S. S. Haykin

# ELECTROMAGNETIC FIELDS, ENERGY, AND FORCES

# ELECTROMAGNETIC FIELDS, ENERGY, AND FORCES


**ROBERT M. FANO**

Professor of Electrical Communications

**LAN JEN CHU**

Professor of Electrical Engineering

**RICHARD B. ADLER**

Professor of Electrical Engineering

Department of Electrical Engineering

Massachusetts Institute of Technology



JOHN WILEY & SONS, INC.

New York · London

SECOND PRINTING, AUGUST, 1963



Library of Congress Catalog Card Number: 60-6453

Printed in the United States of America

TO E. A. G.

# FOREWORD

This book is one of several resulting from a recent revision of the Electrical Engineering Course at the Massachusetts Institute of Technology. The books have the general format of texts and are being used as such. However, they might well be described as reports on a research program aimed at the evolution of an undergraduate core curriculum in Electrical Engineering that will form a basis for a continuing career in a field that is ever-changing.

The development of an educational program in Electrical Engineering to keep pace with the changes in technology is not a new endeavor at the Massachusetts Institute of Technology. In the early 1930's, the Faculty of the Department undertook a major review and reassessment of its program. By 1940, a series of new courses had been evolved, and resulted in the publication of four related books.

The new technology that appeared during World War II brought great change to the field of Electrical Engineering. In recognition of this fact, the Faculty of the Department undertook another reassessment of its program. By about 1952, a pattern for a curriculum had been evolved and its implementation was initiated with a high degree of enthusiasm and vigor.

The new curriculum subordinates option structures built around areas of industrial practice in favor of a common core that provides a broad base for the engineering applications of the sciences. This core structure includes a newly developed laboratory program which stresses the role of experimentation and its relation to theoretical model-making in the solution of engineering problems. Faced with the time limitation of a four-year program for the Bachelor's degree, the entire core curriculum gives priority to basic principles and methods of analysis rather than to the presentation of current technology.

J. A. STRATTON

# PREFACE

This textbook documents part of a coordinated effort within the Electrical Engineering Department of the Massachusetts Institute of Technology to meet the educational challenge presented by the unprecedented growth and rate of change of the Electrical Engineering field in the last decade. This effort led to the development of an undergraduate "core curriculum" consisting of some eight subjects, intended to form a broad foundation on which each student could later build specialized knowledge in the subfield of his choice.

It was readily agreed, when plans for this core curriculum were laid out six years ago, that the student's preparation in circuit theory should be complemented and supplemented by an equally thorough preparation in electromagnetic theory beyond that provided by the sophomore physics subject on electricity and magnetism. Much time and effort was consumed in defining more precisely by trial and error the appropriate topics to be covered, and in developing suitable methods of presenting them to undergraduate students.

The process of trial and error led to the development of two subjects dealing primarily with electromagnetic field theory: a first-term junior subject on electromagnetic fields, energy, and forces based on the material presented in this textbook, and a first-term senior subject on electromagnetic energy transmission and radiation, based on the material presented in a companion textbook by the same authors.[1]

The manuscript of this textbook is the fourth edition of class notes written while the material was being developed and taught, and

[1] Adler, Chu, Fano, *Electromagnetic Energy Transmssion and Radiation*, John Wiley & Sons, New York, 1960.

produced rapidly for use by a large student body. Although only a small fraction of it bears any resemblance to the first edition, we hope the reader will make allowances for those shortcomings that still remain in this version, which is the latest in a series of drafts.

We are greatly indebted to the many colleagues who taught in the last five years the classroom and laboratory sections of the subject from which this textbook originates; their interest, suggestions, constructive criticism, and wholehearted cooperation provided the material and moral support without which the project could not have been completed. We are particularly grateful to Professor Hermann Haus who rough-drafted part of the manuscript and reviewed most of it, and to Professor David Epstein who led the development of the laboratory program which forms an indispensable part of the subject.

The development of the material presented in this text was greatly aided by the exceptional research environment provided by the Research Laboratory of Electronics. We take this opportunity to express our deep appreciation to the Director of the Laboratory, Prof. Jerome B. Wiesner, to our colleagues, and to our graduate students for providing such a stimulating and enjoyable atmosphere.

We wish to thank also those who did the typing and the illustrations for the various editions of class notes which led to this textbook; in particular Miss Lucia Hunt, Mrs. Bertha Hornby, Miss Dorothea Scanlon, and the M.I.T. Illustration Service. Their careful, competent, and prompt help was a great asset to us.

It is a pleasure, above all, to acknowledge our debt of gratitude to Dean Gordon S. Brown, whose courageous leadership, vision and great investment of personal effort as Head of the Electrical Engineering Department made possible the development of the core curriculum. This textbook could not have been written without his constant encouragement, understanding, and administrative support.

R. M. Fano
L. J. Chu
R. B. Adler

*Cambridge, Mass.*
*August 1959*

# CONTENTS

# Introduction

This textbook has been developed for use by junior students in electrical engineering at the Massachusetts Institute of Technology. It is intended to build upon two years of physics, including a full term on electricity and magnetism, two years of mathematics, and a two-term sequence on circuit theory. It does not presuppose any knowledge of vector analysis or of partial differential equations. The material is organized along two interwoven lines of thought, corresponding to the two main objectives of the book, namely the development of a consistent macroscopic theory of electromagnetism and the investigation of the relation between circuit theory and field theory, as outlined below.

The presentation in this text begins where most sophomore-physics subjects terminate, i.e., with a statement of Maxwell's equations in integral form. Maxwell's equations and the expression for the Lorentz force on a moving charge are postulated as the laws of electromagnetism. The Lorentz-force-expression provides a definition of the electric field and of the magnetic field in terms of forces exerted on electric charges, and Maxwell's equations specify the dependence of these two fields on each other and on the charges and currents present in the space. The charges themselves are considered from a macroscopic point of view as forming smooth space distributions, i.e., the discrete character of the elementary electronic charge is disregarded.

From these fundamental postulates the theory is then developed in four successive steps. First, the differential form of Maxwell's equations for fields produced by free charges and free currents alone and the associated boundary conditions are derived from the corresponding integral relations. The necessary tools of vector analysis are provided in a separate, preparatory chapter.

The action of stationary matter as a field source is discussed next. It is shown that the presence of polarized matter can be taken into account macroscopically by means of appropriate distributions of electric charges and currents, which are functions, respectively, of the space dependence and of the time dependence of the polarization vector, i.e., of the macroscopic density of the molecular electric-dipole moments. Magnetized matter is shown by analogy to be representable macroscopically by means of appropriate distributions of magnetic charges and magnetic currents, which are functions, respectively, of the space dependence and of the time dependence of the magnetization vector, i.e., of the macroscopic density of the molecular magnetic-dipole moments. The reader is repeatedly reminded that isolated magnetic charges and currents analogous to free electric charges and currents have never been conclusively observed experimentally. Magnetic charges and magnetic currents are used merely as quantities that are mathematically convenient in describing distributions of magnetic dipoles in their role of field sources; they could be eliminated from the theory without any change of substance at the expense of the mathematical simplicity of the equations expressing the macroscopic field laws.

The manner in which magnetized matter is taken into account in the macroscopic field laws, and the corresponding choice of the magnetic-field intensity $\boldsymbol{H}$ as the fundamental magnetic vector rather than the flux density $\boldsymbol{B}$ constitute a substantial departure from the formulation of electromagnetism found in most other books. This departure appears necessary to preserve simultaneously the internal consistency of the theory and its agreement with experimental evidence. In the formulation presented here, a sharp distinction is made between field quantities, i.e., the electric-field intensity $\boldsymbol{E}$ and the magnetic-field intensity $\boldsymbol{H}$, and material (or source) quantities, i.e., the free-charge density, the free-current density, the polarization vector, and the magnetization vector which represent the macroscopic electromagnetic state of matter. The electric-flux density $\boldsymbol{D}$ and the magnetic-flux density $\boldsymbol{B}$ are regarded as mixed vectors with little physical significance, and are used for the sake of mathematical convenience in certain special situations.

The influence of the electromagnetic field on the electromagnetic state of matter, i.e., on the polarization, magnetization, and current conduction of matter, depends on the microscopic structure of matter. For this reason, the *constituent relations* expressing the electromagnetic state of matter in terms of the electromagnetic field are discussed in this text only at the empirical level, as experimentally obtained relations.

The third step in the development of the theory is the introduction of the concepts of electromagnetic energy and of power flow. It is first shown that the experimentally observed forces on a moving electric charge and on a magnetic dipole imply the existence of a force on a moving magnetic charge analogous to the Lorentz force on a moving electric charge. Then, with the help of the Lorentz force and of its magnetic analog, the expression known as Poynting's theorem—a direct consequence of Maxwell's equations—is interpreted as the law of conservation of energy for electromagnetic fields. Three of the terms in the expression are identified with power dissipated or absorbed by matter because of current conduction or because of its changing state of polarization and magnetization. The remaining terms, which are functions of $\boldsymbol{E}$ and $\boldsymbol{H}$ alone, are then interpreted as representing the time rate of change of the electromagnetic energy stored in the field and the electromagnetic power flow.

In the fourth and final step the macroscopic field laws and the associated power and energy concepts are extended to systems involving matter in relative motion. It is shown that the motion of polarized matter can be taken into account by means of an additional distribution of electric current, which is a function of the velocity field and of the space variation of the polarization. The motion of magnetized matter is taken into account by an analogous magnetic-current distribution. The corresponding generalization of Poynting's theorem includes an additional term equal to the product of the velocity of each grain of matter and the density of the electromagnetic force acting on it. This term is readily identified with the density of the power converted from electromagnetic to mechanical form, or vice versa. Finally, the virtual-work method of evaluating electromagnetic forces on rigid bodies is shown to follow from the generalized Poynting's theorem.

The extension of the macroscopic field laws and of the associated energy relations to systems involving matter in relative motion is carried out without introducing any of the concepts of special relativity. No low-velocity approximations are made either in the field laws or in the generalization of Poynting's theorem. Only in deducing the constituent relations for matter in motion from those for matter at rest it becomes necessary to assume that the velocity of the body in question is much smaller than that of light. For the sake of completeness, the corresponding four-dimensional, relativistic formulation of the theory is presented in Appendix 1, and compared with two different formulations found in other textbooks.

The investigation of the relation between circuit theory and field theory is the second main objective of this book. It is carried out simultaneously with the development of the theory of electromagnetism outlined above because, in addition to being interesting and useful on its own merit, it provides a wealth of illustrative examples.

Circuit theory deals with the behavior of voltages and currents in a network consisting of idealized elements, each of them being completely characterized by a voltage-current relation at its terminals. As such, circuit theory does not take into account the geometry of a physical circuit, except for the manner in which the elements are interconnected. In this very fact lie both the strength and the limitations of circuit theory.

A simple illustration will set the issues involved in the proper frame of reference. A device consisting of a coil of conducting wire may be a resistor, an air-core inductor, a resonant element, a television antenna, part of the helix of a traveling-wave amplifier, or perhaps just a bed spring or a corkscrew. This point is by no means trivial. It stresses that there is no unique correspondence between the physical appearance of the device and its function, even if the device is known to produce an electromagnetic field. The salient characteristics of the electromagnetic field that might be observed in the space surrounding the device depend to a large extent on the frequency of excitation. In turn, the characteristics of the field determine the function that the device might properly perform in an electric system. When connected to a d-c source, or to a very-low-frequency a-c source, the coil plays the circuit role of a resistance. At somewhat higher frequencies, its behavior is controlled primarily by the magnetic field produced by the current, and its terminal characteristics closely resemble those of an inductance, as defined in circuit theory. At still higher frequencies, the energy stored in the electric field produced by charges on the wire becomes equal to the energy stored in the magnetic field, and the coil acts as a resonant circuit. Finally, when the wave length corresponding to the frequency of excitation becomes smaller than the dimensions of the coil, the coil can be used to guide electromagnetic waves, as in a traveling-wave tube, or as an antenna.

This simple illustration stresses the importance of relating the circuit functions and properties of the three basic elements, i.e., resistance, capacitance, and inductance, to corresponding characteristics of electromagnetic fields. The fields associated with distributed-element systems, i.e., transmission lines, are discussed in a separate book by the same authors (see Ref. 2, Chapter 8).

The relation between field characteristics and circuit elements is investigated by expanding the pertinent electromagnetic quantities in power series, whose successive terms can be evaluated in order by solving only field problems of the static type. These terms become appreciable in succession with increasing time rate of change of the electromagnetic quantities they represent. It is shown then, with the help of these series expansions, that the basic elements of circuit theory —resistance, capacitance, and inductance—result from the *quasi-static* electromagnetic field described by the first two terms of each series. The stray effects associated with physical circuit elements result from higher order terms. As a matter of fact, it is possible in some cases to evaluate by recursion all the terms of the series, thereby obtaining the complete electromagnetic field.

The properties of circuit elements are investigated in three successive steps. First, the power-series technique is developed in general terms, and the various possible types of quasi-static fields are analyzed individually and related to the corresponding circuit elements. Next, the same quasi-static fields are studied from the energy point of view, and relations are thereby obtained between resistance, capacitance, and inductance on the one hand, and power dissipation, storage of electric energy, and storage of magnetic energy on the other hand. The same energy relations yield proofs of the reciprocity theorem for electromagnetic systems representable by networks of elements of the same type; the positive character of all the elements of the networks, with the exception of the mutual inductances, is demonstrated at the same time.

Finally, the behavior of quasi-static fields in the sinusoidal steady state is investigated with the help of complex notations. The input impedance (or admittance) of a network is expressed in terms of the average power dissipated in the network, the average electric energy stored, and the average magnetic energy stored. This expression indicates, in particular, that the condition of resonance from a circuit point of view corresponds to the condition in which equal average amounts of electric and magnetic energy are stored in the network. It is shown, furthermore, that the figure of merit, i.e., the $Q$ of a resonant circuit is given by the product of the angular frequency and the total average energy stored divided by the average power dissipated. Next, the series expansions previously introduced in general terms are shown to become power series in the frequency variable. Thus, the successive terms of the series become significant in order with increasing frequency, thereby providing a convenient technique for studying the frequency behavior of circuit components. These results are illustrated with additional examples of quasi-static fields representing various circuit components. The discussion of the sinusoidal steady state is concluded with the proof of the reciprocity theorem for linear, passive electromagnetic systems, from which the usual reciprocity theorem of circuit theory is derived by defining appropriate terminal voltages and terminal currents.

It is clear from the above outline that the solution of the special boundary-value problems of electromagnetic theory is not one of the objectives of this book. The reasons for not including such classical topics are, of course, the complexity of the mathematical techniques involved and the lack of familiarity on the part of junior students with the properties of the special mathematical functions that are encountered. Nevertheless, some mathematical techniques for evaluating fields had to be included to permit the presentation of a sufficient variety of illustrative examples. Chapter 4 is devoted to the study of general properties of the solutions of Poisson's and Laplace's equations, and to the derivation of a few representative classes of solutions of Laplace's equation in two and three dimensions.

Among the nontrivial solutions of Laplace's equation, the dipole field is the one used most frequently for illustrative purposes. It is first introduced in Chapter 3 as the field produced by an electric dipole, and it is used thereafter in every chapter to describe either an electric or a magnetic field. By the end of the book the reader should be thoroughly familiar with the properties of this very important field, the simplest field, after that of a point charge, that can be produced by sources located in a finite region of space.

The illustrative examples and the methods of analysis used in their connection have been selected primarily on the basis of two guiding principles. The first one is to give preference to the mathematical simplicity of the field over the extent to which the system under consideration resembles a device used in engineering practice. The properties of greatest interest are exhibited directly by the electromagnetic field rather than by the material boundaries that shape it. Thus, more can be learned from a thorough study of the simplest field that exhibits the property of interest than from a necessarily more qualitative study of a device that meets practical requirements extraneous to the question under consideration.

The second guiding principle is that it is often more convenient in a design problem to find a field which has the desired properties, and then design around it material boundaries and sources that can support it, rather than to start out with a material structure and determine from it whether the resulting field has the desired properties. In other words, it is usually easier to synthesize an electromagnetic system with prescribed properties than to analyze one that is completely specified. This synthesis point of view is often emphasized in the main body of the text as well as in the illustrative examples.

A final remark is in order with regard to the material that can be covered in one term. The main body of the text, excluding the sections marked with the sign ▶ as well as Appendix 1, can be covered in one term by junior or senior students who are good candidates for graduate education. The last two chapters as well may have to be left out of a program designed for the average junior or senior student. The entire text with the exception of Appendix 1 should be appropriate for a graduate subject. Appendix 1 has been included primarily as a reference for advanced graduate students and research workers; it presents the relativistic macroscopic formulation of electromagnetism recently developed by one of the authors (L. J. Chu).

# CHAPTER ONE

# The Integral Laws in Free Space

The development of electromagnetism in the nineteenth century went hand in hand with a very significant modification of the point of view from which the pertinent experimental evidence was interpreted and pieced together. The original point of view of "action at a distance," characteristic of Coulomb's law, had led to considering forces of electric and magnetic origin as exerted directly by electric charges on electric charges, and by magnetic poles or current elements on other magnetic poles or other current elements. It was Faraday, in the first half of the nineteenth century, who first conceived of the space surrounding electric charges as filled with "lines of force," indicating everywhere the direction and (through their density) the magnitude of the force that would be acting on a positive unit charge if such a charge were present. Faraday, furthermore, thought of the space—whether empty or occupied by polarizable matter—as an elastic medium under stress, tension being present along the lines of force, and pressure being exerted in all directions normal to them. Mutual forces between charges could then be conceived as being "transmitted" by the medium.

Faraday's line of thought shifted the focus of attention from the properties of geometric configurations of charges and conductors to those of the surrounding medium and of the field of force hypothesized within it. Maxwell, in the second half of the nineteenth century, was much impressed by the importance of this shift of emphasis, and set out to express Faraday's ideas in a precise mathematical form. He stated in the preface to the first edition of his famous *A Treatise on Electricity and Magnetism* [1]: [1]

[1] Numbers set in brackets refer to references at end of chapter.

When I had translated what I considered to be Faraday's ideas into a mathematical form, I found that in general the results of the two methods [that of Faraday and that of action at a distance, which was the most popular among the theoretical physicists and mathematicians of the time] coincided, so that the same phenomena were accounted for, and the same laws of action deduced by both methods, but that Faraday's methods resembled those in which we begin with the whole and arrive at the parts by analysis, while the ordinary mathematical methods were founded on the principle of beginning with the parts and building up the whole by synthesis. I also found that several of the most fertile methods of research discovered by the mathematicians could be expressed much better in terms of ideas derived from Faraday than in their original form. The whole theory, for instance, of the potential, considered as a quantity which satisfies a certain partial differential equation, belongs essentially to the method which I have called that of Faraday.

Maxwell's interest in the inherent mathematical properties of electric and magnetic fields, as contrasted with those that depend on the geometry and strength of their sources, led him to the formulation of his famous field equations and to the theoretical discovery of electromagnetic waves. Although electromagnetic waves can also be interpreted as the result of "delayed action at a distance," their discovery by Maxwell as a necessary consequence of the properties of electromagnetic fields constitutes the single most striking example of the much greater power of the field point of view.

In deference to the mechanistic attitude of the nineteenth-century physicists, Maxwell kept alive Faraday's conception of free space as an appropriate elastic medium through which electromagnetic actions are transmitted, although his formulation of the field equations did not depend in the least upon it. Only the repeated failure to observe any one of the expected physical consequences of the existence of such a medium, the ether, led modern physicists to disregard such an hypothesis as unwarranted and, furthermore, as totally unnecessary. Yet, because of the similarity between the mathematics of electromagnetism and that of elasticity, the concept of an elastic medium is still useful in providing helpful, suggestive analogies.

The historical approach, beginning with Coulomb's law, is followed in most elementary treatments of electromagnetism because it permits one to develop slowly the abstract concept of field while discussing the experimental laws leading to Maxwell's formulation of the field equations. On the other hand, it seems more appropriate, in a second and more profound study of electromagnetism, to postulate Maxwell's field equations as the laws of electromagnetism, from which the simpler laws of Coulomb, Ampere, Faraday, etc., can be derived as special cases. This approach has the advantage of making a clear-cut separation between the sources of an electromagnetic field, the field itself, and the action exerted by the field on charges, currents, and neutral matter. The important fact, in this regard, is that in any given region of space the same field can be produced by a variety of source distributions outside the region. However, the field within the region must satisfy conditions entirely independent of the sources located outside the region. These conditions, which may be looked upon as physical realizability conditions, are expressed by Maxwell's field equations, so that the solutions of Maxwell's equations represent the physically realizable fields. Thus we see that the field approach permits us to split any design problem into three parts:

1. The determination of the class of fields able to produce the desired type of action on charges, currents, and matter;
2. the selection within such a class of a physically realizable field, i.e., a field that satisfies Maxwell's equations;
3. the determination of primary sources (charges and currents) and of secondary sources (polarizable and magnetizable matter) able to produce the desired field.

This field-synthesis point of view will guide our thinking in most of this volume.

## 1.1 Review of Basic Postulates and Definitions

Basic postulates and definitions are always a troublesome subject in the exposition of any physical theory. Educationally speaking, we are faced with a vicious circle. On the one hand, the exposition of the theory should be preceded by a thorough discussion of the postulates on which it is based and by precise definitions of the physical quantities involved. On the other hand, both postulates and definitions cannot be properly justified or even stated precisely without exploring their consequences and comparing them with the available experimental evidence; thus it would seem that postulates and definitions should be discussed after the presentation of the theory rather than before it. Furthermore, questions concerning their consistency, necessity, and sufficiency are often very difficult and involve not only the theory that stems from them but also other related physical theories.

Serious difficulties of this type confront us in connection with the field theory of electromagnetism. We are thus forced to compromise and be satisfied with postulates and definitions that are not so clear and precise as we should like them to be, and which appear somewhat arbitrary. Some of the questions that are left open will be answered later on; others are beyond the scope of this text.

The evidence available from a wide variety of experiments on electromagnetic forces is consistent with the following basic postulates:

1. There exist two kinds of electric charges: a positive charge and a negative charge.
2. Electric charge is conserved; in the sense that whenever any positive charge appears, an equal amount of negative charge also appears. Conversely, whenever any positive charge disappears, an equal amount of negative charge also disappears. Thus the algebraic sum of all charges is constant in any isolated system.
3. All charges are integral multiples of the electronic charge, whose magnitude is given by

$$e = 1.60 \times 10^{-19} \text{ coulomb} \tag{1.1}$$

4. An electric charge in motion may be acted on by a force independent of its velocity and also by a force proportional to its velocity and directed at right angles to it. More precisely, the total force $\boldsymbol{F}$ known as the Lorentz force can be expressed in the form

$$\boldsymbol{F} = q(\boldsymbol{E} + \boldsymbol{v} \times \mu_0 \boldsymbol{H}) \tag{1.2}$$

where $q$ represents the charge and $\boldsymbol{v}$ its velocity. The vector $\boldsymbol{E}$, the electric-field intensity, and the vector $\boldsymbol{H}$, the magnetic-field intensity, are thereby defined in terms of the force, the charge, and its velocity relative to the observer. The quantity $\mu_0$ is the permeability of vacuum, a constant whose value depends on the system of units.

In the mks rationalized system of units, used throughout this volume, the force is measured in newtons, the velocity in meters per second, and the charge in coulombs. The coulomb is the basic electric unit which, together with the meter, the kilogram, and the second, permits the definition of all other electromagnetic units, as discussed in Appendix 2. Its definition requires, of course, an additional relation independent of Eq. 1.2. The unit of electric-field intensity is specified by Eq. 1.2 in terms of the units of force and charge. In practice, the electric-field intensity is measured in volts per meter, a volt being a joule per coulomb. The unit of $\mu_0 \boldsymbol{H}$ is specified, similarly, in terms of the units of force, velocity, and charge. The dimensions and the value of the permeability of vacuum

$$\mu_0 = 4\pi \times 10^{-7} \text{ henry/meter} \tag{1.3}$$

are selected in such a way that the magnetic-field intensity be measured in amperes per meter, that is in coulombs per meter-second, as we shall see in Sec. 1.3.

We shall need in our study the concepts of charge density, current, and current density. The charge density $\rho$ at any point $P$ is defined as the ratio of the charge $\delta q$ contained in a small region about $P$ to the volume $\delta V$ of the region, in the limit when the region shrinks to the point $P$; i.e.,

$$\rho = \lim_{\delta V \to 0} \frac{\delta q}{\delta V} \tag{1.4}$$

Conversely, the charge density is a scalar function of position such that the total charge in any volume $V$ shall be representable as the volume integral

$$q = \int_V \rho \, dv \tag{1.5}$$

Strictly speaking, this definition is inconsistent with postulate 3 above, because the limit of Eq. 1.4 cannot exist if the charge $\delta q$ must remain an integral multiple of the electronic charge. Conversely, the total charge in a finite region cannot be an integral multiple of the electronic charge for all regions if the charge density is a finite function of position. On the other hand, the quantization of charge implied by postulate 3 is so fine compared with the charge involved in the large-scale phenomena with which we shall be concerned that the inaccuracies resulting from the assumption of a smooth charge distribution with a finite density are completely negligible.

The current $I$ flowing through a surface $S$ is defined as the limit of the ratio of $\delta q$, the amount of charge that crosses $S$ in the time $\delta t$, to the time interval $\delta t$, when $\delta t$ approaches zero, i.e.,

$$I = \lim_{\delta t \to 0} \frac{\delta q}{\delta t} \tag{1.6}$$

Current is measured in amperes, one ampere being equal to a coulomb per second. The sign of $I$ is arbitrarily defined as positive for a current flowing in the direction of motion of positive charges or opposite to the direction of motion of negative charges.

The current density $\boldsymbol{J}$, a vector, is defined in turn as follows. Let us consider a small element of surface $\delta a$, and indicate with $\boldsymbol{n}$ a unit vector normal to it. Clearly, the current $\delta I$ flowing through $\delta a$ is a maximum when the direction of $\boldsymbol{n}$ coincides with the direction of motion of the charge; with $\boldsymbol{n}$ so oriented, the magnitude of $\boldsymbol{J}$ is defined as

$$|\boldsymbol{J}| = \lim_{\delta a \to 0} \frac{\delta I}{\delta a} \tag{1.7}$$

The direction of $\boldsymbol{J}$ coincides with the direction of motion of positive charge and is opposite to the direction of motion of negative charge, in agreement with the above convention regarding the sign of $I$. Thus the current density in an electron beam has a direction opposite to the direction of motion of the electrons. The current density can also be defined in an equivalent manner as a vector function of position such that the current through any surface $S$ shall be representable as the surface integral

$$I = \int_S J_n \, da \tag{1.8}$$

where $da$ is a differential element of surface, and $J_n$ is the component of $\boldsymbol{J}$ normal to the surface.

It is clear that the above definitions of current and current density are just as inconsistent with postulate 3 as the definition of charge density. Again the inconsistency may be disregarded as long as we are dealing with large-scale phenomena.

The definition of charge density and current density, together with the law of conservation of charge (postulate 2), implies that, for any surface $S$ enclosing a volume $V$,

$$\oint_S J_n \, da = -\frac{d}{dt} \int_V \rho \, dv \tag{1.9}$$

where $J_n$ is the component of $\boldsymbol{J}$ normal to $S$, and outwardly directed. The left-hand side of this equation represents the current flowing out of the closed surface $S$, i.e., the net outgoing positive charge per unit time. The right-hand side is the negative time rate of change of the net charge within $V$. We shall use this equation as a formal statement of the law of conservation of charge.

## 1.2 Convection and Conduction Currents

The current through a given surface was defined, in the preceding section, as the amount of charge crossing the given surface per unit time, without reference to any other characteristics of the motion of the charge. On the other hand, it is convenient for the purposes of our discussion, to classify currents according to their physical origins in three categories: convection currents, conduction currents, and polarization currents. Convection currents and conduction currents result from the free motion of electric charges; for this reason, they are often referred to as free currents. Polarization currents result from the relative displacement of charged particles in the atomic structure of matter, when such particles remain bound to the atom or molecule to which they belong. The current resulting from the motion of such bound charges is discussed in Sec. 5.2, as part of our study of dielectric polarization. We shall focus our attention here on convection currents and conduction currents.

We regard a current as being of the convection type when it results from the motion of charge whose density and velocity are explicitly stated. Thus, for instance, the current in a vacuum tube is regarded as a convection current because it originates from the motion of a well-identified space charge. The same is true for the current of an electron beam in a cathode-ray tube, and for the current resulting from the motion of a charged conductor. If $\rho$ is the density of the moving charge at a given point in a stationary system of coordinates, and $\boldsymbol{v}$ is its velocity, the corresponding convection-current density is

$$\boldsymbol{J} = \rho \boldsymbol{v} \tag{1.10}$$

Conduction currents result from the drift of free electrons and ions in matter under the influence of an electric field, as, for instance, in metals and electrolytic solutions respectively. The motion of such charged particles is opposed by frictionlike forces within the conducting material that balance the forces exerted by the electric field. In metals and in electrolytic solutions these frictionlike forces are proportional to the velocity of the charged particles over a large range of values, with the result that the latter must be proportional to the electric-field intensity in order for the particles to be in dynamic equilibrium. It follows that the current density, which is proportional to the velocity of the particles, becomes proportional to the electric-field intensity, i.e.,

$$\boldsymbol{J}_c = \sigma \boldsymbol{E} \tag{1.11}$$

where $\sigma$ is the conductivity of the material at the point at which $\boldsymbol{J}_c$ and $\boldsymbol{E}$ are measured. This equation is readily recognized as expressing Ohm's law in terms of field vectors.

It is important to note that the presence of conduction current does not imply the presence of a net charge density. In a metal, for instance, conduction current results from the drift of free atomic electrons in the presence of stationary atoms, which are positively charged because of the loss of electrons. The net charge density may or may not be equal to zero; in any case, it bears no relation to the current density beyond that required by the law of conservation of charge. Furthermore, the actual density of the moving charge and its velocity are of no interest from a macroscopic point of view; we are only concerned with their product which constitutes the current density. By comparison, in the case of a convection current, both the charge density and its velocity are individually of interest.

## 1.3 The Field Equations in Free Space

The electric field $\boldsymbol{E}$ and the magnetic field $\boldsymbol{H}$ have been defined in Sec. 1.1 in terms of the Lorentz force exerted on a moving charge. In the first six chapters we shall focus our attention on the properties of these two fields without reference to their original definition, following the field approach to electromagnetism developed by Faraday and Maxwell. We shall return to their significance in terms of electromagnetic forces in Chapter 7 in order to develop the concepts of electromagnetic energy and electromagnetic power from the work done by such forces.

Let us begin by reconsidering the integral form of Maxwell's equations in free space, which culminates most elementary discussions of electromagnetism. For this purpose, let us consider an arbitrary, two-sided, simply connected [1] surface $S$, bounded by a closed contour $C$, as illustrated in Fig. 1.1. The direction of the arrow along the contour is related to that of the unit vector $\boldsymbol{n}$, normal to the surface, by the right-handed-screw rule; i.e., if the surface is continuously deformed into a plane, a right-handed screw turning in the direction indicated on the resulting contour should move axially in the direction of the unit vector $\boldsymbol{n}$, normal to the plane. The two fundamental equations of Maxwell can be written in the form:

$$\oint_C E_t\, ds + \frac{d}{dt}\int_S \mu_0 H_n\, da = 0 \tag{1.12}$$

$$\oint_C H_t\, ds - \frac{d}{dt}\int_S \epsilon_0 E_n\, da = \int_S J_n\, da \tag{1.13}$$

[1] A simply connected surface is a surface without holes, i.e., a surface bounded by a contour consisting of a single continuous line. We shall see later on that any surface with holes (multiply connected) can be reduced for our purpose to a simply connected surface by means of appropriate cuts. An example of a one-sided surface is the Moebian strip constructed by joining the two ends of a twisted strip of paper in such a way that one edge of the strip is made to coincide with the other edge.

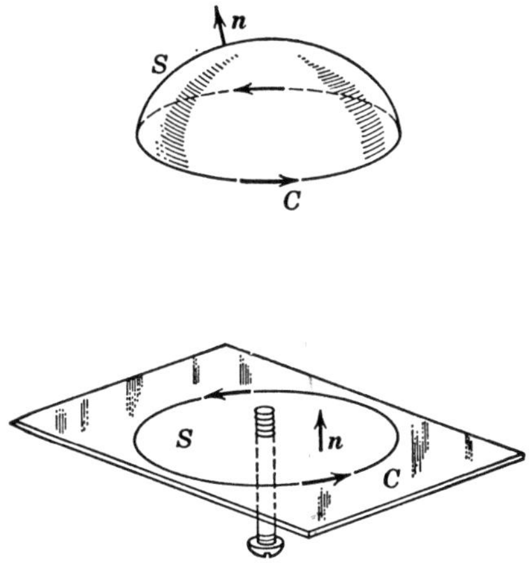


**Fig. 1.1.** The use of the right-handed-screw rule in determining reference directions on a surface and on the contour bounding it.

where $E_t$ and $H_t$ are the components of $\boldsymbol{E}$ and $\boldsymbol{H}$ tangent to the contour $C$ in the direction indicated by the arrow, and $E_n$ and $H_n$ are the components of the same vectors normal to the surface $S$ and in the direction of the unit vector $\boldsymbol{n}$; $da$ represents a differential element of the surface $S$, and $ds$ represents a differential element of the contour $C$. The value of the constant $\epsilon_0$, the permittivity of vacuum, is obtained from the equation

$$c = \frac{1}{\sqrt{\epsilon_0 \mu_0}} = 2.998 \times 10^8 \text{ meters/second} \tag{1.14}$$

where $c$ is the velocity of light in vacuum, as determined by measurements. This equation yields for $\epsilon_0$ the value

$$\epsilon_0 = 8.854 \times 10^{-12} \tag{1.15}$$

Equation 1.14 is a direct consequence of Maxwell's equations, although it cannot be derived at this point. Since it relates the values of $\mu_0$ and $\epsilon_0$ to the velocity of light in vacuum, a measurable physical quantity, only one of these two constants of vacuum can be selected arbitrarily in devising a system of units. As stated in Sec. 1.1, the value of $\mu_0$ is selected, in the mks rationalized system, in such a way that the magnetic-field intensity is measured in amperes per meter, as evidenced by Eq. 1.13; this selection fixes both the value and the dimensions of $\epsilon_0$.

The first equation, Eq. 1.12, expresses Faraday's induction law, namely, that the electromotive force around any closed contour must equal the negative time rate of change of the magnetic flux linking the contour. In fact, the contour integral represents the work that would be done by the electric field in moving a unit positive charge once around the contour, i.e., the electromotive force. The surface integral represents the flux of the magnetic field through the given surface $S$. Since the contour integral depends only on the field and the contour $C$, the surface integral must also depend only on the field and on the contour; in particular, the time rate of change of the flux must be the same for all two-sided surfaces bounded by $C$. We shall see in Sec. 3.1 that this requirement implies that the magnetic flux through any closed surface is always equal to zero, i.e.,

$$\oint_S \mu_0 H_n \, da = 0 \tag{1.16}$$

This equation is sometimes stated as a separate field law known as Gauss' law for the magnetic field. Actually it is a direct consequence of Eq. 1.12.

The second field equation, Eq. 1.13, is a statement of Ampere's circuital law, modified by the addition of the term involving the time rate of change of the flux of $\epsilon_0 \boldsymbol{E}$. The contour integral is the magnetomotive force around the contour; the surface integral of the current density represents, of course, the net current flowing through $S$. The role played by the second term on the left-hand side, sometimes misleadingly referred to as the "displacement current," becomes evident when we move it to the right-hand side and require that the sum of the two surface integrals be the same for all two-sided surfaces bounded by the same contour, just as we did in connection with Eq. 1.12. This requirement could not be met by the current term alone; for instance, the surfaces $S$ and $S'$ in Fig. 1.2 would yield different current fluxes, since $S$ cuts through a wire leading to a capacitor whereas $S'$ passes between the plates of the capacitor without cutting through any wire.

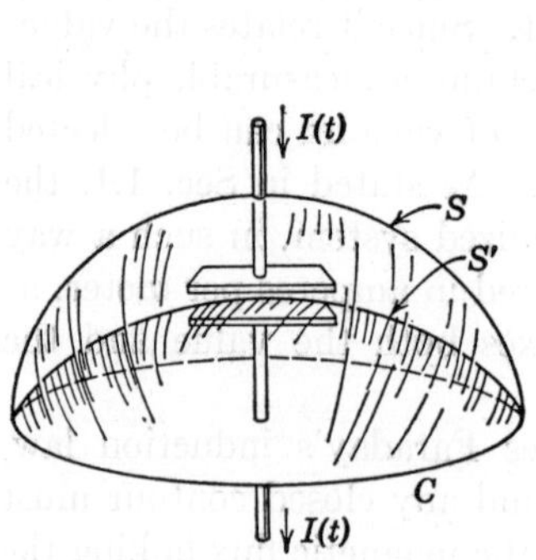


**Fig. 1.2.** An example of two surfaces bounded by the same contour $C$ through which different amounts of current flow.

Thus the circuital law as stated originally by Ampere cannot be correct for time-varying fields.

We shall see in Sec. 3.1 that the requirement that the sum of the two surface integrals in Eq. 1.13 be the same for all surfaces bounded by the same contour implies that the outward flux of $\epsilon_0 \boldsymbol{E}$ through any closed surface must be equal to the net charge $q$ in the volume $V$ enclosed by the surface: i.e.,

$$\oint_S \epsilon_0 E_n \, da = \int_V \rho \, dv = q \tag{1.17}$$

Again, this equation is sometimes stated as a separate law, known as Gauss' law for the electric field. Actually it is a direct consequence of Eq. 1.13 and of the law of conservation of charge expressed by Eq. 1.9. Historically, however, the discovery of Gauss' law preceded the formulation of the second basic field equation. Maxwell noted that Ampere's circuital law (similar to Eq. 1.13 but without the term involving $\epsilon_0 E_n$) was mathematically inconsistent for time-varying fields because the flux of $\boldsymbol{J}$ could depend on the particular surface $S$ selected, as discussed above. He then showed, on the basis of Gauss' law and the law of conservation of charge, that mathematical consistency could be obtained by adding the term involving $\epsilon_0 E_n$. It is important to note that the addition of this term was the key to the theoretical discovery of electromagnetic waves.

The name "displacement current" originated from Maxwell's argument about an additional current term being required, for mathematical consistency, and from his views about free space being some sort of a material medium. Actually, nothing is displaced in free space, and the new term introduced by Maxwell in Eq. 1.13 should be thought of as being parallel to the corresponding term in Eq. 1.12. Thus, a finite magnetomotive force is associated with a time-varying flux of $\epsilon_0 \boldsymbol{E}$, just as a finite electromotive force is associated with a time-varying flux of $\mu_0 \boldsymbol{H}$.

## 1.4 Usefulness and Limitations of Integral Laws

It is important to stress that the integral laws discussed in the preceding section must be satisfied for *every closed contour $C$ and every closed surface $S$*. Clearly, it would be very difficult to ascertain whether any particular pair of fields $\boldsymbol{E}$ and $\boldsymbol{H}$ does or does not satisfy such laws for all possible contours and surfaces, and it would be even more difficult to find directly a pair of fields that would satisfy them for a given distribution of charges and currents. We shall see in Chapter 3 that the problem can be considerably simplified by substituting for the integral laws equivalent differential laws. Yet, there are important special cases in which the integral form of the field laws is not only adequate but also more illuminating. These special cases are characterized by particular geometric symmetries, such as spherical or cylindrical. This point is best explained in terms of specific examples.

Let us consider a time-independent charge $q$, uniformly distributed within a sphere of radius $a$ centered at the origin. We wish to determine the electric field produced by this charge, both inside and outside the sphere. We note, first of all, that because of the spherical symmetry of the charge distribution, the electric field must have everywhere a direction radial from the origin. This follows from the fact that a radial direction is the only direction that can have a complete spherical symmetry. For the same reason, the intensity of the electric field must be constant over any concentric spherical surface. Then, if we take any such spherical surface as the closed surface $S$ of Eq. 1.17, and indicate with $r$ its radius, this equation becomes

$$4\pi r^2 \epsilon_0 E_n = \begin{cases} q\left(\dfrac{r}{a}\right)^3 & \text{for } r < a \\ q & \text{for } r \geq a \end{cases} \tag{1.18}$$

from which we obtain

$$E_n = \begin{cases} \dfrac{q}{4\pi\epsilon_0 a^3}\, r & \text{for } r < a \\ \dfrac{q}{4\pi\epsilon_0 r^2} & \text{for } r \geq a \end{cases} \tag{1.19}$$

where $E_n$ is the electric-field intensity in the outward direction.

It is important to observe that Eq. 1.17 together with the spherical symmetry requirement was sufficient to determine uniquely the electric-field intensity. This means that Eq. 1.12 must be automatically satisfied, or, in other words, that the constraint imposed on the electric field by this equation is already implied by the spherical-symmetry requirement. It can be shown, in fact, that, in the absence of any time-varying magnetic field, Eq. 1.12 is satisfied by any radial, spherically symmetrical electric field. This property of spherically symmetrical fields is very readily proved with the tools of vector analysis, discussed in the following chapter.

Let us consider next the case of an infinite straight wire of radius $a$, carrying a steady current $I$, parallel to the axis of the wire and uniformly distributed through its cross section. We wish to determine the magnetic field produced by this current distribution, both inside and outside the wire. We shall show, first, that the magnetic field must be tangent to any circular cylinder coaxial with the wire. For this purpose, we observe, first of all, that, because of the circular cylindrical symmetry of the current distribution, the magnetic field can depend only on the radial distance $r$ from the axis of the wire, besides on the magnitude and the direction of the current. In particular, if the magnetic field includes a radial component, this component must have the same direction (either toward the axis of the wire or away from it) at all points. Furthermore, if the magnetic field has a component parallel to the axis of the wire, this component must be constant over any straight line parallel to the wire.

Let us consider then Eq. 1.16, using for $S$ the surface of any circular cylinder of finite length, coaxial with the wire. The flux of $\boldsymbol{H}$ entering the cylinder from either end surface must be equal to the flux leaving the cylinder from the opposite end surface, because the component of the magnetic field parallel to the wire must be independent of the position along the wire. Thus this component cannot contribute to the surface integral. On the other hand, any flux through the circular part of the surface can only be caused by a radial component; furthermore, because of the circular symmetry requirement on the radial component, this flux can vanish only if this component is equal to zero. Thus, we can conclude that Eq. 1.16 requires the magnetic field to be tangent to any circular cylinder coaxial with the wire.

Let us consider next Eq. 1.13 and use as contour $C$ a circle concentric with the wire, drawn on a plane normal to it, as illustrated in Fig. 1.3. Assuming that the current flows upward from the paper, Eq. 1.13 requires the current flowing through the circle to be equal to the line integral, in the direction indicated by the arrow, of $H_t$, the component

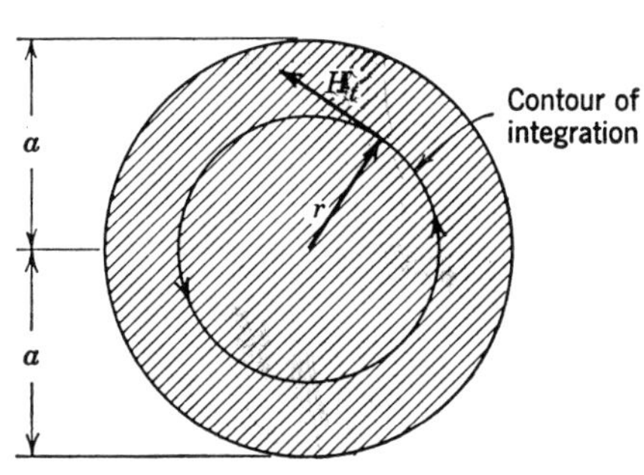


**Fig. 1.3.** Contour of integration used in connection with Eq. 1.20.

of the magnetic field tangent to the circle. Since $H_t$ must be constant over the circle, because of the circular symmetry of the current distribution, Eq. 1.13 yields for a circle of radius $r$,

$$2\pi r H_t = \begin{cases} I\left(\dfrac{r}{a}\right)^2 & \text{for } r < a \\ I & \text{for } r \geq a \end{cases} \tag{1.20}$$

from which we obtain

$$H_t = \begin{cases} \dfrac{I}{2\pi a^2}\, r & \text{for } r < a \\ \dfrac{I}{2\pi r} & \text{for } r \geq a \end{cases} \tag{1.21}$$

It remains to be shown that, if there is any component of the magnetic field parallel to the axis of the wire, the magnitude of such a component must be constant throughout the entire space and independent of the current in the wire; in other words, this component plays the role of an "arbitrary additive constant." For this purpose, let us use for $C$ the rectangular closed path illustrated in Fig. 1.4, drawn on a plane containing the axis of the wire. The two radial sides of the rectangle do not contribute to the line integral in Eq. 1.13 because the magnetic field has no radial component. Furthermore the entire line integral must vanish because no current flows through the

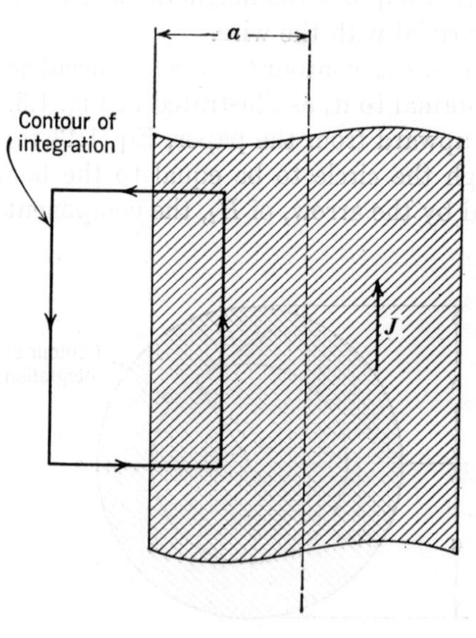


**Fig. 1.4.** Contour of integration used in determining the magnetic field parallel to the wire.

rectangular closed contour. It follows that the contributions to the line integral of the two remaining sides must be equal in magnitude and opposite in sign. Since this must be true for all similar rectangular paths, the component of the magnetic field parallel to the axis of the wire must be constant through the entire space. This uniform field is independent of the current in the wire and must be thought of as being produced by currents at infinity.

The above two examples illustrate how static fields can be determined from their sources with the help of the integral laws when the sources have special geometric symmetries. The simplicity of the procedure results from the selection of surfaces and contours on which the pertinent field components are known to be constant because of the symmetry of the sources. In the two examples considered above, the fields turn out to depend on a single spacial coordinate; there are cases, however, in which fields that depend on two spacial coordinates can be determined directly from the integral laws by following a similar procedure. In other words, the adequacy of the integral laws for the solution of a particular problem depends on the possibility of finding appropriate contours and surfaces rather than on the dimensionality of the field, although these two characteristics of the problem are related to some extent.

## 1.5 Matter as a Field Source

Matter is known to consist of positively charged nuclei surrounded by electrons. The negatively charged electrons revolve in orbits around the nuclei, and carry a total charge equal in magnitude and opposite in sign to that of the nuclei. Thus matter, in its normal state, is macroscopically neutral.

The field produced by atomic charges is, clearly, extremely complex. In dealing with large-scale phenomena, however, we can disregard its fine structure, and focus our attention on the smoothed field obtained by averaging the actual field over volumes large compared to atomic dimensions, yet small compared with the dimensions of the system under consideration. We shall use the adjective "macroscopic" in referring to these smoothed fields.

Usually, no macroscopic electric field is produced by neutral matter, mainly because of the mutual cancellation of the fields produced by neighboring atoms, and the averaging effect of thermal agitation. However, when the atomic structure of a material is modified, or the averaging action of thermal agitation is counteracted by an external electric field (or by other external forces), the contributions of the individual atoms may add up to yield a macroscopic field comparable in intensity to the external applied field. Two distinct situations arise: the first one characteristic of conducting materials when electrons or ions are relatively free to move about under the influence of an electric field, as in metals and electrolytic solutions; the second one characteristic of dielectric materials, when positive and negative charges are held together by such strong forces that they cannot be pulled apart completely, but only slightly displaced.

The ordered drift of charges resulting in the first situation constitutes macroscopically a conduction current which is found to depend at each point on the local electric-field intensity and on the local structure of matter, as discussed in Sec. 1.2. Such free charges may accumulate within a conducting body and on its surface, giving rise thereby to a net macroscopic charge distribution. In the second situation, in which charges are held together by strong forces, only small changes of their relative mean positions can result. When a net macroscopic electric field results from such displacements, the material is said to be electrically polarized. We shall see in Chapter 5 that the state of polarization of a material can be taken into account by associating to the material a distribution of electric dipoles whose moment density at each point is a function of the local state of matter. The macroscopic charge and current densities resulting from such dipole distributions and from their time rates of change will then be incorporated in the field equations as polarization components of $\rho$ and $\boldsymbol{J}$.

Electrons are known to possess a magnetic-dipole moment in addition to a negative electric charge. This is evidenced by the magnetic field produced by them as well as by the force and torque exerted on them by an external magnetic field. This magnetic-dipole moment is associated to an angular momentum, or spin, and, therefore, is usually regarded as resulting from the current loop formed by the spinning electric charge. In some substances the spin dipole moments of the various electrons cancel completely within each atom or molecule; in others they do not cancel completely, so that each of their atoms or molecules has a resultant net dipole moment. These atomic or molecular magnetic dipoles are usually randomly oriented, mainly because of thermal agitation, so that they produce no net macroscopic field. However, a partial orientation in a particular direction may occur under the influence of an external magnetic field, or as a result of strong interatomic or intermolecular forces. In such cases the individual contributions of each atom or molecule add up to yield a finite macroscopic field and the material is said to be magnetized.

We shall see in Chapter 5 that the state of magnetization of a material can be taken into account macroscopically by associating with it a distribution of magnetic dipoles, whose moment density at each point is a function of the local state of matter. This representation is entirely analogous to that of electrically polarized materials. However, it is not immediately clear how a distribution of magnetic dipoles should be incorporated in the field equations as a field source. We shall see in Chapter 5 that, if each dipole of the distribution is regarded as a microscopic current loop, the entire dipole distribution is equivalent to a macroscopic current distribution whose density can be treated as a magnetization component of $\boldsymbol{J}$. However, the use of such a current model for magnetized materials makes it impossible to develop a macroscopic theory of electromagnetism that is both self-consistent and in agreement with experimental evidence. We shall see, on the other hand, that a satisfactory model can be obtained by treating magnetic dipoles in a manner entirely analogous to electric dipoles, just as if they consisted of magnetic charges with properties analogous to those of electric charges. This will require introducing in the field laws a magnetic-charge density $\rho^*$ and a magnetic-current density $\boldsymbol{J}^*$, analogous to $\rho$ and $\boldsymbol{J}$; Eqs. 1.12 and 1.16 will then become

$$\oint_C E_t\, ds + \frac{d}{dt}\int_S \mu_0 H_n\, da = -\int_S J_n{}^*\, da \tag{1.22}$$

$$\oint_S \mu_0 H_n\, da = \int_V \rho^*\, dv \tag{1.23}$$

The purpose of the above qualitative remarks about the role of matter as a source of electromagnetic fields is to introduce at this early stage the point of view that will characterize our treatment of macroscopic electromagnetic phenomena, and to justify the fact that, in the first four chapters, we shall confine our attention to free-space fields. It is convenient, for our purposes, to regard the phenomena of electric polarization and of magnetization of matter as consisting of two distinct parts: the action of an electromagnetic field in changing the state of polarization and magnetization of matter, and the action of polarized and magnetized matter in producing an electromagnetic field. The first part involves the functional relations between the state of polarization and the state of magnetization of matter on the one hand, and the electromagnetic field acting on matter on the other hand. These functional relations are often referred to as "constituent relations of matter." The physical origin of these relations and the microscopic characteristics of matter that are responsible for them are outside the scope of our discussion. We shall treat them instead empirically as experimentally determined properties of matter. The second part, namely, the role of polarized and magnetized matter as a source of electromagnetic fields is not only within the scope of our discussion but is a central part of it.

Another way of describing the same point of view is to say that matter behaves like a "controlled source," in the sense that matter is a source of electromagnetic field, but, at the same time, its source strength is a function of the field itself. In other words, the phenomena of polarization and magnetization involve a sort of "feedback control," whose characteristics are assumed to be given, or otherwise experimentally determinable, for each material.

This point of view leads us to consider any macroscopic electromagnetic field in matter as a free-space field in the presence of source distributions, which are either directly specified, or are expressible in terms of the field itself with the help of the constituent relations of the material involved. It follows that all field properties that do not involve the feedback link represented by the constituent relations can be studied without any reference to whether the sources are independent of the field or result from polarization and magnetization of matter. In particular, the field laws for macroscopic fields are the same within matter as outside matter, as long as the source densities which appear in the field laws are understood to include the components contributed by matter. We must keep in mind in this regard that, whereas electric sources can be present in the absence of polarized matter, magnetic sources can arise only from magnetized matter. For this reason, magnetic sources are not usually included in the free-space field equations; we have followed this convention in Sec. 1.3, and we shall continue to follow it in the next three chapters to avoid generating any misunderstanding as to the physical nature of magnetic charges and currents.

In view of the above arguments, we shall focus our attention first on free-space fields, produced by specified source distributions. Metallic conductors, however, will be included from the start in our discussion because they provide a wealth of interesting illustrations, and because of the simplicity of the constituent relation between electric field and conduction current, namely, Ohm's law. Polarizable and magnetizable materials will be taken up in detail in Chapter 5.

## 1.6 Summary and Conclusions

This chapter has been devoted to a review of the basic postulates of electromagnetism and of the laws governing the behavior of electromagnetic fields in free space. The main purpose of this review was to place in evidence the foundations on which we shall build our more advanced discussion of electromagnetic phenomena, free from the intermediate steps necessary in a first presentation to develop gradually the abstract concept of electromagnetic field. These foundations are

1. The law of conservation of charge.
2. The expression for the Lorentz force on a moving charge in terms of which the electric field and the magnetic field are defined.
3. The field laws in integral form that relate the electric field and magnetic field to each other and to the charge and current distributions.

These fundamental laws form a self-consistent set of relations in terms of which observable mutual forces between charges, whether stationary or in motion, can be described and predicted. The description and prediction of macroscopic forces between material bodies will require the additional postulation in Chapter 5 of macroscopic models for polarized and magnetized matter.

An important characteristic of the law of conservation of charge and of the field laws as expressed in Secs. 1.1 and 1.3 is that they relate contour integrals, surface integrals, and volume integrals of electromagnetic quantities. They are not equations of the type in which physical quantities are related to space or time derivatives of other physical quantities at the same point in space. On the other hand, such integral relations must be valid for all closed contour and associated surfaces, and for all closed surfaces and associated volumes. This arbitrary nature of the contours and surfaces suggests, as it is actually the case, that there should exist equivalent point relations between the same electromagnetic quantities and their time and space derivatives. For instance, the elementary derivation of plane waves found in many texts [2, Sec. 15.1] provides a good illustration of how the field equations in integral form yield point relations between the time derivative of one field vector and the space derivatives of the other.

Differential point relations describe the variations of vector fields from point to point rather than their properties over extended regions of space. As a result, they are much more convenient than integral relations, both conceptually and mathematically. The next chapter is devoted to the development of the mathematical tools necessary to express the laws of electromagnetism in the appropriate differential form.

## 1.7 Selected References

The following selected references should be helpful in reviewing the elementary aspects of electromagnetism, in acquiring a better historical perspective of the development of electromagnetism, and in developing a clearer understanding of the basic postulates and definitions discussed in this chapter, and a better appreciation of the problems involved in their choice.

1. J. C. Maxwell, *A Treatise on Electricity and Magnetism*, 3rd ed., reprinted by Dover Publications, New York, 1954. The preface to the first edition, dated February 1, 1873, gives the reader a good appreciation of Maxwell's point of view and of his fundamental contribution to the theory of electromagnetism.
2. N. H. Frank, *Introduction to Electricity and Optics*, 2nd ed., McGraw-Hill, New York, 1950. This is the physics textbook most appropriate in content and point of view for reviewing the elementary aspects of electromagnetism with which the reader is expected to be familiar.
3. A. Sommerfeld, *Electrodynamics*, Academic Press, New York, 1952. Section 1 of Part I is an historical review including some interesting biographical notes on the great men of electromagnetism. This review is particularly illuminating because Sommerfeld lived through the period in which electromagnetic theory became of age. Sections 2, 7, and 8 present a careful discussion of units and dimensions.
4. J. C. Slater and N. H. Frank, *Electromagnetism*, McGraw-Hill, New York, 1947. The introduction to Chapter 1 provides a good discussion of the development of electromagnetism.

## PROBLEMS

**Problem 1.1.** An electron moves with a velocity $v$ along the $z$-axis of a Cartesian coordinate system. A uniform magnetic field of magnitude $H$ is applied in the positive $x$-direction. What electric field is required to force the electron to follow a straight path along the $z$-axis?

**Problem 1.2.** An electron (charge $e = 1.6 \times 10^{-19}$ coulomb, mass $m = 9.1 \times 10^{-31}$ kg) moves in a uniform magnetic field $H = 10^6$ amp/m in a plane at right angles to the direction of $\boldsymbol{H}$. Show that the electron moves in a circular path of radius $r$, and find $r$ for an electron velocity of $v = 10^4$ m/sec.

**Problem 1.3.** In a cathode-ray oscilloscope, the electrons emitted from a heated filament are accelerated through a potential difference of 1000 v. The electrons then pass between two parallel deflecting plates, $2 \times 2$ cm, spaced 0.5 cm apart.

The electrons finally strike a fluorescent screen 30 cm from the rear edge of the deflecting plates.

What is the deflection of the spot on the fluorescent screen when a potential difference of 10 v is applied to the deflecting plates? Neglect the fringing field near the edges of the deflecting plates.

**Problem 1.4.** A cloud of charged particles is distributed in a hollow spherical cavity carved out of a perfectly conducting material. The charge density is

$$\rho(r) = \rho_0 \left(1 - \frac{r^2}{R^2}\right) \frac{\text{coulombs}}{\text{meter}^3}$$

where $\rho_0$ is a constant, $R$ is the radius of the cavity, and $r$ is the distance from the center of the cavity. Find the electric-field intensity at every point within the cavity. What is the surface-charge density on the surface of the cavity?

**Problem 1.5.** A spherical drop of fluid carries a charge of $q$ coulombs. Assume that the charge is uniformly distributed throughout the volume.

(a) Calculate the electric field and the potential both inside and outside the sphere.

(b) Two identical drops as above coalesce to form a single spherical drop. What is the potential at the surface of the new drop?

**Problem 1.6.** Given a very large plane sheet of charge (not a conductor) with uniform surface-charge density $\sigma$, find the *difference* of the electric-field vectors on either side of the sheet, far from the edges of the sheet.

**Problem 1.7.** The static electric field between two infinite parallel conducting plates held at a potential difference $V_0$ is perpendicular to the plates, and uniform.

(a) Show that the field satisfies Eq. 1.12 for all rectangular paths normal and parallel to the plates.

(b) Show that the field satisfies Eq. 1.17 for all parallelepipeds with faces normal and parallel to the plates. Show that the same equation is satisfied for any spherical surface.

(c) Find the surface-charge density on the plates by applying Eq. 1.17 to an appropriate surface.

**Problem 1.8.** (a) Find the electrostatic field produced by a point charge $q$.

(b) Show that Eq. 1.17 of the text is satisfied for a closed surface whose sides are formed by a circular cone with the apex at the point charge, and whose two endfaces are two spherical caps of radii $R_1$ and $R_2$ respectively ($R_2 > R_1$).

(c) Show that the field satisfies Eq. 1.12 for any planar contour consisting of two arcs of circles centered at the charge and two segments of straight lines passing by the charge.

**Problem 1.9.** Two infinite coaxial metallic cylinders are uniformly charged with a density $\lambda_i$ per unit length on the inner cylinder (outer radius $r_0$), and a charge $\lambda_0$ per unit length on the outer cylinder (inner radius $R_i$ and outer radius $R_0$). Determine the electric field between the cylinders, and in the outside space, and show that it satisfies both Eqs. 1.12 and 1.17.

**Problem 1.10.** A direct current is uniformly distributed over the cross section of a straight, infinitely long, circular cylindrical copper conductor of radius $r_0$. An equal amount of current flows in the opposite direction through a coaxial conductor of inner radius $R_i$ and outer radius $R_0$, and it is uniformly distributed over its cross section. Find the magnetic field both inside and outside the conductors, and show that it satisfies Eqs. 1.13 and 1.16.

**Problem 1.11.** The Supreme Council of Lower Slabovia has decreed that in honor of its famous scientist Popin, a new unit of flux be introduced, the popin (abbreviation "pop," dimensional symbol $P$).

$$1 \text{ pop} = 10 \text{ webers}$$

The coulomb has been abolished. Derive a table of dimensions as used by the Slabovian scientists. Use only the four fundamental dimensions, meter, second, kilogram, and popin. Find the explicit values and dimensions of the electric permittivity $\epsilon_0$ and the permeability $\mu_0$, as used by the Slabovians.

# CHAPTER TWO

# Vector Analysis

The purpose of this chapter is to review the elementary properties of vectors and to introduce some of the more advanced concepts useful in the study of vector fields.

In view of the over-all objective of this text, we shall most often select illustrative examples involving electric and magnetic fields. We should keep in mind, however, that the mathematical concept of vector field is basic to the study of many other physical phenomena; as a matter of fact, it is so fundamental in physics that it has become to many a "physical concept."

## 2.1 Vectors and Addition of Vectors

*Vectors*[1] are used to represent physical quantities, such as forces or velocities, which have a direction in space as well as a magnitude. They are represented geometrically by means of straight lines with an arrowhead indicating the direction of the vector, the length of the line being proportional to its magnitude. The end marked by the arrowhead is called the *terminus* and the other end is called the *origin*.

It is customary to stress the difference between vector quantities and quantities that can be described by a single number (because they do not have a direction) by referring to the latter as *scalars*. The product of a vector and a scalar is defined as a vector having a magnitude equal to the numerical product of the magnitude of the vector and the magnitude of the scalar, and a direction coinciding with that of the original vector or opposite to it, depending on whether the scalar is positive or negative. Thus, multiplying a vector by $-1$ is equivalent to reversing its direction.

[1] Vectors are indicated by symbols in italic boldface, and their components as well as other scalar quantities by symbols in italic lightface.

The sum of two vectors $\boldsymbol{A}$ and $\boldsymbol{B}$ is defined geometrically, as illustrated in Fig. 2.1, as a vector $\boldsymbol{C}$ forming with $\boldsymbol{A}$ and $\boldsymbol{B}$ a triangle in which the origin of $\boldsymbol{B}$ is made to coincide with the terminus of $\boldsymbol{A}$. The origin of $\boldsymbol{C}$ coincides with that of $\boldsymbol{A}$, and its terminus coincides with the terminus of $\boldsymbol{B}$. It is clear from Fig. 2.1 that interchanging $\boldsymbol{A}$ and $\boldsymbol{B}$ does not affect the resultant $\boldsymbol{C}$. Thus

$$\boldsymbol{A} + \boldsymbol{B} = \boldsymbol{B} + \boldsymbol{A} \tag{2.1}$$

or, expressed in words, the operation of addition defined above follows the commutative law. The addition of several vectors may be performed by iterating the operation for two vectors. It can readily be shown that such an addition follows the associative law, i.e.,

$$(\boldsymbol{A} + \boldsymbol{B}) + \boldsymbol{C} = \boldsymbol{A} + (\boldsymbol{B} + \boldsymbol{C}) \tag{2.2}$$

Vectors have been defined above without reference to any system of coordinates. Furthermore, vector addition and all other vector operations can be defined similarly without reference to any system of coordinates. Although the usefulness of vector notations results primarily from this property of the basic definitions, it is convenient in some instances to refer a vector to a particular system of coordinates by resolving it into components along directions specified by the system. We shall be concerned in these notes only with components in mutually orthogonal directions, and therefore, we shall limit the present discussion to this special case.

Let us consider three mutually orthogonal directions which we may identify with the $x$-, $y$-, $z$-axes of a system of Cartesian coordinates, and let us define unit vectors (vectors of unit magnitude) $\boldsymbol{i}_x$, $\boldsymbol{i}_y$, $\boldsymbol{i}_z$ in the directions of such axes. Representing a vector in terms of its Cartesian components amounts to expressing it as the sum of three vectors parallel to the orthogonal axes, i.e.,

$$\boldsymbol{A} = \boldsymbol{i}_x A_x + \boldsymbol{i}_y A_y + \boldsymbol{i}_z A_z \tag{2.3}$$

The scalars $A_x$, $A_y$, $A_z$ are the components of $\boldsymbol{A}$ and may be obtained

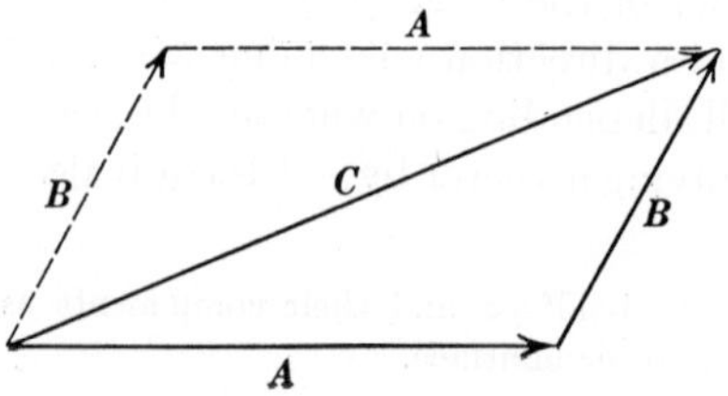


**Fig. 2.1.** Addition of vectors.

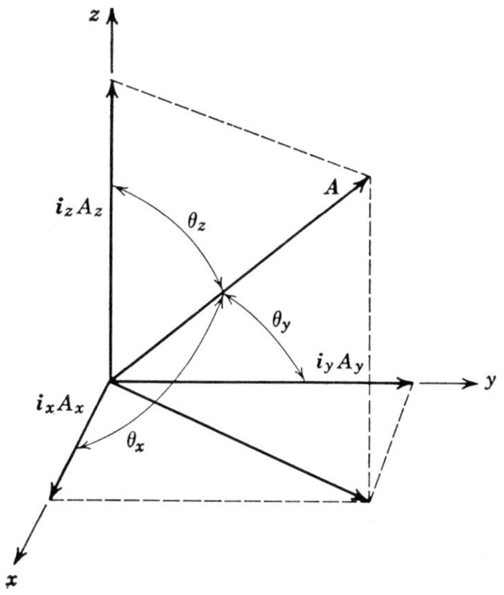


**Fig. 2.2.** Cartesian components of the vector $\boldsymbol{A}$.

by projecting $\boldsymbol{A}$ on the three axes, as indicated in Fig. 2.2. Thus, if $\theta_x$, $\theta_y$, $\theta_z$ are the angles between $\boldsymbol{A}$ and the positive directions of the axes,

$$\begin{aligned} A_x &= |A| \cos \theta_x \\ A_y &= |A| \cos \theta_y \\ A_z &= |A| \cos \theta_z \end{aligned} \tag{2.4}$$

where $|A|$ represents the magnitude of $\boldsymbol{A}$, a positive number.

The component of the vector sum of $\boldsymbol{A}$ and $\boldsymbol{B}$ in the direction of any axis is the sum of the components of $\boldsymbol{A}$ and $\boldsymbol{B}$ along the same axis. We thus have

$$\begin{aligned} \boldsymbol{A} + \boldsymbol{B} &= (\boldsymbol{i}_xA_x + \boldsymbol{i}_yA_y + \boldsymbol{i}_zA_z) + (\boldsymbol{i}_xB_x + \boldsymbol{i}_yB_y + \boldsymbol{i}_zB_z) \\ &= \boldsymbol{i}_x(A_x + B_x) + \boldsymbol{i}_y(A_y + B_y) + \boldsymbol{i}_z(A_z + B_z) \end{aligned} \tag{2.5}$$

This equation follows directly from the associative property of vector addition.

## 2.2 Products of Vectors

There are two types of products of interest to us: the *scalar product* and the *vector product*. As the names indicate, the scalar product of two vectors is a *scalar quantity* whereas the vector product is a *vector*.

The *scalar product* (dot product) of $\boldsymbol{A}$ and $\boldsymbol{B}$ is indicated by $\boldsymbol{A}\cdot\boldsymbol{B}$, and is defined by

$$\boldsymbol{A}\cdot\boldsymbol{B} = |A|\,|B|\cos\theta \tag{2.6}$$

where $\theta$ is the angle between $\boldsymbol{A}$ and $\boldsymbol{B}$. Noting that $|A|\cos\theta$ is the component of $\boldsymbol{A}$ in the direction of $\boldsymbol{B}$, we may say that the scalar product $\boldsymbol{A}\cdot\boldsymbol{B}$ is the numerical product of the magnitude of $\boldsymbol{B}$ and the component of $\boldsymbol{A}$ in the direction of $\boldsymbol{B}$. Alternatively, we may say that $\boldsymbol{A}\cdot\boldsymbol{B}$ is the product of the magnitude of $\boldsymbol{A}$ and the component of $\boldsymbol{B}$ in the direction of $\boldsymbol{A}$.

An example of scalar product is provided, for instance, by the work done by a force $\boldsymbol{A}$ in moving an object a distance $\boldsymbol{B}$ along a straight line. This work is equal to the product of the magnitude of the displacement and the component of the force in the direction of the displacement, and therefore to the scalar product $\boldsymbol{A}\cdot\boldsymbol{B}$ in accordance with the above definition.

It is clear from the above definition that the scalar product obeys the commutative law, i.e.,

$$\boldsymbol{A}\cdot\boldsymbol{B} = \boldsymbol{B}\cdot\boldsymbol{A} \tag{2.7}$$

It obeys also the distributive law,

$$(\boldsymbol{A} + \boldsymbol{B})\cdot\boldsymbol{C} = \boldsymbol{A}\cdot\boldsymbol{C} + \boldsymbol{B}\cdot\boldsymbol{C} \tag{2.8}$$

because the component of $\boldsymbol{A} + \boldsymbol{B}$ in the direction of $\boldsymbol{C}$ is the sum of the components of $\boldsymbol{A}$ and $\boldsymbol{B}$ in the same direction. The associative law does not apply to the scalar product because no more than two vectors can be so multiplied. It might be well to stress in this connection that

$$(\boldsymbol{A}\cdot\boldsymbol{B})\boldsymbol{C} \neq \boldsymbol{A}(\boldsymbol{B}\cdot\boldsymbol{C}) \tag{2.9}$$

In fact, the vector on the left is parallel to $\boldsymbol{C}$, whereas that on the right is parallel to $\boldsymbol{A}$.

The scalar product of $\boldsymbol{A}$ and $\boldsymbol{B}$ may be readily expressed in terms of their components by noting that

$$\begin{aligned} \boldsymbol{i}_x\cdot\boldsymbol{i}_x &= \boldsymbol{i}_y\cdot\boldsymbol{i}_y = \boldsymbol{i}_z\cdot\boldsymbol{i}_z = 1 \\ \boldsymbol{i}_x\cdot\boldsymbol{i}_y &= \boldsymbol{i}_x\cdot\boldsymbol{i}_z = \boldsymbol{i}_y\cdot\boldsymbol{i}_z = 0 \end{aligned} \tag{2.10}$$

We thus have

$$\begin{aligned} \boldsymbol{A}\cdot\boldsymbol{B} &= (\boldsymbol{i}_xA_x + \boldsymbol{i}_yA_y + \boldsymbol{i}_zA_z)\cdot(\boldsymbol{i}_xB_x + \boldsymbol{i}_yB_y + \boldsymbol{i}_zB_z) \\ &= A_xB_x + A_yB_y + A_zB_z \end{aligned} \tag{2.11}$$

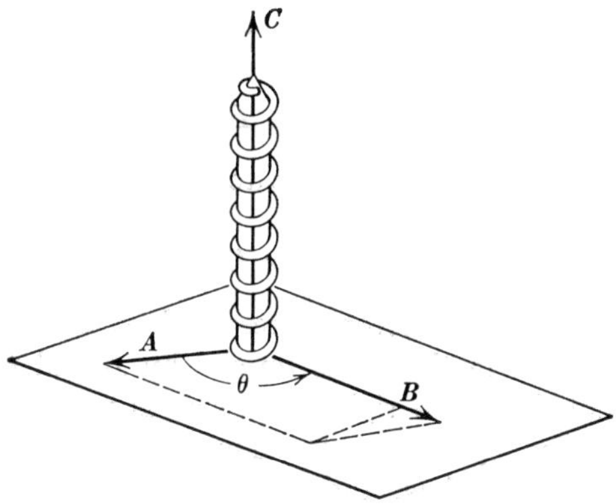


**Fig. 2.3.** Vector product.

That is, the scalar product of two vectors is equal to the sum of the products of the corresponding components.

The *vector product* (cross product) of $\boldsymbol{A}$ and $\boldsymbol{B}$ is a vector

$$\boldsymbol{C} = \boldsymbol{A} \times \boldsymbol{B} \tag{2.12}$$

normal to both $\boldsymbol{A}$ and $\boldsymbol{B}$, i.e., to the plane defined by them. The direction of $\boldsymbol{C}$ is obtained from $\boldsymbol{A}$ and $\boldsymbol{B}$ by the right-handed-screw rule, as indicated in Fig. 2.3; i.e., if the origins of $\boldsymbol{A}$ and $\boldsymbol{B}$ are made to coincide, a right-handed screw turning from $\boldsymbol{A}$ to $\boldsymbol{B}$ through the smaller angle $\theta$ will advance in the direction of $\boldsymbol{C}$. The magnitude of $\boldsymbol{C}$ is given by

$$|C| = |A|\,|B| \sin\theta \tag{2.13}$$

where the value of $\sin\theta$ is never negative because $\theta \leq \pi$. Since $|A| \sin\theta$ is the component of $\boldsymbol{A}$ normal to $\boldsymbol{B}$, $|C|$ is equal to the area of the parallelogram formed by $\boldsymbol{A}$ and $\boldsymbol{B}$, as illustrated in Fig. 2.3.

An example of vector product is the force exerted by a magnetic field, represented by a vector $\mu_0\boldsymbol{H}$, on a unit charge moving with a velocity $\boldsymbol{v}$. In accordance with Eq. 1.2, this force is given by the vector product $\boldsymbol{v} \times \mu_0\boldsymbol{H}$. It is therefore normal to both $\boldsymbol{v}$ and $\mu_0\boldsymbol{H}$, and its magnitude is equal to the product of the magnitudes of the two vectors and of the sine of the angle between them. Another example is the moment of a force $\boldsymbol{F}$ about a point $P$, displaced a distance $\boldsymbol{r}$ from the point at which the force is applied. This moment is, by definition, a vector normal to the plane of $\boldsymbol{F}$ and $\boldsymbol{r}$; its magnitude is equal to the product of the magnitude of $\boldsymbol{r}$ and the component of $\boldsymbol{F}$ normal to $\boldsymbol{r}$. Thus, in accordance with the above definition, the moment of $\boldsymbol{F}$ about $P$ can be expressed as the vector product $\boldsymbol{F} \times \boldsymbol{r}$.

It is clear, from the preceding definition of the direction of the vector product, that

$$\boldsymbol{B} \times \boldsymbol{A} = -\boldsymbol{A} \times \boldsymbol{B} \tag{2.14}$$

Thus the vector product does not obey the commutative law. Furthermore,

$$(\boldsymbol{A} \times \boldsymbol{B}) \times \boldsymbol{C} \neq \boldsymbol{A} \times (\boldsymbol{B} \times \boldsymbol{C}) \tag{2.15}$$

In fact, the vector represented by the left-hand side is normal to $\boldsymbol{C}$ and lies in the plane formed by $\boldsymbol{A}$ and $\boldsymbol{B}$, whereas the vector represented by the right-hand side is normal to $\boldsymbol{A}$ and lies in the plane formed by $\boldsymbol{B}$ and $\boldsymbol{C}$. Thus the vector product does not obey the associative law, and the triple product $\boldsymbol{A} \times \boldsymbol{B} \times \boldsymbol{C}$ does not have a unique meaning unless the order in which the operations are to be performed is specified. On the other hand, it can be shown that the vector product obeys the distributive law, i.e.,

$$(\boldsymbol{A} + \boldsymbol{B}) \times \boldsymbol{C} = \boldsymbol{A} \times \boldsymbol{C} + \boldsymbol{B} \times \boldsymbol{C} \tag{2.16}$$

The vector product $\boldsymbol{A} \times \boldsymbol{B}$ may be conveniently expressed in terms of the rectangular components of $\boldsymbol{A}$ and $\boldsymbol{B}$ by noting that

$$\begin{gathered} \boldsymbol{i}_x \times \boldsymbol{i}_x = \boldsymbol{i}_y \times \boldsymbol{i}_y = \boldsymbol{i}_z \times \boldsymbol{i}_z = 0 \\ \boldsymbol{i}_x \times \boldsymbol{i}_y = \boldsymbol{i}_z \qquad \boldsymbol{i}_y \times \boldsymbol{i}_z = \boldsymbol{i}_x \qquad \boldsymbol{i}_z \times \boldsymbol{i}_x = \boldsymbol{i}_y \end{gathered} \tag{2.17}$$

We have then

$$\begin{aligned} \boldsymbol{A} \times \boldsymbol{B} &= (\boldsymbol{i}_x A_x + \boldsymbol{i}_y A_y + \boldsymbol{i}_z A_z) \times (\boldsymbol{i}_x B_x + \boldsymbol{i}_y B_y + \boldsymbol{i}_z B_z) \\ &= \boldsymbol{i}_x(A_y B_z - A_z B_y) + \boldsymbol{i}_y(A_z B_x - A_x B_z) \\ &\quad + \boldsymbol{i}_z(A_x B_y - A_y B_x) \end{aligned} \tag{2.18}$$

This expression can be readily obtained by expanding the determinant

$$\boldsymbol{A} \times \boldsymbol{B} = \begin{vmatrix} \boldsymbol{i}_x & \boldsymbol{i}_y & \boldsymbol{i}_z \\ A_x & A_y & A_z \\ B_x & B_y & B_z \end{vmatrix} \tag{2.19}$$

in terms of the elements of the first row, i.e., in terms of the unit vectors.

Vector and scalar products are combined in the *scalar triple product* $\boldsymbol{A} \cdot (\boldsymbol{B} \times \boldsymbol{C})$. The value of this triple product is equal to the volume of the parallelepiped formed by the three vectors, as illustrated in Fig. 2.4. In fact, the magnitude of $\boldsymbol{B} \times \boldsymbol{C}$ is equal to the area of the base of the parallelepiped, and the component of $\boldsymbol{A}$ in the direction of $\boldsymbol{B} \times \boldsymbol{C}$ is equal to the height of the parallelepiped.

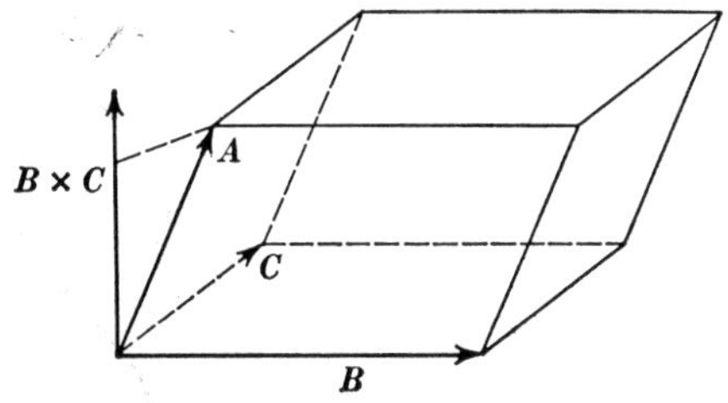


**Fig. 2.4.** Scalar triple product.

It may be readily seen from Eqs. 2.11 and 2.19 that the scalar triple product is equal to the value of the determinant

$$\boldsymbol{A}\cdot(\boldsymbol{B}\times\boldsymbol{C}) = \begin{vmatrix} A_x & A_y & A_z \\ B_x & B_y & B_z \\ C_x & C_y & C_z \end{vmatrix} \tag{2.20}$$

Noting that the value of a determinant changes sign when any two rows are interchanged leads immediately to the useful relations:

$$\boldsymbol{A}\cdot(\boldsymbol{B}\times\boldsymbol{C}) = \boldsymbol{B}\cdot(\boldsymbol{C}\times\boldsymbol{A}) = \boldsymbol{C}\cdot(\boldsymbol{A}\times\boldsymbol{B}) = -(\boldsymbol{C}\times\boldsymbol{B})\cdot\boldsymbol{A}$$

$$= -(\boldsymbol{A}\times\boldsymbol{C})\cdot\boldsymbol{B} = -(\boldsymbol{B}\times\boldsymbol{A})\cdot\boldsymbol{C} \tag{2.21}$$

Another set of useful relations may be derived from the vector triple product $\boldsymbol{A}\times(\boldsymbol{B}\times\boldsymbol{C})$. It was noted above that this vector lies in the plane defined by $\boldsymbol{B}$ and $\boldsymbol{C}$. Thus it must be possible to express it as the sum of two vectors proportional to $\boldsymbol{B}$ and $\boldsymbol{C}$. Detailed evaluation of this triple product shows that

$$\boldsymbol{A}\times(\boldsymbol{B}\times\boldsymbol{C}) = (\boldsymbol{A}\cdot\boldsymbol{C})\boldsymbol{B} - (\boldsymbol{A}\cdot\boldsymbol{B})\boldsymbol{C} \tag{2.22}$$

We obtain similarly

$$(\boldsymbol{A}\times\boldsymbol{B})\times\boldsymbol{C} = (\boldsymbol{A}\cdot\boldsymbol{C})\boldsymbol{B} - (\boldsymbol{B}\cdot\boldsymbol{C})\boldsymbol{A} \tag{2.23}$$

## 2.3 Orthogonal Coordinates

The physical quantities with which we shall be concerned in connection with electromagnetism are, in general, functions of position as well as of time. In other words, the magnitude and the direction of the vector representing, let us say, the electric-field intensity vary from point to point as well as from time to time. Thus, to describe

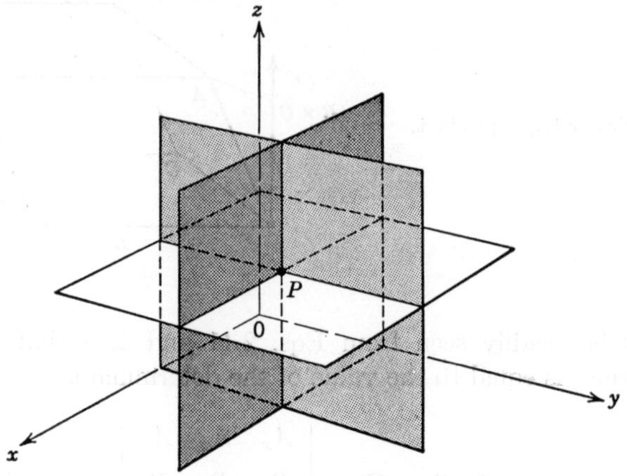


**Fig. 2.5.** Identification of a point as the intersection of three orthogonal planes.

the spatial variations of such physical quantities, we must be able to label in a suitable manner all points of space.

A point in a three-dimensional space can be identified as the intersection of three suitably chosen surfaces; for instance, we may identify a point $P$ as the intersection of three mutually orthogonal planes, as illustrated in Fig. 2.5. The planes are identified, in turn, by their normal distances from a reference point 0. Clearly, their distances from 0 are just the Cartesian coordinates of the point. Similarly, a point $P$ may be identified as the intersection of three spheres centered at three different reference points. Since the spheres must be identified in turn by giving their radii, this method is equivalent to specifying the position of $P$ in terms of its distance from the three reference points.

In general, given three independent families of surfaces,

$$f_1(x, y, z) = u_1 \tag{2.24}$$

$$f_2(x, y, z) = u_2 \tag{2.25}$$

$$f_3(x, y, z) = u_3 \tag{2.26}$$

each of which covering the entire space, any point $P$ can be identified by the values of the three parameters $u_1$, $u_2$, $u_3$ corresponding, respectively, to the particular surface of each family that passes by $P$. Thus the parameters $u_1$, $u_2$, $u_3$ form a new set of coordinates and constitute a generalization of the Cartesian coordinates $x$, $y$, $z$. Suppose. for instance, that the three families of surfaces are given by the equations

$$\sqrt{x^2 + y^2} = u_1 = r \tag{2.27}$$

$$\cos^{-1} \frac{x}{\sqrt{x^2 + y^2}} = u_2 = \varphi \tag{2.28}$$

$$z = u_3 \tag{2.29}$$

with the understanding that the square root is taken with the positive sign, and $0 \leq \varphi < 2\pi$. Then the first family consists of coaxial circular cylinders of radius $r$, with their axis coinciding with the $z$-axis, as illustrated in Fig. 2.6. The second family consists of radial planes parallel to the $z$-axis and intersecting on it, each member of the family being identified by the angle $\varphi$ formed with the $xz$-plane. The third family consists of planes normal to the $z$-axis and identified by their distance from the origin, i.e., by their $z$ coordinate. Thus each point $P$ can be identified by the values of the three new coordinates $r$, $\varphi$, and $z$, corresponding, respectively, to the particular surfaces of the three families that pass by $P$. We refer to this system of coordinates as *circular-cylindrical.* It will be noted that, if we disregard the $z$ coordinate and focus our attention on the family of concentric circles and on the family of radial lines formed by the intersection of the cylinders and

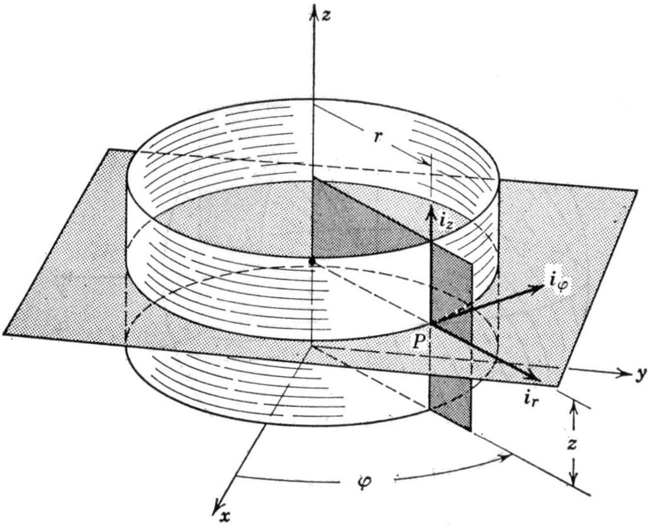


**Fig. 2.6.** Circular-cylindrical coordinates.

the radial planes with the $xy$-plane, the three-dimensional circular-cylindrical system reduces to a two-dimensional *polar system* of coordinates.

As a second example, let us consider the three families of surfaces defined by the equations

$$\sqrt{x^2 + y^2 + z^2} = u_1 = r \tag{2.30}$$

$$\cos^{-1} \frac{z}{\sqrt{x^2 + y^2 + z^2}} = u_2 = \theta \tag{2.31}$$

$$\cos^{-1} \frac{x}{\sqrt{x^2 + y^2}} = u_3 = \varphi \tag{2.32}$$

with the understanding that both square roots are taken with the positive sign, that $0 \leq \theta \leq \pi$, and that $0 \leq \varphi < 2\pi$. The first family consists of spheres of radius $r$ centered at the origin, as illustrated in

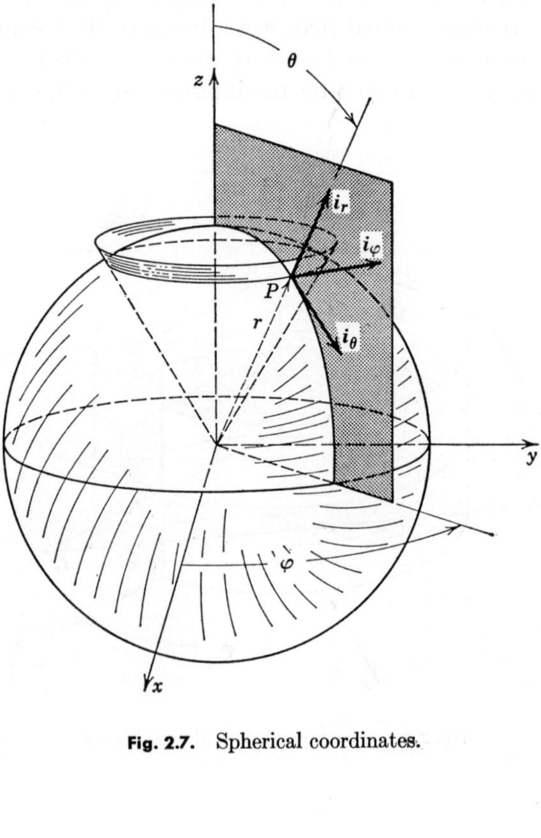


**Fig. 2.7.** Spherical coordinates.

Fig. 2.7. The second family consists of cones of aperture $\theta$, all with their apex at the origin and their axis coinciding with the $z$-axis. The third family consists of radial (meridian) half-planes, parallel to the $z$-axis and intersecting on it, with each plane identified by the meridian angle $\varphi$ formed with the $xz$-plane. Thus each point $P$ can be identified by the three *spherical coordinates* $r$, $\theta$, and $\varphi$ corresponding, respectively, to the particular surfaces of the three families that pass by $P$.

The Cartesian system, the circular-cylindrical system, and the spherical system are the three best known examples of *orthogonal systems of coordinates.* Orthogonal systems are characterized by the fact that the three families of surfaces are mutually orthogonal. Other orthogonal systems are the *elliptic-cylindrical,* the *bipolar-cylindrical,* the *ellipsoidal,* the *spheroidal,* etc. Nonorthogonal systems are of little practical importance because of the mathematical complexity associated with them. For this reason, we shall limit our general discussion to orthogonal systems, with the circular-cylindrical and the spherical used throughout as illustrations.

Let us now turn our attention to how the three orthogonal coordinates $u_1$, $u_2$, $u_3$ vary from point to point, and to how differential elements of distance, area, and volume can be expressed in terms of increments of these three new variables. We observe, first of all, that the value of a coordinate remains constant over any particular surface of the family corresponding to it. For instance, the coordinate $r$ of a spherical system assumes the same value at all points of any particular spherical surface centered at the origin; similarly, the coordinate $\varphi$ is constant over any meridian half-plane (a half-plane containing the $z$-axis). We observe next that two of the coordinates remain constant over any line formed by the intersection of two surfaces belonging to different families, namely, the two coordinates associated with the two surfaces. Thus, the coordinates $r$ and $\varphi$ of a spherical system are constant over a meridian semicircle formed by the intersection of a sphere centered at the origin with a meridian half-plane. The position of a point over this meridian semicircle is specified by the third coordinate $\theta$, so that the circle plays the role of a coordinate line. Similarly, each radial line from the origin, formed by the intersection of a meridian half-plane with a cone of aperture $\theta$, constitutes a coordinate line over which the coordinate $r$ varies while the coordinates $\theta$ and $\varphi$ are constant. In general, the three families of coordinate surfaces generate, through pairwise intersection, three corresponding families of coordinate lines. The lines of each family are the loci over which two of the variables remain constant—namely, those corresponding to the generating families of surfaces—and the third one varies. In the spherical system, illustrated in Fig. 2.7, the family of lines over which only $r$ varies consists of all radial lines from the origin. The family of lines over which only $\theta$ varies consists of the meridian semicircles formed by the intersection of spheres with meridian half-planes. The family of lines over which only $\varphi$ varies consists of the circles formed by the intersection of spheres centered at the origin with coaxial cones having their apex also at the origin. In the circular-cylindrical system illustrated in Fig. 2.6, the family of lines over which only $r$ varies consists of the radial lines normal to the $z$-axis. The family of lines over which only $\varphi$ varies consists of the concentric circles formed by the intersection of coaxial cylinders with planes normal to the $z$-axis. The family of lines over which only $z$ varies consists of all straight lines parallel to the $z$-axis.

It is convenient to define, at each point of space, three unit vectors tangent to the three coordinate lines passing by the point, and with directions coinciding with those in which the values of the three coordinates increase. In a circular-cylindrical system, the unit vectors are $\boldsymbol{i}_r$, $\boldsymbol{i}_\varphi$, $\boldsymbol{i}_z$, as indicated in Fig. 2.6; in a spherical system, the unit vectors are $\boldsymbol{i}_r$, $\boldsymbol{i}_\theta$, $\boldsymbol{i}_\varphi$, as indicated in Fig. 2.7. The directions of these vectors vary from point to point; but, because of the mutual orthogonality between the families of surfaces, each unit vector is normal to the coordinate surface corresponding to the same variable. For instance, in a spherical system, $\boldsymbol{i}_r$ is normal to the spherical surface of radius $r$ passing by the point, $\boldsymbol{i}_\theta$ is normal to the cone, and $\boldsymbol{i}_\varphi$ is normal to the meridian plane. It follows, of course, that for any orthogonal system the unit vectors at any point are mutually orthogonal, and that the families of coordinate lines are also mutually orthogonal and consist of the trajectories normal to the corresponding families of coordinate surfaces.

If the points along the coordinate lines of a family are labeled with the corresponding values of the coordinate variable, equal increments of the variable do not necessarily correspond to line segments of equal length. In general, if $du_i$ is a differential increment of one of the variables, and $ds_i$ is the differential length of the corresponding line segment, we have

$$ds_i = h_i\,du_i \tag{2.33}$$

where the *metrical coefficient* $h_i$ may be a function of all three coordinates. The proper expression for $h_i$ may be obtained directly by inspection, in simple cases, or formally from the equations defining the families of coordinate surfaces, as follows. The differential element of length $ds_i$ is first expressed in terms of the differentials of the Cartesian variables,

$$ds_i^2 = dx^2 + dy^2 + dz^2 \tag{2.34}$$

Next, the differentials of the Cartesian variables are expressed in terms of the differential $du_i$ of the coordinate $u_i$,

$$dx = \frac{\partial x}{\partial u_i} du_i \tag{2.35}$$

$$dy = \frac{\partial y}{\partial u_i} du_i \tag{2.36}$$

$$dz = \frac{\partial z}{\partial u_i} du_i \tag{2.37}$$

where the partial derivatives are obtained from Eqs. 2.24, 2.25, and 2.26. Finally, substitution of Eqs. 2.35, 2.36, and 2.37 into Eq. 2.34 yields, by comparison with Eq. 2.33,

$$h_i^2 = \left(\frac{\partial x}{\partial u_i}\right)^2 + \left(\frac{\partial y}{\partial u_i}\right)^2 + \left(\frac{\partial z}{\partial u_i}\right)^2 \tag{2.38}$$

The differential element of area corresponding to differential increments of any pair of variables is a rectangle with sides equal to the coordinate-line segments corresponding to the differential increments of the variables, as illustrated in Fig. 2.8. Thus, for instance, the differential element of area corresponding to the increments $du_2$, $du_3$,

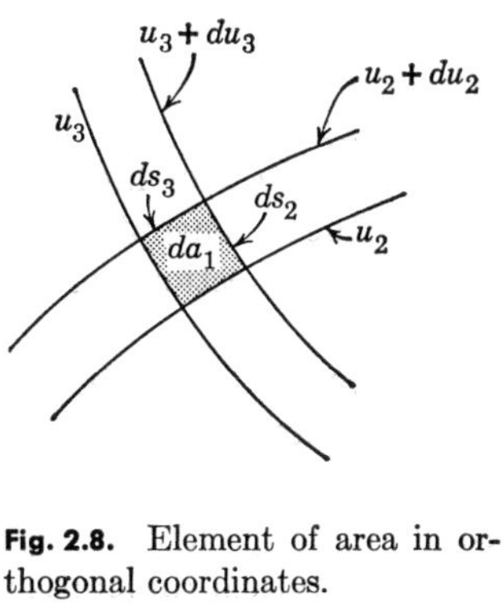


**Fig. 2.8.** Element of area in orthogonal coordinates.

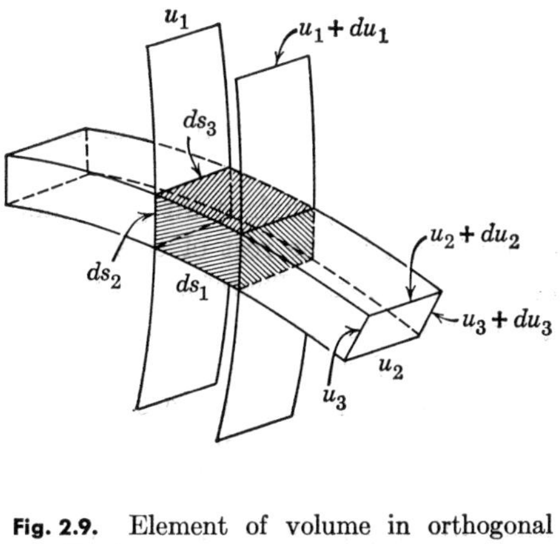


**Fig. 2.9.** Element of volume in orthogonal coordinates.

and normal to the coordinate line $u_1$ is

$$da_1 = ds_2\, ds_3 = h_2 h_3\, du_2\, du_3 \tag{2.39}$$

Similarly, the differential element of volume corresponding to increments of all three variables is a rectangular parallelepiped with edges equal to the corresponding line segments, as illustrated in Fig. 2.9. Thus we have

$$dv = ds_1\, ds_2\, ds_3 = h_1 h_2 h_3\, du_1\, du_2\, du_3 \tag{2.40}$$

The above expressions yield, for circular-cylindrical coordinates,

$$x = r\cos\varphi \qquad y = r\sin\varphi \qquad z = z \tag{2.41}$$

$$h_r = 1 \qquad h_\varphi = r \qquad h_z = 1 \tag{2.42}$$

$$ds_r = dr \qquad ds_\varphi = r\, d\varphi \qquad ds_z = dz \tag{2.43}$$

$$da_r = r\, d\varphi\, dz \qquad da_\varphi = dr\, dz \qquad da_z = r\, dr\, d\varphi \tag{2.44}$$

$$dv = r\, dr\, d\varphi\, dz \tag{2.45}$$

For spherical coordinates we obtain

$$x = r\sin\theta\cos\varphi \qquad y = r\sin\theta\sin\varphi \qquad z = r\cos\theta \tag{2.46}$$

$$h_r = 1 \qquad h_\theta = r \qquad h_\varphi = r\sin\theta \tag{2.47}$$

$$ds_r = dr \qquad ds_\theta = r\, d\theta \qquad ds_\varphi = r\sin\theta\, d\varphi \tag{2.48}$$

$$da_r = r^2\sin\theta\, d\theta\, d\varphi \qquad da_\theta = r\sin\theta\, dr\, d\varphi \qquad da_\varphi = r\, dr\, d\theta \tag{2.49}$$

$$dv = r^2\sin\theta\, dr\, d\theta\, d\varphi \tag{2.50}$$

## 2.4 Line, Surface, and Volume Integrals

Line integrals, surface integrals, and volume integrals play an important part in the rest of this chapter, and, as a matter of fact, in this entire book. Therefore, it is wise to review these concepts and agree on the terminology that we shall use in their connection before making any further extensive use of them.

It is important to make a sharp distinction between the definitions of line integral, surface integral, and volume integral, and the methods for evaluating them. Although we shall occasionally evaluate some of these integrals, we are primarily interested in their geometric significance. Thus, it is important to prevent the analytical difficulties often encountered in their evaluation from obscuring their conceptual simplicity.

The definitions of line integral, surface integral, and volume integral are natural extensions of the definition of the usual one-dimensional integral as the limit of a sum. Let us review briefly this definition of the one-dimensional integral. If $f(x)$ is a function of $x$, defined for a range of values of $x$ including the points $a < b < c$, the definite integral

$$\int_a^c f(x)\,dx$$

is an additive function of the interval of integration, in the sense that

$$\int_a^c f(x)\,dx = \int_a^b f(x)\,dx + \int_b^c f(x)\,dx \tag{2.51}$$

Let $f(x)$ be continuous and single-valued over the range of values of $x$ considered, and subdivide a particular interval, such as $a$, $b$, into $n$ contiguous intervals of lengths $\delta x_1, \delta x_2, \cdots, \delta x_i, \cdots, \delta x_n$. Then, if $f_i$ represents the value of $f(x)$ at any point within the interval $\delta x_i$, it can be shown that the limit

$$\lim_{n\to\infty} \sum_{i=1}^{n} f_i\,\delta x_i = \int_a^b f(x)\,dx \tag{2.52}$$

is independent of the manner in which the interval $a$, $b$ is subdivided as long as all the lengths of all the intervals $\delta x_i$ approach zero when $n$ approaches infinity. Thus this limit can be taken as a definition of the definite integral on the right-hand side of Eq. 2.52. Conversely, it can be shown that

$$f(b) = \frac{d}{db}\int_a^b f(x)\,dx \tag{2.53}$$

In other words, the operations of differentiation and integration, as defined by Eq. 2.52, are the inverse of each other.

The integral of a scalar function over a prescribed path in three-dimensional space can be defined in a similar manner. Let $C$ be a curve joining the points $P$ and $Q$, and $f(x, y, z)$ be a function of position, defined in a region of space including $C$. The line integral of $f(x, y, z)$ over the curve $C$ is an additive function of the interval of integration along $C$, in the same sense as indicated by Eq. 2.51 for a one-dimensional integral. Let $s$ be the distance along the curve $C$, measured from an arbitrary origin in the direction from $P$ to $Q$, and subdivide $C$ in $n$ contiguous intervals of lengths $\delta s_1, \delta s_2, \cdots, \delta s_i, \cdots,$

$\delta s_n$. Then, if $f(x, y, z)$ is continuous and single-valued in a region including $C$, and $f_i$ is its value at some point of the interval $\delta s_i$, it can be shown that the limit

$$\lim_{n \to \infty} \sum_{i=1}^{n} f_i \, \delta s_i = \int_{s(P)}^{s(Q)} f(x, y, z) \, ds \qquad (2.54)$$

is independent of the manner in which the curve is subdivided, as long as all the lengths $\delta s_i$ approach zero when $n$ approaches infinity. Thus, this limit can be used to define the line integral on the right-hand side of Eq. 2.54.

The limitation on this definition resulting from the requirement that the function $f(x, y, z)$ be continuous and single-valued is not serious in connection with physical problems because all functions of interest are at least piecewise continuous and single-valued over any given curve. Then, if the function is not singular, the integral over the entire curve can be defined as the sum of the integrals over the contiguous intervals over which the function meets the above requirements. Singularities at the boundaries between intervals can be handled as usual by means of suitable limiting processes.

In the most common type of line integral the function $f(x, y, z)$ is the tangential component of some vector. For instance, the work per unit charge done by an electrostatic field in moving a positive charge from a point $P$ to a point $Q$ along a path $C$ is

$$\int_{s(P)}^{s(Q)} E_t \, ds = \int_C \boldsymbol{E} \cdot \boldsymbol{ds} \qquad (2.55)$$

where $E_t$ is the component of $\boldsymbol{E}$ tangent to $C$ in the direction from $P$ to $Q$, and $\boldsymbol{ds}$ is a differential vector tangent to $C$ of magnitude equal to $ds$ and directed from $P$ to $Q$, as illustrated in Fig. 2.10. It is clear that the scalar product of $\boldsymbol{E}$ and $\boldsymbol{ds}$ is equal to the tangential component of $\boldsymbol{E}$ multiplied by the scalar increment of length $ds$. When the symbol $C$ is used to represent the path of integration as on the right-hand side of Eq. 2.55, it is understood that the specification of $C$ includes not only the path of integration but also its direction, i.e., the direction of $\boldsymbol{ds}$. When the end points of $C$ coincide, i.e., when $C$ forms a closed contour, this characteristic of the path of integration is emphasized by adding a circle to the sign of integral as in

$$\oint_C \boldsymbol{E} \cdot \boldsymbol{ds}$$

The definition of surface integral proceeds also along similar lines. Given a surface $S$ and a function $f(x, y, z)$ defined in a region including

$S$, the surface integral of $f(x, y, z)$ is an additive function of the elements of area of $S$ in the sense that, if $S_1$ and $S_2$ are two, nonoverlapping parts of $S$, the integral over $S_1 + S_2$ is the sum of the integrals over $S_1$ and $S_2$, separately. Let us subdivide $S$ into $n$ contiguous elements, of areas $\delta a_1, \delta a_2, \cdots, \delta a_i, \cdots, \delta a_n$, and assume that $f(x, y, z)$ is continuous and single-valued over a region including $S$. Then, if $f_i$ is the value of $f(x, y, z)$ at some point within the element of area $\delta a_i$, it can be shown that the limit

$$\lim_{n \to \infty} \sum_{i=1}^{n} f_i \, \delta a_i = \int_S f(x, y, z) \, da \tag{2.56}$$

is independent of the manner in which $S$ is subdivided, provided the linear dimensions of all elements of area approach zero when $n$ approaches infinity. Thus, this limit can be used as a definition of the surface integral on the right-hand side of Eq. 2.56.

Again, the requirement of continuity and single-valuedness does not seriously limit this definition in connection with physical problems because the functions of interest meet this requirement at least in a piecewise sense. Then the surface integral of a nonsingular function $f(x, y, z)$ can be defined as the sum of the integrals over the regions of $S$ over which the function meets the above requirements. Singularities over the boundaries between such regions can then be handled by suitable limiting processes.

In the most common type of surface integral the function $f(x, y, z)$ represents the normal component of a vector. For instance, the total current flowing through a two-sided surface $S$ can be expressed as the surface integral of $J_n$, the normal component of the current density,

$$I_S = \int_S J_n \, da = \int_S \boldsymbol{J} \cdot \boldsymbol{n} \, da \tag{2.57}$$

where $\boldsymbol{n}$ is a unit vector, normal to $S$, whose direction coincides with the positive reference direction of the current. The normal component $J_n$ is, by definition, equal to the scalar product of $\boldsymbol{J}$ and $\boldsymbol{n}$. When the surface $S$ is closed, this fact is placed in evidence by adding a circle to the sign of integral, as in

$$\oint_S \boldsymbol{J} \cdot \boldsymbol{n} \, da$$

In this case, the unit vector $\boldsymbol{n}$ is usually taken to be outwardly directed; this convention will be followed throughout this book unless otherwise stated.

The volume integral of a function $f(x, y, z)$ is, similarly, an additive function of the volume of integration. Its definition as the limit of a sum should be obvious by now, and it does not need to be stated in detail. The integral over a volume $V$ is usually indicated by

$$\int_V f(x, y, z)\, dv$$

where $dv$ is a differential element of volume. Thus, this integral can be interpreted as the sum of the contributions $f(x, y, z)\, dv$ of each differential element of volume. A circle will be added to the sign of integral, as in

$$\oint f(x, y, z)\, dv$$

when the integral is evaluated over the entire space.

Let us turn our attention next to the evaluation of these integrals. To evaluate a line integral over a specified path, we must reduce it to a sum of definite integrals involving a single independent variable. Let us suppose, for instance, that the coordinates of each point of the curve $C$ are given in parametric form by three functions $x(t)$, $y(t)$, $z(t)$ of an independent variable $t$, with the end points of $C$ corresponding to the values $t_P$ and $t_Q$ of $t$. As a help in visualizing this independent variable, we may think of it as the time at which an object moving along $C$ occupies each position on $C$. The three coordinates, functions of $t$, can then be regarded as the components of a distance vector

$$\boldsymbol{r}(t) = \boldsymbol{i}_x\, x(t) + \boldsymbol{i}_y\, y(t) + \boldsymbol{i}_z\, z(t) \tag{2.58}$$

indicating the position of the object at time $t$, relative to the origin. The displacement of the object along $C$ in a time $dt$ is then given by

$$\boldsymbol{ds} = \frac{\boldsymbol{dr}}{dt}\, dt = \left(\boldsymbol{i}_x \frac{dx}{dt} + \boldsymbol{i}_y \frac{dy}{dt} + \boldsymbol{i}_z \frac{dz}{dt}\right) dt \tag{2.59}$$

where $\boldsymbol{ds}$ is the differential vector appearing in Eq. 2.55 and illustrated in Fig. 2.10. Thus $\boldsymbol{ds}$ can be readily expressed in terms of the independent variable $t$, and so can its magnitude

$$ds = \sqrt{\left(\frac{dx}{dt}\right)^2 + \left(\frac{dy}{dt}\right)^2 + \left(\frac{dz}{dt}\right)^2}\, dt \tag{2.60}$$

The function $f(x, y, z)$ in Eq. 2.54 can be transformed into a function of $t$ by substituting for the variables $x$, $y$, and $z$ their expressions as functions of $t$. Then the line integral can be written as a one-dimen-

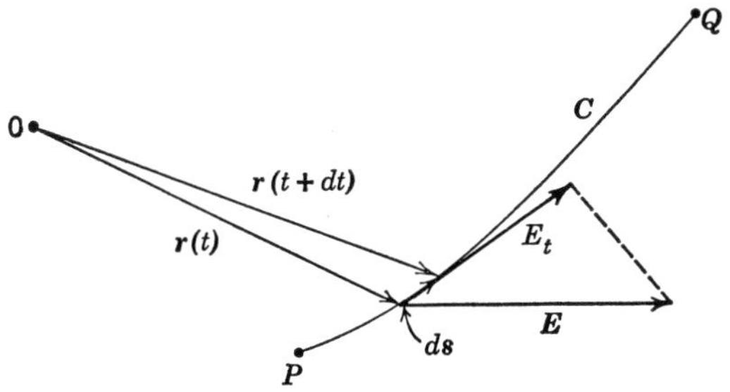


**Fig. 2.10.** Geometry used in connection with Eqs. 2.55 and 2.59.

sional integral in the independent variable $t$, and can be evaluated separately over each interval of $t$ in which the integrand is continuous and single-valued. The entire integral will be the sum of these partial integrals.

When the function $f(x, y, z)$ is the tangential component of a vector given in terms of its Cartesian coordinates, it is often more convenient to evaluate the line integral by integrating separately its three components, as follows. The integral of Eq. 2.55, for instance can be written in the form

$$\int_C \mathbf{E}\cdot d\mathbf{s} = \int_{x_P}^{x_Q} E_x\, dx + \int_{y_P}^{y_Q} E_y\, dy + \int_{z_P}^{z_Q} E_z\, dz \tag{2.61}$$

The component $E_x$, for instance, is, in general, a function of all three coordinates. However, it can be readily transformed into a function of $x$ alone by substituting for $y$ and $z$ their expressions as functions of $x$ obtained from the equations specifying the curve $C$. The component $E_y$ can be similarly expressed in terms of the variable $y$ alone, and $E_z$ in terms of the variable $z$ alone. Then, Eq. 2.61 becomes the sum of three one-dimensional integrals that can be evaluated between the specified limits if the integrands are continuous and single-valued. If this condition on the integrands is not met, the integrals can be usually computed as sums of integrals evaluated over subintervals in which the integrands are continuous and single-valued. The same procedure can be followed when the vector is given in terms of its components in any orthogonal system of coordinates, by expressing the differential vector $d\mathbf{s}$ in the same system of coordinates, as discussed in Sec. 2.3. This procedure becomes particularly simple when the path of integration coincides with one of the coordinate lines of the system, in which case two of the three integrals disappear.

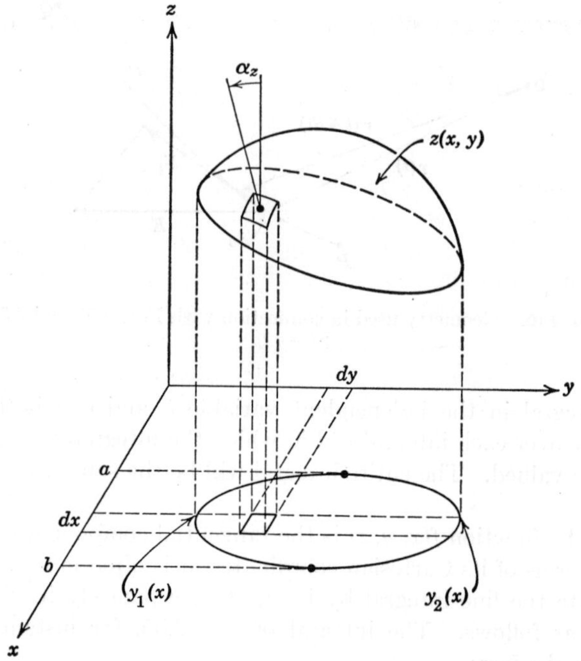


**Fig. 2.11.** Evaluation of a surface integral.

To evaluate a surface integral, we must reduce it first to a double integral in two independent variables. Suppose, for instance, that the surface $S$ is specified by a function $z = z(x, y)$, and that the projection of its boundary on the $xy$-plane is a closed contour specified by a function $y = y(x)$. Let us consider an element of surface whose projection on the $xy$-plane is a rectangle of sides $dx$ and $dy$, as illustrated in Fig. 2.11. The area of this element of surface is given by

$$da = \frac{dx\,dy}{\cos\alpha_z} \tag{2.62}$$

where $\cos\alpha_z$ is the direction cosine of the normal to the surface with the $z$-axis. The value of this direction cosine is given by

$$\cos\alpha_z = \left[1 + \left(\frac{\partial z}{\partial x}\right)^2 + \left(\frac{\partial z}{\partial y}\right)^2\right]^{-\frac{1}{2}} \tag{2.63}$$

The function $f(x, y, z)$ can be transformed into a function of $x$ and $y$ by substituting for $z$ the function of $x$ and $y$ that defines the surface $S$.

Then, the surface integral of Eq. 2.56 can be rewritten in the form

$$\int_S f(x, y, z)\, da = \int_{S_{xy}} f[x, y, z(x, y)] \left[1 + \left(\frac{\partial z}{\partial x}\right)^2 + \left(\frac{\partial z}{\partial y}\right)^2\right]^{1/2} dx\, dy \tag{2.64}$$

which is a double integral in the variables $x$ and $y$ over the projection $S_{xy}$ of $S$ on the $xy$-plane. If the function $z(x, y)$ defining the surface is single-valued, and the entire integrand on the right-hand side of Eq. 2.64 is continuous and single-valued, the double integral can be evaluated by conventional means. Let $a$ and $b$ ($b > a$) be the extreme values of $x$ on the contour of the projection $S_{xy}$, and $y_1(x)$ and $y_2(x)$ be the values of $y$ ($y_2 > y_1$) on the two parts of the same contour, as indicated in Fig. 2.11. Then the integral of Eq. 2.64 can be written in the form

$$\int_S f(x, y, z)\, da = \int_a^b \int_{y_1(x)}^{y_2(x)} f[x, y, z(x, y)] \left[1 + \left(\frac{\partial z}{\partial x}\right)^2 + \left(\frac{\partial z}{\partial y}\right)^2\right]^{1/2} dx\, dy \tag{2.65}$$

thereby reducing it to two successive one-dimensional integrals. If the function $z(x, y)$ is not single-valued or the integrand on the right-hand side of Eq. 2.64 is not continuous and single-valued, it is usually possible to subdivide the surface $S$ in parts for which these conditions are met. Then the entire surface integral can be evaluated as the sum of the integrals over these parts.

When the surface $S$ coincides with a coordinate surface of an orthogonal system of coordinates, the integral is more conveniently evaluated as a double integral in the two orthogonal coordinates that vary over $S$. Thus, for instance, if the surface is a sphere, the integral should be evaluated in terms of the $\theta$ and $\varphi$ coordinates of a spherical system concentric with the sphere. The function $f(x, y, z)$ can then be expressed in terms of the appropriate orthogonal coordinates by substitution; multiplication of the resulting expression by the appropriate differential element of surface as derived in Sec. 2.3, yields directly a double integral that can be evaluated by conventional means. Most of the surface integrals that we will have occasion to evaluate are of this simpler type.

The evaluation of volume integrals is, in principle at least, straightforward, because such integrals are written, from the start, in the form of triple integrals in three independent variables. If the three integrations are performed in the order $z$, $y$, $x$, the limits for the integral with respect to $z$ are functions of $x$ and $y$, the limits for the integral with respect to $y$ are functions of $x$, and the limits for the integral with respect to $x$ are the maximum and minimum values assumed by $x$ on the surface enclosing the volume. The same is true when other systems of coordinates are used. It must be stressed, however, that although the volume element in Cartesian coordinates is simply $dx$, $dy$, $dz$, the volume element in other systems of orthogonal coordinates is not just equal to the product of the differentials of the three coordinates but involves also a function of position as a factor, as discussed in Sec. 2.3. Thus, for instance, the volume element in spherical coordinates is equal to $r^2 \sin \theta \, dr \, d\theta \, d\varphi$.

Integrals of vectors, as opposed to integrals of scalar quantities, are defined as vectors whose Cartesian components are the integrals of the corresponding components of the vector. Thus, for instance,

$$\int_S \boldsymbol{E} \, da = \boldsymbol{i}_x \int_S E_x \, da + \boldsymbol{i}_y \int_S E_y \, da + \boldsymbol{i}_z \int_S E_z \, da \tag{2.66}$$

This definition is consistent with the fact that, if we regard the integral of a vector as the limit of a sum, the sum of any number of vectors is a vector whose Cartesian components are the sums of corresponding components of the vectors. Thus, the evaluation of the integral of a vector is reduced to the evaluation of the integrals of its three Cartesian components. It must be stressed, in this connection, that, although the three integrals may be evaluated in any convenient system of coordinates, the integrands must be the Cartesian components of the vector. This follows from the fact that, in order to evaluate the sum of a number of vectors, the components of each vector that we add must be in the same direction. This requirement is met only by the Cartesian components. For instance, the direction of the radial component in a spherical system, indicated by the unit vector $\boldsymbol{i}_r$, varies with position. Thus, if we were to add the radial components of a vector at different points in space, these components would not represent projections of the vectors on the same line and, therefore, their sum would not represent any particular component of the vector sum.

## 2.5 The Gradient

Scalar functions of position are of direct importance in the study of electromagnetic phenomena. For instance, the electric potential, in terms of which electrostatic fields are most conveniently studied, is a scalar function of position. Furthermore, the three-dimensional behavior of a scalar function is much easier to visualize and to describe mathematically than that of a vector function. We shall see also that the mathematical concepts useful in connection with scalar functions are either directly useful also in connection with vector functions or suggest appropriate generalizations.

Let $U$ be a single-valued function of position, i.e., one and only one value of $U$ corresponds to each point, although, of course, the same value of $U$ may correspond to many different points. The spatial behavior of $U$ can be described geometrically by means of the family of constant-$U$ surfaces, i.e., the surfaces over which $U$ remains constant. For instance, if $U$ is equal to the distance from a given reference point, the constant-$U$ surfaces are concentric spheres. It would seem, intuitively, that the normal trajectories to this family of surfaces are the lines in the direction of which $U$ changes most rapidly; furthermore, we should be able to represent, at each point, both the direction of the normal trajectory and the corresponding maximum rate of change of $U$ by means of an appropriately defined vector. This is actually the case, as shown below. The appropriate vector is known as the *gradient* of $U$, which is written, for brevity, as grad $U$.

Let us focus our attention on a pair of constant-$U$ surfaces separated in value by a differential increment $dU$. Let $P_1$ and $P_2$ be the intersections of a normal trajectory with the two surfaces, and $dn$ the distance between the two points, as illustrated in Fig. 2.12. Let $P_3$ be a

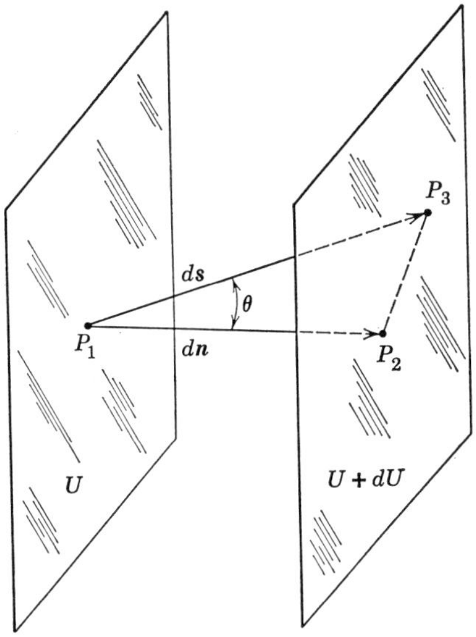


**Fig. 2.12.** Geometry used in the definition of the gradient of a scalar function $U$.

second point on the same surface as $P_2$, and $ds$ the distance between $P_1$ and $P_3$. In view of the differential character of the distances involved, we may, for our purpose, substitute for the two surfaces the planes tangent to them at $P_1$ and $P_2$, and consider these two planes as parallel. Then the distance from $P_1$ to $P_2$ is related to the distance from $P_1$ to $P_3$ by

$$dn = ds \cos \theta \tag{2.67}$$

where $\theta$ is the angle between the directions from $P_1$ to $P_2$ and from $P_1$ to $P_3$.

The directional derivative of $U$ in a particular direction, i.e., the ratio of the increment $dU$ to the corresponding displacement $ds$, depends, of course, on the direction of the displacement. On the other hand, for a given increment $dU$, the magnitude of the corresponding displacement varies with its direction, in accordance with Eq. 2.67. It follows that the directional derivative in an arbitrary direction is related to the normal derivative by

$$\frac{dU}{ds} = \frac{dU}{dn} \cos \theta \tag{2.68}$$

Thus the directional derivative at any point assumes its maximum value in the direction of the normal trajectory to the constant-$U$ surfaces; furthermore, its value in any direction can be obtained by multiplying this maximum value by the cosine of the angle between the prescribed direction and that tangent to the normal trajectory, and pointing toward increasing values of $U$. We can conclude, therefore, that the directional derivative of $U$ can be represented by the component in the prescribed direction of a vector to which we shall refer as grad $U$. More precisely, if $\boldsymbol{i}_n$ is a unit vector normal to the constant-$U$ surface passing by a point $P$, and $\boldsymbol{i}_s$ is a unit vector in an arbitrary direction,

$$\text{grad } U = \boldsymbol{i}_n \frac{\partial U}{\partial n} \tag{2.69}$$

and,

$$\frac{\partial U}{\partial s} = \boldsymbol{i}_s \cdot \text{grad } U = \boldsymbol{i}_s \cdot \boldsymbol{i}_n \frac{\partial U}{\partial n} \tag{2.70}$$

where the partial derivative of $U$ with respect to $n$ is taken in the direction of the unit vector $\boldsymbol{i}_n$, and the partial derivative with respect to $s$ is taken in the direction of the unit vector $\boldsymbol{i}_s$; the two variables $n$ and $s$ may be thought of as measuring the distances from $P$ in the two corresponding directions.

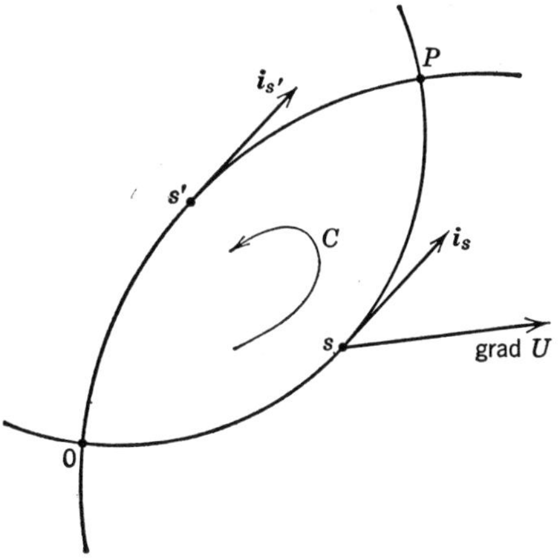


**Fig. 2.13.** Paths of integration used in computing the increment of $U$ from 0 to $P$, when grad $U$ is given.

Let us consider next the inverse problem of determining the increment of the function $U$ from some point 0 to some other point $P$, on the assumption that we know the vector function grad $U$. We consider for this purpose any line joining 0 to $P$, as shown in Fig. 2.13, and call $s$ the distance along this line measured, for instance, from 0. We have, by definition,

$$U(P) - U(0) = \int_0^{s(P)} \frac{\partial U}{\partial s} ds \tag{2.71}$$

On the other hand, because of Eq. 2.70,

$$U(P) - U(0) = \int_0^P \boldsymbol{i}_s \cdot \text{grad } U \, ds \tag{2.72}$$

where $\boldsymbol{i}_s$ is a unit vector tangent to the line and pointing toward $P$, and $P$, the upper limit of the integral, is a shorthand notation for $s(P)$. We refer to the integral in this last equation as the *line integral* of grad $U$ from 0 to $P$ along the specified path. Sometimes the unit vector $\boldsymbol{i}_s$ is combined with the differential displacement $ds$ to form the differential vector $\boldsymbol{ds}$, in which case the expression grad $U \cdot \boldsymbol{ds}$ is substituted in Eq. 2.72 for $\boldsymbol{i}_s \cdot$grad $U\, ds$.

It is clear that, if the integral on the right-hand side of Eq. 2.72 is to represent the increment of $U$ from 0 to $P$, the integral cannot depend on the particular line selected, i.e., on the path of integration. Thus, if we select a different line joining 0 to $P$, as shown in Fig. 2.13, and call $s'$ the distance measured along this line, with $\boldsymbol{i}_{s'}$ as the corresponding unit vector tangent to the line, we obtain

$$\int_0^P \boldsymbol{i}_s \cdot \text{grad } U \, ds - \int_0^P \boldsymbol{i}_{s'} \cdot \text{grad } U \, ds' = 0 \tag{2.73}$$

On the other hand, interchanging the limits of integration in the second integral amounts to computing the increment of $U$ from $P$ to 0 instead of from 0 to $P$. The sign of the integral changes, of course, as a result of reversing the direction of integration. Thus,

$$\int_0^P \boldsymbol{i}_s \cdot \text{grad } U \, ds + \int_P^0 \boldsymbol{i}_{s'} \cdot \text{grad } U \, ds' = 0 \tag{2.74}$$

Finally, if $s$ is redefined as the distance along the closed path $C$ from 0 to $P$ and back to 0 by the way of the primed path, the last equation can be written in the form

$$\oint_C \boldsymbol{i}_s \cdot \text{grad } U \, ds = 0 \tag{2.75}$$

where the circle over the integral sign indicates that the path of integration $C$ is closed. In words, *the line integral of grad $U$ over a closed path is always equal to zero.* This is a very important property of the vector function grad $U$ to which we shall return in a later section in connection with our discussion of the line integrals of arbitrary vector functions.

The vector grad $U$ can be readily expressed in terms of components in any system of orthogonal coordinates. It is sufficient to remember, for this purpose, that the component of grad $U$ in any direction is the partial derivative of $U$ in the corresponding direction. Thus, at any point $P$, the component of grad $U$ in the direction of the unit vector $\boldsymbol{i}_1$ (normal to the constant-$u_1$ surface and tangent to the $u_1$ coordinate line) is given by

$$(\text{grad } U)_1 = \frac{\partial U}{\partial s_1} = \frac{\partial U}{\partial u_1}\frac{\partial u_1}{\partial s_1} = \frac{1}{h_1}\frac{\partial U}{\partial u_1} \tag{2.76}$$

where $h_1$ is the metrical coefficient defined by Eq. 2.33. Similarly,

$$(\text{grad } U)_2 = \frac{1}{h_2}\frac{\partial U}{\partial u_2} \tag{2.77}$$

$$(\text{grad } U)_3 = \frac{1}{h_3}\frac{\partial U}{\partial u_3} \tag{2.78}$$

In Cartesian coordinates the metrical coefficients are all equal to one. Thus,

$$\operatorname{grad} U = \boldsymbol{i}_x \frac{\partial U}{\partial x} + \boldsymbol{i}_y \frac{\partial U}{\partial y} + \boldsymbol{i}_z \frac{\partial U}{\partial z} \tag{2.79}$$

The expressions in other systems of orthogonal coordinates are listed in Appendix 3.

The simplicity of Eq. 2.79 suggests defining a vector differential operator

$$\nabla = \boldsymbol{i}_x \frac{\partial}{\partial x} + \boldsymbol{i}_y \frac{\partial}{\partial y} + \boldsymbol{i}_z \frac{\partial}{\partial z} \tag{2.80}$$

whose components are the partial-derivative operators with respect to the three Cartesian coordinates. We refer to this operator as *del*. When this operator is multiplied by a scalar function, it yields a vector whose components are the products of the components of the operator and the scalar function, which, in turn, are to be interpreted as the partial derivatives of the function. Thus,

$$\nabla U = \boldsymbol{i}_x \frac{\partial}{\partial x} U + \boldsymbol{i}_y \frac{\partial}{\partial y} U + \boldsymbol{i}_z \frac{\partial}{\partial z} U = \operatorname{grad} U \tag{2.81}$$

We shall see that when this vector operator is multiplied scalarly and vectorially by a vector function, it yields the expressions in Cartesian coordinates for the two most important differential characteristics of vector functions.

The gradient of the product of two scalar functions $U$ and $V$ can be readily expressed in terms of the individual gradients of the two functions. We have, for the $x$ component of the gradient,

$$(\operatorname{grad} UV)_x = \frac{\partial}{\partial x} UV = U \frac{\partial V}{\partial x} + V \frac{\partial U}{\partial x} \tag{2.82}$$

and similarly for the other components. It follows that

$$\operatorname{grad} UV = U \operatorname{grad} V + V \operatorname{grad} U \tag{2.83}$$

Let us turn our attention next to the spacial derivative of a vector in a prescribed direction. Let $\boldsymbol{A}$ be the vector, and $\boldsymbol{i}_s$ a unit vector indicating the direction in which the derivative is to be evaluated. The derivative of a vector with respect to any variable is defined as the vector whose Cartesian components are the derivatives of the corresponding components of the original vector. Thus, if $s$ is a variable that measures distance in the direction of $\boldsymbol{i}_s$,

$$\begin{aligned}\frac{\partial \boldsymbol{A}}{\partial s} &= \boldsymbol{i}_x \frac{\partial A_x}{\partial s} + \boldsymbol{i}_y \frac{\partial A_y}{\partial s} + \boldsymbol{i}_z \frac{\partial A_z}{\partial s} \\ &= \boldsymbol{i}_x(\boldsymbol{i}_s \cdot \nabla A_x) + \boldsymbol{i}_y(\boldsymbol{i}_s \cdot \nabla A_y) + \boldsymbol{i}_z(\boldsymbol{i}_s \cdot \nabla A_z) \\ &= (\boldsymbol{i}_s \cdot \nabla)\boldsymbol{A} \end{aligned} \tag{2.84}$$

In the last expression, the differential operator formed by the scalar product of $\boldsymbol{i}_s$ and $\nabla$ must be understood to operate on the Cartesian components of the vector $\boldsymbol{A}$.

More often we are interested in expressing the product of the manitude of a vector $\boldsymbol{B}$, by the derivative of $\boldsymbol{A}$ evaluated in the direction of $\boldsymbol{B}$. The desired expression is obtained simply by substituting the vector $\boldsymbol{B}$ for $\boldsymbol{i}_s$ in Eq. 2.84. We obtain

$$(\boldsymbol{B} \cdot \nabla)\boldsymbol{A} = \left(B_x \frac{\partial}{\partial x} + B_y \frac{\partial}{\partial y} + B_z \frac{\partial}{\partial z}\right) \boldsymbol{A} \tag{2.85}$$

where again the differential operator on the right-hand side of the equation must be understood to operate on the Cartesian components of the vector $\boldsymbol{A}$. We shall have occasion to use this differential expression in Chapters 9 and 10 in connection with moving bodies.

## 2.6 The Divergence and Gauss' Theorem

A vector field is a region of space in which a vector function of position is defined. The earth's gravitational field of force, the velocity field of a fluid, the electric field between the plates of a capacitor, and the magnetic field around a coil are examples of vector fields.

A great deal of insight into the properties of a vector field may be obtained by picturing it in terms of *flow lines*, also called *field lines* or *lines of force*. Such lines are defined as curves tangent at all points to the vector; therefore they indicate how the direction of the vector varies throughout the field. An arrowhead is often added to each line to indicate the positive direction of the vector. The density of lines can be used to represent the magnitude of the vector. For this purpose, we draw through any unit surface normal to the lines a number of lines proportional to the magnitude of the vector. Changes of line density from point to point in the field may come about automatically through lines moving closer to one another, or they may have to be forced by starting additional lines or ending existing ones. Figure 2.14*a* illustrates

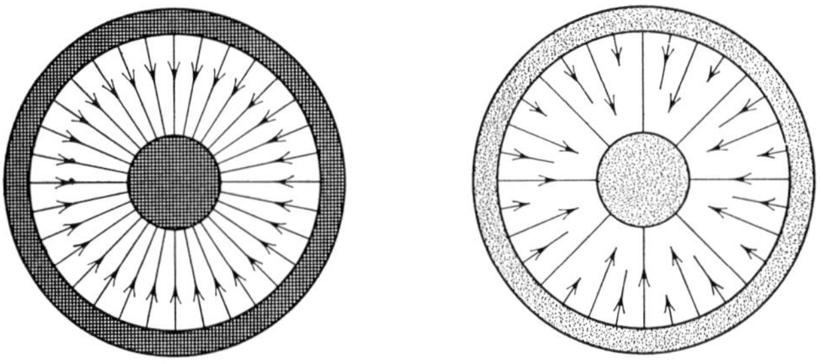

(a) (b)

**Fig. 2.14.** (a) Electric field between coaxial conductors. (b) Electric field between plate and cathode of a coaxial diode.

the electric field between two coaxial conductors in which the natural gathering of the lines takes care automatically of the variations of the magnitude of the vector. Figure 2.14b illustrates the electric field between the cathode and the plate of a space-charge-limited diode, in which lines must end at various points of the field. We shall refer to any point at which a line starts as a *source* of the field; and a point at which a line ends, as a *sink*. It is clear that the difference between the number of sources and the number of sinks within any given volume $V$ equals the net number of lines crossing, in the outward direction, the surface enclosing $V$.

Let us consider, as an example, the field map of an electric vector $\boldsymbol{E}$. Because of the assumed proportionality between the density of the lines and the magnitude of the vector, the net number of lines going out of a given closed surface $S$ is proportional (within the precision limits permitted by the scale of the map) to the flux of $\boldsymbol{E}$ through $S$. However, because of Eq. 1.17, the flux of $\epsilon_0\boldsymbol{E}$ is equal to the total charge enclosed by $S$. It follows that each of the sources and sinks in the map represents the same amount of positive or negative charge. In other words, each line starts from a positive charge (lumped at one point because of the quantization of the map) and ends on a negative charge of equal magnitude. The sinks in Fig. 2.14b, for instance, represent the negative space charge distributed between the electrodes of the diode.

It seems clear from the above geometric considerations that an important characteristic of a vector field is the distribution of its sources (and sinks), and that the net amount of sources within any given region is measured by the outward flux of the vector through the surface enclosing the region. Let us, then, consider a closed surface $S$ enclosing a volume $V$, and compute the outward flux of a vector function $\boldsymbol{A}$

through $S$. We have

$$\Phi_S = \oint_S A_n\, da = \oint_S \boldsymbol{A}\cdot\boldsymbol{n}\, da \tag{2.86}$$

where $\boldsymbol{n}$ is a unit vector normal to $S$ and outwardly directed, $da$ is a differential element of $S$, and

$$A_n = \boldsymbol{A}\cdot\boldsymbol{n} \tag{2.87}$$

is the component of $\boldsymbol{A}$ normal to $S$. The ratio of $\Phi_S$ to the volume $V$ enclosed by $S$ measures the mean source density within the region, i.e., the mean source strength per unit volume. Then, if $S$ is made to shrink about any particular point $P$, the limiting value of this ratio will measure the actual source density at $P$. We define the *divergence* of a vector field $\boldsymbol{A}$ at any given point as the limit

$$\operatorname{div} \boldsymbol{A} = \lim_{V\to 0} \frac{\oint_S \boldsymbol{A}\cdot\boldsymbol{n}\, da}{V} \tag{2.88}$$

where the surface $S$ enclosing $V$ shrinks about $P$. The shape of the surface does not matter as long as all its dimensions vanish in the limit; obviously, a cylinder of vanishing radius but of fixed length would not constitute a suitable surface.

The limit in Eq. 2.88 can be readily evaluated in terms of any set of orthogonal coordinates. For this purpose, we take as $V$ the element of volume illustrated in Fig. 2.9, of which an enlarged view is shown in Fig. 2.15. This element of volume consists of the space enclosed by three pairs of coordinate surfaces with values differing by differential increments of the three variables $u_1$, $u_2$, $u_3$. The vector $\boldsymbol{A}$ can be represented at any point in terms of its components in the directions of the unit vectors $\boldsymbol{i}_1$, $\boldsymbol{i}_2$, $\boldsymbol{i}_3$, normal to the corresponding coordinate surfaces

$$\boldsymbol{A} = \boldsymbol{i}_1 A_1 + \boldsymbol{i}_2 A_2 + \boldsymbol{i}_3 A_3 \tag{2.89}$$

It should be clear that only one component of $\boldsymbol{A}$ can contribute to the flux through each part of the surface $S$ enclosing the element of volume; in fact, $S$ consists of pieces of coordinate surfaces. Thus, for instance, only $A_2$ contributes to the flux through the part of $S$ that coincides with the coordinate surface $u_2$. Furthermore, the flux entering the element of volume through the coordinate surface $u_2$, indicated in Fig. 2.15, is given by

$$d\Phi_2(u_2) = A_2\, da_2 = A_2 h_1 h_3\, du_1\, du_3 \tag{2.90}$$

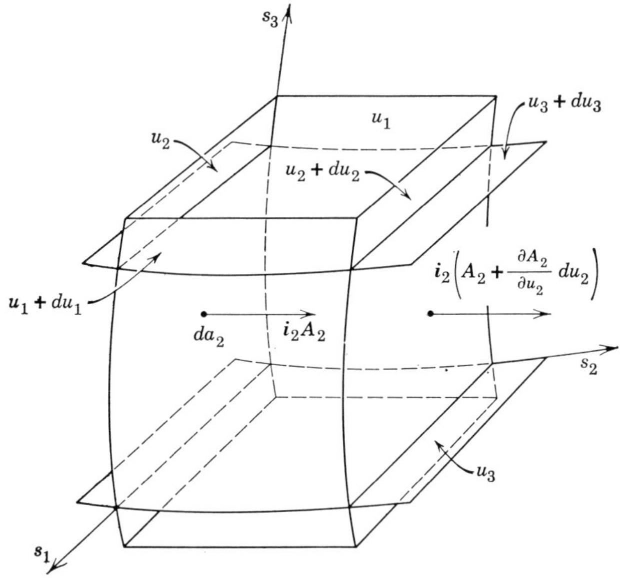


**Fig. 2.15.** The element of volume used in evaluating div $\boldsymbol{A}$.

where use is made of Eq. 2.39. On the other hand, the flux going out of the element of volume through the opposite coordinate surface $u_2 + du_2$ differs from that given by Eq. 2.90 because the element of area $da_2$ as well as the component $A_2$ changes in passing from one surface to the other. More precisely, we have

$$d\Phi_2(u_2 + du_2) = \left(A_2 h_1 h_3 + \frac{\partial(A_2 h_1 h_3)}{\partial u_2} du_2\right) du_1\, du_3 \qquad (2.91)$$

Thus the net flux going out of the element of volume through the pair of constant-$u_2$ surfaces is

$$d\Phi_2(u_2 + du_2) - d\Phi_2(u_2) = \frac{\partial(A_2 h_1 h_3)}{\partial u_2} du_1\, du_2\, du_3 \qquad (2.92)$$

The net fluxes going out of the element of volume through the other two pairs of coordinate surfaces are given by similar expressions, so that the total outgoing flux is

$$d\Phi = \left[\frac{\partial(A_1 h_2 h_3)}{\partial u_1} + \frac{\partial(A_2 h_1 h_3)}{\partial u_2} + \frac{\partial(A_3 h_1 h_2)}{\partial u_3}\right] du_1\, du_2\, du_3 \quad (2.93)$$

Finally, division by the volume $dv$ of the element, given by Eq. 2.40, yields

$$\text{div}\,\boldsymbol{A} = \frac{1}{h_1h_2h_3}\left[\frac{\partial(A_1h_2h_3)}{\partial u_1} + \frac{\partial(A_2h_1h_3)}{\partial u_2} + \frac{\partial(A_3h_1h_2)}{\partial u_3}\right] \tag{2.94}$$

In the simple case of Cartesian coordinates, all the metrical coefficients $h_i$ are equal to one, with the result that opposite surface elements are exactly equal, and the net outgoing flux through each pair of them depends only on the derivative of the vector component normal to them. We have, in this simple case,

$$\text{div}\,\boldsymbol{A} = \frac{\partial A_x}{\partial x} + \frac{\partial A_y}{\partial y} + \frac{\partial A_z}{\partial z} = \nabla\cdot\boldsymbol{A} \tag{2.95}$$

where it is recognized that the resulting expression can be interpreted as the scalar product of the del operator, defined in Eq. 2.80, and the vector $\boldsymbol{A}$. The expressions for the divergence of $\boldsymbol{A}$ in other important systems of orthogonal coordinates are given in Appendix 3.

The operation of taking the divergence of a vector field can be readily combined with the operation of taking the gradient of a scalar function; we obtain

$$\text{div grad}\,U = \nabla\cdot\nabla U = \frac{\partial^2 U}{\partial x^2} + \frac{\partial^2 U}{\partial y^2} + \frac{\partial^2 U}{\partial z^2} \tag{2.96}$$

an expression known as the *Laplacian* of $U$. The operator $\nabla\cdot\nabla$ is sometimes written in abbreviated form as $\nabla^2$, at other times, as $\Delta$. It represents the sum of the second partial derivatives with respect to the three Cartesian coordinates.

The divergence of a vector field can also be interpreted as the rate of change of the flux through a surface $S$ with respect to the volume enclosed by the surface. In fact, if the volume is increased by an amount $dv$ by attaching a small bulge to its surface, it is readily recognized that the flux through the resulting outer surface is increased by an amount $d\Phi$ just equal to the flux through the surface enclosing the bulge. Thus the ratio of the increment of flux to the increment of volume is just the divergence of the vector field at the point where the bulge is located. Conversely, the outward flux of a vector $\boldsymbol{A}$ through any closed surface $S$ can be expressed as the integral of div $\boldsymbol{A}$ over the volume enclosed by the surface, i.e.,

$$\oint_S \boldsymbol{A}\cdot\boldsymbol{n}\,da = \int_V \text{div}\,\boldsymbol{A}\,dv \tag{2.97}$$

This relation is known as Gauss' theorem. A proof may be obtained by dividing the volume into differential elements, and noting that the net flux through the surface $S$ may be expressed as the sum of the fluxes through the differential surfaces of the individual elements. In fact, all the terms of this sum contributed by the internal elements cancel, leaving only the contributions of the surface elements that are part of $S$. On the other hand, the flux through the surface of each differential volume element is equal, by definition, to the volume element multiplied by div $\boldsymbol{A}$. Thus, the flux through $S$ is equal to the volume integral of div $\boldsymbol{A}$.

Let us consider again, as an example, the field of the electric vector $\epsilon_0\boldsymbol{E}$. Each source of its line map was said to represent a fixed amount of charge. Therefore the density of such sources must represent the charge density, and

$$\text{div}\ \epsilon_0\boldsymbol{E} = \rho \tag{2.98}$$

Conversely, with the help of Gauss' theorem,

$$\oint_S \epsilon_0\boldsymbol{E}\cdot\boldsymbol{n}\,da = \int_V \text{div}\ \epsilon_0\boldsymbol{E}\,dv = \int_V \rho\,dv \tag{2.99}$$

Equation 2.98 expresses in differential form the same physical law stated by Eq. 2.99 in integral form. In the next chapter we shall see how Eq. 2.98 follows from one of Maxwell's equations in differential form.

## 2.7 The Curl and Stokes' Theorem

We saw in Sec. 2.5 that the vector grad $U$ has the important property that its line integral around any closed path is always equal to zero. Clearly, not all vector fields have this property. For instance, the lines of force of the magnetic field produced by a steady current in a straight circular conductor are concentric circles; therefore the line integral of the magnetic field around any one of these concentric circles must necessarily be different from zero. It is natural, then, to inquire about the characteristics of a vector field that determine whether the line integral around any particular closed path will or will not be equal to zero.

This problem is in some respects similar to that discussed in the preceding section. There, we started by considering the net flux going out of a closed surface, and attributed its being different from zero to the presence of *sources* within the volume enclosed by the surface. The divergence of the vector field was then defined as the density of such sources. Here, we start by considering the line integral of the field vector $\boldsymbol{A}$ around an arbitrary closed path $C$:

$$F = \oint_C \boldsymbol{A} \cdot d\boldsymbol{s} \tag{2.100}$$

By analogy, we attribute its being different from zero to the presence of *vortex lines* or *lines of rotation* threading the closed path. The physical significance of such vortex lines can be readily appreciated in the case of the velocity field of an incompressible fluid in rotary motion in which these lines act as the centers of rotation of the fluid. As a matter of fact, the hydrodynamic interpretation of a vector field is responsible for most of the terminology employed here as well as in the preceding section. Furthermore, the vortex lines may be thought of, from a geometric point of view, as describing the field of a new vector tangent to the lines and of magnitude proportional to their density. This vector, to which we shall refer as *curl* $\boldsymbol{A}$, is then the counterpart of the divergence, being a measure of the density of the vortex lines threading the closed path $C$.

To define precisely the vector curl $\boldsymbol{A}$, let us consider a closed path $C$ lying on a plane, and indicate with $\boldsymbol{n}$ a unit vector normal to the plane, and directed relative to $C$ according to the right-handed-screw rule. By analogy with the definition of the divergence, we form the ratio of the line integral of $\boldsymbol{A}$ around $C$ to the area $a$ enclosed by $C$, and take the limit of this ratio when the closed path shrinks to a point $P$. In anticipation of future results, let us denote this limit by

$$(\text{curl } \boldsymbol{A})_n = \lim_{a \to 0} \frac{\oint_C \boldsymbol{A} \cdot d\boldsymbol{s}}{a} \tag{2.101}$$

For any given point $P$, the result of this limiting process depends on the orientation of the plane on which $C$ lies, i.e., on the direction of the unit vector $\boldsymbol{n}$. It can be shown that the quantity defined by Eq. 2.101 behaves as the component of a vector; i.e., if $\boldsymbol{n}_m$ is the direction of $\boldsymbol{n}$ for which it assumes its maximum value, its value for all other orientations can be obtained by multiplying this maximum value by the cosine of the angle between $\boldsymbol{n}$ and $\boldsymbol{n}_m$. The proof of this statement is somewhat involved and is not particularly illuminating; it can be found in [1]. It is worth pointing out, in this connection, that, in order to arrive at the definition of grad $U$ in Sec. 2.5, it was similarly necessary to prove that the directional derivative of a scalar function behaves as

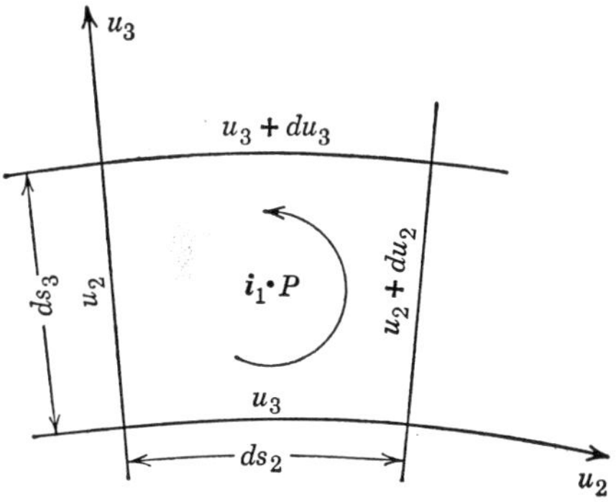


**Fig. 2.16.** Closed path used in the evaluation of (curl $\boldsymbol{A}$)$_1$.

the component of a vector. In that case, however, the proof was so simple that its significance could easily have been overlooked.

Once it has been determined that the quantity defined by Eq. 2.101 behaves as the component of a vector, this equation provides a complete definition of the vector curl $\boldsymbol{A}$, by giving the value of its component in the arbitrary direction of the unit vector $\boldsymbol{n}$. We can then proceed to evaluate the components of curl $\boldsymbol{A}$ in any arbitrary system of orthogonal coordinates.

For this purpose, let us consider the closed path on a constant-$u_1$ surface, illustrated in Fig. 2.16. Because of the differential dimensions of the path, we can regard the path as lying on the plane tangent to the surface at the point $P$, and normal to the unit vector $\boldsymbol{i}_1$. It will be noticed that, if the reference directions on the coordinate lines form a right-handed system in the order $u_1$. $u_2$, $u_3$, the unit vector $\boldsymbol{i}_1$ points in Fig. 2.16 upward from the paper. Then the reference direction on the closed path must be counterclockwise in order for the computation to yield the component of curl $\boldsymbol{A}$ in the direction of $\boldsymbol{i}_1$.

In evaluating the line integral around the path of Fig. 2.16, we observe first of all that only the component $A_3$ contributes to the integral on the two opposite sides of the path marked $u_2$ and $u_2 + du_2$. The contribution of the side marked $u_2$ is

$$dF_3(u_2) = -A_3\, ds_3 = -A_3 h_3\, du_3 \tag{2.102}$$

where $h_3$ is the metrical coefficient associated with $u_3$. The contribution of the side marked $u_2 + du_2$ differs in magnitude from $dF_3(u_2)$ because both $A_3$ and $h_3$ change as a result of the increment $du_2$. We obtain

$$dF_3(u_2 + du_2) = \left[ A_3 h_3 + \frac{\partial(A_3 h_3)}{\partial u_2}\, du_2 \right] du_3 \tag{2.103}$$

Thus the total contribution of these two opposite sides of the path is

$$dF_3(u_2) + dF_3(u_2 + du_2) = \frac{\partial(A_3h_3)}{\partial u_2}\, du_2\, du_3 \tag{2.104}$$

Similarly, we obtain for the contribution of the other two sides of the path:

$$dF_2(u_3) + dF_2(u_3 + du_3) = -\frac{\partial(A_2h_2)}{\partial u_3}\, du_2\, du_3 \tag{2.105}$$

Adding Eqs. 2.104 and 2.105 and dividing by the area $h_2h_3\, du_2\, du_3$ enclosed by the path yield the desired component of curl $\boldsymbol{A}$:

$$(\text{curl}\, \boldsymbol{A})_1 = \frac{1}{h_2h_3}\left[\frac{\partial(A_3h_3)}{\partial u_2} - \frac{\partial(A_2h_2)}{\partial u_3}\right] \tag{2.106}$$

The other two components of curl $\boldsymbol{A}$ can be obtained in a similar manner by operating on differential closed paths lying on the constant-$u_2$ and constant-$u_3$ surfaces. The expressions for these components are

$$(\text{curl}\, \boldsymbol{A})_2 = \frac{1}{h_1h_3}\left[\frac{\partial(A_1h_1)}{\partial u_3} - \frac{\partial(A_3h_3)}{\partial u_1}\right] \tag{2.107}$$

$$(\text{curl}\, \boldsymbol{A})_3 = \frac{1}{h_1h_2}\left[\frac{\partial(A_2h_2)}{\partial u_1} - \frac{\partial(A_1h_1)}{\partial u_2}\right] \tag{2.108}$$

All three components together are conveniently expressed by the determinant

$$\text{curl}\, \boldsymbol{A} = \frac{1}{h_1h_2h_3}\begin{vmatrix} h_1\boldsymbol{i}_1 & h_2\boldsymbol{i}_2 & h_3\boldsymbol{i}_3 \\ \dfrac{\partial}{\partial u_1} & \dfrac{\partial}{\partial u_2} & \dfrac{\partial}{\partial u_3} \\ A_1h_1 & A_2h_2 & A_3h_3 \end{vmatrix} \tag{2.109}$$

In the simple case of Cartesian coordinates, the metrical coefficients $h_i$ are all equal to one, and the above determinant reduces to

$$\text{curl}\, \boldsymbol{A} = \boldsymbol{i}_x\left(\frac{\partial A_z}{\partial y} - \frac{\partial A_y}{\partial z}\right) + \boldsymbol{i}_y\left(\frac{\partial A_x}{\partial z} - \frac{\partial A_z}{\partial x}\right) + \boldsymbol{i}_z\left(\frac{\partial A_y}{\partial x} - \frac{\partial A_x}{\partial y}\right) \tag{2.110}$$

Again, the *del* operator provides a shorthand notation for curl $\boldsymbol{A}$ in Cartesian coordinates. We have, by inspection,

$$\text{curl}\, \boldsymbol{A} = \nabla \times \boldsymbol{A} \tag{2.111}$$

It will be remembered in this regard that products such as $\partial/(\partial x)$ by $A_y$ are to be interpreted as partial derivatives, such as $(\partial A_y)/(\partial x)$.

A very important property of the field of curl $\boldsymbol{A}$ is that it is purely rotational, i.e., its divergence is identically zero:

$$\text{div curl } \boldsymbol{A} = 0 \tag{2.112}$$

This property can be readily checked by performing successively the required operations on the Cartesian components of curl $\boldsymbol{A}$. An important consequence of this identity is that the flux of curl $\boldsymbol{A}$ through any two-sided surface $S$ bounded by a contour $C$, as illustrated in Fig. 2.17*a* depends only on $C$ and not on the surface itself. In other words, the flux of curl $\boldsymbol{A}$ through a closed contour is a uniquely defined quantity. To prove this statement, let us consider a second surface $S'$ bounded by the same contour, as illustrated in Fig. 2.17*b*. The two surfaces $S$ and $S'$ taken together form a closed surface, and the total flux of curl $\boldsymbol{A}$ going out of such a closed surface is zero because of Eq. 2.112. Thus the outgoing fluxes through the two surfaces $S$ and $S'$ must be equal in magnitude and opposite in sign; this implies, of course, that the fluxes through $S$ and $S'$ are both considered as outgoing relatively to the closed surface. On the other hand, if $S'$ is considered as resulting from a deformation of $S$, the unit vector $\boldsymbol{n}$ should have the same direction relative to the contour for both surfaces, as illustrated in Figs. 2.17*a* and *b*. The net result is that the flux through $S'$ changes sign when $S'$ is considered as an open surface rather than part of the closed surface. We may conclude, therefore, that the fluxes through the two open surfaces $S$ and $S'$, bounded by the same contour $C$, are equal in both magnitude and sign.

A further important property of the curl operation is the identity

$$\text{curl grad } U = 0 \tag{2.113}$$

where $U$ is a scalar function of position. This identity can be easily

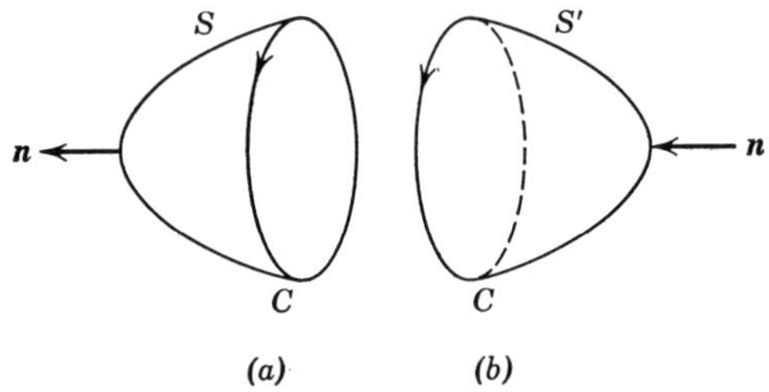


**Fig. 2.17.** Two surfaces bounded by the same contour.

proved by direct evaluation in Cartesian coordinates; its validity is evident from the fact that the line integral of grad $U$ around any closed path is equal to zero, by the very definition of grad $U$, as shown in Sec. 2.5.

The approximate notion, introduced above, that the line integral of the vector $\boldsymbol{A}$ around a closed path $C$ is related to the number of vortex lines threading $C$ can now be expressed in a precise form. If $S$ is any two-sided surface bounded by a contour $C$, then it can be shown that

$$\oint_C \boldsymbol{A}\cdot d\boldsymbol{s} = \int_S \text{curl}\, \boldsymbol{A}\cdot \boldsymbol{n}\, da \tag{2.114}$$

where $\boldsymbol{n}$ is directed, relatively to $d\boldsymbol{s}$, according to the right-handed-screw rule as, for example, in Fig. 2.17. In words, *the contour integral of $\boldsymbol{A}$ is equal to the flux of curl $\boldsymbol{A}$ through the contour.* This relation is known as Stokes' theorem.

Stokes' theorem may be readily proved by dividing the surface $S$ into differential elements, as indicated in Fig. 2.18. By the definition of curl $\boldsymbol{A}$, the integral of $\boldsymbol{A}$ around the contour of each differential element is equal to the product of the component of curl $\boldsymbol{A}$ normal to the element and the area of the element; i.e.,

$$\oint_{da} \boldsymbol{A}\cdot d\boldsymbol{s} = \text{curl}\, \boldsymbol{A}\cdot \boldsymbol{n}\, da \tag{2.115}$$

If we add together the values of the right-hand side of Eq. 2.115 for all elements of $S$, we obtain the flux of curl $\boldsymbol{A}$ through $S$, i.e., the right-hand side of Eq. 2.114. If we add up similarly the elementary contour integrals, we observe that all terms cancel out but for the contributions of the parts of the elementary contours that belong to $C$. This follows from the fact that the common part of two adjacent elementary contours is transversed in opposite directions by the two contours. Thus, the summation over $S$ of the left-hand side of Eq. 2.115 reduces to the

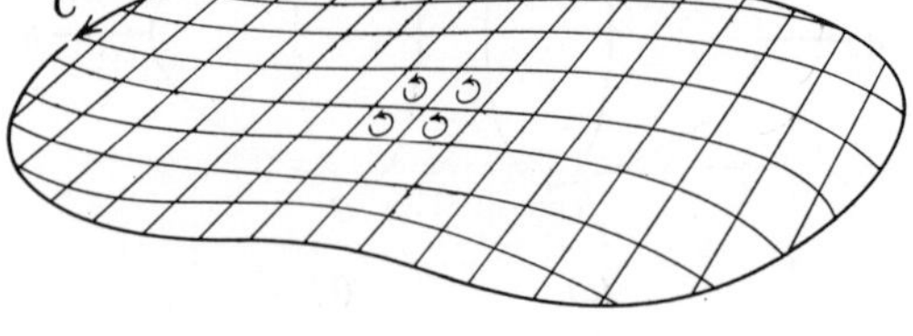


**Fig. 2.18.** Surface divided into differential elements.

left-hand side of Eq. 2.114. This completes the proof of Stokes' theorem on the assumption that curl $\boldsymbol{A}$ exists and is finite at all points of $S$.

An illuminating physical interpretation of the curl of a vector can be developed with the help of the relation

$$\oint_S \boldsymbol{A} \times \boldsymbol{n}\, da = -\int_V \operatorname{curl} \boldsymbol{A}\, dv \tag{2.116}$$

where $S$ is a closed surface and $V$ is the volume enclosed by $S$, which can be derived from Gauss' theorem, as shown in the next section. Let us consider a rigid spherical shell of radius $R$ covered with a uniform charge distribution of surface density $\sigma$ (charge per unit area). If this spherical shell is subjected to a rotational electric field $\boldsymbol{E}$, the torque about the center of the sphere exerted by $\boldsymbol{E}$ on a differential element of surface $da$ is a vector

$$d\boldsymbol{T} = -R\sigma \boldsymbol{E} \times \boldsymbol{n}\, da \tag{2.117}$$

where the unit vector $\boldsymbol{n}$ is normal to the sphere and outwardly directed. Thus the total torque on the spherical shell is, with the help of Eq. 2.116,

$$\boldsymbol{T} = -R\sigma \oint_S \boldsymbol{E} \times \boldsymbol{n}\, da = R\sigma \int_V \operatorname{curl} \boldsymbol{E}\, dv \tag{2.118}$$

where $S$ represents the spherical surface. If, furthermore, $R$ is so small that curl $\boldsymbol{E}$ is constant over the volume of the sphere, we obtain

$$\operatorname{curl} \boldsymbol{E} = \frac{\boldsymbol{T}}{R\sigma V} \tag{2.119}$$

Thus the vector curl $\boldsymbol{E}$ is proportional to the vector representing the torque exerted by $\boldsymbol{E}$ on the spherical shell; in other words, the spherical shell could be used—in principle, at least—to measure the curl of an electric field.

We may note also that, if the spherical shell is elastic in the radial direction and the displacement of each point of the shell is proportional to the applied force, the net change of volume resulting from the action of the electric field is (because of Gauss' theorem):

$$\delta V = \alpha\sigma \oint_S \boldsymbol{E} \cdot \boldsymbol{n}\, da = \alpha\sigma \int_V \operatorname{div} \boldsymbol{E}\, dv \tag{2.120}$$

where $\alpha$ is the proportionality factor between displacement and force.

If, furthermore, div $\boldsymbol{E}$ does not vary appreciably within the sphere, we obtain

$$\text{div}\, \boldsymbol{E} = \frac{\delta V}{\alpha \sigma V} \tag{2.121}$$

## ► 2.8 Miscellaneous Theorems

(*a*) Let $U$ be a scalar function of position which is differentiable within a volume $V$ and on its surface, and $\boldsymbol{n}$ a unit vector normal to $S$ and outwardly directed. Then

$$\int_V \text{grad}\, U\, dv = \oint_S U\boldsymbol{n}\, da \tag{2.122}$$

To prove this theorem, we apply Gauss' theorem to the divergence of the vector $\boldsymbol{i}U$, where $\boldsymbol{i}$ is a constant unit vector. We have

$$\int_V \text{div}\, \boldsymbol{i}U\, dv = \oint_S \boldsymbol{i}U \cdot \boldsymbol{n}\, da \tag{2.123}$$

On the other hand,

$$\text{div}\, \boldsymbol{i}U = \boldsymbol{i} \cdot \text{grad}\, U \tag{2.124}$$

so that Eq. 2.123 becomes

$$\boldsymbol{i} \cdot \int_V \text{grad}\, U\, dv = \boldsymbol{i} \cdot \oint_S U\boldsymbol{n}\, da \tag{2.125}$$

This equation must hold for all orientations of the unit vector $\boldsymbol{i}$, and in particular when $\boldsymbol{i}$ coincides with the unit vectors $\boldsymbol{i}_x$, $\boldsymbol{i}_y$, $\boldsymbol{i}_z$ of a Cartesian system of coordinates. This completes the proof of Eq. 2.122.

(*b*) Let $\boldsymbol{A}$ be a vector function of position whose components are differentiable within a volume $V$ and on its surface $S$, and $\boldsymbol{n}$ a unit vector normal to $S$ and outwardly directed. Then,

$$\int_V \text{curl}\, \boldsymbol{A}\, dv = \oint_S \boldsymbol{n} \times \boldsymbol{A}\, dv \tag{2.126}$$

To prove this theorem, we apply Gauss' theorem to the divergence of the vector $\boldsymbol{i} \times \boldsymbol{A}$, where $\boldsymbol{i}$ is a constant unit vector. Then,

$$\int_V \text{div}\, (\boldsymbol{i} \times \boldsymbol{A})\, dv = \oint_S (\boldsymbol{i} \times \boldsymbol{A}) \cdot \boldsymbol{n}\, da \tag{2.127}$$

On the other hand

$$\operatorname{div}(\boldsymbol{i} \times \boldsymbol{A}) = -\boldsymbol{i} \cdot \operatorname{curl} \boldsymbol{A} \tag{2.128}$$

and

$$(\boldsymbol{i} \times \boldsymbol{A}) \cdot \boldsymbol{n} = -\boldsymbol{i} \cdot (\boldsymbol{n} \times \boldsymbol{A}) \tag{2.129}$$

Thus,

$$\boldsymbol{i} \cdot \int_V \operatorname{curl} \boldsymbol{A}\, dv = \boldsymbol{i} \cdot \oint_S (\boldsymbol{n} \times \boldsymbol{A})\, da \tag{2.130}$$

This equation must hold for all orientations of the unit vector $\boldsymbol{i}$, and in particular when $\boldsymbol{i}$ coincides with the unit vectors $\boldsymbol{i}_x$, $\boldsymbol{i}_y$, $\boldsymbol{i}_z$ of a Cartesian system of coordinates. This completes the proof of Eq. 2.126.

(*c*) Let $U$ be a scalar function of position, which is differentiable within a volume $V$, and let $S$ be a two-sided surface bounded by a contour $C$ and wholly contained in $V$. Then, if $d\boldsymbol{s}$ is a differential vector tangent to $C$ and $\boldsymbol{n}$ a unit vector normal to $S$ and oriented according to the right-handed-screw rule,

$$\int_S \boldsymbol{n} \times \operatorname{grad} U\, da = \oint_C U\, d\boldsymbol{s} \tag{2.131}$$

To prove this theorem, we apply Stokes' theorem to the vector $\boldsymbol{i}U$, where $\boldsymbol{i}$ is a constant unit vector. We have

$$\int_S (\operatorname{curl} \boldsymbol{i}U) \cdot \boldsymbol{n}\, da = \oint_C \boldsymbol{i}U \cdot d\boldsymbol{s} \tag{2.132}$$

On the other hand,

$$\operatorname{curl} \boldsymbol{i}U = -\boldsymbol{i} \times \operatorname{grad} U \tag{2.133}$$

and

$$-\boldsymbol{n} \cdot (\boldsymbol{i} \times \operatorname{grad} U) = \boldsymbol{i} \cdot (\boldsymbol{n} \times \operatorname{grad} U) \tag{2.134}$$

Thus,

$$\boldsymbol{i} \cdot \int_S \boldsymbol{n} \times \operatorname{grad} U\, da = \boldsymbol{i} \cdot \oint_C U\, d\boldsymbol{s} \tag{2.135}$$

This equation must hold for all orientations of $\boldsymbol{i}$, and in particular when $\boldsymbol{i}$ coincides with the unit vectors $\boldsymbol{i}_x$, $\boldsymbol{i}_y$, $\boldsymbol{i}_z$ of a Cartesian system of coordinates. This completes the proof of Eq. 2.131.

(*d*) Let $U$ and $V$ be two scalar functions which, together with their gradients and Laplacians, are nonsingular within a volume $V$ and on the surface $S$ enclosing $V$. Applying Gauss' theorem to the vector $V$ grad $U$ yields

$$\int_V \operatorname{div}(V \operatorname{grad} U)\, dv = \oint_S (V \operatorname{grad} U) \cdot \boldsymbol{n}\, da \tag{2.136}$$

On the other hand,

$$\text{div}\,(V\,\text{grad}\,U) = \text{grad}\,V\cdot\text{grad}\,U + V\,\Delta U \tag{2.137}$$

Thus

$$\int_V (\text{grad}\,V\cdot\text{grad}\,U + V\,\Delta U)\,dv = \oint_S V\,\text{grad}\,U\cdot\boldsymbol{n}\,da \tag{2.138}$$

and similarly,

$$\int_V (\text{grad}\,U\cdot\text{grad}\,V + U\,\Delta V)\,dv = \oint_S U\,\text{grad}\,V\cdot\boldsymbol{n}\,da \tag{2.139}$$

Subtracting Eq. 2.139 from Eq. 2.138 yields finally

$$\int_V (V\,\Delta U - U\,\Delta V)\,dv = \oint_S (V\,\text{grad}\,U - U\,\text{grad}\,V)\cdot\boldsymbol{n}\,da \tag{2.140}$$

This expression is known as Green's theorem.

(*e*) Let $\boldsymbol{A}$ be a conservative vector (curl $\boldsymbol{A} = 0$) and $\boldsymbol{B}$ a solenoid vector (div $\boldsymbol{B} = 0$) whose magnitudes vanish at infinity at least as fast as the reciprocal of the square of the distance from a fixed origin. Then,

$$\oint \boldsymbol{A}\cdot\boldsymbol{B}\,dv = 0 \tag{2.141}$$

where the volume integral includes the entire space.

In fact, expressing $\boldsymbol{A}$ in terms of its potential $U$,

$$\boldsymbol{A} = -\text{grad}\,U$$

we have

$$\text{div}\,(U\boldsymbol{B}) = \boldsymbol{B}\cdot\text{grad}\,U + U\,\text{div}\,\boldsymbol{B} = -\boldsymbol{A}\cdot\boldsymbol{B} \tag{2.142}$$

Then, applying Gauss' theorem to a sphere of radius $R$ yields

$$\int_V \boldsymbol{A}\cdot\boldsymbol{B}\,dv = -\oint_S U\boldsymbol{B}\cdot\boldsymbol{n}\,da \tag{2.143}$$

where $V$ is the volume of the sphere and $S$ is its surface. In the limit when $R$ approaches infinity, the surface integral vanishes because $U\boldsymbol{B}\cdot\boldsymbol{n}$ vanishes at least as fast as $R^{-3}$, and the surface of the sphere approaches infinity as $R^2$.

(*f*) Let $\boldsymbol{A}$ be a solenoidal vector (div $\boldsymbol{A} = 0$) which vanishes outside a volume $V$ and on the surface $S$ enclosing $V$. Then,

$$\int_V \boldsymbol{A}\,dv = 0 \tag{2.144}$$

In fact, $\boldsymbol{A}$, because of its solenoidal character, can be expressed as

$$\boldsymbol{A} = \text{curl}\, \boldsymbol{B} \tag{2.145}$$

where $\boldsymbol{B}$ is another vector. Then, the volume integral can be transformed into a surface integral with the help of Eq. 2.126,

$$\int_V \boldsymbol{A}\, dv = \int_V \text{curl}\, \boldsymbol{B}\, dv = \oint_S \boldsymbol{n} \times \boldsymbol{B}\, da \tag{2.146}$$

where $\boldsymbol{n}$ is a unit vector normal to $S$ and outwardly directed. On the other hand, since $\boldsymbol{A}$ vanishes on $S$ and outside $V$, the vector $\boldsymbol{B}$ is conservative on $S$ and outside $V$, and, therefore, it can be expressed as the gradient of a scalar function $\phi$, i.e.,

$$\boldsymbol{B} = \text{grad}\, \phi \tag{2.147}$$

Substitution for $\boldsymbol{B}$ in Eq. 2.146 yields then,

$$\int_V \boldsymbol{A}\, dv = \oint_S \boldsymbol{n} \times \text{grad}\, \phi\, da \tag{2.148}$$

Finally, the surface integral can be transformed into a line integral with the help of Eq. 2.131,

$$\int_V \boldsymbol{A}\, dv = \oint_C \phi\, d\boldsymbol{s} = 0 \tag{2.149}$$

and the latter vanishes because the surface $S$ is closed and, therefore, the contour $C$ bounding it consists of a single point. This completes the proof of Eq. 2.144.

(*g*) Let $r$ be the distance between a point $P_1$ of coordinates $x_1$, $y_1$, $z_1$ and a point $P_2$ of coordinates $x_2$, $y_2$, $z_2$,

$$r = \sqrt{(x_1 - x_2)^2 + (y_1 - y_2)^2 + (z_1 - z_2)^2} \tag{2.150}$$

and let $\boldsymbol{i}_r$ be a unit vector pointing from $P_2$ to $P_1$. We have

$$\frac{\partial r^n}{\partial x_1} = n r^{n-2}(x_1 - x_2) = -\frac{\partial r^n}{\partial x_2} \tag{2.151}$$

Thus,

$$\begin{aligned} \text{grad}_1\, r^n &= -\text{grad}_2\, r^n = n r^{n-2}[\boldsymbol{i}_x(x_1 - x_2) + \boldsymbol{i}_y(y_1 - y_2) + \boldsymbol{i}_z(z_1 - z_2)] \\ &= n r^{n-1}\boldsymbol{i}_r \end{aligned} \tag{2.152}$$

where the subscripts to the gradient symbol indicate the point with respect to which the differentiations are to be carried out. If

$$\boldsymbol{r} = \boldsymbol{i}_r r = \boldsymbol{i}_x(x_1 - x_2) + \boldsymbol{i}_y(y_1 - y_2) + \boldsymbol{i}_z(z_1 - z_2) \tag{2.153}$$

is the vector distance from $P_2$ to $P_1$,

$$\text{div}_1\, \boldsymbol{r} = \text{div}_1\, \boldsymbol{i}_r r = 3 = -\text{div}_2\, \boldsymbol{r} \tag{2.154}$$

It follows that

$$\begin{aligned}\text{div}_1\, \boldsymbol{i}_r r^n &= r^{n-1}\, \text{div}_1\, \boldsymbol{i}_r r + \boldsymbol{i}_r r \cdot \text{grad}_1\, r^{n-1} \\ &= 3r^{n-1} + (n-1)r^{n-1} = (n+2)r^{n-1} = -\,\text{div}_2\, \boldsymbol{i}_r r^n\end{aligned} \tag{2.155}$$

and

$$\Delta_1 r^n = \text{div}_1\, \text{grad}_1\, r^n = n(n+1)r^{n-2} = \Delta_2 r^n \tag{2.156}$$

In particular,

$$\text{grad}_1 \frac{1}{r} = -\frac{\boldsymbol{i}_r}{r^2} = -\,\text{grad}_2 \frac{1}{r} \tag{2.157}$$

$$\Delta_1 \frac{1}{r} = 0 = \Delta_2 \frac{1}{r} \tag{2.158}$$

Furthermore, Eq. 2.152 states that any vector $\boldsymbol{i}_r r^m$ is proportional to the gradient of a scalar function. It follows that

$$\text{curl}_1\, \boldsymbol{i}_r r^m = 0 = \text{curl}_2\, \boldsymbol{i}_r r^m \tag{2.159}$$

This identity can be checked by direct computation.

## 2.9 Summary and Conclusions

This chapter has been devoted to a review of vector algebra and to the study of the basic differential properties of scalar and vector fields. We saw, first of all, that the directional derivative of a scalar function of position $U$ could be expressed as the component, in the given direction, of the vector grad $U$. We saw next that the flux of a vector $\boldsymbol{A}$ through a closed surface could be attributed to the presence of sources within the surface; the divergence of the vector was then defined as a measure of the density of such sources. Conversely, Gauss' theorem permitted us to express the flux through the closed surface as a volume integral of the divergence of the vector, i.e., of the source density. Similarly, we were led to relate the line integral of a vector $\boldsymbol{A}$ around a closed path to the presence of vortex lines threading the path, and we were able to show that these vortex lines were the lines of force of a vector curl $\boldsymbol{A}$. Conversely, Stokes' theorem permitted us to express the line integral of $\boldsymbol{A}$ in terms of the flux of curl $\boldsymbol{A}$ through any two-sided surface bounded by the closed path.

Fields of which either the curl or the divergence is equal to zero play very important roles in the study of electromagnetic fields, as we shall see in Chapter 4. Fields whose curl is equal to zero are said to be *conservative*. This name stems from the fact that energy is conserved in a force field having this property, for any motion that ends at the point of origin, i.e., for any motion around a closed path. For instance, the net work done by an electrostatic field on a unit charge is equal to zero when the charge is returned to its point of origin; therefore, the work done by the field in moving the charge from one point to another is independent of the path followed. For this reason, the charge possesses at each point a well-defined *potential energy* relative to any given reference point. In mathematical terms, as we shall see in Chapter 4, a conservative vector can be represented as the negative gradient of a scalar *potential* function.

Fields whose divergence is equal to zero are said to be *solenoidal*. The name stems from the Greek word "solen," meaning channel or tube. It implies that the lines of force form endless tubes, without sources or sinks. This is just the characteristic that was associated with the vanishing of the divergence, and that resulted in the fact that the flux through any closed surface was equal to zero. One might say that, whereas energy is conserved in a conservative field, flux is conserved in a solenoidal field. The name *solenoid* is used in referring to an inductor, just because the magnetic field in free space is solenoidal. We shall see in Chapter 4 that a solenoidal field can be represented as the curl of a *vector potential*; this representation is analogous to that of a conservative field as the negative gradient of a scalar potential. As a matter of fact, we shall see later on that the vector potential associated with the magnetic field is related to the potential energy of a closed-current filament in a magnetic field.

The sources whose density is measured by the divergence, and the vortex lines whose direction and density are represented by the curl, are the seats of vector fields. More precisely, it can be shown that the field within any closed surface $S$ is uniquely specified by its curl and its divergence within $S$, and by either its tangential component or its normal component on $S$. This is equivalent to saying that a field which is both solenoidal and conservative within $S$, and of which either the normal component or the tangential component vanishes over $S$, is identically zero within $S$. This important property of vector fields will be discussed in Chapter 4. It is a generalization of the well-known fact that a one-dimensional function is uniquely specified by its derivative together with its value at a single point.

Our discussion of the differential properties of vector fields involved the implicit assumption that all the components of the vector are finite and differentiable. On the other hand, our discussion of electromagnetic fields will confront us very often with situations in which certain vector components are discontinuous and, therefore, nondifferentiable. A simple way of circumventing the difficulties arising in such situations, is to substitute for the discontinuities very fast but continuous variations. But we shall see in the next chapter that the discontinuities associated with electromagnetic fields have deep physical significance, and that an appreciation of the phenomena involved is of great help in resolving the related mathematical difficulties. For this reason we have purposely avoided such questions in this chapter. It should be remembered, however, that expressions such as Gauss' and Stokes' theorems are valid only when the vector components are differentiable throughout the region of space involved, and that great care, therefore, should be exercised in their application.

It is well to point out that vector notations were not used in the early days of electromagnetism; for instance, vector notations are not used in Maxwell's famous treatise. A glance at any of the older books will show the great advantage of such notations. The main point is that all the vector operations discussed in this chapter are defined and can be used without reference to any system of coordinates. It is only in dealing with the details of specific problems that coordinates have to be introduced to fit the particular geometry involved. There is no question that the simplicity and elegance which result from the use of vector notations are well worth the additional effort necessary to become familiar with them.

The fact that vectors and certain operations on vectors can be defined without reference to a particular system of coordinates deserves much more attention than it was possible to give to it in this chapter. The geometric definition of a vector as a quantity representable by means of a directed segment of line implies that a vector must have the same mathematical properties as the distance between two points. In particular, the Cartesian components of a vector must transform like the Cartesian coordinates of a point when the coordinate axes are rotated. As a matter of fact, it can be shown that the concept of a vector can be defined, for an $n$-dimensional space, simply as a set of $n$ numbers that transform like the Cartesian coordinates of a point. Vector analysis can be developed in a more direct and precise, but more abstract, manner from this definition. The main advantage of such an approach is that it leads directly to the development of tensor analysis as a generalization of vector analysis. For an introductory discussion of this approach, see [2].

## 2.10 Selected References


1. E. A. Guillemin, *The Mathematics of Circuit Analysis*, The Technology Press and John Wiley and Sons, New York, 1949, Chapter V. A more complete discussion of vector analysis, similar in point of view to that presented in this chapter.
2. J. A. Stratton, *Electromagnetic Theory*, McGraw-Hill, New York, 1941. Sections 1.19 and 1.20 present an introductory discussion of vector analysis and tensor analysis from a transformation point of view.
3. H. B. Phillips, *Vector Analysis*, John Wiley and Sons, New York, 1933. A very thorough and complete, yet readable, treatment of vector analysis.
4. W. E. Rogers, *Introduction to Electric Fields*, McGraw-Hill, New York, 1954. A clear exposition of electromagnetism at an intermediate level. The first chapter covers vector algebra and coordinate systems; the differential operations are introduced in the discussion of electrostatics and magnetostatics.


## PROBLEMS

**Problem 2.1.** Given the three vectors

$$\boldsymbol{A} = \boldsymbol{i}_x + \boldsymbol{i}_y + \boldsymbol{i}_z$$

$$\boldsymbol{B} = \boldsymbol{i}_x - \boldsymbol{i}_y$$

$$\boldsymbol{C} = \boldsymbol{i}_x + \boldsymbol{i}_y 2 - \boldsymbol{i}_z 2$$

Find

(a) $\boldsymbol{A} + \boldsymbol{B}$.
(b) $\boldsymbol{A} + \boldsymbol{C}$.
(c) $\boldsymbol{B} \cdot \boldsymbol{C}$.
(d) $|\boldsymbol{A} - \boldsymbol{C}|$.
(e) $\boldsymbol{A} \cdot \boldsymbol{B}$.
(f) $\boldsymbol{A} \cdot \boldsymbol{C}$.
(g) The cosine of the angle between $\boldsymbol{A}$ and $\boldsymbol{C}$.
(h) $\boldsymbol{A} \times \boldsymbol{B}$.
(i) The sine of the angle between $\boldsymbol{A}$ and $\boldsymbol{B}$.
(j) $\boldsymbol{A} \cdot (\boldsymbol{B} \times \boldsymbol{C})$.
(k) $\boldsymbol{A} \times (\boldsymbol{B} \times \boldsymbol{C})$.
(l) $(\boldsymbol{A} \times \boldsymbol{B}) \times \boldsymbol{C}$.

**Problem 2.2.** When drawn from the origin, the tips of the three vectors $\boldsymbol{A}$, $\boldsymbol{B}$, and $\boldsymbol{C}$ determine a plane. Show that the shortest distance from this plane to the origin is given by

$$d = \frac{\boldsymbol{A} \cdot [(\boldsymbol{A} - \boldsymbol{B}) \times (\boldsymbol{A} - \boldsymbol{C})]}{|(\boldsymbol{A} - \boldsymbol{B}) \times (\boldsymbol{A} - \boldsymbol{C})|}$$

Evaluate $d$ for the vectors:

$$A = i_x + 2i_y$$

$$B = i_y - i_z$$

$$C = i_x + i_z$$

What is the significance of the sign of $d$?

**Problem 2.3.** The vector $A = i_x y - i_y x$ represents a force in newtons when $x$ and $y$ are given in meters. Find the work done by this force on a *closed* path in the $xy$-plane that follows the parabola $y = x^2$ from the point $x = -1$, $y = 1$ to the point $x = 2$, $y = 4$ and returns along the straight line $y = x + 2$.

**Problem 2.4.** Find the flux of the vector

$$A = i_x x + i_y y + i_z z$$

over a spherical surface of radius $R$, centered at the origin. (*Hint:* Use spherical coordinates.)

**Problem 2.5.** Find the value of the derivative of

$$V = x^2 + 4y^2 + 16z^2$$

at the point (2, 2, 1) in the direction of the vector

$$A = -i_x + i_y 2 + i_z 2$$

**Problem 2.6.** A vector $A$ is defined by

$$A = i_x(x^2 - y^2) - i_y 2xy$$

(a) Can the vector $A$ be represented as the gradient of a scalar function?

(b) Find the value of the line integral of $A$ over the contour of a square lying in the $xy$-plane with sides parallel to the two axes and one corner located at the origin.

**Problem 2.7.** Consider the nine fields $F$ described by

$$F = i_j$$

where $i_j$ is one of the three unit vectors in a Cartesian, cylindrical, and spherical coordinate system. Sketch the field lines in appropriately chosen cross-sectional planes. Find the curls and divergences of these nine fields.

**Problem 2.8.** Consider the nine potentials given by

$$\phi = u_i$$

where $u_i$ is any one of the coordinates of a Cartesian, cylindrical, and spherical system ($u_1 = x$, $u_2 = y$, $u_3 = z$; $u_1 = r$, $u_2 = \varphi$, $u_3 = z$; $u_1 = r$, $u_2 = \theta$, $u_3 = \varphi$). Sketch the equipotential lines and the field lines of these potentials in appropriately chosen cross-sectional planes. Find div grad $\phi$ for these nine potentials.

**Problem 2.9.** Determine the contour integral of

$$A = i_x yz + i_y xz + i_z 3z^3$$

over a contour formed by the intersections of the four planes $x = \pm a$, $y = \pm b$ with another plane not parallel to any one of them.

**Problem 2.10.** Given a spherical volume $V$ enclosed by a surface $S$ show that

$$-\oint_S \boldsymbol{A} \times \boldsymbol{n}\, da = \int_V \text{curl}\, \boldsymbol{A}\, dv$$

for the vector

$$\boldsymbol{A} = \boldsymbol{i}_r \frac{\theta}{r} + \boldsymbol{i}_\theta \frac{1}{r} + \boldsymbol{i}_\varphi \frac{\ln r}{r}$$

**Problem 2.11.** Show that

(a) div curl $\boldsymbol{A} = 0$.
(b) curl grad $\phi = 0$.
(c) curl curl $\boldsymbol{A}$ = grad div $\boldsymbol{A} - \nabla^2 \boldsymbol{A}$.

# CHAPTER THREE

# The Differential Laws in Free Space

It was stated at the end of Chapter 1 that the integral field equations of electromagnetism can be transformed into equivalent differential point relations. These differential relations lend themselves more readily to mathematical manipulations, and thereby lead to a more profound understanding of electromagnetic fields. We shall see in this chapter how the *general field equations* can be written in terms of the differential quantities discussed in the preceding chapter, and how discontinuities of the field components can be taken into account by means of supplementary *boundary conditions.* These boundary conditions will reflect the presence of surface charge distributions and surface current distributions, having finite surface densities but infinite volume densities.

The differential expressions of the field laws will permit us to classify fields according to their mathematical properties, thereby providing an outline for a systematic study of their properties. This chapter includes a discussion of electric and magnetic dipole fields that will provide a basis for a variety of illustrative examples throughout this book.

## 3.1 Maxwell's Equations in Free Space

We shall assume in this section that all field components are differentiable to insure that their curl and divergence have no singularities anywhere in the space. In this connection, we may think of any spatial discontinuity as substituted by a fast variation with a finite rate of change; discontinuities will be discussed explicitly in the next section.

Let us consider first the equation representing the law of conservation of charge, which is reproduced below in vector notations, for convenience of reference.

$$\oint_S \boldsymbol{J}\cdot\boldsymbol{n}\, da = -\frac{d}{dt}\int_V \rho\, dv \tag{3.1}$$

where $\boldsymbol{J}$ is the current density, $\rho$ is the charge density, $S$ is a closed surface, $\boldsymbol{n}$ is a unit vector normal to the surface and outwardly directed, $da$ is a differential element of surface, $dv$ is a differential element of volume, and $V$ is the volume enclosed by $S$. If we divide this equation by $V$ and shrink the surface $S$ about any internal point $P$, the left-hand side coincides, in the limit when $V$ approaches zero, with the definition of div $\boldsymbol{J}$, given by Eq. 2.88. The volume integral on the right-hand side approaches, by definition, the value of the charge density at the same point $P$. We thus have

$$\text{div}\, \boldsymbol{J} = -\frac{\partial \rho}{\partial t} \tag{3.2}$$

where the sign of partial differentiation with respect to time has been substituted for that of total differentiation in view of the fact that $\rho$ is a function of the space coordinates as well as of time, whereas the volume integral in Eq. 3.1 is a function of $t$ alone, for a fixed surface $S$. Equation 3.2 expresses the law of conservation of charge in differential form. The integral form from which we started can be obtained from Eq. 3.2 by the reverse process of applying Gauss' theorem to the latter equation.

Let us consider next the two fundamental field equations in free space, which are again reproduced below in vector notations for convenience of reference,

$$\oint_C \boldsymbol{E}\cdot d\boldsymbol{s} + \frac{d}{dt}\int_S \mu_0 \boldsymbol{H}\cdot\boldsymbol{n}\, da = 0 \tag{3.3}$$

$$\oint_C \boldsymbol{H}\cdot d\boldsymbol{s} - \frac{d}{dt}\int_S \epsilon_0 \boldsymbol{E}\cdot\boldsymbol{n}\, da = \int_S \boldsymbol{J}\cdot\boldsymbol{n}\, da \tag{3.4}$$

where $C$ is a closed path, $S$ is any two-sided surface bounded by $C$, $d\boldsymbol{s}$ is a vector differential element of $C$, $\boldsymbol{n}$ is a unit vector normal to $S$ and directed relative to $d\boldsymbol{s}$ according to the right-handed-screw rule illustrated in Fig. 1.1, $\boldsymbol{E}$ is the electric-field intensity, and $\boldsymbol{H}$ is the magnetic-field intensity. Let us select, as $C$, a closed path lying on a plane and, as $S$, the area enclosed by $C$ on the plane, so that $\boldsymbol{n}$ is normal to the plane. Then let us divide both equations by the area $a$ enclosed by $C$, and shrink $C$ about any internal point $P$. In the limit when $a$

approaches zero, the left-hand sides of the resulting equations coincide with the definitions of the components of curl $\boldsymbol{E}$ and curl $\boldsymbol{H}$ in the direction of $\boldsymbol{n}$ given by Eq. 2.101. The surface integrals on the right-hand sides become equal, by definition, to the components in the direction of $\boldsymbol{n}$ of the vectors involved. We thus obtain

$$\boldsymbol{n}\cdot\text{curl}\,\boldsymbol{E} + \frac{\partial}{\partial t}(\boldsymbol{n}\cdot\mu_0\boldsymbol{H}) = 0 \tag{3.5}$$

$$\boldsymbol{n}\cdot\text{curl}\,\boldsymbol{H} - \frac{\partial}{\partial t}(\boldsymbol{n}\cdot\epsilon_0\boldsymbol{E}) = (\boldsymbol{n}\cdot\boldsymbol{J}) \tag{3.6}$$

where the sign of partial derivative has been substituted for that of total derivative in view of the fact that the vector components are functions of the space coordinates as well as of time, while the surface integrals are functions of time alone, for a fixed closed path $C$. On the other hand, since the direction of $\boldsymbol{n}$, i.e., the orientation of the plane, is arbitrary, Eqs. 3.5 and 3.6 are valid for any three mutually orthogonal directions of $\boldsymbol{n}$, and therefore imply that

$$\text{curl}\,\boldsymbol{E} + \mu_0\frac{\partial \boldsymbol{H}}{\partial t} = 0 \tag{3.7}$$

$$\text{curl}\,\boldsymbol{H} - \epsilon_0\frac{\partial \boldsymbol{E}}{\partial t} = \boldsymbol{J} \tag{3.8}$$

The time derivatives of $\boldsymbol{H}$ and $\boldsymbol{E}$ are vectors whose components are time derivatives of the corresponding components of $\boldsymbol{H}$ and $\boldsymbol{E}$. It may be readily checked that this definition of the time derivative of a vector is equivalent to

$$\frac{\partial \boldsymbol{H}}{\partial t} = \lim_{\delta t\to 0}\frac{\boldsymbol{H}(t+\delta t) - \boldsymbol{H}(t)}{\delta t} \tag{3.9}$$

where the increment of $\boldsymbol{H}$ from $t$ to $t + \delta t$ is a vector difference. Equations 3.7 and 3.8 express in differential form the fundamental laws governing the behavior of electromagnetic fields in free space; they are known as Maxwell's equations in free space. The integral forms of the same laws from which we started can be obtained from Eqs. 3.7 and 3.8 by the reverse process of applying Stokes' theorem to the latter equations.

It was pointed out in Sec. 1.3 that mathematical consistency in the field laws requires that the parts of Eqs. 3.3 and 3.4 that involve surface integrals over $S$ be independent of the particular surface $S$ selected, as long as the surface is bounded by the given contour $C$. This requirement was said to imply that the two field vectors must satisfy two additional equations, which are reproduced below in vector notations for convenience of reference,

$$\oint_S \mu_0 \boldsymbol{H} \cdot \boldsymbol{n} \, da = 0 \tag{3.10}$$

$$\oint_S \epsilon_0 \boldsymbol{E} \cdot \boldsymbol{n} \, da = \int_V \rho \, dv \tag{3.11}$$

where $S$ is now a closed surface and $V$ is the volume enclosed by $S$. These equations state that the flux of $\mu_0 \boldsymbol{H}$ through any closed surface must be equal to zero, and that the flux of $\epsilon_0 \boldsymbol{E}$ through any closed surface must be equal to the net charge enclosed by the surface. We shall see now that Maxwell's equations imply corresponding differential relations, from which, in turn, Eqs. 3.10 and 3.11 can be obtained with the help of Gauss' theorem.

It was pointed out in Sec. 2.7 (Eq. 2.112) that the divergence of the curl of any vector field is identically equal to zero. Thus, taking the divergence of Eqs. 3.7 and 3.8 and interchanging the order of the differentiations with respect to time and with respect to the space coordinates yields

$$\frac{\partial}{\partial t} \operatorname{div} \mu_0 \boldsymbol{H} = 0 \tag{3.12}$$

$$\operatorname{div} \boldsymbol{J} + \frac{\partial}{\partial t} \operatorname{div} \epsilon_0 \boldsymbol{E} = 0 \tag{3.13}$$

On the other hand, div $\boldsymbol{J}$ is equal to the negative time rate of change of the charge density, because of the law of conservation of charge, expressed by Eq. 3.2. Substitution for div $\boldsymbol{J}$ in Eq. 3.13 yields

$$\frac{\partial}{\partial t} (\operatorname{div} \epsilon_0 \boldsymbol{E} - \rho) = 0 \tag{3.14}$$

Finally, integration with respect to time of Eqs. 3.12 and 3.14 yields

$$\operatorname{div} \mu_0 \boldsymbol{H} = \text{constant} \tag{3.15}$$

$$\operatorname{div} \epsilon_0 \boldsymbol{E} - \rho = \text{constant} \tag{3.16}$$

These last two equations state that the divergence of $\mu_0 \boldsymbol{H}$ and the difference between the divergence of $\epsilon_0 \boldsymbol{E}$ and the charge density are quantities independent of time. However, experimental evidence indicates that $\boldsymbol{H}$ can be made to vanish within any desired region of space of finite dimensions, at least at some one instant of time. Thus the constant in Eq. 3.15 must be equal to zero at all points of space. Similarly, all the charge can be removed from any finite region of space, and the electric field can be made to vanish in the same region, at least at some one instant of time. Thus the constant in Eq. 3.16 is also equal to zero. It follows that Eqs. 3.15 and 3.16 reduce to

$$\text{div } \mu_0 \boldsymbol{H} = 0 \tag{3.17}$$

$$\text{div } \epsilon_0 \boldsymbol{E} = \rho \tag{3.18}$$

These are the differential expressions corresponding to Eqs. 3.10 and 3.11. These expressions follow from Maxwell's equations and from the fact that the charge density and the two fields can be made to vanish at some time within any finite region of space. Equations 3.10 and 3.11 can be obtained from Eqs. 3.17 and 3.18 with the help of Gauss' theorem. Conversely, if we had accepted from the start the validity of Eqs. 3.10 and 3.11, Eqs. 3.17 and 3.18 could have been derived from them by the same procedure used in obtaining Eq. 3.2 from Eq. 3.1.

Equations 3.17 and 3.18 state that the field of $\mu_0\boldsymbol{H}$ is solenoidal, and charge is the source of the field $\epsilon_0\boldsymbol{E}$. Both fields are, in general, turbulent, as indicated by Eqs. 3.7 and 3.8. The negative time rate of change of $\mu_0\boldsymbol{H}$ is the vortex field of $\boldsymbol{E}$, and the current density, together with the time rate of change of $\epsilon_0\boldsymbol{E}$, is the vortex field of $\boldsymbol{H}$. In the particular case of time-invariant fields, the field of $\boldsymbol{E}$ becomes conservative, and the current density constitutes the entire vortex field of $\boldsymbol{H}$.

## 3.2 Surface Charges and Surface Currents

The validity of the differential field equations derived in the preceding section was restricted by the assumption that the components of all field vectors had to be differentiable in all directions throughout the entire space. This stringent requirement is met in free space if the charge density and the current density are finite at all points. Most types of charge and current singularities are of interest only as mathematical idealizations of finite distributions, and, therefore, are best handled by corresponding limiting processes. Some of these singularities are discussed in the next chapter. On the other hand, surface charge distributions and surface current distributions are of direct physical significance in connection, for instance, with the behavior of electromagnetic fields on the boundaries of conductors, and, in general, as we shall see in Chapter 5, on all surfaces where the properties of matter change abruptly. In preparation for the discussion of these questions, it is helpful to investigate at this time the behavior of free-space fields in the presence of surface charge distributions and surface current distributions, although these distributions are not physically realizable in free space.

A surface charge distribution can be defined as the limit of a charge distribution in a surface layer of finite thickness $\delta$, when $\delta$ approaches zero, but the charge per unit area of surface, i.e., the surface charge density $\sigma$, remains finite. Clearly, the volume charge density within the layer approaches infinity, and for this reason it is said to be singular on the surface. A surface current distribution can be defined similarly, as the limit of a current distribution flowing within a surface layer of finite thickness $\delta$, when $\delta$ approaches zero, but the current per unit width of the surface in the direction normal to that of current flow, i.e., the surface current density $\boldsymbol{K}$, remains finite. Clearly, the volume current density, i.e., the current per unit area normal to its direction of flow, approaches infinity when $\delta$ approaches zero, and becomes singular on the surface. The surface charge density $\sigma$ is measured in coulombs per square meter, and the surface current density $\boldsymbol{K}$ is measured in amperes per meter.

The two surface densities must still satisfy the law of conservation of charge, together with any current density that might be present on the two sides of the surface. Let us consider, in this connection, a surface $\Sigma$ on which a surface charge distribution of density $\sigma$ and a surface current distribution of density $\boldsymbol{K}$ are present, and let $\boldsymbol{J}$ represent the volume current density on the two sides of $\Sigma$. In order to investigate the form of the law of conservation of charge on $\Sigma$, we take for $S$ in Eq. 3.1 the pillbox surface illustrated in Fig. 3.1, consisting of two open

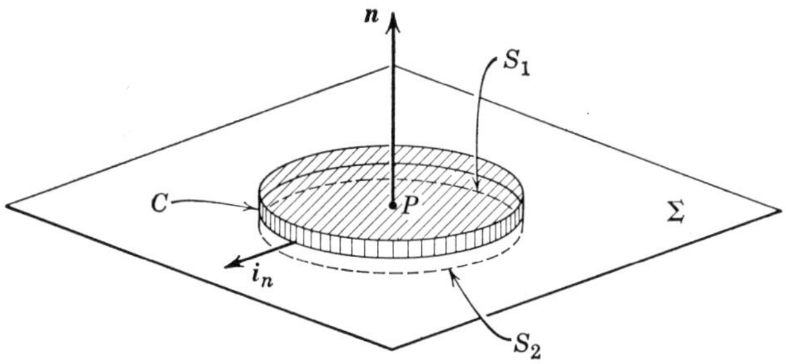


**Fig. 3.1.** The pillbox-surface $S$ employed in connection with surface charge distributions and discontinuities of the normal components of field vectors.

surfaces $S_1$ and $S_2$ parallel to each other and to $\Sigma$, and of the thin ribbon-like side surface normal to $\Sigma$ and intersecting it on the closed contour $C$. Let us then divide Eq. 3.1 by the common area $a$ of the two parallel surfaces $S_1$ and $S_2$, and evaluate its limit when the thickness of the pill-box and the area $a$ approach zero together while the contour $C$ shrinks about some internal point $P$ of $\Sigma$. The current flowing out of $S$ consists of three components: a component $I_1$ resulting from the flux of $\boldsymbol{J}$ through $S_1$, a component $I_2$ resulting from the flux of $\boldsymbol{J}$ through $S_2$, and a component $I_C$ resulting from the flux of the surface current density $\boldsymbol{K}$ through the contour $C$. We obtain for these three components:

$$\lim_{a\to 0} \frac{I_1}{a} = \boldsymbol{J}_1 \cdot \boldsymbol{n} \tag{3.19}$$

$$\lim_{a\to 0} \frac{I_2}{a} = -\boldsymbol{J}_2 \cdot \boldsymbol{n} \tag{3.20}$$

$$\lim_{a\to 0} \frac{I_C}{a} = \lim_{a\to 0} \frac{\oint_C \boldsymbol{K} \cdot \boldsymbol{i}_n \, ds}{a} = \operatorname{div}_\Sigma \boldsymbol{K} \tag{3.21}$$

where $\boldsymbol{n}$ is a unit vector normal to $\Sigma$ and pointing from $S_2$ to $S_1$, $\boldsymbol{J}_1$ and $\boldsymbol{J}_2$ are the values of $\boldsymbol{J}$ at the point $P$ on opposite sides of $\Sigma$, $\boldsymbol{i}_n$ is a unit vector tangent to $\Sigma$ and outwardly normal to $C$, and $\operatorname{div}_\Sigma \boldsymbol{K}$ is the two-dimensional divergence of $\boldsymbol{K}$, defined by the limit of Eq. 3.21. The charge enclosed by $S$ consists, in the limit, of only the portion of the surface charge enclosed by $C$, which, when divided by $a$, becomes (by definition) the surface charge density $\sigma$. It follows that

$$(\boldsymbol{J}_1 - \boldsymbol{J}_2) \cdot \boldsymbol{n} + \operatorname{div}_\Sigma \boldsymbol{K} = -\frac{\partial \sigma}{\partial t} \tag{3.22}$$

This equation states that the negative time rate of change of the surface charge density consists of two components: a component equal to the discontinuity suffered by the normal component of the volume current density in passing through $\Sigma$, and a component equal to the two-dimensional divergence of the surface current density $\boldsymbol{K}$.

## 3.3 Boundary Conditions

Let us investigate next the behavior of the field vectors $\boldsymbol{E}$ and $\boldsymbol{H}$ on a surface $\Sigma$ on which charges and currents are distributed, with the help of the two fundamental laws in integral form—namely, Eqs. 3.3 and 3.4—and of the two subsidiary equations derived from them—namely, Eqs. 3.10 and 3.11. We use the latter two equations first, and take as $S$ the same surface used in connection with the law of conservation of charge and illustrated in Fig. 3.1. Proceeding as in Sec. 3.2, we divide these two equations by the area $a$ of the two parallel surfaces $S_1$ and $S_2$, and evaluate their limits when the thickness of the pillbox and the area $a$ approach zero together while the contour $C$ shrinks about some internal point $P$ of $\Sigma$. We observe, first of all, that the contribution of the flux through the ribbonlike side surface vanishes in the limit because the thickness of the pillbox and the area $a$ are assumed to approach zero together, which implies that the ratio of the area of the side surface to $a$ vanishes in the limit. The fluxes through the surfaces $S_1$ and $S_2$, when divided by $a$, yield in the limit expressions similar to those for the components $I_1$ and $I_2$ given by Eqs. 3.19 and 3.20, with $\boldsymbol{H}$ and $\boldsymbol{E}$ substituted for $\boldsymbol{J}$. On the other hand, the total charge enclosed by $S$, when divided by $a$, yields in the limit the surface charge density $\sigma$, as pointed out above. It follows that Eqs. 3.10 and 3.11, when divided by $a$, yield in the limit

$$\mu_0(\boldsymbol{H}_1 - \boldsymbol{H}_2)\cdot\boldsymbol{n} = 0 \tag{3.23}$$

$$\epsilon_0(\boldsymbol{E}_1 - \boldsymbol{E}_2)\cdot\boldsymbol{n} = \sigma \tag{3.24}$$

The first equation states that the component of $\boldsymbol{H}$ normal to $\Sigma$ is continuous. The second equation states that the component of $\epsilon_0\boldsymbol{E}$ normal to $\Sigma$ suffers a discontinuity equal to $\sigma$ in passing through $\Sigma$.

Let us turn next to Eqs. 3.3 and 3.4 and select as $C$ the planar contour illustrated in Fig. 3.2, consisting of two line segments $L_1$ and $L_2$ parallel to and on opposite sides of $\Sigma$, and of two much shorter seg-

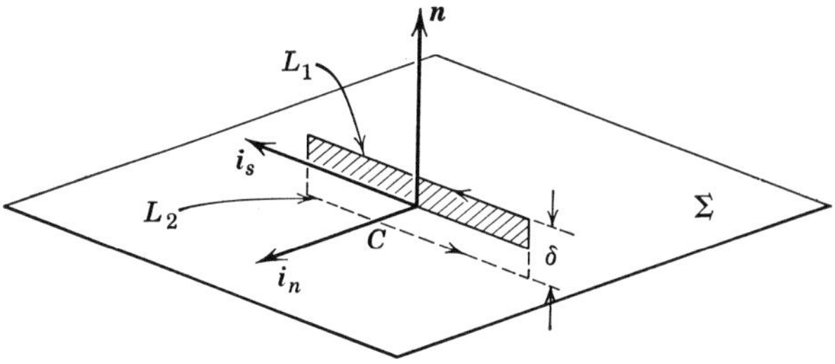


**Fig. 3.2.** Planar loop employed in connection with surface current distributions and discontinuities of the tangential components of field vectors.

ments normal to $\Sigma$. The surface $S$ may be taken as the area enclosed by the contour on the plane normal to $\Sigma$ and containing $L_1$ and $L_2$. Let us divide Eqs. 3.3 and 3.4 by the common length $L$ of the line segments $L_1$ and $L_2$, and evaluate their limits when both the height $\delta$ of the planar loop and its length $L$ approach zero, but in such a way that the ratio $\delta/L$ also approaches zero. Considering first Eq. 3.3, we observe that the contributions to the contour integral of the two sides of the rectangular loop normal to $\Sigma$ become, in the limit, proportional to $\delta$, and therefore vanish when divided by $L$. The other two sides of the loop yield, in the limit,

$$\lim_{L\to 0} \frac{\int_{L_1} \boldsymbol{E}\cdot d\boldsymbol{s}}{L} = \boldsymbol{E}_1\cdot\boldsymbol{i}_s \tag{3.25}$$

and

$$\lim_{L\to 0} \frac{\int_{L_2} \boldsymbol{E}\cdot d\boldsymbol{s}}{L} = -\boldsymbol{E}_2\cdot\boldsymbol{i}_s \tag{3.26}$$

where $\boldsymbol{i}_s$ is a unit vector parallel to $L_1$ and $L_2$, and $\boldsymbol{E}_1$ and $\boldsymbol{E}_2$ are the values of $\boldsymbol{E}$ at the point $P$ on opposite sides of $\Sigma$. On the other hand, the flux of $\mu_0\boldsymbol{H}$ through the rectangular loop becomes, in the limit, proportional to the area enclosed by the loop on the plane normal to $\Sigma$, namely, $\delta L$. It follows that the ratio of the flux to $L$ vanishes in the limit together with $\delta$. Thus we obtain

$$(\boldsymbol{E}_1 - \boldsymbol{E}_2)\cdot\boldsymbol{i}_s = 0 \tag{3.27}$$

This equation states that the component of $\boldsymbol{E}$ tangent to $\Sigma$ in the direction of $\boldsymbol{i}_s$ is continuous through $\Sigma$. On the other hand, the direction of $\boldsymbol{i}_s$ is arbitrary on the plane tangent to $\Sigma$. It follows that the entire component of $\boldsymbol{E}$ tangent to $\Sigma$ is continuous; this fact can be stated in the form

$$\boldsymbol{n} \times (\boldsymbol{E}_1 - \boldsymbol{E}_2) = 0 \tag{3.28}$$

Considering next Eq. 3.4, the two contributions to the contour integral of $\boldsymbol{H}$ of the two sides of the loop normal to $\Sigma$ vanish in the limit when divided by $L$, just as in the case of the contour integral of $\boldsymbol{E}$. The contributions of the other two sides divided by $L$ yield, in the limit, expressions similar to Eqs. 3.25 and 3.26 with $\boldsymbol{H}$ substituted for $\boldsymbol{E}$. Similarly, the flux of $\epsilon_0\boldsymbol{E}$ through the loop, divided by $L$, vanishes in the limit with $\delta$. The ratio of the current through the loop to the length

$L$ of the sides of the loop becomes, in the limit,

$$\lim_{L \to 0} \frac{\int_L \boldsymbol{K} \cdot \boldsymbol{i}_n \, ds}{L} = \boldsymbol{K} \cdot \boldsymbol{i}_n \tag{3.29}$$

where $\boldsymbol{i}_n$ is a unit vector tangent to $\Sigma$ and normal to the plane of the loop. We obtain thus,

$$(\boldsymbol{H}_1 - \boldsymbol{H}_2) \cdot \boldsymbol{i}_s = \boldsymbol{K} \cdot \boldsymbol{i}_n \tag{3.30}$$

In words: the component of $\boldsymbol{H}$ tangent to $\Sigma$, in passing through $\Sigma$, suffers a discontinuity equal to the component of the surface current density at right angles to it. A more convenient expression for the discontinuity of $\boldsymbol{H}$ can be obtained by orienting the loop of Fig. 3.2 in such a way that $\boldsymbol{i}_n$ is parallel to $\boldsymbol{K}$. For this loop orientation the component of $\boldsymbol{H}$ parallel to $\boldsymbol{i}_n$ is continuous, i.e. $(\boldsymbol{H}_1 - \boldsymbol{H}_2) \cdot \boldsymbol{i}_n$ vanishes. Then, multiplying Eq. 3.30 by $\boldsymbol{i}_n$ yields, with the help of Eq. A4.4 of Appendix 4

$$\begin{aligned}[(\boldsymbol{H}_1 - \boldsymbol{H}_2) \cdot \boldsymbol{i}_s]\boldsymbol{i}_n &= (\boldsymbol{H}_1 - \boldsymbol{H}_2) \times (\boldsymbol{i}_n \times \boldsymbol{i}_s) + [(\boldsymbol{H}_1 - \boldsymbol{H}_2) \cdot \boldsymbol{i}_n]\boldsymbol{i}_s \\ &= \boldsymbol{n} \times (\boldsymbol{H}_1 - \boldsymbol{H}_2) = \boldsymbol{K} \end{aligned} \tag{3.31}$$

where

$$\boldsymbol{n} = \boldsymbol{i}_s \times \boldsymbol{i}_n \tag{3.32}$$

is a unit vector normal to $\Sigma$.

Equations 3.23, 3.24, 3.28, and 3.31 specify completely the behavior of the field vectors $\boldsymbol{E}$ and $\boldsymbol{H}$ at any surface over which surface distributions of charge and current are present. Summarizing, the tangential component of $\boldsymbol{E}$ is continuous, while its normal component suffers a discontinuity equal to the surface charge density divided by $\epsilon_0$. The normal component of $\boldsymbol{H}$, on the other hand, is continuous, while its tangential component suffers a discontinuity equal in magnitude to the surface current density, and at right angles to it. It is worth noting further that, whereas div $\boldsymbol{E}$ and curl $\boldsymbol{H}$ are singular on $\Sigma$, div $\boldsymbol{H}$ and curl $\boldsymbol{E}$ are finite, in spite of the fact that some of the vector components are discontinuous. This fact can be readily checked by evaluating div $\boldsymbol{H}$ and curl $\boldsymbol{E}$ with one of the coordinate lines normal to $\Sigma$.

## 3.4 Classification of Fields in Free Space and in Linear Conductors

The form of Maxwell's equations in free space suggests that electromagnetic fields might be conveniently classified for the purposes of studying their properties, on the basis of whether their divergence alone, their curl alone, or both their divergence and their curl vanish in a given region of space.

1. Both the divergence and the curl of the field vanish throughout a region of space. This condition is met by:

(*a*) The electrostatic field $\boldsymbol{E}$ in a charge-free region. In fact,

$$\text{curl}\,\boldsymbol{E} = -\mu_0 \frac{\partial \boldsymbol{H}}{\partial t} = 0 \tag{3.33}$$

$$\text{div}\,\boldsymbol{E} = \frac{\rho}{\epsilon_0} = 0 \tag{3.34}$$

(*b*) The magnetostatic field $\boldsymbol{H}$ in a current-free region. In fact,

$$\text{curl}\,\boldsymbol{H} = \boldsymbol{J} + \epsilon_0 \frac{\partial \boldsymbol{E}}{\partial t} = 0 \tag{3.35}$$

$$\text{div}\,\boldsymbol{H} = 0 \tag{3.36}$$

(*c*) The static-current field $\boldsymbol{J}$ within a linear, homogeneous, isotropic conductor. The current field in a conductor is not, of course, a free-space field. Nevertheless, we wish to include it in our classification because of the wealth of interesting examples that it can provide. If $\sigma$ is the conductivity of the conductor, we have for such a current field,

$$\text{curl}\,\boldsymbol{J} = \sigma\,\text{curl}\,\boldsymbol{E} = 0 \tag{3.37}$$

$$\text{div}\,\boldsymbol{J} = -\frac{\partial \rho}{\partial t} = 0 \tag{3.38}$$

It should be noted also that the electric field $\boldsymbol{E}$, being proportional to $\boldsymbol{J}$, satisfies the same two conditions.

2. The curl of the field vanishes, but its divergence does not. This condition is met by:

(*a*) The electrostatic field $\boldsymbol{E}$ in any region of space because curl $\boldsymbol{E}$ vanishes in the absence of a time-varying magnetic field. We have in the entire space

$$\text{curl}\,\boldsymbol{E} = 0 \tag{3.39}$$

$$\text{div}\,\boldsymbol{E} = \frac{\rho}{\epsilon_0} \tag{3.40}$$

with the understanding that the normal component of $\boldsymbol{E}$ suffers a discontinuity given by Eq. 3.24 in the presence of a surface charge distribution.

3. The divergence of the field vanishes, but its curl does not. This condition is met by:

(*a*) The magnetic field $\boldsymbol{H}$ in any free-space region. We have

$$\text{div}\,\boldsymbol{H} = 0 \tag{3.41}$$

and, in the absence of a time-varying electric field,

$$\text{curl}\,\boldsymbol{H} = \boldsymbol{J} \tag{3.42}$$

with the understanding that the tangential component of $\boldsymbol{H}$ suffers a discontinuity given by Eq. 3.31 in the presence of a surface current distribution.

(*b*) The static-current field $\boldsymbol{J}$. Because of its time independence, and barring a continuous accumulation of charge,

$$\text{div}\,\boldsymbol{J} = -\frac{\partial\rho}{\partial t} = 0 \tag{3.43}$$

In the case of a current field in a linear, isotropic, but inhomogeneous conductor, we have

$$\text{curl}\,\boldsymbol{J} = \text{curl}\,\sigma\boldsymbol{E} = \sigma\,\text{curl}\,\boldsymbol{E} + (\text{grad}\,\sigma) \times \boldsymbol{E} = \frac{\text{grad}\,\sigma}{\sigma} \times \boldsymbol{J} \tag{3.44}$$

(*c*) The time-varying electromagnetic field in a charge- and current-free region. In this case,

$$\text{div}\,\boldsymbol{E} = \text{div}\,\boldsymbol{H} = 0 \tag{3.45}$$

$$\text{curl}\,\boldsymbol{E} = -\mu_0\frac{\partial\boldsymbol{H}}{\partial t} \tag{3.46}$$

$$\text{curl}\,\boldsymbol{H} = \epsilon_0\frac{\partial\boldsymbol{E}}{\partial t} \tag{3.47}$$

from which we obtain, by substitution,

$$\text{curl curl } \boldsymbol{E} = -\epsilon_0\mu_0 \frac{\partial^2 \boldsymbol{E}}{\partial t^2} \tag{3.48}$$

$$\text{curl curl } \boldsymbol{H} = -\epsilon_0\mu_0 \frac{\partial^2 \boldsymbol{H}}{\partial t^2} \tag{3.49}$$

4. Neither the divergence nor the curl of the field vanish in the region of interest. This general type of field can be treated, at least in principle, as the sum of two fields, one belonging to group 2 and one to group 3.

## 3.5 The Electric Dipole

This section is devoted to the study of the electric-dipole field, which is the simplest three-dimensional field beyond that of a spherically symmetrical charge distribution, discussed in Sec. 1.4. We turn our attention to it at this time for two main reasons. In the first place, we wish to become familiar with it at the earliest possible stage in our discussion, because we shall use it very frequently in illustrative examples. In the second place, it affords an opportunity to illustrate the field point of view mentioned in the introduction to Chapter 1, and to contrast it with the Coulomb approach characteristic of the elementary treatment of field problems.

The electric dipole is defined as a complex of two point charges, of equal magnitude and opposite sign, in the limit when their magnitude approaches infinity, their spacing approaches zero, but the product of magnitude and spacing remains constant. With reference to Fig. 3.3, if $q$ is the magnitude of the point charges, and $2\delta$ is their spacing, the magnitude of the moment of the dipole is defined as

$$p = 2q\delta \tag{3.50}$$

We shall review now the elementary derivation of the field of an electric dipole. We know from Sec. 1.4 that a point charge produces a radial, spherically symmetrical field of magnitude inversely proportional to the square of the radial distance from the charge. With reference to Fig. 3.3, the distance from the positive charge to the point $P$ is

$$r_+ = r - \delta \cos \theta \tag{3.51}$$

where $r$ is the distance from the origin 0, and $\theta$ is the angle between the direction of the point $P$ from the origin and the $z$-axis on which the two

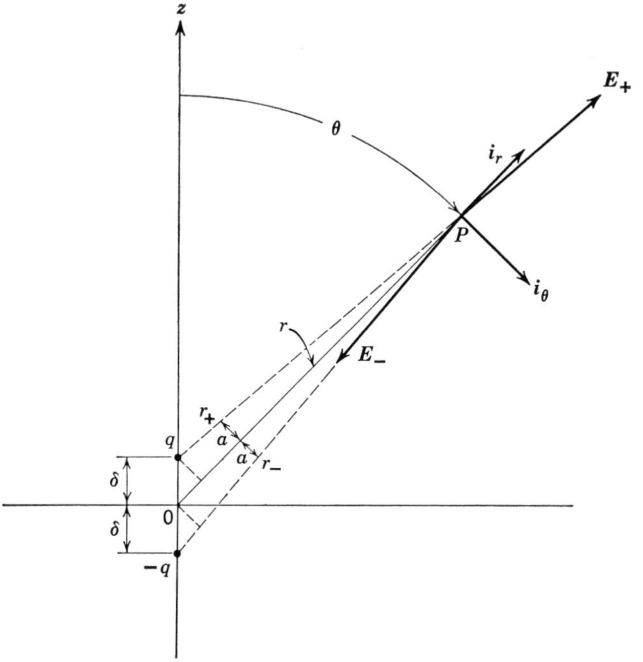


**Fig. 3.3.** Geometry used in the determination of the field of an electric dipole.

charges are located. Similarly, the distance from the negative charge to the point $P$ is

$$r_- = r + \delta \cos \theta \tag{3.52}$$

Let us express the total electric field in terms of its components in spherical coordinates. With the help of Eq. 1.19 expressing the field of a spherically symmetrical charge, we have for the total radial component

$$\begin{aligned} E_r &= \frac{q}{4\pi\epsilon_0}\left[\frac{1}{(r - \delta \cos \theta)^2} - \frac{1}{(r + \delta \cos \theta)^2}\right] \cos \alpha \\ &= \frac{q}{4\pi\epsilon_0} \frac{4r\delta \cos \theta \cos \alpha}{(r^2 - \delta^2 \cos^2 \theta)^2} \end{aligned} \tag{3.53}$$

where $\alpha$ is the angle between the line joining $P$ to the origin and that joining $P$ to either the positive charge or the negative charge. In the limit when $\delta$ approaches zero, and $2q\delta$ approaches $p$, this expression reduces to

$$E_r = \frac{2p \cos \theta}{4\pi\epsilon_0 r^3} \tag{3.54}$$

The total $\theta$ component is, similarly,

$$\begin{aligned} E_\theta &= \frac{q}{4\pi\epsilon_0}\left[\frac{1}{(r - \delta \cos \theta)^2} + \frac{1}{(r + \delta \cos \theta)^2}\right] \sin \alpha \\ &= \frac{q}{4\pi\epsilon_0} \frac{2(r^2 + \delta^2 \cos^2 \theta)}{(r^2 - \delta^2 \cos^2 \theta)^2} \frac{\delta \sin \theta}{r} \end{aligned} \tag{3.55}$$

In the limit when $\delta$ approaches zero and $2q\delta$ approaches $p$, this expression reduces to

$$E_\theta = \frac{p \sin \theta}{4\pi\epsilon_0 r^3} \tag{3.56}$$

Thus, the field of an electric dipole is

$$\boldsymbol{E} = \frac{p}{4\pi\epsilon_0 r^3} (\boldsymbol{i}_r 2 \cos \theta + \boldsymbol{i}_\theta \sin \theta) \tag{3.57}$$

A map of this field is shown in Fig. 3.4.

The approach used in this derivation is that of Coulomb's law, in the sense that the field was determined as the sum of the fields produced by two point charges. Let us now consider this field as a solution of Maxwell's equation. The electric field given by Eq. 3.57 must satisfy the static-field equations

$$\text{curl } \boldsymbol{E} = 0 \tag{3.58}$$

$$\text{div } \boldsymbol{E} = 0 \tag{3.59}$$

at all points of space except at the origin where the dipole is located. This can be readily checked by direct evaluation of the divergence and curl of $\boldsymbol{E}$, with the help of the expressions in spherical coordinates given in Appendix 3. On the other hand, any field that satisfies Eqs. 3.58 and 3.59 in a charge-free region $V$ is a "physically realizable" static field in such a region. The field must, of course, be produced by charges located outside $V$, but there is, in general, a variety of charge distributions that can produce the same field in $V$. In other words, the question of whether a particular static field is physically realizable in a given charge-free region depends entirely on whether it satisfies Eqs. 3.58 and 3.59 within the region, and, therefore, it can be considered independently of how the field can actually be generated. Thus, the field given by Eq. 3.57 is a physically realizable field in any charge-

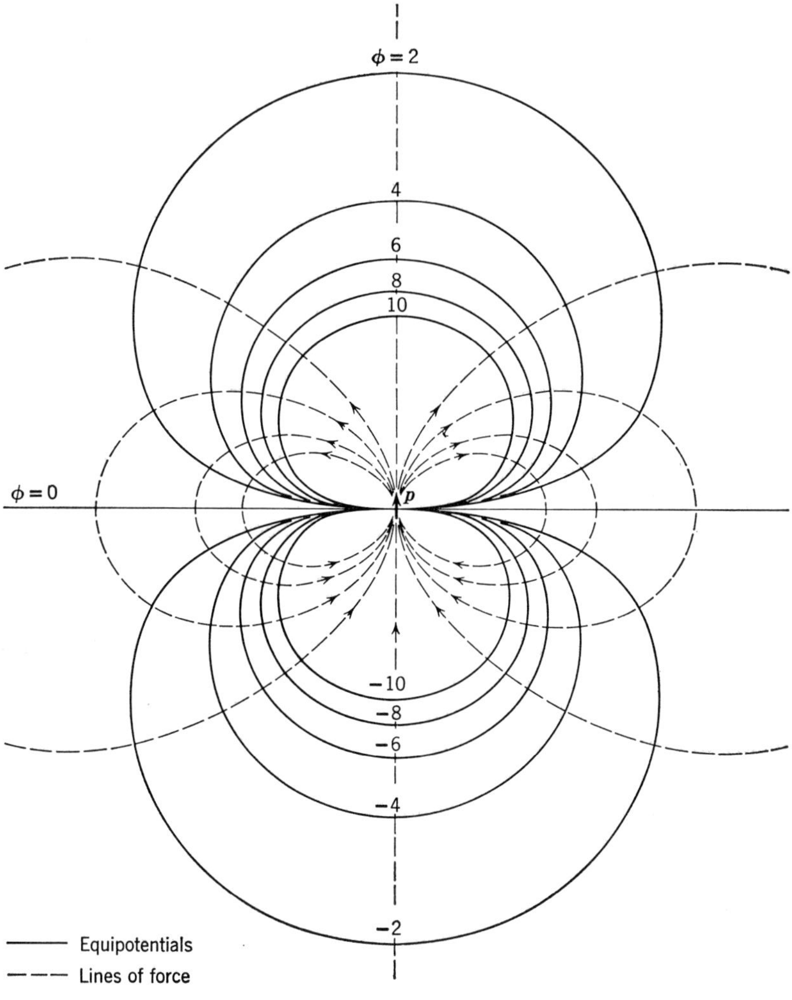


**Fig. 3.4.** The field of a dipole on a meridian plane.

free region $V$ not including the origin. However, it can be produced by a variety of charge distributions located outside $V$ as well as by the dipole from which it was derived. We derived it from a particular charge distribution, namely, the dipole, because this type of derivation is the only way of finding solutions to the differential Eqs. 3.58 and 3.59 with which we are familiar at this point. However, we shall see in Chapter 4 how entire families of solutions can be obtained directly without any reference to particular charge distributions; as a matter of fact, the field given by Eq. 3.57 is a member of one of these families, namely, the family of solutions in spherical coordinates.

The point of view of separating the physical realizability of a field from the manner in which the field is actually produced can be illustrated by inquiring how a dipole field can be generated outside a sphere of radius $R$, centered at the origin, by charge distributed on the surface of the same sphere. For this purpose, we observe, first of all, that, if $\sigma$ is the density of the surface charge, $\boldsymbol{E}_o$ the field outside the sphere, and $\boldsymbol{E}_i$ the field inside the sphere, then Eq. 3.24 requires

$$\boldsymbol{i}_r \cdot (\boldsymbol{E}_o - \boldsymbol{E}_i)_{r=R} = E_{or} - E_{ir} = \frac{\sigma}{\epsilon_0} \tag{3.60}$$

In words, the radial component of the electric field must suffer a discontinuity at the surface of the sphere equal to the surface charge density divided by $\epsilon_0$. On the other hand, because of Eq. 3.27,

$$\boldsymbol{i}_\theta \cdot (\boldsymbol{E}_o - \boldsymbol{E}_i)_{r=R} = E_{o\theta} - E_{i\theta} = 0 \tag{3.61}$$

In words, the tangential $\theta$-component of the electric field must be continuous through the surface of the sphere.

Next we note that the electric field must satisfy Eqs. 3.58 and 3.59 inside the sphere as well as outside the sphere. Thus, we must search for a field which satisfies these two equations inside the sphere, and whose $\theta$-component becomes equal to the $\theta$-component of the dipole field on the surface of the sphere, according to Eq. 3.61. The only way that we know at this point of finding such a field is to make an educated guess. A little thought will show that the tangential component of a uniform field parallel to the $z$-axis is proportional to $\sin\theta$, just as the tangential component of the dipole field. More precisely, a uniform field, parallel to the $z$-axis, can be expressed in spherical coordinates as follows,

$$\boldsymbol{E}_i = A(\boldsymbol{i}_r \cos\theta - \boldsymbol{i}_\theta \sin\theta) \qquad r < R \tag{3.62}$$

where $A$ is an arbitrary constant representing the intensity of the field. Equations 3.58 and 3.59 are obviously satisfied by a uniform field because all of its spacial derivatives are equal to zero. Furthermore, since the field outside the sphere is given by

$$\boldsymbol{E}_o = \frac{p}{4\pi\epsilon_0 r^3}(\boldsymbol{i}_r 2\cos\theta + \boldsymbol{i}_\theta \sin\theta) \qquad r > R \tag{3.63}$$

the condition imposed by Eq. 3.61 can be met by setting

$$A = -\frac{p}{4\pi\epsilon_0 R^3} \tag{3.64}$$

Thus,

$$\boldsymbol{E}_i = -\frac{p}{4\pi\epsilon_0 R^3}(\boldsymbol{i}_r \cos\theta - \boldsymbol{i}_\theta \sin\theta) \qquad r < R \tag{3.65}$$

The surface charge density $\sigma$ can now be computed from the discontinuity of the radial component of the electric field. We have from Eqs. 3.60, 3.63, and 3.65,

$$\sigma = \frac{3p}{4\pi R^3}\cos\theta \tag{3.66}$$

We must conclude, therefore, that this surface distribution of charge on a sphere of radius $R$ must produce a dipole field of moment $p$ outside the sphere, and a uniform field of intensity given by Eq. 3.64 inside the sphere. A map of the entire field is shown in Fig. 3.5. It must be kept in mind with regard to the scale of the map that the same lines must be thought as drawn on a set of equally spaced meridian planes, of which

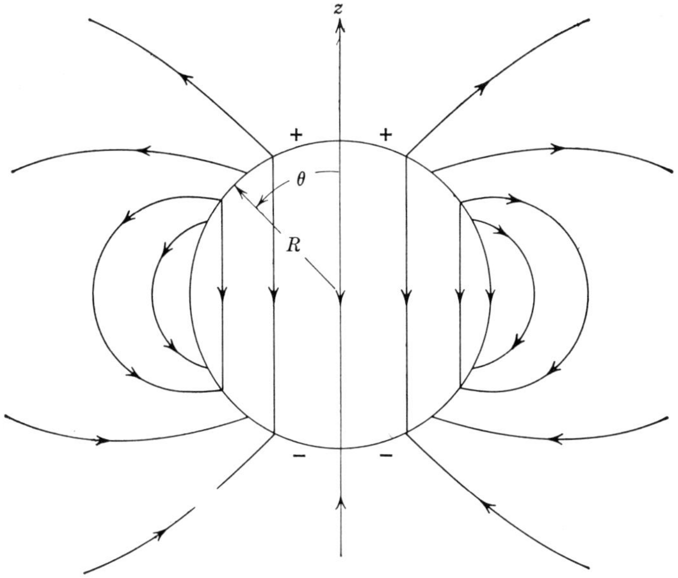


**Fig. 3.5.** The electric field produced by an electric dipole consisting of charge distributed on a spherical surface.

one is shown in the figure. Thus, in order for the lines to have a uniform volume density inside the sphere, their spacing on each meridian plane must be nonuniform.

Let us consider, finally, the relation between the dipole moment associated with the field outside the sphere and the charge distribution on the surface of the sphere. The limiting process involved in the definition of the dipole can be interpreted by saying that the spacing between the two charges forming the dipole must be vanishingly small compared to the distance from the two charges to the point at which the field is measured; in other words, a distance can be said to be vanishingly small only in a relative sense. Thus, if we consider the field produced by the surface charge for values of $r$ large compared to the radius of the sphere, we can regard each positive element of charge and the corresponding negative element on the same meridian plane as forming a dipole of moment

$$dp = 2R\sigma \cos \theta \, da \tag{3.67}$$

where $2R \cos \theta$ is the distance between the two charge elements at the points $\theta$ and $\pi - \theta$, and $da$ is the differential surface element. The total dipole moment should then be equal to the sum of all such differential dipole moments; that is,

$$p = \int_S 2R\sigma \cos \theta \, da \tag{3.68}$$

where $S$ is the positive half of the surface of the sphere. Since the surface element $da$ is given, in spherical coordinates, by

$$da = R^2 \sin \theta \, d\theta \, d\varphi \tag{3.69}$$

we obtain

$$p = 4\pi R^3 \int_0^{\pi/2} \sigma \sin \theta \cos \theta \, d\theta = 3p \int_0^{\pi/2} \sin \theta \cos^2 \theta \, d\theta$$

$$= 3p \int_0^1 \cos^2 \theta \, d(\cos \theta) = p \tag{3.70}$$

as expected. We shall see in Sec. 4.2 that a dipole moment can be assigned to any charge distribution of zero net charge, and that this dipole moment is equal to the first geometric moment of the charge distribution with respect to any arbitrary point.

## 3.6 The Magnetic Dipole

We saw in Sec. 3.4 that a static magnetic field in a current-free region has the same mathematical properties as a static electric field in a charge-free region. More precisely, the divergence and the curl of both fields must be equal to zero. It follows that, if the electric-dipole field given by Eq. 3.57 is a physically realizable electric field in any charge-free region not including the origin, the magnetic field

$$\boldsymbol{H} = \frac{m}{4\pi r^3}(\boldsymbol{i}_r 2\cos\theta + \boldsymbol{i}_\theta \sin\theta) \tag{3.71}$$

must be physically realizable in any current-free region of space not including the origin. In other words, this magnetic field must satisfy the equations

$$\text{curl}\ \boldsymbol{H} = 0 \tag{3.72}$$

$$\text{div}\ \boldsymbol{H} = 0 \tag{3.73}$$

in any such region of space. We refer to the constant $m$ appearing in Eq. 3.71 as the magnetic-dipole moment associated with the field. Comparison of this equation with Eq. 3.57 indicates that $m$ is analogous to $p/\epsilon_0$, rather than to $p$; although it would be conceptually more satisfying to divide the right-hand side of Eq. 3.71 by $\mu_0$, thereby making $m$ analogous to $p$, the resulting definition of $m$ would be at variance with accepted usage.

Let us inquire now how the magnetic field given by Eq. 3.71 could be generated in the space outside a sphere of radius $R$ by placing an appropriate current distribution on the surface of the same sphere. Let us indicate with $\boldsymbol{K}$ the density of the surface current, with $\boldsymbol{H}_o$ the magnetic field outside the sphere, and with $\boldsymbol{H}_i$ the magnetic field inside the sphere. Then, Eq. 3.23 requires the normal component of $\boldsymbol{H}$ to be continuous through the surface of the sphere,

$$\boldsymbol{i}_r \cdot (\boldsymbol{H}_o - \boldsymbol{H}_i)_{r=R} = (H_{or} - H_{ir})_{r=R} = 0 \tag{3.74}$$

while Eq. 3.31 requires the tangential component of $\boldsymbol{H}$ to suffer a discontinuity equal in magnitude to the current density,

$$\boldsymbol{i}_r \times (\boldsymbol{H}_o - \boldsymbol{H}_i)_{r=R} = \boldsymbol{K} \tag{3.75}$$

The magnetic field inside the sphere must satisfy Eqs. 3.72 and 3.73, and, because of Eq. 3.74, its radial component must be proportional to $\cos\theta$ on the surface of the sphere. By analogy with the electric case discussed in the preceding section, we attempt to meet these requirements with a uniform magnetic field

$$\boldsymbol{H}_i = A(\boldsymbol{i}_r \cos\theta - \boldsymbol{i}_\theta \sin\theta) \qquad r < R \tag{3.76}$$

where $A$ is an arbitrary constant. Such a magnetic field satisfies Eqs. 3.72 and 3.73 because all the spacial derivatives of the components are equal to zero; furthermore its radial component is proportional to $\cos\theta$, just like the radial component of the dipole field. Then, Eq. 3.74 can be satisfied by setting

$$A = \frac{m}{2\pi R^3} \tag{3.77}$$

The resulting field is given by

$$\boldsymbol{H}_i = \frac{m}{2\pi R^3}(\boldsymbol{i}_r \cos\theta - \boldsymbol{i}_\theta \sin\theta) \qquad r < R \tag{3.78}$$

and

$$\boldsymbol{H}_o = \frac{m}{2\pi r^3}\left(\boldsymbol{i}_r \cos\theta + \boldsymbol{i}_\theta \frac{1}{2}\sin\theta\right) \qquad r > R \tag{3.79}$$

We are now in a position to determine the surface current distribution required to produce the desired magnetic field. We have from Eq. 3.75

$$\boldsymbol{K} = (\boldsymbol{i}_r \times \boldsymbol{i}_\theta)\frac{m}{2\pi R^3}\left(\frac{1}{2} + 1\right)\sin\theta = \boldsymbol{i}_\varphi \frac{3m}{4\pi R^3}\sin\theta \tag{3.80}$$

Thus, the surface current circulates in the $\varphi$ direction with a density proportional to $\sin\theta$. Such a current distribution could be approximated by means of a coil, wound on the surface of the sphere with uniform turn density in the direction of the $z$-axis, as illustrated in Fig. 3.6. If $N$ is the total number of turns in the coil, the current in the coil must be equal to

$$I = \frac{3m}{4\pi R^3}\frac{2R}{N} = \frac{3m}{2\pi R^2 N} \tag{3.81}$$

The map of the resulting magnetic field is illustrated in Fig. 3.6. It is interesting to note that, for the same field intensity outside the sphere, the magnetic field inside the sphere is twice as intense as the electric field in the case discussed in the preceding section, and oppositely directed.

Let us consider, finally, the relation between the dipole moment associated with the field outside the sphere and the current distribution on the surface of the sphere. A magnetic dipole is defined by a limiting process similar to that used in the definition of an electric dipole. Let

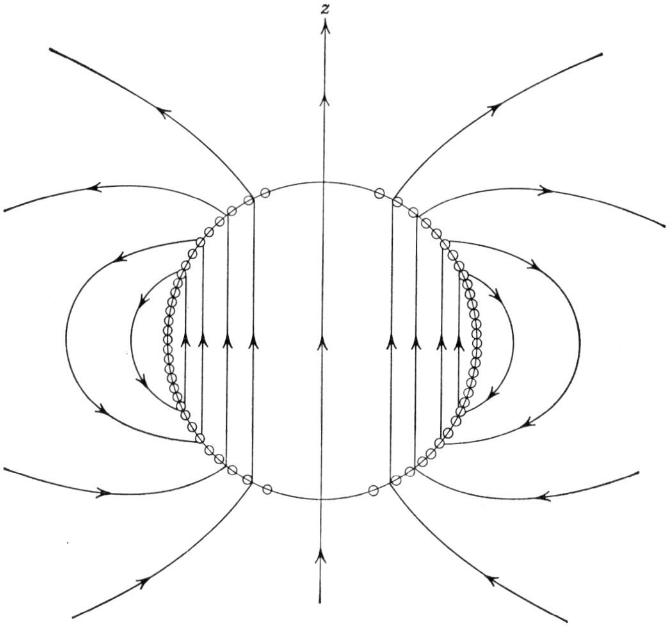


**Fig. 3.6.** The magnetic field produced by a coil wound on a sphere with uniform axial density.

us consider a planar, closed current filament of intensity $I$, and let $A$ be the area of the plane enclosed by the filament. A magnetic dipole is the limit of such a current filament when $I$ approaches infinity, the linear dimensions of the filament approach zero, but the product $IA$ remains constant. The moment of the dipole is just the product

$$m = IA \tag{3.82}$$

We shall see in Sec. 4.5 that the magnetic field produced by such a current filament is just that given by Eq. 3.71. Accepting for the present this result, we can regard the current distribution on the sphere of radius $R$ as consisting of current filaments of radius

$$a = R \sin \theta \tag{3.83}$$

and differential intensity

$$dI = K_\varphi R \, d\theta \tag{3.84}$$

Then, as far as the field at distances $r \gg a$ is concerned, each of these current filaments must contribute a differential dipole moment

$$dm = \pi a^2\, dI = \pi R^3\, K_\varphi \sin^2 \theta\, d\theta \tag{3.85}$$

so that the total moment of the current distribution must be

$$m = \pi R^3 \int_0^\pi K_\varphi \sin^2 \theta\, d\theta \tag{3.86}$$

Evaluation of this integral yields, with the help of Eq. 3.80,

$$m = \frac{3m}{4} \int_0^\pi \sin^3 \theta\, d\theta = \frac{3m}{4} \int_{-1}^1 (1 - \cos^2 \theta)\, d(\cos \theta) = m \tag{3.87}$$

as expected.

## 3.7 Summary and Conclusions

This chapter has been devoted to the derivation of the fundamental laws of free-space electromagnetism in differential form and of the boundary conditions that control the behavior of electromagnetic fields in free space over all surfaces at which any of the field components are discontinuous. It should be stressed in this connection, that, although the validity of the integral expressions of the fundamental laws is quite general, the corresponding differential expressions are valid only at points where the field components are differentiable and, therefore, they must be supplemented by the associated boundary conditions. In other words, the boundary conditions express the laws of electromagnetism over all surfaces at which the field components are not differentiable.

The illustrative examples presented in Secs. 3.5 and 3.6 have provided an introduction to the field point of view, fundamental to our study of electromagnetic phenomena. Maxwell's equations are regarded, from this point of view, as the conditions of physical realizability for an electromagnetic field in any given region of space rather than as equations that permit us to determine a field from its sources. The problem of finding physically realizable fields can thereby be separated from the problem of determining source distributions that can actually generate such fields. Thus, although the dipole field used in the illustrative examples was originally found as the electric field produced by a particular charge distribution, we were able, by focusing our attention on the differential equations satisfied by it, to interpret it also as a physically realizable magnetic field and to find a current distribution that could generate it.

This field point of view will lead us, in the next chapter, to inquire how physically realizable fields can be determined from the differential equations that they must satisfy, without regard to the source distributions by which they can be generated. We shall see, in particular, that all fields with zero curl and zero divergence can be found as solutions of a second-order partial-differential equation, known as Laplace's equation. Various families of solutions of this differential equation will be derived, one of which will include the dipole field used in the preceding sections.

## PROBLEMS

**Problem 3.1.** The electric potential inside a spherical surface of radius $R$ is

$$\phi_i = -A \frac{r}{R} \cos \theta$$

and the potential outside the same surface is

$$\phi_0 = -A \left(\frac{R}{r}\right)^2 \cos \theta$$

where $r$ and $\theta$ are polar coordinates, and $A$ is a constant. What is the electric field inside and outside the sphere? What surface charge distribution on the spherical surface will produce this electric field?

**Problem 3.2.** Two infinite perfectly conducting plates are parallel to the $xy$-plane and are separated by a distance $a$. An electric field

$$\boldsymbol{E} = \boldsymbol{i}_x A \sin\left(\pi \frac{z}{a}\right) \cos\left(\pi \frac{ct}{a}\right)$$

exists in the space between the two plates, where $A$ is a constant, and $c$ is the velocity of light. No field is present in the rest of the space.

(a) Find div $\boldsymbol{E}$ and curl $\boldsymbol{E}$.
(b) Can $\boldsymbol{E}$ be expressed as the negative gradient of a scalar function of position?
(c) Obtain the magnetic field $\boldsymbol{H}$ associated with the given $\boldsymbol{E}$.
(d) Determine the surface currents on the two plates.
(e) Determine the surface charges on the two plates.

**Problem 3.3.** The dielectric strength of air is approximately $3 \times 10^6$ v/m. If a charge of $2 \times 10^{-6}$ coulomb is to be placed on an isolated conducting sphere immersed in air, what is the minimum allowable sphere diameter? What is the resulting potential of the sphere with respect to infinity?

**Problem 3.4.** Given two vector fields

$$\boldsymbol{E} = \boldsymbol{i}_x x \qquad \boldsymbol{H} = \boldsymbol{i}_x y$$

(a) Classify these fields by taking the curl and the divergence of the vectors.

(b) Determine the distribution of charges and currents required to form these fields.

**Problem 3.5.** In a parallel-plate vacuum diode the electric potential $\phi$ as a function of the distance $d$ from the cathode is given by

$$\phi = KJ^{2/3}d^{4/3}$$

where $K$ is a constant and $J$ is the current density (directed entirely toward the plate). Find the space charge density $\rho$ as a function of distance. (*Note:* the electrons emerge from the cathode with a negligible velocity.)

**Problem 3.6.** Given a time-varying electric field

$$\boldsymbol{E} = \left[\boldsymbol{i}_r \left(\frac{r_0}{r}\right)^2 + \boldsymbol{i}_\theta \left(\frac{r_0}{r \sin\theta}\right)\right] \sin\omega t$$

where $r$ and $\theta$ are spherical coordinates and $r_0$ is a constant,

(a) Determine the magnetic field $\boldsymbol{H}$ associated with $\boldsymbol{E}$.

(b) Determine the sources necessary to generate the electromagnetic field.

**Problem 3.7.** Show that the electric field associated with a two-dimensional electric dipole is given, in polar coordinates, by

$$\boldsymbol{E} = \frac{p_\lambda}{2\pi\epsilon_0 r^2}(\boldsymbol{i}_r \cos\varphi + \boldsymbol{i}_\theta \sin\varphi)$$

where $p_\lambda$ is the magnitude of the dipole moment. Define the two-dimensional dipole by analogy with the three-dimensional one.

**Problem 3.8.** Charge is distributed over a circular cylindrical surface, with a density independent of the coordinate parallel to the axis of the cylinder. Determine the surface charge density that produces the dipole field of Prob. 3.7 outside the surface, and a uniform field inside the surface.

**Problem 3.9.** Current flows on the surface of a circular cylinder in a direction parallel to the axis of the cylinder. Determine the surface current density that produces a magnetic field analogous to the dipole field of Prob. 3.7 outside the surface, and a uniform field inside the surface. Express the surface current density in terms of an appropriately defined magnetic-dipole moment.

# CHAPTER FOUR

# Static Fields

The elegance and simplicity of Maxwell's formulation of the laws of electromagnetism disappear in a cloud of involved mathematical techniques as soon as we attempt to determine the field associated with a given system. The fact of the matter is that very few systems of practical interest give rise to a field that can be described by means of a single known mathematical function. In most cases, only approximate descriptions of the field can be obtained. Furthermore, there is no single technique on which one can rely, but rather imagination, experience, and insight play a key role in the successful solution of any particular problem. In other words, the determination of the electromagnetic field associated with a given system is often as much an art as a science. It is fortunate that in engineering practice one is more often called upon to design a system which will give rise to a field with prescribed properties rather than to analyze the field associated with a given system. Furthermore, a good share of the design can often be done efficiently through physical experimentation as long as the starting point of the design is judiciously selected and the experimenter has a good "feeling" for how the field will be affected by slight modifications of the system. Needless to say that engineering judgment and physical feeling are, to a large extent, the product of experience. Yet their foundations lie in a thorough understanding of the properties of simple fields and in the appreciation of the ways of thinking that have proved successful in the past.

The main objective of this chapter is to help the reader develop a basic understanding of the behavior of static fields rather than to provide a working knowledge of the mathematical techniques employed in the solution of static-field problems. More specifically, in line with the point of view suggested in the introduction to this book, and illustrated in Secs. 3.5 and 3.6, we shall make a sharp distinction between the problem of finding fields that are physically realizable in a given region of space and that of determining the particular field existing in a given system. Most of our attention will be devoted to the first problem, with the second one being almost entirely disregarded. The main reason for this emphasis is that the second problem is mathematically intricate, and its detailed consideration would be very time-consuming, particularly in view of the little additional light it would shed on the behavior of electromagnetic fields.

We shall see in Chapter 6 that the time-varying fields associated with electric circuits can be considered as sums of static fields. Furthermore, we shall see in Chapter 9 that the fields associated with slowly moving material bodies can also be considered as sums of static fields in the presence of stationary bodies. Thus, the study of static fields is fundamental to the discussion of all the electromagnetic phenomena discussed in this book. The fields associated with wave propagation are not considered here; their study is the main objective of a separate book by the same authors.[1]

## 4.1 The Coulomb Field of Fixed Charges

It is convenient to begin our discussion of static fields by focusing our attention on the electrostatic field associated with fixed charges in an otherwise free space. This discussion will serve as an introduction to the study of the fields classified as groups 1, 2, and 3 in Sec. 3.4.

Our first objective is to derive an expression for the electric field in terms of the given charge distribution. It is convenient, for this purpose, to write the electric field as the negative gradient of a scalar potential $\phi$.

$$\boldsymbol{E} = -\operatorname{grad} \phi \tag{4.1}$$

This is always possible because all electrostatic fields are conservative. We shall show presently that the desired expression is the generalized Coulomb's law

$$\phi = \frac{1}{4\pi\epsilon_0} \int \frac{dq}{r_{QP}} \tag{4.2}$$

where $dq$ is a differential element of charge located at a point $Q$, $r_{QP}$ is the distance between the charge element and the point $P$ at which $\phi$ is measured, and the integral is extended over the entire charge distribution.

[1] R. B. Adler, L. J. Chu, R. M. Fano, *Electromagnetic Energy Transmission and Radiation*, John Wiley & Sons, New York, 1960.

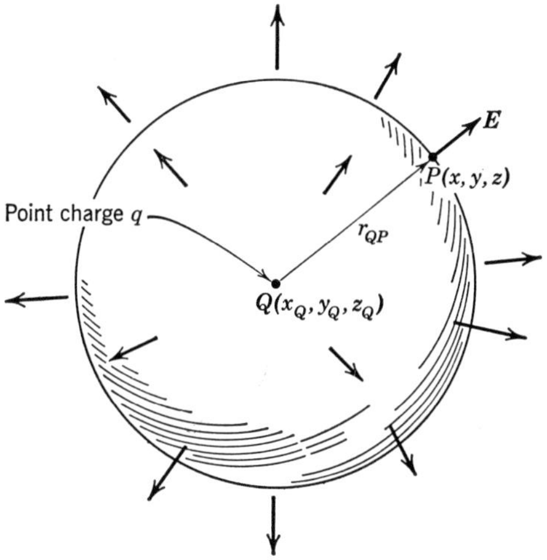


**Fig. 4.1.** Electric field associated with a point charge.

We observe first that Coulomb's law for the potential associated with a point charge $q$, namely,

$$\phi_q = \frac{q}{4\pi\epsilon_0 r_{QP}} \tag{4.3}$$

is a direct consequence of Gauss' law (namely, that the flux of $\epsilon_0 \boldsymbol{E}$ out of any closed surface must be equal to the total charge enclosed). In fact, if we draw a spherical surface $S$ of radius $r_{QP}$ around the point charge, as illustrated in Fig. 4.1, the electric field must be normal to $S$, and its magnitude must be constant over it because of the spherical symmetry of the system. Then, by Gauss' law,

$$4\pi r_{QP}^2 \epsilon_0 E_r = q \tag{4.4}$$

and

$$E_r = \frac{q}{4\pi\epsilon_0 r_{QP}^2} \tag{4.5}$$

where $E_r$ is the radial component of the electric field. Finally, integration with respect to $r_{QP}$ yields,

$$\phi_q = \int_{r_{QP}}^{\infty} \frac{q}{4\pi\epsilon_0 r_{QP}^2}\, dr_{QP} = \frac{q}{4\pi\epsilon_0 r_{QP}} \tag{4.6}$$

We argue next that, because of the linearity of Eq. 4.1 and of Gauss' law, the potentials produced by any number of point charges is the sum of the potentials produced separately by each point charge. Then, the potentials produced by a spatial distribution of charge must be equal to the sum of the potentials produced, separately, by the charge in each volume element, and, therefore, it must be given by the integral in Eq. 4.2.

The differential $dq$ in Eq. 4.3 represents a differential amount of charge. Thus, we have for a charge distribution of finite volume density $\rho$

$$\phi = \frac{1}{4\pi\epsilon_0} \int_V \frac{\rho}{r_{QP}} \, dv \tag{4.7}$$

where $\rho \, dv$ has been substituted for $dq$, and $V$ is a volume containing the entire charge distribution. On the other hand, if charge is distributed over a surface $S$ with a finite surface density $\sigma$ (which implies that the volume density becomes infinite on $S$), the potential produced by such a surface charge is given by

$$\phi = \frac{1}{4\pi\epsilon_0} \int_S \frac{\sigma}{r_{QP}} \, da \tag{4.8}$$

where $\sigma \, da$ has been substituted for $dq$ in Eq. 4.2. Similarly, the potential produced by charge distributed over a line $L$ with a finite linear density $\lambda$ is given by

$$\phi = \frac{1}{4\pi\epsilon_0} \int_L \frac{\lambda}{r_{QP}} \, ds \tag{4.9}$$

where $ds$ is a differential element of the line and $\lambda \, ds$ has been substituted for $dq$ in Eq. 4.2. Finally, the potential produced by all point charges is given by

$$\phi = \frac{1}{4\pi\epsilon_0} \sum_k \frac{q_k}{r_{QP}} \tag{4.10}$$

where $q_k$ represents the $k$th point charge, and $r_{QP}$ represents its distance from the point $P$ at which $\phi$ is measured. Thus, we have for an arbitrary distribution of charge

$$\phi = \frac{1}{4\pi\epsilon_0} \left( \int_V \frac{\rho}{r_{QP}} \, dv + \int_S \frac{\sigma}{r_{QP}} \, da + \int_L \frac{\lambda}{r_{QP}} \, ds + \sum_k \frac{q_k}{r_{QP}} \right) \tag{4.11}$$

It must be carefully noted that $\phi$ is a function of the coordinates of the point $P$ alone, $\rho$, $\sigma$, $\lambda$, are functions of the coordinates of the point $Q$ alone, while

$$r_{QP} = \sqrt{(x - x_Q)^2 + (y - y_Q)^2 + (z - z_Q)^2} \tag{4.12}$$

is a symmetrical function of the coordinates of $P$ and $Q$. All three integrations are carried out with respect to the coordinates of the point $Q$.

It is clear from Eq. 4.11 that the potential becomes infinite (singular) as $1/r_{QP}$ at the locations of the point charges. Similarly, the potential becomes infinite on any line charge of finite linear density; in fact, in the immediate vicinity of any line charge, the electric field intensity must be inversely proportional to the distance from the line, and, therefore, the potential must become proportional to the negative logarithm of the distance. On the other hand, we saw in Chapter 3 that a surface distribution of charge produces merely a discontinuity of the normal component of the electric field, of magnitude proportional to the surface charge density. Thus, the potential remains finite and continuous across a surface charge distribution of finite density. Similarly, both the potential and its first derivatives remain finite throughout any region occupied by a charge distribution of finite volume density; in fact, the electric field intensity remains both finite and continuous.

The electric field intensity can be computed from Eq. 4.11 with the help of Eq. 4.1. We observe in this regard, that the differentiations involved in computing the potential gradient must be carried out with respect to the coordinates of the point $P$ which are independent of the coordinates with respect to which the integrations in Eq. 4.11 are carried out. It follows that the order of the two operations can be interchanged. Thus, noting that $\rho$ is not a function of $P$, we have, for instance,

$$-\operatorname{grad}_P \int_V \frac{\rho}{r_{QP}}\, dv = -\int_V \rho \left(\operatorname{grad}_P \frac{1}{r_{QP}}\right) dv \tag{4.13}$$

On the other hand (see sec. 2.8-g),

$$\begin{aligned}\operatorname{grad}_P \frac{1}{r_{QP}} &= -\frac{1}{r_{QP}^2}\left(\boldsymbol{i}_x \frac{x - x_Q}{r_{QP}} + \boldsymbol{i}_y \frac{y - y_Q}{r_{QP}} + \boldsymbol{i}_z \frac{z - z_Q}{r_{QP}}\right) \\ &= -\frac{\boldsymbol{i}_{QP}}{r_{QP}^2}\end{aligned} \tag{4.14}$$

where $\boldsymbol{i}_{QP}$ is a unit vector directed from $Q$ to $P$. It follows that

$$\boldsymbol{E} = \frac{1}{4\pi\epsilon_0}\left(\int_V \frac{\boldsymbol{i}_{QP}\rho}{r_{QP}^2}\, dv + \int_S \frac{\boldsymbol{i}_{QP}\sigma}{r_{QP}^2}\, da + \int_L \frac{\boldsymbol{i}_{QP}\lambda}{r_{QP}^2}\, ds + \sum_K \frac{\boldsymbol{i}_{QP} q_k}{r_{QP}^2}\right) \tag{4.15}$$

where the vectorial integrals are vectors whose Cartesian components are the integrals of the corresponding components of the integrand.

We are often confronted, in practice, with charge distributions that have cylindrical symmetry in the sense that they are uniform in some particular direction. Taking this direction as that of $z$-axis, the charge densities are then functions of the $x$ and $y$ coordinates alone, i.e., the charge distribution becomes two-dimensional. Then, if we focus our attention on a unit length of the distribution (along the $z$-axis), the volume density $\rho$ measures the charge per unit area of the cross section normal to the $z$-axis. Similarly, the surface density $\sigma$ (on a cylindrical surface parallel to the $z$-axis) measures the charge per unit length of the cross-sectional line, and the line density $\lambda$ (on a line parallel to the $z$-axis) plays the role of a two-dimensional point charge.

The two-dimensional Coulomb's law is obtained from the field produced by an infinite, straight, line charge of density $\lambda$. If we consider the flux of $\boldsymbol{E}$ per unit length through a circular cylindrical surface around the line charge, we find that Gauss' law requires the electric field intensity to be radially directed, uniformly distributed around the line charge, and inversely proportional to the distance from the line charge. That is,

$$E_r = \frac{\lambda}{2\pi\epsilon_0 r_{QP}} \tag{4.16}$$

where $r_{QP}$ is the cross-sectional distance between the point $P$ at which

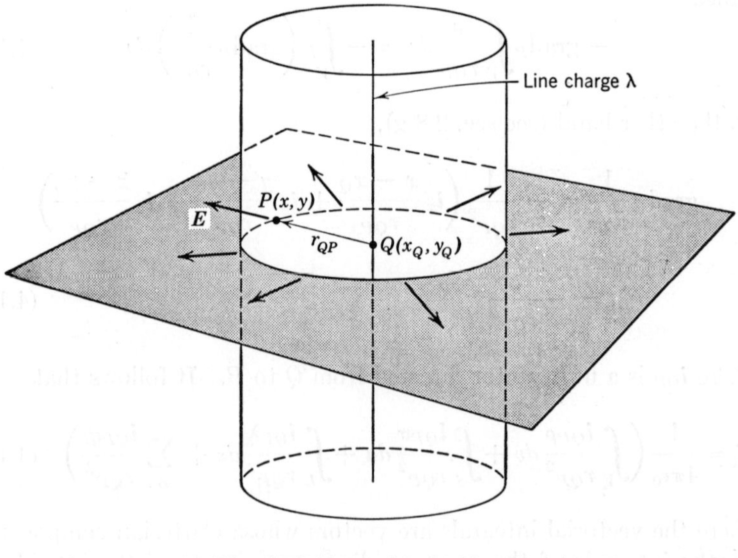


**Fig. 4.2.** Electric field associated with a line charge.

the field is measured and the intersection $Q$ of the line charge with the cross-sectional plane containing $P$, as illustrated in Fig. 4.2. The two-dimensional potential is obtained from Eq. 4.16 by integration

$$\phi = -\int_R^{r_{QP}} E_r \, dr_{QP} = \frac{\lambda}{2\pi\epsilon_0} \ln \frac{R}{r_{QP}} \tag{4.17}$$

where $R$ is the radius of the cylindrical surface chosen as a zero-potential reference.

A derivation analogous to that leading to Eqs. 4.11 and 4.15 yields for a two-dimensional potential

$$\phi = \frac{1}{2\pi\epsilon_0}\left(\int_S \rho \ln \frac{R}{r_{QP}} \, da + \int_L \sigma \ln \frac{R}{r_{QP}} \, ds + \sum_k \lambda_k \ln \frac{R}{r_{QP}}\right) \tag{4.18}$$

and

$$\boldsymbol{E} = \frac{1}{2\pi\epsilon_0}\left(\int_S \frac{\boldsymbol{i}_{QP}\rho}{r_{QP}} \, da + \int_L \frac{\boldsymbol{i}_{QP}\sigma}{r_{QP}} \, ds + \sum_k \frac{\boldsymbol{i}_{QP}\lambda_k}{r_{QP}}\right) \tag{4.19}$$

where $S$ is the cross-sectional area occupied by the volume distribution $\rho$, $L$ is the cross-sectional line corresponding to the surface distribution $\sigma$, and the summation is extended over all line charges.

## ► 4.2 Charge Singularities and Their Uses

The concepts of point charge, line charge, and dipole are of great value in the study of static electric fields, as idealized representations of charge distributions confined to regions of negligibly small dimensions. Their role in field theory is similar to that of the impulse and the doublet in circuit theory. For instance, a current impulse represents a current pulse of vanishing small duration, corresponding, nevertheless, to the flow of a finite amount of charge. Similarly, a point charge is a spatial impulse packing a finite amount of charge into a volume of vanishing small dimensions. By vanishing small duration or dimensions we mean, of course, a duration or dimensions much smaller than those that need to be resolved in each particular instance.

Let us suppose, for instance, that we wish to determine the electric field produced by a charge distribution contained in its entirety within a sphere of radius $R$. Suppose further that we are only interested in the field at a point $P$ whose distance $r$ from the center of the sphere is much greater than the radius $R$. Inspection of Eq. 4.2 indicates immediately that the field at $P$ depends primarily on the total charge $q$

enclosed by the sphere and relatively little on the way the charge is distributed within it. Thus, we may identify, to a first approximation, the field at $P$ with the field produced by a point charge $q$ located at the center of the sphere.

Let us suppose next that the total charge $q$ of the distribution is equal to zero. Then, the predominant character of the field for $r > R$ must depend on the relative positions of the positive and negative charges. In order to investigate this character, we consider the center of the sphere as the origin of a Cartesian system of coordinates and expand the reciprocal of the distance between $P$ and $Q$

$$\frac{1}{r_{QP}} = \frac{1}{\sqrt{(x - x_Q)^2 + (y - y_Q)^2 + (z - z_Q)^2}} \tag{4.20}$$

in powers of $x_Q, y_Q, z_Q$ about the origin, while holding fixed the coordinates $x, y, z$ of $P$. We have

$$\begin{aligned}\frac{1}{r_{QP}} = \left(\frac{1}{r_{QP}}\right)_0 &+ \left(\frac{\partial}{\partial x_Q}\frac{1}{r_{QP}}\right)_0 x_Q + \left(\frac{\partial}{\partial y_Q}\frac{1}{r_{QP}}\right)_0 y_Q + \left(\frac{\partial}{\partial z_Q}\frac{1}{r_{QP}}\right)_0 z_Q \\ &+ \frac{1}{2}\left(\frac{\partial^2}{\partial x_Q^2}\frac{1}{r_{QP}}\right)_0 x_Q^2 + \frac{1}{2}\left(\frac{\partial^2}{\partial y_Q^2}\frac{1}{r_{QP}}\right)_0 y_Q^2 + \frac{1}{2}\left(\frac{\partial^2}{\partial z_Q^2}\frac{1}{r_{QP}}\right)_0 z_Q^2 \\ &+ \left(\frac{\partial^2}{\partial x_Q\,\partial y_Q}\frac{1}{r_{QP}}\right)_0 x_Q y_Q + \left(\frac{\partial^2}{\partial x_Q\,\partial z_Q}\frac{1}{r_{QP}}\right)_0 x_Q z_Q \\ &+ \left(\frac{\partial^2}{\partial y_Q\,\partial z_Q}\frac{1}{r_{QP}}\right)_0 y_Q z_Q + \cdots\end{aligned} \tag{4.21}$$

where the subscript 0 indicates that the quantity in parentheses is evaluated for $x_Q = y_Q = z_Q = 0$, i.e., for $Q$ coinciding with the origin. On the other hand, since $r_{QP}$ is a function of the differences between the coordinates of $P$ and $Q$, we have for the derivatives with respect to $x_Q$ and with respect to $x_Q$ and $y_Q$,

$$\left(\frac{\partial}{\partial x_Q}\frac{1}{r_{QP}}\right)_0 = -\left(\frac{\partial}{\partial x}\frac{1}{r_{QP}}\right)_0 = -\frac{\partial}{\partial x}\frac{1}{r} \tag{4.22}$$

$$\left(\frac{\partial^2}{\partial x_Q\,\partial y_Q}\frac{1}{r_{QP}}\right)_0 = \left(\frac{\partial^2}{\partial x\,\partial y}\frac{1}{r_{QP}}\right)_0 = \frac{\partial^2}{\partial x\,\partial y}\frac{1}{r} \tag{4.23}$$

and similarly for all other derivatives. It follows that the power series of Eq. 4.21 can be written in the form

$$\frac{1}{r_{QP}} = \frac{1}{r} - \left(x_Q \frac{\partial}{\partial x} + y_Q \frac{\partial}{\partial y} + z_Q \frac{\partial}{\partial z}\right)\frac{1}{r}$$

$$+ \frac{1}{2}\left(x_Q \frac{\partial}{\partial x} + y_Q \frac{\partial}{\partial y} + z_Q \frac{\partial}{\partial z}\right)^2 \frac{1}{r} - \cdots$$

$$= \frac{1}{r} - \boldsymbol{r}_Q \cdot \nabla \frac{1}{r} + \frac{1}{2}(\boldsymbol{r}_Q \cdot \nabla)^2 \frac{1}{r} - \cdots \tag{4.24}$$

where $\boldsymbol{r}_Q$ is the vector distance from the origin to $Q$, whose components are the coordinates of $Q$. This series can be shown to converge for $r > R$; when substituted for $1/r_{QP}$ in Eq. 4.2, the constant term yields a component of potential

$$\phi_0 = \frac{1}{4\pi\epsilon_0 r}\int dq = \frac{q}{4\pi\epsilon_0 r} \tag{4.25}$$

which is readily recognized as the potential produced by a point charge located at the origin, and of magnitude equal to the total charge $q$ within the sphere of radius $R$, as discussed above.

The first-order term in the series yields a component of potential given by

$$\phi_1 = -\frac{1}{4\pi\epsilon_0}\boldsymbol{p}\cdot\text{grad}\,\frac{1}{r} = \frac{\boldsymbol{i}_r \cdot \boldsymbol{p}}{4\pi\epsilon_0 r^2} = \frac{|\boldsymbol{p}|\cos\theta}{4\pi\epsilon_0 r^2} \tag{4.26}$$

where the vector

$$\boldsymbol{p} = \int \boldsymbol{r}_Q\, dq = \boldsymbol{i}_x \int x_Q\, dq + \boldsymbol{i}_y \int y_Q\, dq + \boldsymbol{i}_z \int z_Q\, dq \tag{4.27}$$

is, by definition, the dipole moment of the charge distribution; the unit vector $\boldsymbol{i}_r$ and the angle $\theta$ are defined in Fig. 4.3. The electric field corresponding to $\phi_1$ is

$$\boldsymbol{E}_1 = -\,\text{grad}\,\phi_1 = -\boldsymbol{i}_r \frac{\partial \phi_1}{\partial r} - \boldsymbol{i}_\theta \frac{1}{r}\frac{\partial \phi_1}{\partial \theta}$$

$$= \frac{\boldsymbol{i}_r 2\cos\theta + \boldsymbol{i}_\theta \sin\theta}{4\pi\epsilon_0 r^3}|\boldsymbol{p}| \tag{4.28}$$

The lines of force and the equipotential surfaces of this field are illustrated in Fig. 3.4.

It can be readily seen that, if the origin of the system of coordinates is displaced from the center of the sphere to a point of coordinates

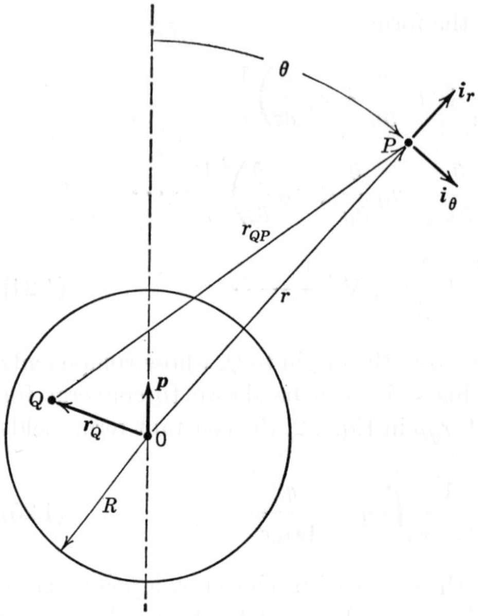


**Fig. 4.3.** Geometry used in connection with the dipole moment of a charge distribution.

$x_0$, $y_0$, $z_0$, the $x$ component of the dipole moment becomes

$$p_x' = \int (x_Q - x_0)\, dq = p_x - qx_0 \tag{4.29}$$

Similar expressions are obtained for the other two components. Thus, the dipole moment is independent of the origin selected if $q = 0$. Conversely, if $q \neq 0$, the dipole moment can be made equal to any desired value, including zero, by a proper choice of the origin. Thus, the dipole moment is a characteristic quantity of a charge distribution only when the net charge in the distribution is equal to zero.

The dipole potential $\phi_1$ is inversely proportional to the square of the distance $r$. Thus, it is negligible compared to the point charge potential $\phi_0$ for sufficiently large values of $r$. The higher order terms in the series can be readily shown to be inversely proportional to successively higher powers of the distance $r$. In other words, when the right-hand side of Eq. 4.24 is substituted for $1/r_{QP}$ in Eq. 4.2, the potential becomes a series in inverse powers of the distance $r$. Thus, when the net charge $q$ in the distribution is equal to zero, the dipole potential becomes the dominant term for large values of $r$. The second-order term is inversely proportional to $r^3$ and represents the potential associated with the quadrupole moment of the charge distribution as discussed below;

it becomes the dominant term when both the net charge $q$ and the dipole moment $\boldsymbol{p}$ are equal to zero.

It is clear that the potential $\phi_1$ can be thought as being produced by a dipole. This charge singularity, defined in Sec. 3.5, is the space analog of the doublet used in circuit theory. It is redefined here to emphasize the process by which higher order singularities are defined. Let us consider two point charges of equal magnitude $q$ and opposite polarities, separated by a vector distance $\boldsymbol{s}_1$ directed from the negative charge to the positive charge, as shown in Fig. 4.4. The dipole moment of this complex of charges is, from Eq. 4.27

$$\boldsymbol{p} = q\boldsymbol{s}_1 \tag{4.30}$$

A dipole is, by definition, the charge singularity obtained in the limit when $q$ approaches infinity and $\boldsymbol{s}_1$ approaches zero while $\boldsymbol{p}$ remains constant. It can be shown that all potential terms of order higher than the first vanish in such a limit and that $\phi_1$ alone represents the potential produced by a dipole of moment $\boldsymbol{p}$.

The component of potential arising from the second-order terms in the series Eq. 4.24 can be associated with a charge singularity known as a quadrupole. This charge singularity can be constructed from a pair of identical dipoles symmetrically located with respect to the origin, as illustrated in Fig. 4.5. A quadrupole is the charge singularity obtained in the limit when the distance $\boldsymbol{s}_2$ between the dipoles approaches zero while the magnitude of the dipole moments approaches infinity. The magnitude and the two directions that characterize the quadrupole associated with a given charge distribution are specified by the second-order moments of the distribution.

In general, each component of potential can be associated to a charge singularity obtained in a similar manner from a pair of charge singular-

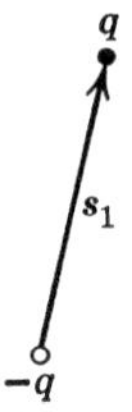


**Fig. 4.4.** Structure of a dipole.

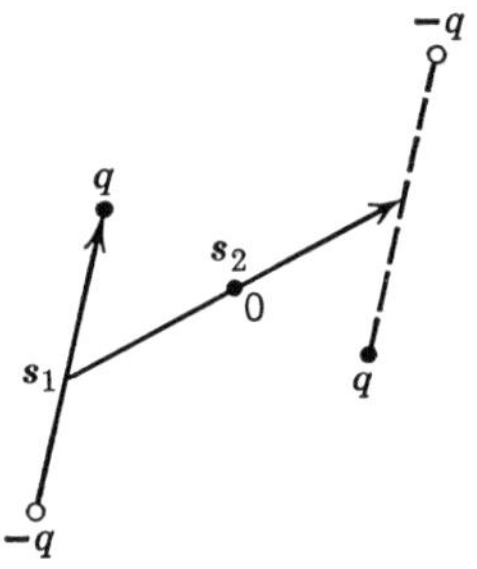


**Fig. 4.5.** Structure of a quadrupole.

ities of the next lower order. Thus, any charge distribution within a sphere of radius $R$ is equivalent, with regard to the electric field outside the sphere, to a series of charge singularities located at the origin. Furthermore, since the potential produced by the singularity of order $n$ is inversely proportional to the $(n+1)$th power of the distance $r$ from the center of the sphere, only the lowest singularity of nonvanishing magnitude is of any consequence for $r \gg R$. In particular, as stated above, a charge distribution of zero net value is equivalent to a dipole at sufficiently large distances.

The field associated with a two-dimensional charge distribution within a circular cylinder of radius $R$ can be analyzed in a similar manner by expanding in a power series the function $\ln R/r_{QP}$, appearing in Eq. 4.18. We have by analogy with Eq. 4.24

$$\ln \frac{R}{r_{QP}} = \ln \frac{R}{r} - \left( x_Q \frac{\partial}{\partial x} + y_Q \frac{\partial}{\partial y} \right) \ln \frac{R}{r} + \frac{1}{2} \left( x_Q \frac{\partial}{\partial x} + y_Q \frac{\partial}{\partial y} \right)^2 \ln \frac{R}{r} + \cdots$$

$$= \ln \frac{R}{r} - \boldsymbol{r}_Q \cdot \nabla \ln \frac{R}{r} + \frac{1}{2} (\boldsymbol{r}_Q \cdot \nabla)^2 \ln \frac{R}{r} - \cdots \tag{4.31}$$

where $\boldsymbol{r}_Q$ is the vector distance from the axis of the cylindrical system to the point $Q$. When this series is substituted for $\ln \dfrac{R}{r_{QP}}$ in the first integral in Eq. 4.18, the zero-order term yields a component of potential

$$\phi_0 = \frac{\lambda}{2\pi\epsilon_0} \ln \frac{R}{r} \tag{4.32}$$

where $\lambda$ is the net charge per unit length in the cylindrical charge distribution. This component represents the potential produced by a line charge of density $\lambda$, parallel to the $z$-axis (the direction in which the charge distribution is uniform), and passing by the origin. Thus, for sufficiently large values of $r$, the charge distribution is equivalent to a line charge.

The first-order term gives rise to a component of potential

$$\phi_1 = -\frac{1}{2\pi\epsilon_0} \boldsymbol{p}_\lambda \cdot \nabla \ln \frac{R}{r} = \frac{1}{2\pi\epsilon_0} \frac{\boldsymbol{p}_\lambda \cdot \boldsymbol{i}_r}{r} = \frac{|\boldsymbol{p}_\lambda| \cos \varphi}{2\pi\epsilon_0 \, r} \tag{4.33}$$

where the two-dimensional vector

$$\boldsymbol{p}_\lambda = \boldsymbol{i}_x \int x_Q \rho \, da + \boldsymbol{i}_y \int y_Q \rho \, da = \int \boldsymbol{r}_Q \rho \, da \tag{4.34}$$

represents the two-dimensional dipole moment per unit length of the cylindrical charge distribution. The radial unit vector $\boldsymbol{i}_r$ and the angle $\varphi$ are defined in Fig. 4.6. It can be seen by analogy with Eq. 4.29 that $\boldsymbol{p}_\lambda$ is independent of the origin selected when the net charge per unit length is equal to zero.

The electric field corresponding to $\phi_1$ can be obtained by computing the negative gradient of $\phi_1$ in circular cylindrical coordinates

$$\begin{aligned} \boldsymbol{E}_1 &= -\operatorname{grad} \phi_1 = -\boldsymbol{i}_r \frac{\partial \phi_1}{\partial r} - \boldsymbol{i}_\varphi \frac{1}{r} \frac{\partial \phi_1}{\partial \varphi} \\ &= \frac{|\boldsymbol{p}_\lambda|}{2\pi\epsilon_0 r^2} (\boldsymbol{i}_r \cos \varphi + \boldsymbol{i}_\varphi \sin \varphi) \end{aligned} \tag{4.35}$$

The lines of force and the traces of the equipotential surfaces for this two-dimensional dipole field are shown in Fig. 4.7. Both sets of lines turn out to be mutually orthogonal families of circles. The circles of each family are mutually tangent at the origin. The radius of the

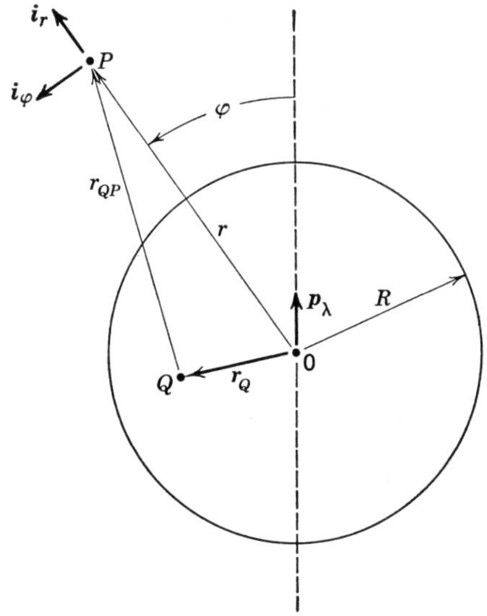


**Fig. 4.6.** Geometry used in connection with the two-dimensional dipole moment of a charge distribution.

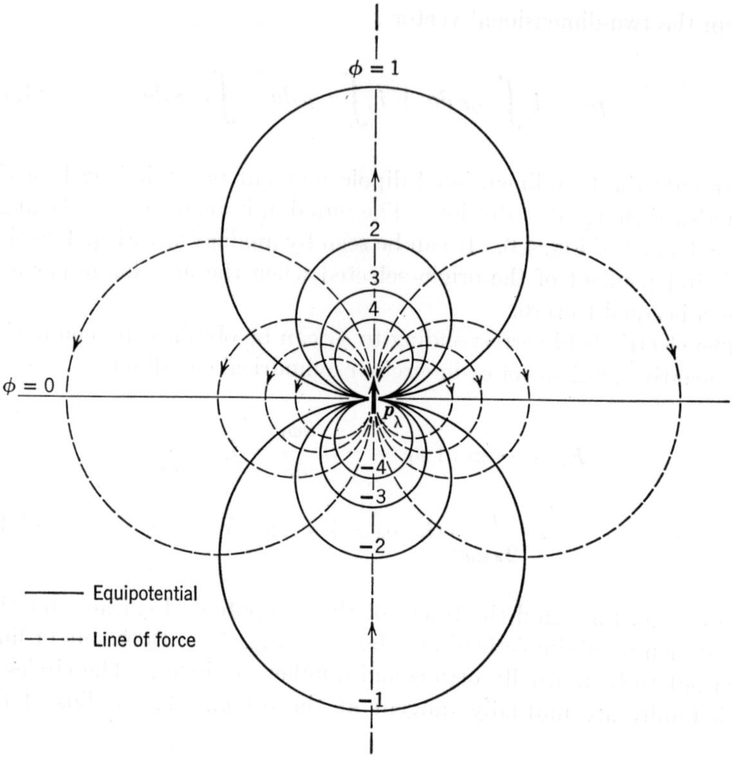


**Fig. 4.7.** The field of a two-dimensional dipole.

equipotential circle corresponding to a potential $\phi_1$ is given by

$$R(\phi_1) = \frac{|\boldsymbol{p}_\lambda|}{4\pi\epsilon_0\phi_1} \tag{4.36}$$

The charge singularity associated with $\phi_1$ consists of two parallel line charges of equal magnitudes $\lambda$ and opposite polarities, displaced a distance $\boldsymbol{s}_1$. The two-dimensional dipole moment of the two-line charges is, from Eq. 4.34,

$$\boldsymbol{p}_\lambda = \lambda \boldsymbol{s}_1 \tag{4.37}$$

It can be shown that all components of potential arising from the higher order terms in Eq. 4.31 vanish in the limit when $\lambda$ approaches infinity and $\boldsymbol{s}_1$ approaches zero. Thus, the two-dimensional dipole so obtained is the charge singularity associated with $\phi_1$.

The second-order term in Eq. 4.31 is associated with a two-dimensional quadrupole which can be constructed from two two-dimensional dipoles just as the three-dimensional quadrupole was constructed from two three-dimensional dipoles. Each of the singularities associated with higher order terms in Eq. 4.31 can be constructed from the next lower singularity in a similar manner. It can be shown that the potential term of order $n$ is inversely proportional to $r^n$. Thus, a cylindrical charge distribution is equivalent, for sufficiently large values of $r$, to the lowest nonvanishing charge singularity associated with it. In particular, if the net charge per unit length is equal to zero, the charge distribution is equivalent, for large values of $r$, to a two-dimensional dipole.

## 4.3 The Differential Equations for the Scalar Potential

The preceding two sections have been devoted to a preliminary discussion of the fields associated with given charge distributions, from the point of view of Coulomb's law. In particular, Eq. 4.2 allows us to determine a conservative field (the electrostatic field) when its divergence (the charge density divided by $\epsilon_0$) is given at all points of space. It is important to note that the integral in Eq. 4.2 must be evaluated over the entire charge distribution. Thus, Eq. 4.2 is of limited value in its present form, when we are interested in determining the conservative fields that are physically realizable in a limited region of space. Let us turn our attention now to this more general problem.

A conservative field, by virtue of the fact that its curl is identically equal to zero, can always be expressed as the gradient of a scalar potential. Using the electrostatic field as a specific example of conservative field, we set

$$\boldsymbol{E} = -\text{grad}\,\phi \tag{4.38}$$

Thus, the divergence of $\boldsymbol{E}$ can be expressed in the form

$$\text{div}\,\boldsymbol{E} = -\text{div grad}\,\phi = -\Delta\phi \tag{4.39}$$

where $\Delta\phi$ is known as the Laplacian of $\phi$. In Cartesian coordinates we have

$$\Delta\phi = \nabla\cdot\nabla\phi = \frac{\partial^2\phi}{\partial x^2} + \frac{\partial^2\phi}{\partial y^2} + \frac{\partial^2\phi}{\partial z^2} \tag{4.40}$$

On the other hand,

$$\text{div}\,\boldsymbol{E} = \frac{\rho}{\epsilon_0} \tag{4.41}$$

It follows that, if the space charge density is equal to zero within the region of interest,

$$\Delta\phi = 0 \tag{4.42}$$

whereas, if the space charge density is finite but different from zero,

$$\Delta\phi = -\frac{\rho}{\epsilon_0} \tag{4.43}$$

Equation 4.42, known as Laplace's equation, expresses in differential form the physical realizability conditions for the fields classified as group 1 in Sec. 3.4, whereas Eq. 4.43, known as Poisson's equation, expresses the corresponding conditions for the fields classified as group 2. It is important to note that the requirement that the field be conservative is automatically imposed by expressing the field in terms of a scalar potential; thus Eq. 4.42 is equivalent to Eqs. 3.33 and 3.34 and Eq. 4.43 is equivalent to Eqs. 3.39 and 3.40.

Let us consider now a region of space $V$, in which charge is distributed with a finite volume density $\rho$. Because of the linearity of Poisson's equation, if $\phi'$ is a function that satisfies Poisson's equation within $V$ and $\phi''$ is a function that satisfies Laplace's equation in the same region, their sum

$$\phi = \phi' + \phi'' \tag{4.44}$$

must also satisfy Poisson's equation at all points of $V$. In fact,

$$\Delta\phi = \Delta\phi' + \Delta\phi'' = \Delta\phi' = -\frac{\rho}{\epsilon_0} \tag{4.45}$$

Conversely, if $\phi$ and $\phi'$ satisfy Poisson's equation within $V$, their difference $\phi''$ must satisfy Laplace's equation in the same region. It follows that the family of functions that satisfy Poisson's equation within $V$ can be generated from the family of functions that satisfy Laplace's equation in the same region, by adding any one particular member of the former family to each member of the latter family. In other words, the problem of finding the family of fields that is physically realizable in a region $V$ in which charge is distributed with a finite density $\rho$, can be reduced to the problem of finding a single realizable field together with the family of fields that would be realizable in $V$ if $V$ were free of charge.

We observe, on the other hand, that the potential given by Eq. 4.7, when the integral is evaluated over the volume $V$, namely

$$\phi' = \frac{1}{4\pi\epsilon_0}\int_V \frac{\rho}{r_{QP}}\,dv \tag{4.46}$$

must be a solution of Poisson's equation at all points of $V$, because it represents the potential that would exist in the entire space if no charge were present outside $V$. Thus, all solutions of Poisson's equation within $V$ can be written in the form

$$\phi = \frac{1}{4\pi\epsilon_0} \int_V \frac{\rho}{r_{QP}} \, dv + \phi'' \tag{4.47}$$

where $\phi''$ is a solution of Laplace's equation within $V$. Physically, this amounts to regarding the potential within $V$ as the sum of two terms: a first term representing the potential produced by the charges in $V$, and a second term representing the potential produced by charges located outside $V$ and on the surface $S$ enclosing $V$. The latter term must satisfy Laplace's equation within $V$ and, therefore, can be identified with $\phi''$. We shall see in Sec. 4.5 that $\phi''$ is uniquely specified when either its value or the value of its normal derivative is given at all points of the surface $S$ enclosing $V$. For instance, if $V$ is the entire space outside (or inside) a conductor, the knowledge that the potential must be constant on $S$ is sufficient to specify uniquely the particular solution of Laplace's equation that must be used as $\phi''$ in Eq. 4.47.

We conclude from the above discussion that the determination of a field of group 2 when its divergence is given within a region $V$ can be reduced to the determination of a field of group 1 by subtracting from it the Coulomb field associated with the given divergence. Furthermore, although the charge above was assumed to be distributed with finite density to avoid singularities in Poisson's equation, it is clear, at least from a physical point of view, that our conclusions are still valid in the presence of charge singularities, provided these are included in the evaluation of $\phi'$ as discussed in Sec. 4.1.

Let us consider, as a simple illustration, the case of a dipole located at the center of a spherical cavity in a conducting material. The dipole potential

$$\phi' = \frac{p \cos\theta}{4\pi\epsilon_0 r^2} \tag{4.48}$$

expressed in spherical coordinates, is the Coulomb potential that would be produced by the dipole in free space, and, therefore, it must be a solution of Poisson's equation in the spherical cavity of radius $a$. It follows that the actual potential in the cavity must be given by

$$\phi = \frac{p \cos\theta}{4\pi\epsilon_0 r^2} + \phi'' \tag{4.49}$$

where $\phi''$ is an appropriate solution of Laplace's equation. We observe, on the other hand, that $\phi$ must be constant within the conducting material and on its surface; otherwise, an electric field would be present in the conducting material which would produce a steady current flow. Then, in order that $\phi$ be constant for $r = a$, the function $\phi''$ must be proportional to $\cos\theta$.

By analogy with the example discussed in Sec. 3.5, let us consider the potential corresponding to a uniform electric field, parallel to the direction of the dipole, i.e., to the $z$-axis of the spherical system of coordinates. This potential must decrease linearly in the direction of the field, and therefore it must be of the form

$$\phi'' = -Az = -Ar\cos\theta \tag{4.50}$$

where $A$ is a constant. Clearly, this potential satisfies Laplace's equation in view of the fact that all its second derivatives are equal to zero. Furthermore, it is proportional to $\cos\theta$, so that the potential $\phi$ can be constant over the surface of the cavity. Since a potential is defined apart from an additive constant, we can require $\phi$ to vanish for $r = a$,

$$\phi(a) = \frac{p\cos\theta}{4\pi\epsilon_0 a^2} - Aa\cos\theta = 0 \tag{4.51}$$

from which we obtain

$$A = \frac{p}{4\pi\epsilon_0 a^3} \tag{4.52}$$

Thus the potential inside the spherical cavity is given by

$$\phi = \frac{p}{4\pi\epsilon_0 a^2}\left[\left(\frac{a}{r}\right)^2 - \left(\frac{r}{a}\right)\right]\cos\theta \tag{4.53}$$

## 4.4 The Vector Potential and Its Differential Equations

The mathematical role played by the scalar potential in connection with the fields classified as group 2, in Sec. 3.4, is played, in connection with the fields of group 3, by a vector potential. In fact, the requirement that the divergence of the field vanish throughout a given region $V$ can be imposed by requiring the vector field to be expressible as the curl of a vector potential $\boldsymbol{A}$. This follows from the fact that, for any vector $\boldsymbol{A}$,

$$\operatorname{div}\operatorname{curl}\boldsymbol{A} = 0 \tag{4.54}$$

Therefore, if the field of interest, for instance, the magnetic field, satisfies the equation

$$\mu_0\boldsymbol{H} = \operatorname{curl}\boldsymbol{A} \tag{4.55}$$

within $V$, its divergence must necessarily vanish throughout $V$. Clearly, this technique of requiring the divergence of the field to vanish is analogous to expressing a field vector as the negative gradient of a scalar potential in order to require its curl to vanish. A further analogy between the scalar potential associated with an electric field and the vector potential associated with a magnetic field will become evident in our study of electric and magnetic energies.

Turning our attention now specifically on the magnetic field within a region $V$ in which current is distributed with a finite density $\boldsymbol{J}$, we have at all points of $V$,

$$\text{curl}\ \mu_0 \boldsymbol{H} = \mu_0 \boldsymbol{J} \tag{4.56}$$

On the other hand,

$$\text{curl curl}\ \boldsymbol{A} = \text{grad div}\ \boldsymbol{A} - \Delta \boldsymbol{A} \tag{4.57}$$

where the Laplacian operator $\Delta$ must be understood to operate on each *Cartesian* component of $\boldsymbol{A}$, i.e.,

$$\Delta \boldsymbol{A} = \boldsymbol{i}_x\, \Delta A_x + \boldsymbol{i}_y\, \Delta A_y + \boldsymbol{i}_z\, \Delta A_z \tag{4.58}$$

Then, if we set

$$\text{div}\ \boldsymbol{A} = 0 \tag{4.59}$$

which we can do in any case without affecting the curl of $\boldsymbol{A}$, Eqs. 4.56 and 4.57 yield,

$$\Delta \boldsymbol{A} = -\mu_0 \boldsymbol{J} \tag{4.60}$$

This equation, known as the vector Poisson equation, amounts to three scalar Poisson equations one for each *Cartesian* component,

$$\Delta A_x = -\mu_0 J_x \tag{4.61}$$

$$\Delta A_y = -\mu_0 J_y \tag{4.62}$$

$$\Delta A_z = -\mu_0 J_z \tag{4.63}$$

Thus, the problem of determining each Cartesian component of $\boldsymbol{A}$ is mathematically identical to the problem of determining the scalar potential associated with a charge density proportional to the corresponding Cartesian component of the current density. Thus, a particular solution of Eq. 4.61 in a region $V$ is

$$A_x = \frac{\mu_0}{4\pi} \int_V \frac{J_x}{r_{QP}}\, dv \tag{4.64}$$

and similar expressions are solutions of Eqs. 4.62 and 4.63. Thus,

$$\boldsymbol{A} = \frac{\mu_0}{4\pi} \int_V \frac{\boldsymbol{J}}{r_{QP}}\, dv \tag{4.65}$$

is a solution of Eq. 4.60.

The magnetic field corresponding to the vector potential given by Eq. 4.65 can be obtained by computing its curl. We observe, in this regard, that the differentiations involved in curl $\boldsymbol{A}$ are to be carried out with respect to the coordinates $x$, $y$, $z$ of the point $P$ at which $\boldsymbol{A}$ is measured, whereas the volume integration in Eq. 4.65 is carried out with respect to the coordinates $x_Q$, $y_Q$, $z_Q$, of the point $Q$ at which $\boldsymbol{J}$ is measured. It follows that the order of the two operations can be interchanged so that

$$\mu_0 \boldsymbol{H} = \text{curl}_P\, \boldsymbol{A} = \frac{\mu_0}{4\pi} \int_V \left(\text{curl}_P \frac{\boldsymbol{J}}{r_{QP}}\right) dv \tag{4.66}$$

On the other hand, we have with the help of Eq. A4.15,

$$\text{curl}_P \frac{\boldsymbol{J}}{r_{QP}} = \left(\text{grad}_P \frac{1}{r_{QP}}\right) \times \boldsymbol{J} + \frac{1}{r_{QP}}\, \text{curl}_P\, \boldsymbol{J} \tag{4.67}$$

and with the help of Eq. 2.157,

$$\text{grad}_P \frac{1}{r_{QP}} = -\boldsymbol{i}_{QP} r_{QP}^{-2} \tag{4.68}$$

where $\boldsymbol{i}_{QP}$ is a unit vector pointing from $Q$ to $P$. Since $\boldsymbol{J}$ is not a function of the coordinates of the point $P$, we obtain finally

$$\boldsymbol{H} = \frac{1}{4\pi} \int_V \frac{(\boldsymbol{J} \times \boldsymbol{i}_{QP})}{r_{QP}^2}\, dv \tag{4.69}$$

which is the desired expression for $\boldsymbol{H}$ in terms of $\boldsymbol{J}$.

It is interesting to note that $\boldsymbol{H}$ is expressed as the sum of the differential contributions

$$d\boldsymbol{H} = \frac{(\boldsymbol{J} \times \boldsymbol{i}_{QP})\, dv}{4\pi r_{QP}^2} \tag{4.70}$$

of each current element $\boldsymbol{J}\, dv$. This equation, known as Biot-Savart's law, is often considered as the magnetic counterpart of Coulomb's law. It should be kept in mind, however, that it leads to a physically possible magnetic field only when integrated over a physically possible distribution of steady currents, i.e., a distribution for which div $\boldsymbol{J} = 0$.

Let us consider now the problem of determining the vector potentials that are physically realizable within a region $V$, in which currents are distributed with a finite density $\boldsymbol{J}$. Because of the linearity of Eq. 4.60, if $\boldsymbol{A}'$ is a particular solution of Eq. 4.60 in $V$, every other solution of the same equation can be expressed as

$$\boldsymbol{A} = \boldsymbol{A}' + \boldsymbol{A}'' \tag{4.71}$$

where $\boldsymbol{A}''$ is a solution of

$$\Delta \boldsymbol{A} = 0 \tag{4.72}$$

in the same region $V$. In particular, $\boldsymbol{A}'$ can be taken as the vector potential obtained from Eq. 4.65 by evaluating the integral over the region $V$. Thus, every solution of Eq. 4.60 can be expressed in the form

$$\boldsymbol{A} = \frac{\mu_0}{4\pi} \int_V \frac{\boldsymbol{J}}{r_{QP}}\, dv + \boldsymbol{A}'' \tag{4.73}$$

Again, as in the case of the scalar potential, we can interpret this result by saying that the vector potential in $V$ can be regarded as the sum of two terms: a first term representing the vector potential produced by the currents in $V$, and a second term representing the vector potential produced by currents located outside $V$ and on the surface enclosing $V$. This second term can be identified with $\boldsymbol{A}''$, a solution of Eq. 4.72.

We observe, on the other hand, that Eqs. 4.55, 4.59, and 4.72, taken together, are equivalent to requiring both the divergence and the curl of $\boldsymbol{H}$ to vanish within $V$. In other words, the field corresponding to $\boldsymbol{A}''$ is a conservative field, and therefore it can be obtained as the gradient of a potential satisfying Laplace's equation. It follows that any physically realizable magnetic field can also be expressed, with the help of Eq. 4.69, in the form

$$\boldsymbol{H} = \frac{1}{4\pi} \int_V \frac{(\boldsymbol{J} \times \boldsymbol{i}_{QP})}{r_{QP}^2}\, dv - \operatorname{grad} \phi'' \tag{4.74}$$

where $\phi''$ is a solution of Laplace's equation in the region $V$ considered. Thus, again, the problem of finding the family of physically realizable fields is reduced to the problem of finding the family of scalar functions that satisfy Laplace's equation. There is an important difference, however, between the case of a field which is conservative throughout the entire space and the case of a field which is solenoidal throughout the entire space. In the case of a conservative field, only single-valued solutions of Laplace's equations are physically realizable, because the potential associated with the entire field must be single-valued. In the case of solenoidal fields, multivalued solutions may be physically realizable if the region $V$ considered is multiply connected; i.e., if there is at least one closed path within $V$ which cannot be shrunk to a point without cutting through the surface $S$ enclosing $V$, as, for instance, in the case of a doughnut-shaped region. We shall discuss this matter further in connection with magnetic circuits.

## ► 4.5 Current Singularities

The similarity between the forms of Eqs. 4.7 and 4.65 suggests that we might be able to investigate the behavior of the vector potential at large distances from a current distribution by using the series expression for $1/r_{QP}$ developed in Sec. 4.2. Let us suppose, for this purpose, that a steady current distribution of density $\boldsymbol{J}$ is contained within a sphere of radius $R$, whose center coincides with the origin of a spherical system of coordinates. When the series given by Eq. 4.24 is substituted for $1/r_{QP}$ in Eq. 4.65, the zero-order term of the series gives rise to a component of vector potential

$$\boldsymbol{A}_0 = \frac{\mu_0}{4\pi r} \int_V \boldsymbol{J}\, dv \tag{4.75}$$

where $V$ is the volume of the sphere and $r$ is the radial coordinate of the point $P$ at which the vector potential is measured. The current density $\boldsymbol{J}$ is a function of the coordinates of the point $Q$, with respect to which the integral is evaluated.

Since the fields with which we are concerned are time-invariant, the current distribution must be solenoidal, i.e.,

$$\operatorname{div} \boldsymbol{J} = -\frac{\partial \rho}{\partial t} = 0 \tag{4.76}$$

This means that the current flows in closed paths and, therefore, roughly speaking, there must be as much current flowing in one direction as in the opposite direction. Thus, it seems reasonable to expect the integral in Eq. 4.75 to vanish when evaluated over the entire current distribution. Theorem ($f$) of Sec. 2.8 shows that this is actually the case, namely,

$$\int_V \boldsymbol{J}\, dv = 0 \tag{4.77}$$

where $V$ is the volume of the sphere which contains, by assumption, the entire current distribution. Thus, $\boldsymbol{A}_0$ vanishes for all steady current distributions.

The first-order term of the series gives rise to a component of vector potential

$$A_1 = -\frac{\mu_0}{4\pi}\int_V J\left(r_Q\cdot\text{grad}\,\frac{1}{r}\right)dv = \frac{\mu_0}{4\pi}\int_V \frac{J}{r^2}(i_r\cdot r_Q)\,dv \qquad (4.78)$$

where $i_r$ is a unit vector pointing from the origin to the point $P$, $r$ is the radial coordinate of the point $P$, and $r_Q$ is the vector distance from the origin to the point $Q$ with respect to which the integral is evaluated. Thus $r$ and $i_r$ are independent of the variables of integration.

The integrand in Eq. 4.78 can be expressed in the form

$$J(i_r\cdot r_Q) = \tfrac{1}{2}i_r \times (J \times r_Q) + \tfrac{1}{2}J(i_r\cdot r_Q) + \tfrac{1}{2}r_Q(i_r\cdot J) \qquad (4.79)$$

with the help of Eq. 2.22. Substituting this expression for the integrand in Eq. 4.78 yields

$$A_1 = \frac{\mu_0}{4\pi r^2}(m \times i_r) + \frac{\mu_0}{8\pi r^2}\int_V [J(i_r\cdot r_Q) + r_Q(i_r\cdot J)]\,dv \qquad (4.80)$$

where

$$m = \frac{1}{2}\int_V (r_Q \times J)\,dv \qquad (4.81)$$

is the dipole moment of the current distribution. We shall show below that the remaining integral on the right-hand side of Eq. 4.80 vanishes when the volume $V$ includes the entire current distribution. Thus, the first-order component of the vector potential reduces to

$$A_1 = \frac{\mu_0}{4\pi r^2}(m \times i_r) \qquad (4.82)$$

The dipole moment $m$ is independent of the location of the origin; this follows immediately from Eq. 4.77. In fact we have for the moment evaluated with respect to a different origin $0'$,

$$m' = \frac{1}{2}\int_V (r_Q' \times J)\,dv = \frac{1}{2}\int_V (r_Q \times J)\,dv + \frac{1}{2}r_{0'} \times \int_V J\,dv = m \qquad (4.83)$$

where $r_Q'$ is the vector distance from $0'$ to $Q$ and $r_{0'}$ is the vector distance from $0$ to $0'$.

The higher order terms in the series given by Eq. 4.24 give rise to components of vector potential inversely proportional to the successive powers of $r$, just as in the case of the scalar potential. Thus, since the zero-order component $A_0$ is always equal to zero, the first-order component $A_1$ is the dominant component of the vector potential at large distances from the current distribution. It is important to note in this regard that the vector potential vanishes at infinity at least as fast as $r^{-2}$, because of the vanishing of $A_0$, and the scalar potential produced by a charge distribution vanishes at infinity only as $r^{-1}$ when the total charge is different from zero.

Let us evaluate the magnetic field associated with $\boldsymbol{A}_1$. We have from Eq. 4.55

$$\boldsymbol{H}_1 = \frac{1}{4\pi} \operatorname{curl} \frac{\boldsymbol{m} \times \boldsymbol{i}_r}{r^2} \tag{4.84}$$

On the other hand, expressing $\boldsymbol{m}$ in spherical coordinates yields

$$\boldsymbol{m} \times \boldsymbol{i}_r = |\boldsymbol{m}|(\boldsymbol{i}_r \cos\theta - \boldsymbol{i}_\theta \sin\theta) \times \boldsymbol{i}_r = \boldsymbol{i}_\varphi |\boldsymbol{m}| \sin\theta \tag{4.85}$$

where the direction of the $z$-axis of the coordinate system coincides with that of the vector $\boldsymbol{m}$. It follows that

$$\boldsymbol{H}_1 = \frac{1}{4\pi} \operatorname{curl} \frac{\boldsymbol{i}_\varphi |\boldsymbol{m}| \sin\theta}{r^2} = \frac{|\boldsymbol{m}|}{4\pi r^3} (\boldsymbol{i}_r 2 \cos\theta + \boldsymbol{i}_\theta \sin\theta) \tag{4.86}$$

which is readily recognized as a dipole field, having the same spacial behavior as that obtained from the first-order term of the scalar potential associated with a charge distribution, as discussed in Sec. 4.2. Thus, any current distribution confined to a finite region of space has the appearance of a magnetic dipole when viewed from a sufficiently large distance, just like a charge distribution of zero net value has the appearance of an electric dipole under the same conditions. Furthermore, it can be shown that the fields derived from the higher order terms of the vector potential are also proportional to the fields derived from the corresponding terms of the scalar potential.

The fact that a current distribution and a charge distribution confined to a sphere of finite radius can produce similar fields outside the sphere should not be surprising. In fact, the static magnetic field and the static electric field are governed by the same laws in any source-free region; therefore, any field which is physically realizable as a magnetic field in a current-free region is also realizable as an electric field in the same region when free of charge. In other words, both fields can be obtained from the same solution of Laplace's equation.

Let us evaluate, as a simple example, the dipole moment of a current filament of intensity $I$, forming a closed contour $C$. The differential current element appearing in Eq. 4.81 can be expressed as

$$\boldsymbol{J}\, dv = \boldsymbol{J}\, da\, ds = I\, d\boldsymbol{r}_Q \tag{4.87}$$

where $da$ is the differential cross section of the filament, $ds$ is a differential element of the contour $C$, and $d\boldsymbol{r}_Q$ is the increment of $\boldsymbol{r}_Q$ along $C$ in the direction of current flow. Clearly, $d\boldsymbol{r}_Q$ is tangent to $C$, and its magnitude is equal to $ds$. Thus, Eq. 4.81 becomes

$$\boldsymbol{m} = I \oint_C \tfrac{1}{2}\boldsymbol{r}_Q \times d\boldsymbol{r}_Q \tag{4.88}$$

On the other hand, the magnitude of the integrand is the area of the triangle formed by $\boldsymbol{r}_Q$ and $d\boldsymbol{r}_Q$. Thus,

$$\boldsymbol{m} = I \int_S \boldsymbol{n}\, da \tag{4.89}$$

where $S$ is the conical surface formed by the lines joining the origin to the points of the contour, and $\boldsymbol{n}$ is a unit vector normal to this surface and oriented according to the right-handed-screw rule relative to the direction of the current. In the special case of a planar contour, if we take the origin on the plane of the contour, Eq. 4.89 reduces to

$$\boldsymbol{m} = \boldsymbol{n}IA \tag{4.90}$$

where $A$ is the area of the plane enclosed by $C$. This is the familiar expression for the dipole moment of a closed current filament.

It remains to prove that the integral in Eq. 4.80 vanishes when the volume $V$ includes the entire current distribution and the current density is solenoidal. A solenoidal current distribution can be regarded as consisting of closed current filament of differential cross section, so that the volume integral in Eq. 4.80 can be evaluated as the sum of the line integrals over each current filament. Then, expressing the differential current element as in Eq. 4.87, we have for a current filament forming a closed contour $C$,

$$dI \oint_C [(\boldsymbol{i}_r \cdot \boldsymbol{r}_Q)\, d\boldsymbol{r}_Q + (\boldsymbol{i}_r \cdot d\boldsymbol{r}_Q)\boldsymbol{r}_Q] = dI \oint_C d[(\boldsymbol{i}_r \cdot \boldsymbol{r}_Q)\boldsymbol{r}_Q] \tag{4.91}$$

where $dI$ is the intensity of the filament current. The right-hand side of this equation is the line integral of the differential of a vector, and therefore it is equal to the difference between the values assumed by the vector at the end points of the path of integration. On the other hand, the path of integration is closed so that its end points coincide. It follows that the integral is equal to zero. Since this is true for all current filaments of the distribution, the integral on the right-hand side of Eq. 4.80 vanishes when evaluated over a volume including the entire current distribution.

## 4.6 General Properties of Laplace's Equation

We saw in the preceding sections that Laplace's equation plays a key role in connection with static fields because, whenever the divergence and the curl of a field are given in the region of space of interest, the determination of the corresponding field reduces to the problem of finding an appropriate solution of Laplace's equation. Furthermore, most static problems of practical interest involve fields whose divergence and curl are both equal to zero throughout the region of interest, and whose behavior, therefore, is controlled directly by Laplace's equation. For instance, we are often called upon to determine the electric field in the space surrounding conductors held at known potentials or with given amounts of charge on their surfaces. Such problems involve the determination of a solution of Laplace's equation for which the surfaces of the conductors are equipotential surfaces meeting the stated requirements. Because of the serious mathematical difficulties that arise in most cases of practical interest, it is of paramount importance to develop such a grasp of the general properties of Laplace's equation, that it be possible to make intelligent guesses and approximations when exact solutions cannot be found.

Our understanding of the properties of Laplace's equations can be facilitated by bringing into play our familiarity with the behavior of d-c circuits. We observe for this purpose that the electric field in a homogeneous, linear conductor carrying a direct current is both conservative and solenoidal, and, therefore, the potential associated with it satisfies Laplace's equation. On the other hand, our intuition suggests that, if we substitute for the conductor a three-dimensional grid of wires of appropriate resistance having the same external geometry, the potential at each node of the grid should be approximately equal to

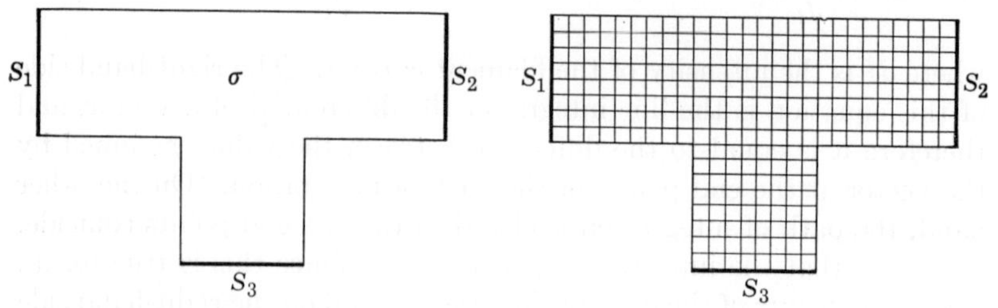


**Fig. 4.8.** A wire-grid approximation of a conductor. $S_1$, $S_2$, $S_3$ are terminal, equipotential surfaces.

the potential at the corresponding point in the solid conductor. For instance, the wire grid illustrated in Fig. 4.8 should be approximately equivalent in this sense to the solid conductor shown in the same figure, when the same voltages are applied between the corresponding terminal surfaces $S_1$, $S_2$, $S_3$. Of course, the terminals of the wires forming each of these surfaces must be held at the same potential, while the terminals of the wires at all other points on the surface of the grid must be left open-circuited. Clearly, the finer the grid, the more closely the solid conductor is approximated by it.

The mathematical justification for the approximate representation of a conductor by means of a wire grid rests on the fact that, if we substitute ratios of finite increments for the derivatives in Laplace's equation, the resulting difference equation can be recognized as the condition that must be satisfied by the potentials of adjacent nodes in the grid. In fact, at any point of coordinates $x$, $y$, $z$, we have

$$\frac{\partial \phi}{\partial x} \simeq \frac{1}{h} [\phi(x + h, y, z) - \phi(x, y, z)] \tag{4.92}$$

and

$$\frac{\partial^2 \phi}{\partial x^2} \simeq \frac{1}{h^2} [\phi(x + h, y, z) - \phi(x, y, z)] - [\phi(x, y, z) - \phi(x - h, y, z)]$$
$$= \frac{1}{h^2} [\phi(x + h, y, z) - 2\phi(x, y, z) + \phi(x - h, y, z)] \tag{4.93}$$

Thus, Laplace's equation becomes, approximately,

$$\Delta\phi = \frac{1}{h^2} [\phi(x + h, y, z) + \phi(x, y + h, z) + \phi(x, y, z + h) - 6\phi(x, y, z)$$
$$+ \phi(x - h, y, z) + \phi(x, y - h, z) + \phi(x, y, z - h)] = 0 \tag{4.94}$$

On the other hand, if we identify $h$ with the length of wire between nodes in the grid, and the point of coordinate $x$, $y$, $z$, with a particular node in the grid, such as the one indicated with 0 in Fig. 4.9, the other six points whose potentials appear in Eq. 4.94 can be identified with the six nodes adjacent to 0, and indicated in Fig. 4.9 with the numbers 1, 2, 3, 4, 5, 6. It can be readily checked that, since all the branches in the grid have the same resistance, Kirchhoff's current law requires that

$$\phi_1 + \phi_2 + \phi_3 + \phi_4 + \phi_5 + \phi_6 - 6\phi_0 = 0 \tag{4.95}$$

which, after making the above identifications, is readily recognized as equivalent to Eq. 4.94.

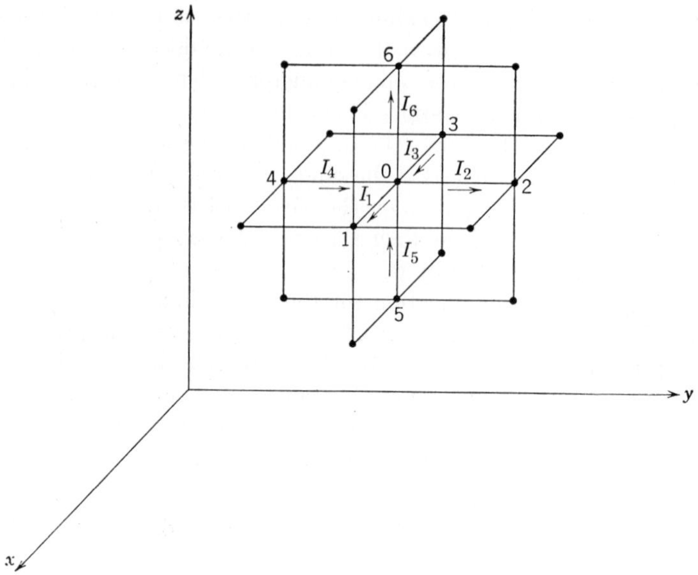


**Fig. 4.9.** Detail of a three-dimensional wire grid.

It is interesting to note, further, that the current distribution in the grid approximates the current distribution in the corresponding conductor. In fact, we have for each component of the current density,

$$J_x = \sigma E_x \simeq -\frac{\sigma}{h}[\phi(x+h, y, z) - \phi(x, y, z)] = -\frac{\sigma}{h}(\phi_1 - \phi_0) \tag{4.96}$$

On the other hand, each branch in the grid corresponds to a cross section of conductor equal to $h^2$, and, therefore, its conductance should be equal to

$$G = \frac{\sigma h^2}{h} = \sigma h \tag{4.97}$$

It follows that

$$h^2 J_x \simeq G(\phi_0 - \phi_1) = I_1 \tag{4.98}$$

In other words, each branch current in the grid is approximately proportional to the component of the current density in the same direction, and, therefore, to the corresponding component of the electric field.

The idea of approximating a conductor by means of a grid of resistive wires is not only helpful from a conceptual point of view, but also as a tool for the numerical solution of static field problems. In fact, the substitution of a wire grid for a conductor reduces any static field problem in a conductor to a network problem which can then be solved numerically by well-known methods. The practical usefulness of such numerical methods has been greatly increased in recent years by the availability of high-speed digital computers.

Equation 4.95 states that the potential of each node is equal to the average value of the potentials of the neighboring nodes. Laplace's equation imposes a similar property on its solutions. It can be shown that, if a function $\phi$ satisfies Laplace's equation within a region $V$, its value at any point $P$ of $V$ is equal to the average value of $\phi$ on the surface of any sphere in $V$ centered at $P$.

Another important property of any function $\phi$ that satisfies Laplace's equation within a region $V$ enclosed by a surface $S$, is that $\phi$ *cannot attain either a maximum value or a minimum value within* $V$; thus $\phi$ must assume its largest and smallest values on $S$. This property can be proved by noting that the second partial derivatives of $\phi$ with respect to $x$, $y$, and $z$ must be all positive at a point where $\phi$ has a minimum, and all negative at a point where $\phi$ has a maximum. This, however, is impossible because their sum must be equal to zero by Laplace's equation. This property permits us to conclude that no electric field can be present in a charge-free region completely enclosed by a conductor. In fact, the largest and smallest values assumed by the potential in such a region must be equal because the potential is forced to be constant on the surface of the conductor. It follows that the potential must be constant throughout the entire region.

A second important conclusion can be drawn from the above property of Laplace's equation, namely, that the *electric field in any charge-free region is uniquely specified by the values assumed by the potential on the surface enclosing the region.* In fact, if there were two potential functions $\phi_1$ and $\phi_2$ that satisfied Laplace's equation within the region and assumed the same values on its surface, their difference $\phi = \phi_1 - \phi_2$ would also satisfy Laplace's equation and would vanish on the surface. Then, it follows from the above property that $\phi$ must vanish throughout the region, or, in other words, that $\phi_1$ must be equal to $\phi_2$. This result becomes physically obvious when we think of it in terms of a wire grid. It states simply that the potentials of all nodes are uniquely specified by the voltages applied to the terminals of the wires on the surface of the grid. Furthermore, it is equally obvious that the node potentials are also uniquely specified if the terminal currents instead of the terminal voltages were given, or, if either the terminal voltage or the terminal current were given for each wire, independently of all other wires. This suggests that the potential within a charge-free region should be uniquely specified when the values assumed on the surface of the region by either the potential or by its normal derivative (the normal component of the electric field) are given; i.e., the potential may be given on a part of the surface, and its normal derivative on the rest of the surface. This is actually the case, as shown below with the help of Green's theorem.

Let us consider Eq. 2.138, and identify $V$ and $U$ with the same function $\phi$, which is assumed to satisfy Laplace's equation within a volume $V$ and on its surface. We have then,

$$\int_V |\operatorname{grad} \phi|^2 \, dv = \oint_S \phi(\boldsymbol{n} \cdot \operatorname{grad} \phi) \, da \tag{4.99}$$

where $S$ is the surface enclosing $V$ and $\boldsymbol{n}$ is a unit vector normal to $S$. The right-hand side of this equation vanishes whenever either $\phi$ or the normal component of grad $\phi$ vanish at all points of $S$. In such a case, the integrand on the left-hand side of the same equation must vanish at all points of $V$ because it is a nonnegative quantity; as a result, $\phi$ must be constant throughout $V$. We can conclude, therefore, that *any solution $\phi$ of Laplace's equation must be constant throughout a region $V$ whenever either $\phi$ or its normal gradient vanishes at all points of the surface $S$ enclosing $V$.*

We shall now prove that *a solution of Laplace's equation is uniquely specified within a region $V$ apart from an additive constant when either its value or the value of its normal gradient is given at all points of the surface $S$ enclosing $V$.* For this purpose, let us suppose that this were not true and that there were two different solutions $\phi_1$ and $\phi_2$ that met the above requirements on the surface $S$. Then, the function

$$\phi = \phi_1 - \phi_2 \tag{4.100}$$

would either vanish or its normal gradient would vanish at all points of $S$. On the other hand, the function $\phi$ is also a solution of Laplace's equation, being the difference between two such solutions. It follows that $\phi$ must be a constant throughout the volume $V$, and, therefore, $\phi_1$ and $\phi_2$ can differ only by a constant.

One final property of Laplace's equation deserves our attention. *If $\phi$ satisfies Laplace's equation in a given region, the derivative and the integral of $\phi$ in any direction satisfy the same equation.* In fact, if the $x$-axis is made to coincide with the desired direction, we have

$$\Delta \frac{\partial \phi}{\partial x} = \frac{\partial^3 \phi}{\partial x^3} + \frac{\partial^3 \phi}{\partial x \, \partial y^2} + \frac{\partial^3 \phi}{\partial x \, \partial z^2} = \frac{\partial}{\partial x} (\Delta \phi) = 0 \tag{4.101}$$

and similarly, for the integral of $\phi$, on the assumption, of course, that the necessary derivatives of $\phi$ are nonsingular. Thus, a whole series of solutions can be constructed from a single solution. It is interesting to note, furthermore, that, if $\phi$ satisfies Poisson's equation for a charge distribution of density $\rho$, its derivative $\partial\phi/\partial x$ satisfies the same equation for a charge density equal to $\partial\rho/\partial x$. This result follows immediately from Eq. 4.101. A similar result is obtained for the integrals of $\phi$ and $\rho$. It can be readily checked, in this connection, that the potential associated with a dipole is the derivative in the direction of the dipole moment of the potential associated with a point charge. The potentials associated with higher order singularities can be obtained similarly by differentiating the potential associated with the singularity of next lower order. This suggests that the charge singularities themselves should form a series of successive derivatives. It can be shown that this is actually the case, just as the doublet used in circuit theory is the derivative of the impulse.

## 4.7 Two-Dimensional Solutions of Laplace's Equation in Rectangular Coordinates

It is helpful, at this point, to study in some detail particular solutions of Laplace's equation. Our main objective in this study will be to abstract from such particular solutions characteristic types of behavior that can be generalized at least qualitatively if not quantitatively. For the sake of simplicity, we shall begin by focusing our attention on two-dimensional solutions of Laplace's equation, i.e., on solutions that depend on the $x$ and $y$ coordinates, but are independent of $z$. Such solutions are associated with systems with cylindrical symmetry, i.e., with systems whose geometry is uniform in the direction of the $z$-axis. Of course, they apply also to fields which are truly two-dimensional, such as the current field in a thin conducting sheet.

Let us start by solving Laplace's equation in Cartesian coordinates,

$$\frac{\partial^2\phi}{\partial x^2} + \frac{\partial^2\phi}{\partial y^2} + \frac{\partial^2\phi}{\partial z^2} = 0 \tag{4.102}$$

Linear, partial-differential equations of this type can often be solved by expressing $\phi$ as the product of three functions, each involving only one of the three variables. In this case, since we seek solutions independent of $z$, we write

$$\phi = X(x)\,Y(y) \tag{4.103}$$

where $X$ is a function of $x$ alone, and $Y$ is a function of $y$ alone. Substituting this expression in Laplace's equation and dividing by $\phi$ yields

$$\frac{1}{X}\frac{d^2X}{dx^2} + \frac{1}{Y}\frac{d^2Y}{dy^2} = 0 \tag{4.104}$$

The first term in this equation is independent of $y$ and the second term is independent of $x$. On the other hand, their sum must vanish for all values of $x$ and $y$. It follows that both terms must be independent of both $x$ and $y$ and, therefore,

$$\frac{d^2X}{dx^2} - k^2X = 0 \tag{4.105}$$

$$\frac{d^2Y}{dy^2} + k^2Y = 0 \tag{4.106}$$

where $k$ is a real constant; substituting $-k^2$ for $k^2$ would merely interchange $x$ and $y$ in the final expression for $\phi$.

The resulting linear, homogeneous, differential equations have solutions of the form

$$X = A_1e^{kx} + A_2e^{-kx} \tag{4.107}$$

$$Y = B_1 \sin ky + B_2 \cos ky \tag{4.108}$$

where $A_1$, $A_2$, $B_1$, and $B_2$ are arbitrary constants. Thus,

$$\phi = (A_1e^{kx} + A_2e^{-kx})(B_1 \sin ky + B_2 \cos ky) \tag{4.109}$$

is a solution of Laplace's equation.

The constant $B_2$ can always be made to vanish by an appropriate shift of the origin along the $y$-axis. Similarly, the magnitudes (not the signs) of the two constants $A_1$ and $A_2$ can always be made equal by an appropriate shift of the origin along the $x$-axis. Thus, depending on the relative signs of $A_1$ and $A_2$, the above solution will behave either as

$$\phi_1 = \sinh kx \sin ky \tag{4.110}$$

or as

$$\phi_2 = \cosh kx \sin ky \tag{4.111}$$

Both functions become infinite when $x$ approaches infinity, but one has odd symmetry the other even symmetry. The equipotential lines and the lines of force of $\phi_1$ are plotted in Fig. 4.10 and those of $\phi_2$ in Fig. 4.11.

We observe, first of all, that apart from a translation in the $y$ direction, the lines of force of $\phi_2$ coincide with the equipotential lines of $\phi_1$, and the lines of force of $\phi_1$ coincide with the equipotential lines of $\phi_2$.

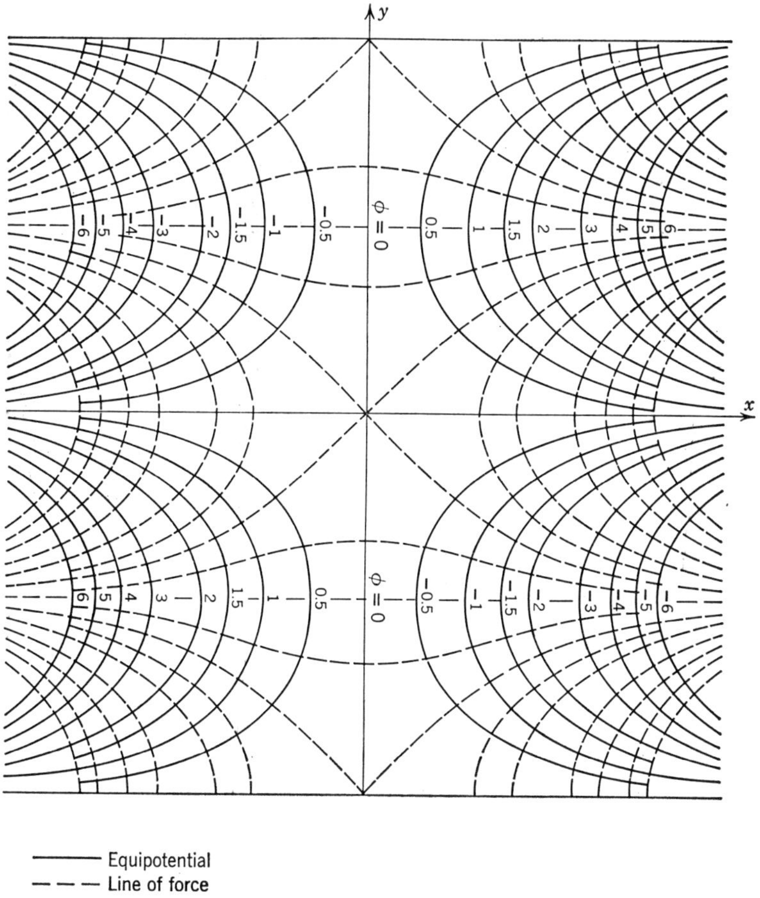


**Fig. 4.10.** Plot of the field $\phi = \sinh x \sin y$.

This property of the two solutions stems from the fact that the two families of lines are mutually orthogonal, and, therefore, either one of the two families can be taken to represent equipotential lines. Clearly to each two-dimensional solution of Laplace's equation must correspond a "conjugate" solution, for which the equipotential lines and the lines of force are interchanged.

Another very important characteristic of the two solutions is that the potential vanishes over all lines parallel to the $x$-axis and displaced from it by an integral multiple of $\pi/k$. Thus, either solution could represent the electrostatic potential between infinite parallel conducting

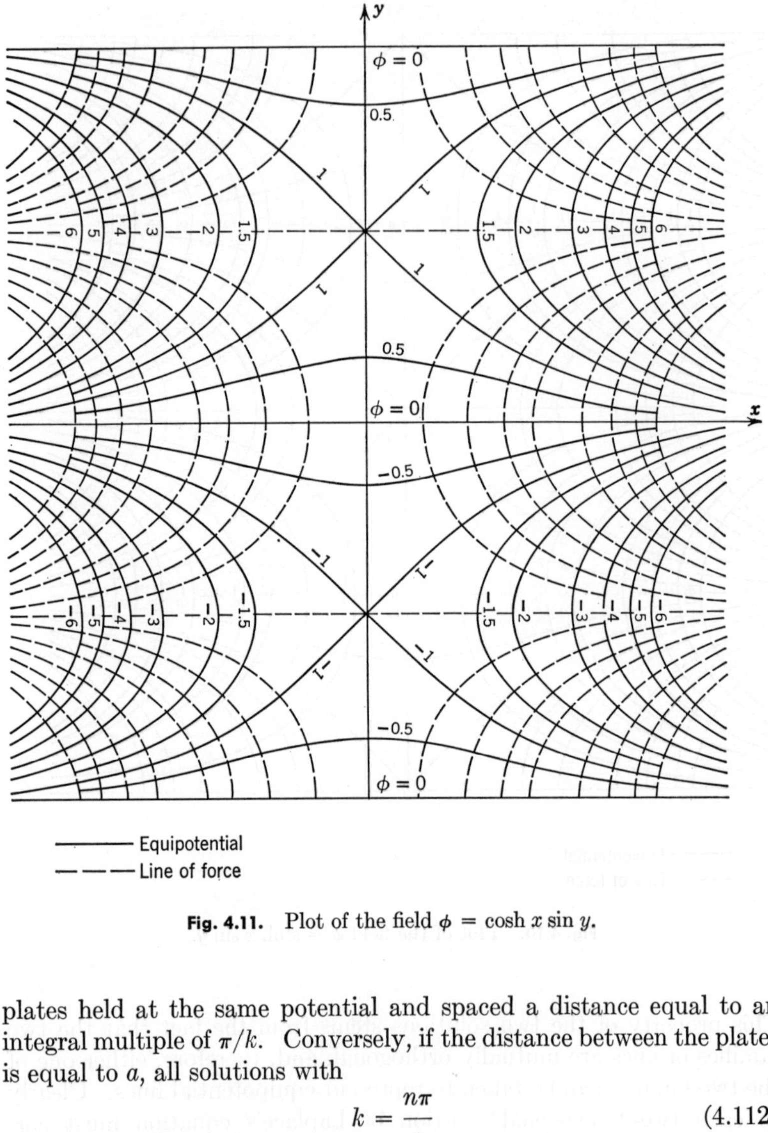


**Fig. 4.11.** Plot of the field $\phi = \cosh x \sin y$.

plates held at the same potential and spaced a distance equal to an integral multiple of $\pi/k$. Conversely, if the distance between the plates is equal to $a$, all solutions with

$$k = \frac{n\pi}{a} \tag{4.112}$$

where $n$ is any positive integer, satisfy the necessary boundary conditions on the plates. It can be shown, furthermore, that the potential between parallel, conducting plates held at the same potential can always be expressed as a linear combination of solutions corresponding to different values of the integer $n$.

Suppose, for instance, that we are interested in determining the extent to which the electric field can penetrate into a conducting slot such as that illustrated in Fig. 4.12. We observe, first of all, that only solutions of the type $\phi_1$ can be present in the slot because the potential must vanish at the bottom of the slot as well as on its sides; thus, the potential in the slot can be written in the form

$$\phi = \sum_n C_n \sinh \frac{n\pi x}{a} \sin \frac{n\pi y}{a} \tag{4.113}$$

where the $C_n$ are constants that must be determined from the potential distribution at the mouth of the slot, i.e., for $x = b$, or on the basis of other data of the problem. We note next that each term of this summation oscillates in the width of the slot, and for $x > a$ grows exponentially toward the mouth of the slot. The shorter is the period of oscillation (i.e., the larger is $n$), the larger is the exponent that controls the growth toward the mouth of the slot. Thus, if the depth of the slot is appreciably greater than its width, the potential is bound to oscillate

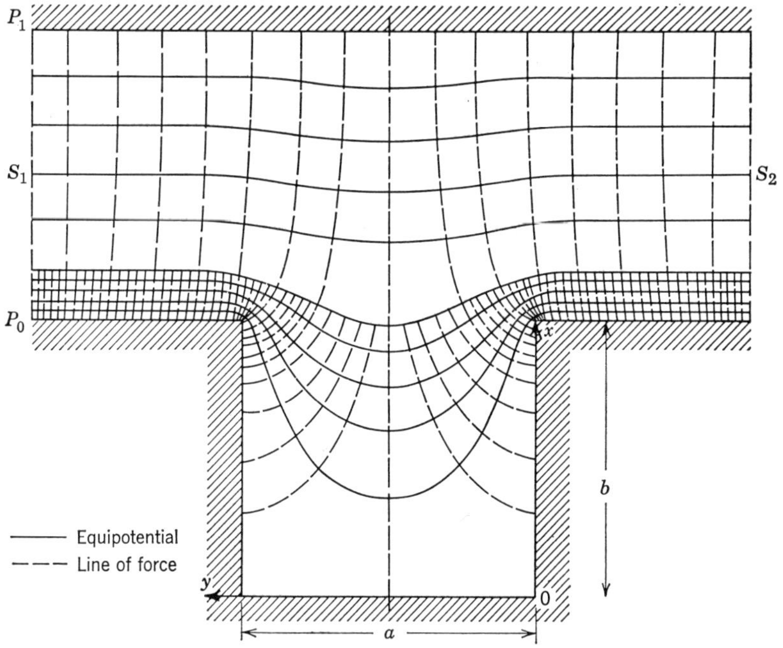


**Fig. 4.12.** Electric field in a slot.

rather violently across the mouth of the slot unless all constants $C_n$ are much smaller than $C_1$. Conversely, if the potential is known to vary rather smoothly across the mouth of the slot so that the contributions of the higher order terms at the mouth are at most of the same order of magnitude as the contribution of the first term, then the potential at distances from the mouth greater than the width of the slot is given approximately by the first term alone. It follows that, to a first approximation, the potential behaves within a deep slot as

$$\phi \simeq C_1 \sinh \frac{\pi x}{a} \sin \frac{\pi y}{a} \sim e^{-\pi(b-x)/a} \sin \frac{\pi y}{a} \qquad (4.114)$$

In other words, the potential decays roughly exponentially from the mouth of the slot; with the exponent inversely proportional to the width of the slot. This situation is illustrated in Fig. 4.12, where a difference of potential is applied between the conducting plate $P_1$ and the plate $P_0$ in which the slot has been cut. The similarity between the field in the slot and that illustrated in Fig. 4.10 is evident. It is interesting to note that the equipotential lines in this figure represent the current-density field in a $T$-shaped conducting sheet when a potential difference is applied between the two terminal lines $S_1$ and $S_2$. Thus, we see that the penetration of the current into the open-circuited side branch of the conducting sheet is governed by the same considerations as the penetration of the electric field into the corresponding slot.

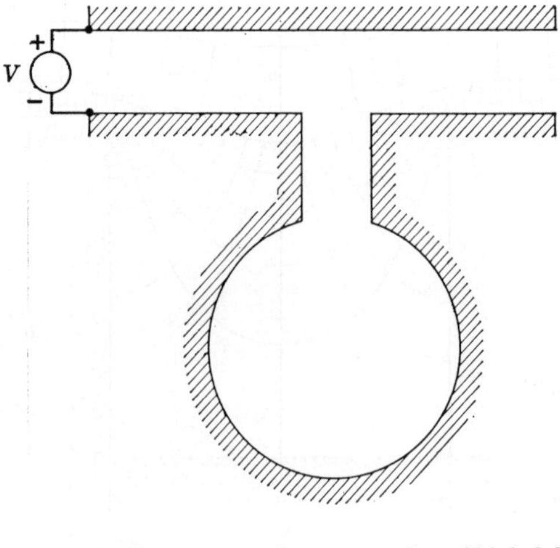


**Fig. 4.13.** Cavity connected by a narrow duct to a region of high field intensity.

A useful generalization can be made on the basis of the above example. We saw that the potential decays exponentially into a slot, and that the exponent involved is inversely proportional to the width of the slot. It follows that, if the width of the slot varies with the depth, the potential will still decay in a roughly exponential manner and that the field will not penetrate far into a slot, regardless of its shape. In particular, very little field will penetrate into a charge-free cavity connected by a narrow duct to a region where the field is strong, as illustrated in Fig. 4.13. In other words, the narrow duct acts as an exponential attenuator. We shall see in the next section that three-dimensional fields have similar properties and that conducting hollow pipes act also as exponential attenuators; as a matter of fact, this property of hollow pipes is exploited in practice in the construction of calibrated high-frequency attenuators and in the shielding of high-frequency amplifiers.

## 4.8 Two-Dimensional Solutions of Laplace's Equation in Polar Coordinates

Other two-dimensional solutions of Laplace's equation can be generated by writing the latter in other systems of orthogonal coordinates. We shall consider here only the solutions obtained by writing Laplace's equation in polar coordinates. We have for a two-dimensional potential,

$$\Delta\phi = \frac{1}{r}\frac{\partial}{\partial r}\left(r\frac{\partial\phi}{\partial r}\right) + \frac{1}{r^2}\frac{\partial^2\phi}{\partial\varphi^2} = 0 \qquad (4.115)$$

where $r$ is the distance from the origin, and $\varphi$ is the angle around the origin, measured counterclockwise from an arbitrary reference direction. Let us write again $\phi$ as the product of two functions, each of which involves only one of the two coordinates,

$$\phi = R(r)\,\Phi(\varphi) \qquad (4.116)$$

Substituting this expression in Eq. 4.115 yields, after multiplication by $r^2/\phi$,

$$\frac{1}{R}\left(r\frac{\partial R}{\partial r} + r^2\frac{\partial^2 R}{\partial r^2}\right) + \frac{1}{\Phi}\frac{\partial^2\Phi}{\partial\varphi^2} = 0 \qquad (4.117)$$

The left-hand side of this equation, just as that of Eq. 4.104, consists of two terms, each one involving only one of the variables. It follows that, in order for the equation to be satisfied, the two terms must be separately equal to constants having the same magnitude and opposite signs. Thus, the partial-differential Eq. 4.117 breaks into the two ordinary differential equations

$$r^2 \frac{d^2R}{dr^2} + r\frac{dR}{dr} = n^2R \tag{4.118}$$

$$\frac{d^2\Phi}{d\varphi^2} = -n^2\Phi \tag{4.119}$$

where $n^2$ is the separation constant. The solutions of these two equations are

$$R = A \ln \frac{a}{r} \tag{4.120}$$

$$\Phi = B_1\varphi + B_2 \qquad \text{for } n = 0 \tag{4.121}$$

and

$$R = A_1r^n + A_2r^{-n} \tag{4.122}$$

$$\Phi = B_1 \sin n\varphi + B_2 \cos n\varphi \qquad \text{for } n \neq 0 \tag{4.123}$$

where $A$, $a$, $A_1$, $A_2$, $B_1$, and $B_2$ are arbitrary constants.

The potential obtained for $n = 0$ by multiplying Eq. 4.120 by Eq. 4.121 is clearly a linear combination of the three potentials.

$$\phi_0 = \ln \frac{a}{r} \tag{4.124}$$

$$\phi_0' = -\varphi \tag{4.125}$$

$$\phi_0'' = \varphi \ln \frac{a}{r} \tag{4.126}$$

The first of these potentials is readily recognized as that associated with a line charge of density $\lambda = 2\pi\epsilon_0$. The corresponding electric field is given by

$$\boldsymbol{E}_0 = -\text{ grad } \phi_0 = \boldsymbol{i}_r \frac{1}{r} \tag{4.127}$$

The second potential $\phi_0'$ has the peculiarity of being multivalued in the sense that its magnitude increases by $2\pi$ each time the point of observation is moved completely around the origin. However, its negative gradient, given by

$$-\text{ grad } \phi_0' = \boldsymbol{i}_\varphi \frac{1}{r} \tag{4.128}$$

is single-valued; it is readily identified with the magnetic field $\boldsymbol{H}$ associated with a current filament of intensity $I = 2\pi$. We shall discuss later on the physical significance of multivalued magnetic potentials.

The third potential $\phi_0''$ is of little practical interest and is not associated with any physically realizable singularity; its equipotential lines and its lines of force form orthogonal families of spirals.

Let us now turn our attention to the more interesting solutions obtained by multiplying Eq. 4.122 by Eq. 4.123. We observe, first of all, that we can always make either $B_1$ or $B_2$ equal to zero by selecting appropriately the reference direction with respect to which the angle $\varphi$ is measured. Thus, no loss of generality results from disregarding the first term in Eq. 4.123. The two terms in Eq. 4.122 give rise to the two potentials

$$\phi_n = \frac{\cos n\varphi}{r^n} \tag{4.129}$$

$$\phi_n' = r^n \cos n\varphi \tag{4.130}$$

No restriction has been placed up to now on the value of the constant $n$. It is clear that if $n$ is an integer, the above potentials are single-valued and, therefore, can represent fields in the entire space. If $n$ is not an integer, both potentials are multivalued and, therefore, can represent physical fields only in a limited region of space. Imaginary values of $n$ are also acceptable, but the corresponding fields are of limited practical interest. Thus, we shall limit our discussion from now on to the potentials associated with integral values of $n$.

The potential

$$\phi_1 = \frac{\cos \varphi}{r} \tag{4.131}$$

is readily recognized as that associated with a two-dimensional electric dipole. Its equipotential lines and its lines of force form orthogonal families of circles as illustrated in Fig. 4.7. The potential

$$\phi_1' = r \cos \varphi \tag{4.132}$$

on the other hand, increases linearly in the direction with respect to which the angle $\varphi$ is measured and, therefore, represents a uniform vector field, parallel to such a direction.

The potential

$$\phi_2 = \frac{\cos 2\varphi}{r^2} \tag{4.133}$$

can be shown to be associated with a two-dimensional quadrupole as discussed in Sec. 4.2. Its equipotential lines and its lines of force are

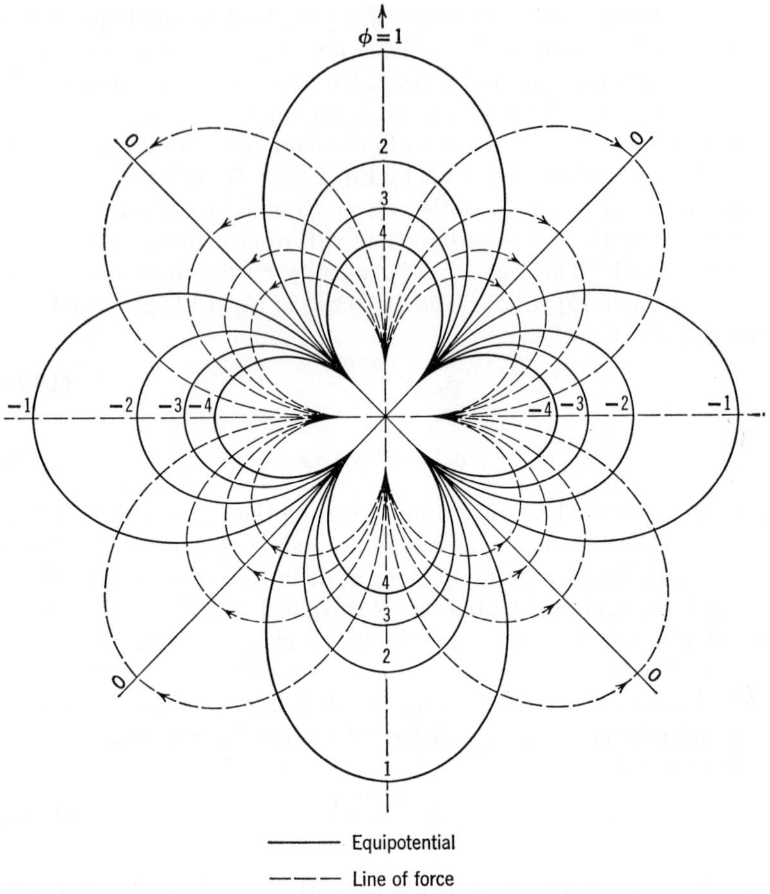


**Fig. 4.14.** Field of a two-dimensional quadrupole, $\phi_2 = (\cos 2\varphi)/r^2$.

illustrated in Fig. 4.14. The potential

$$\phi_2' = r^2 \cos 2\varphi \tag{4.134}$$

whose behavior is illustrated in Fig. 4.15, has a similar angular symmetry, but it becomes singular at infinity instead of at the origin.

The potentials corresponding to larger values of $n$ exhibit similar behaviors with higher order angular symmetries and are associated with correspondingly higher singularities at the origin and at infinity. One important fact should be stressed; the shorter the angular period of oscillation, the faster the decay (or the growth) of the potential in the radial direction. This relationship is similar to that observed for the solutions of Laplace's equation in Cartesian coordinates. Roughly speaking, we can think of the solution in polar coordinates as being obtainable by "wrapping" around the origin the solutions in Cartesian coordinates.

Interesting and useful field patterns are obtained by forming linear combinations of the primed and unprimed potentials corresponding to the same integer $n$. For instance, subtracting Eq. 4.131 from Eq. 4.132 yields the potential

$$\phi = \left(r - \frac{1}{r}\right) \cos \varphi \tag{4.135}$$

whose behavior is illustrated in Fig. 4.16. Its conjugate potential (with

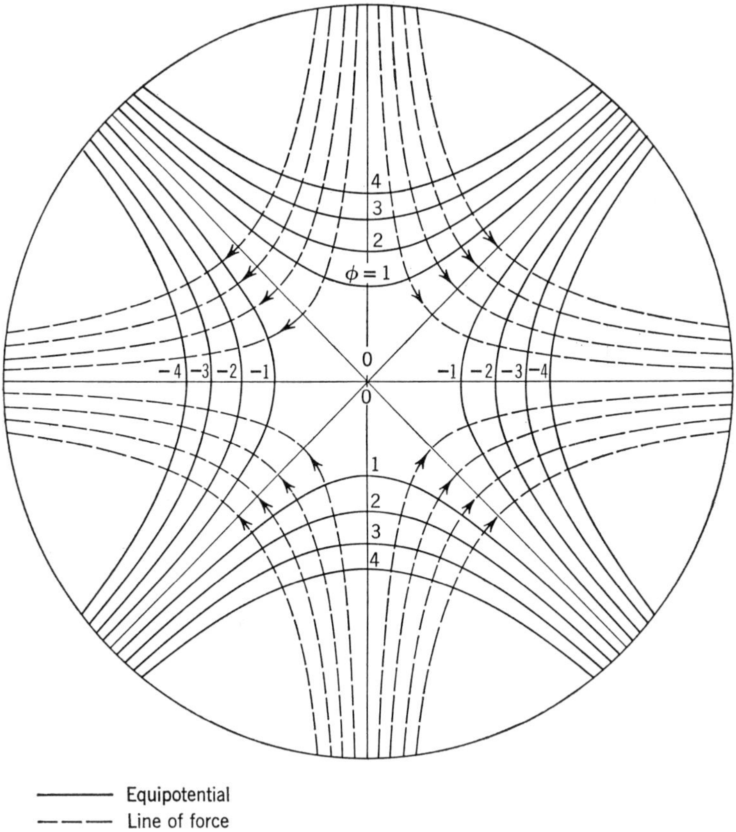


**Fig. 4.15.** The potential $\phi_2{}' = r^2 \cos 2\varphi$.

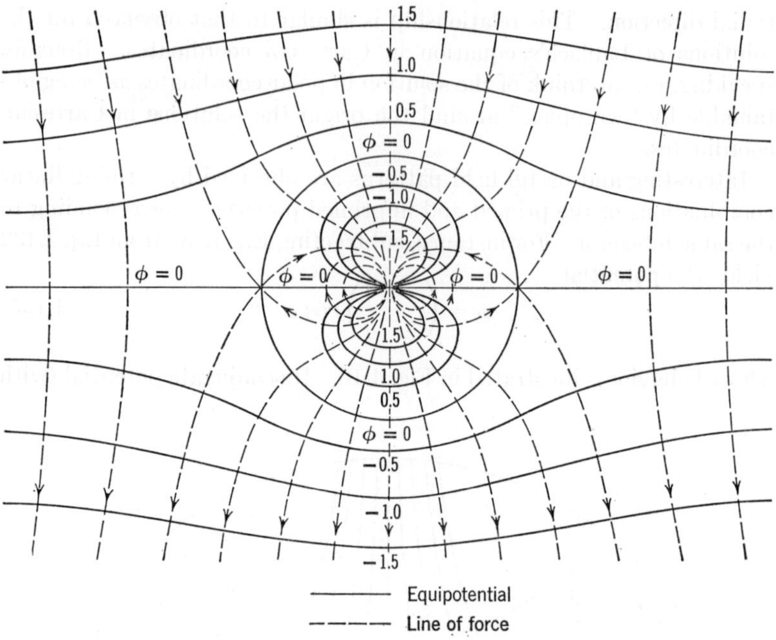


**Fig. 4.16.** The potential $\phi = (r - 1/r)\cos\varphi$.

the equipotential lines interchanged with the lines of force) is obtained by adding Eq. 4.131 and Eq. 4.132 with $\cos\varphi$ replaced by $\sin\varphi$. It should be noted also that multiplying the two equations by arbitrary constants before addition or subtraction would merely change the scale of the field plot.

The circle of unit radius in Fig. 4.16 coincides with the circular parts of the degenerate equipotential lines indicated with $\phi = 0$. We note also that the field becomes uniform at large distances from the origin. It follows that the field illustrated in Fig. 4.16, outside the circle of unit radius, can be identified with the electric field around a circular cylindrical conductor of unit radius immersed in a uniform field normal to its axis. We observe, in this regard, that the dipole field $\phi_1$ which has been subtracted from the uniform field $\phi_1'$ must be associated with the surface charge induced on the conductor. This charge must have a density

$$\sigma = -\epsilon_0(\text{grad}_r\,\phi)_{r=1} = -2\epsilon_0\cos\varphi \tag{4.136}$$

It can be readily checked that its two-dimensional dipole moment has a magnitude just equal to $2\pi\epsilon_0$, and that its higher order moments are all equal to zero. The field produced by the surface charge in the region occupied by the conductor must be equal in magnitude to the uniform field in which the conductor has been immersed and oppositely directed. This follows from the requirement that their sum be zero throughout the region occupied by the conductor. Thus, the field produced by the surface charge given in Eq. 4.136 is uniform inside the circle of unit radius and is equal to the field of a two-dimensional dipole outside the same unit circle.

## 4.9 Three-Dimensional Solutions of Laplace's Equation in Rectangular Coordinates

Three-dimensional solutions of Laplace's equation, although more complex and harder to visualize than two-dimensional solutions, exhibit the same general type of behavior. Let us consider, for instance, the solutions obtained by expressing Laplace's equation in Cartesian coordinates. Substituting into Eq. 4.102 the potential

$$\phi = X(x)\,Y(y)\,Z(z) \tag{4.137}$$

and dividing the whole equation by $\phi$, yields

$$\frac{1}{X}\frac{d^2X}{dx^2} + \frac{1}{Y}\frac{d^2Y}{dy^2} + \frac{1}{Z}\frac{d^2Z}{dz^2} = 0 \tag{4.138}$$

The first term in this equation depends on $x$ only, the second term on $y$ only, and the third term on $z$ only. On the other hand, their sum must vanish for all values of the three variables. It follows that each term separately must be equal to a constant, so that Eq. 4.138 breaks into the three ordinary differential equations

$$\frac{d^2X}{dx^2} = K_xX \tag{4.139}$$

$$\frac{d^2Y}{dy^2} = K_yY \tag{4.140}$$

$$\frac{d^2Z}{dz^2} = K_zZ \tag{4.141}$$

where $K_x$, $K_y$, $K_z$ are the three separation constants whose sum must be equal to zero.

It is clear that one of the three separation constants must be negative if the other two are positive, and vice versa. If two of the separation constants are positive, the resulting potential reduces, after a rotation of the axes, to the two-dimensional solutions discussed in Sec. 4.7. If, instead, one of the constants

$$K_x = \alpha^2 \tag{4.142}$$

is positive, and the other two,

$$K_y = -\beta_y{}^2 \tag{4.143}$$

$$K_z = -\beta_z{}^2 \tag{4.144}$$

are negative, we obtain

$$X = A_1 e^{\alpha x} + A_2 e^{-\alpha x} \tag{4.145}$$

$$Y = B_1 \sin \beta_y y + B_2 \cos \beta_y y \tag{4.146}$$

$$Z = C_1 \sin \beta_z z + C_2 \cos \beta_z z \tag{4.147}$$

where

$$\alpha = \sqrt{\beta_y{}^2 + \beta_z{}^2} \tag{4.148}$$

The potential resulting from the product of the solutions obtained above reduces, after an appropriate translation of the origin, to a function proportional to either

$$\phi = \cosh \alpha x \sin \beta_y y \sin \beta_z z \tag{4.149}$$

or

$$\phi' = \sinh \alpha x \sin \beta_y y \sin \beta_z z \tag{4.150}$$

depending on whether $A_1$ and $A_2$ have the same sign or opposite signs, just as in the corresponding two-dimensional situation. It follows that the three-dimensional solutions differ from the two-dimensional solutions only in the fact that the potential varies sinusoidally in two of the orthogonal directions instead of just one. The potential behaves in the same manner in the third direction, but for the fact that the constant $\alpha$ ($k$ in the two-dimensional solutions) depends on the period of oscillation in both of the other two directions.

The zero-potential surfaces of both $\phi$ and $\phi'$ form two families of parallel, equally spaced planes, normal to the $y$-axis and to the $z$-axis respectively. The zero-potential planes normal to the $y$-axis are spaced a distance equal to $\pi/\beta_y$, and those normal to the $z$-axis are spaced a distance equal to $\pi/\beta_z$. Thus both solutions could satisfy the conditions imposed on the electric potential by a conducting, hollow pipe of rectangular cross section and dimensions equal to integral multiples of

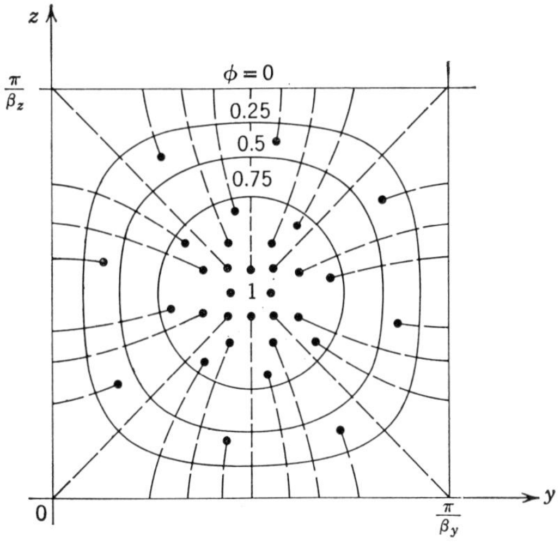


**Fig. 4.17.** Potential $\phi = \sinh ax \sin \beta_y y \sin \beta_z z$ on a plane normal to the $x$-axis.

$\pi/\beta_y$ and $\pi/\beta_z$. The traces of the equipotential surfaces and the lines of force in a plane normal to the $x$-axis are plotted in Fig. 4.17; the field pattern shown is repeated periodically in both the $y$ and $z$ directions. It should be noted in this connection, that both $\phi$ and $\phi'$ yield the same field on any plane normal to the $x$-axis, but for a constant multiplier.

The two potentials $\phi$ and $\phi'$ are the result of combining the two exponential solutions in Eq. 4.145, and, therefore, both of them behave exponentially for large values of $x$. Thus, we can generalize the results obtained in the preceding section by saying that, if an electric field is created at the mouth of a hollow conducting pipe, the field will decay exponentially along the axis of the pipe. More precisely, if we locate the origin at one corner of the mouth with the positive direction of the $x$-axis into the pipe, the potential at the mouth of the pipe will be of the form

$$\phi = \sum_n \sum_m A_{nm} e^{-\alpha_{nm} x} \sin \frac{n\pi y}{y_0} \sin \frac{m\pi z}{z_0} \tag{4.151}$$

where $y_0$ and $z_0$ are the dimensions of the pipe, $n$ and $m$ are integers, and the $A_{nm}$ are constants. The exponent $\alpha_{nm}$ is related to the dimensions of the pipe, in accordance with Eq. 4.148, by

$$\alpha_{nm} = \sqrt{\left(\frac{n\pi}{y_0}\right)^2 + \left(\frac{m\pi}{z_0}\right)^2} \tag{4.152}$$

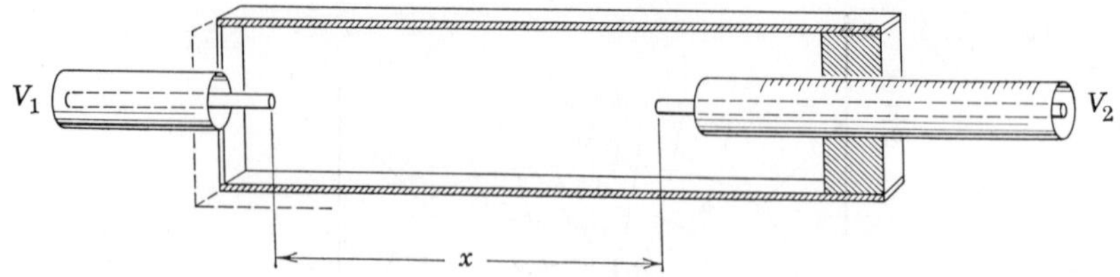


**Fig. 4.18.** Schematic diagram of an attenuator.

and therefore, for given dimensions, it increases with the values of the integers $n$ and $m$. It follows that, for large values of $x$, i.e., at some distance from the mouth of the pipe, the dominant term in Eq. 4.151 will be that corresponding to the smallest values of $\alpha_{nm}$, i.e., $\alpha_{11}$, and the field will look like that illustrated in Fig. 4.17.

An attenuator that operates on this principle is illustrated in Fig. 4.18. If a voltage $V_1$ is applied between the inner conductor and the outer conductor on the left, the output voltage between the inner conductor and the outer conductor on the right is given by

$$V_2 = Ae^{-\alpha_{11}x}V_1 \tag{4.153}$$

where $A$ is an appropriate constant and $x$ is the distance between the two inner conductors. Thus, the ratio of the two voltages expressed in decibels is linearly related to the distance $x$. For $x$ larger than the dimensions of the pipe, the calibration is very accurate up to frequencies for which the wave length becomes comparable with the dimensions of the pipe.

## 4.10 Solutions of Laplace's Equations in Spherical Coordinates

A detailed derivation of the solutions of Laplace's equation in spherical coordinates is beyond the scope of our discussion. We shall present here only the family of solutions corresponding to the terms of the series expansion of the potential discussed in Sec. 4.2, and the corresponding family of solutions with singularities at infinity.

The solutions in spherical coordinates can again be expressed as products of three separate functions of the three coordinates,

$$\phi = R(r)\,\Theta(\theta)\,\Phi(\varphi) \tag{4.154}$$

The function $R(r)$ is a linear combination of the type

$$R(r) = A_1r^n + A_2r^{-(n+1)} \tag{4.155}$$

where $n$ is a positive integer, and the function $\Phi(\varphi)$ is a linear combination of the type

$$\Phi(\varphi) = B_1 \sin m\varphi + B_2 \cos m\varphi \qquad m \leq n \tag{4.156}$$

where $m$ is a positive integer. The function $\Theta(\theta)$ is similarly a linear combination of two types of functions, one of which only is considered here, namely,

$$\Theta(\theta) = C\, P_n{}^m(\cos\theta) \tag{4.157}$$

These functions are known as the associated Legendre functions, and are tabulated in Table 4.1 for $m \leq n \leq 2$.

**TABLE 4.1. Associated Legendre Functions**

With $x = \cos\theta$
$P_0{}^0(x) = 1$
$P_1{}^0(x) = x = \cos\theta$
$P_1{}^1(x) = (1 - x^2)^{1/2} = \sin\theta$
$P_2{}^0(x) = \frac{1}{2}(3x^2 - 1) = \frac{1}{4}(3\cos 2\theta + 1)$
$P_2{}^1(x) = 3x(1 - x^2)^{1/2} = \frac{3}{2}\sin 2\theta$
$P_2{}^2(x) = 3(1 - x^2) = \frac{3}{2}(1 - \cos 2\theta)$

The simplest nontrivial, spherical solution, corresponding to $n = m = 0$ is

$$\phi_0 = \frac{1}{r} \tag{4.158}$$

and represents the potential associated with a point charge. The next two solutions, corresponding to $n = 1$, $m = 0$, are

$$\phi_1 = \frac{\cos\theta}{r^2} \tag{4.159}$$

and

$$\phi_1' = r\cos\theta \tag{4.160}$$

The first of these two solutions represents the potential associated with a dipole with moment parallel to the $z$-axis of the coordinate system. The field corresponding to this solution has been discussed in Secs. 3.5 and 4.2, and is illustrated in Fig. 3.4. The potential represented by the second of these solutions increases linearly in the direction of the $z$-axis, and therefore corresponds to a uniform field parallel to the $z$-axis.

There are four independent solutions with $n = m = 1$. The linear combination of the two solutions proportional to $r^{-2}$ and of the solution given by Eq. 4.159 represents the potential associated with a dipole of arbitrary orientation,

$$\phi = \frac{1}{r^2}(C \cos \theta + B_1 \sin \varphi \sin \theta + B_2 \cos \varphi \sin \theta) \qquad (4.161)$$

where the constants $C$, $B_1$, and $B_2$ are proportional to the Cartesian components of the dipole moment. Similarly, the two solutions proportional to $r$, when combined linearly with the solution given by Eq. 4.160, yield a potential representing an arbitrarily oriented, uniform field; the three arbitrary constants involved in such a linear combination are proportional to the Cartesian components of the field intensity.

The solution with $n = 2$, $m = 0$ and proportional to $r^{-3}$

$$\phi_2 = \frac{3 \cos 2\theta + 1}{4r^3} \qquad (4.162)$$

represents the potential associated with a quadrupole, formed by displacing two dipoles of opposite moments along their common axis; i.e., a quadrupole for which the two displacement vectors $\boldsymbol{s}_1$ and $\boldsymbol{s}_2$, shown in Fig. 4.5, are both parallel to the $z$-axis. The linear combination of this solution and of the other four solutions with $n = 2$, and proportional to $r^{-3}$, represents the potential associated with a quadrupole with arbitrary orientations of $\boldsymbol{s}_1$ and $\boldsymbol{s}_2$. The five arbitrary constants involved in such a linear combination are sufficient to specify independently the magnitude of the quadrupole moment and the directions of the two displacement vectors.

The five independent solutions with $n = 2$ and proportional to $r^2$ form a linear combination which represents a potential analogous to that of a quadrupole, but with its singularity at infinity. This potential is characterized, similarly, by a magnitude and two directions. It should be clear, by now, that the solutions corresponding to higher values of the integer $n$ represent the potentials associated with the higher order singularities mentioned in Sec. 4.2 and the corresponding singularities at infinity. Thus, the series expansion developed in Sec. 4.2 is a summation of solutions of Laplace's equation in spherical coordinates which represent the fields that are physically realizable outside the sphere to which the charge is confined. These solutions of Laplace's equation can represent magnetostatic fields as well as electrostatic fields because the two types of fields obey mathematically identical laws in source-free regions. Thus, in the case of a steady current confined to a sphere of radius $R$, the magnetic field outside the sphere can be expanded in a series mathematically identical to that representing the electric field outside a sphere containing charges, as discussed in Sec. 4.5.

A particularly interesting solution is obtained by subtracting the potential of Eq. 4.159 from that of Eq. 4.160. We obtain

$$\phi = \left(r - \frac{1}{r^2}\right)\cos\theta \tag{4.163}$$

This potential vanishes for $r$ equal to one and, therefore, possesses a spherical equipotential surface. On the other hand, for large values of $r$, it represents a uniform field parallel to the direction with respect to which the angle $\theta$ is measured. It follows that this potential can represent the electric field around a conducting sphere of unit radius, immersed in a uniform field. This is the three-dimensional analog of the problem solved in Sec. 4.8.

## 4.11 Summary and Conclusions

This chapter has been devoted to the study of conservative and solenoidal fields, i.e., fields of which either the curl or the divergence is equal to zero. In this connection our attention has been focused primarily on the electrostatic field, as an example of conservative field, and on the magnetostatic field, as an example of solenoidal field; however, the results obtained apply as well to a variety of special types of electromagnetic fields, as discussed in Sec. 3.4. It was shown, first of all, that the scalar potential associated with the electric field must satisfy the scalar Poisson's equation. It was possible to define, similarly, a vector potential associated with the magnetic field which must satisfy a vector Poisson's equation, i.e., whose Cartesian components must satisfy scalar Poisson's equations involving the corresponding Cartesian components of the current density.

It was shown next that any solution of the scalar Poisson's equation in a region $V$ can always be considered as representing the sum of two fields: the field that would be produced by the charges within $V$ and a field produced by charges outside $V$. The latter field is solenoidal as well as conservative within $V$ and, therefore, the potential associated with it must satisfy Laplace's equation within $V$. Then, since the field produced by charges can be obtained simply by integration of Coulomb's law over the charge distribution, we found that we needed to concern ourselves only with fields that are both solenoidal and conservative, and therefore only with potentials that satisfy Laplace's equation. The same conclusion was reached in connection with the magnetic field in a similar region.

After a general discussion of the properties of Laplace's equation, we studied in detail some of its solutions in two dimensions and three dimensions. On the other hand, the problem of finding solutions of Laplace's equation that satisfy prescribed conditions over the boundary of a given region was not considered, at least not directly. This "boundary-value" problem is rather involved and somewhat frustrating. The fact of the matter is that, in general, the desired solution of Laplace's equation is not expressible in terms of a finite number of functions which are tabulated and whose properties are known. On the other hand, it is always expressible as an infinite sum of known functions, such as those discussed in Secs. 4.7 to 4.10 but the determination of the coefficients in such an infinite sum of functions is usually a very laborious and difficult task, if at all possible. Furthermore, a solution in the form of an infinite sum is of little practical value unless all of its terms, except for a very few, can be neglected. The net result is that very few boundary-value problems of practical interest have ever been solved. On the other hand, digital computers are steadily enlarging the realm of feasible mathematical computations.

The problem that we face most often in engineering work is that of designing a material structure to provide a field with prescribed properties, rather than that of determining the field associated with a given structure. This is the reason for our emphasis on the properties of known solutions of Laplace's equation, and our disregard of the problem of satisfying prescribed boundary conditions. Fortunately, the synthesis problem is easier in practice than the analysis problem. This is true also in network theory; although we are able to design with relative ease very complex filters with prescribed characteristics of practical interest, the determination of the currents and voltages in an arbitrary network of comparable size could be a formidable computational task. As a matter of fact, approximate numerical solutions of boundary-value problems are often carried out by substituting for the field an appropriate network, as discussed in Sec. 4.5.

## 4.12 Selected References

1. W. E. Rogers, *Introduction to Electric Fields,* McGraw-Hill, New York, 1954. This book deals almost entirely with static fields. It proceeds rather slowly from the elementary point of view of Coulomb's law to the advanced point of view of Poisson's equation for both scalar and vector potentials. The material

presented is illustrated by a wealth of detailed examples and by many three-dimensional views of fields. This book should be very helpful to those who find the pace of this chapter too fast and who need a more detailed discussion of the mathematical steps.

2. J. A. Stratton, *Electromagnetic Theory*, McGraw-Hill, New York, 1941, Chapters 3 and 4. These chapters deal with electrostatics and magnetostatics and with the associated boundary-value problems from an advanced point of view.
3. W. R. Smythe, *Static and Dynamic Electricity*, McGraw-Hill, New York, 1939, Chapters 4 to 7. These chapters present an extensive discussion of static-field problems in two dimensions and three dimensions, including the properties of the mathematical functions involved.
4. H. B. Phillips, *Vector Analysis*, John Wiley and Sons, New York, 1933, Chapters 5 to 8. These chapters present a thorough mathematical discussion of potential theory in electrostatics and magnetostatics.

## PROBLEMS

**Problem 4.1.** (a) Determine the potential and electric field caused by a positive charge $q$ located at $+a$ on the $z$-axis and a negative charge $-q$ located at $-a$ on the $z$-axis, at a distance $r \gg a$ from the origin. Use spherical coordinates.

(b) Repeat the calculation for the case of two positive charges $q$ located at $x = \pm a$, $y = 0$, and two negative charges $-q$ at $x = 0$, $y = \pm a$.

**Problem 4.2.** Two concentric cylindrical conductors are insulated by air. The inner radius of the outer conductor is 5 cm. Choose the radius of the inner conductor so as to maximize the potential difference that can be applied between the two conductors. Taking the dielectric strength of air as equal to 3,000,000 v/m, compute the maximum permissible potential difference.

**Problem 4.3.** A cube is placed so that one of its corners is at the origin of a Cartesian system of coordinates, and three of the edges coincide with the axes. The cube is filled with charge of density

$$\rho = \rho_0 xyz \text{ coulombs/m}^3$$

where $\rho_0$ is a constant. No charge is present outside the cube.

(a) What is the dipole moment of this charge distribution?

(b) Does it depend on the choice of origin?

(c) Find the electric field at distances large compared to the edges of the cube.

**Problem 4.4.** Charge is distributed along the $z$-axis with a line density

$$\lambda = \begin{cases} \lambda_0 & \text{for } |z| \leq d \\ 0 & \text{for } |z| > d \end{cases}$$

where $\lambda_0$ is a constant.

(a) Find general expressions for the potential and the electric field.

(b) Find approximate expressions for the potential and the field in the $xy$-plane at a distance $r \ll d$ from the origin. Compare them with the expressions for an infinitely long line charge.

(c) Find approximate expressions for the potential and the field at distances $r \gg d$ from the origin. Compare them with the expressions for a point charge.

**Problem 4.5.** Determine the field and the potential on the axis of a circular disk with a uniform surface charge of density $\sigma_0$.

**Problem 4.6.** Find the vector potential for a planar square loop of thin wire carrying a current $I$, at distances large compared to the sides of the loop. Use a spherical coordinate system.

**Problem 4.7.** A circular cylindrical hole has been drilled through a straight circular conductor. The axis of the hole is parallel to that of the cylinder. A direct current of uniform density $J_0$ flows along the conductor. Calculate the magnetic field in the hole and express the result in rectangular coordinates.

**Problem 4.8.** An infinite planar slab of copper of constant thickness carries a uniform current of density parallel to its faces. Derive an expression for the magnetic vector potential in the slab and determine from it the magnetic field.

**Problem 4.9.** Two adjacent sides of a rectangular sheet of uniformly conducting material are held at zero potential. The other two sides are held at a potential which varies linearly from zero to a common value $V$.

(a) Obtain an expression for the potential in the sheet.
(b) Obtain an expression for the current density.
(c) Sketch the equipotential lines and the current lines.

**Problem 4.10.** Three sides of a very long rectangular sheet of uniformly conducting material are held at zero potential. The remaining short side of the sheet is edged by a thin wire of nonuniform resistance per unit length $R$. A constant-current source is connected between the center of the wire and its two ends. Find the dependence of $R$ on the position along the wire that produces a potential distribution in the sheet proportional to $e^{-\pi z/d}$, where $d$ is the width of the sheet and the $z$-axis is parallel to the long sides. Note that current is drained off from the wire by the sheet.

**Problem 4.11.** A long strip of conducting sheet of width $h$ is used in a calibrated logarithmic attenuator, as follows. One edge of the strip is in contact with a perfectly conducting bar, while a sliding connector makes perfect contact with the other edge. A voltage source is connected across one end of the strip, and the output voltage is measured between the sliding connector and the perfectly conducting bar. Explain the operation of the attenuator and express the output voltage as a function of the position of the sliding connector along the edge of the strip.

**Problem 4.12.** Find the current distribution on the surface of a circular cylinder necessary to produce inside the cylinder a uniform magnetic field normal to the axis of the cylinder.

**Problem 4.13.** A circular cylinder of infinite length has a conductivity $\sigma_1$. The cylinder is imbedded in an infinite medium of conductivity $\sigma_2$. The current density present in the medium is uniform at large distances from the cylinder and normal to the axis of the cylinder. Find the current density and the electric field everywhere. Sketch the current density field for the two cases $\sigma_2 = 0$ and $\sigma_2 = \infty$.

**Problem 4.14.** The outer surface of a hollow, circular, cylindrical conductor is maintained at a potential $A \cos \varphi$, where $A$ is a constant and $\varphi$ is the angular coordinate. The inner surface is maintained at a constant potential. Assuming the cylinder is long enough to ignore end effects, determine the electric potential at all points within the conductor.

**Problem 4.15.** A conducting sphere is immersed in a static electric field which is uniform at large distances from the sphere.

(a) Find the electric field.
(b) Find the maximum field intensity and the position at which it occurs.
(c) Find the surface charge density on the sphere.

**Problem 4.16.** The spherical portion of a hemisphere of uniformly conducting material is maintained at a potential

$$\phi = V_0 \cos \theta$$

where $\theta$ is the angle from the apex of the sphere and $V_0$ is a constant. The flat surface of the hemisphere is held at zero potential. Find the potential inside the hemisphere.

**Problem 4.17.** A surface distribution of electric charge on a sphere of radius $R$ creates an electric field which is uniform inside the sphere and identical, outside the sphere, to that of an electric dipole of moment $\boldsymbol{p}$ located at the center of the sphere. (See Sec. 3.5).

(a) Evaluate the vector $\int_V \boldsymbol{E}\, dv$ in terms of $\boldsymbol{p}$, when $V$ is the volume of the sphere of radius $R$.

(b) Repeat (a) when $V$ is the volume of a sphere of radius $R' > R$, and concentric with the sphere of radius $R$.

**Problem 4.18.** A surface distribution of electric current on a sphere of radius $R$ creates a magnetic field which is uniform inside the sphere and identical, outside the sphere, to that of a magnetic dipole of moment $\boldsymbol{m}$ located at the center of the sphere (see Sec. 3.6).

(a) Evaluate the vector $\int_V \boldsymbol{H}\, dv$ in terms of $\boldsymbol{m}$, when $V$ is the volume of the sphere of radius $R$.

(b) Repeat (a) when $V$ is the volume of a sphere of radius $R' > R$ and concentric with the sphere of radius $R$.

**Problem 4.19.** Show that the results of Prob. 4.17 are valid for *any* distribution of electric charge within and on the sphere of radius $R$ that gives rise to an electric-dipole field of moment $\boldsymbol{p}$ outside the sphere. (*Hint:* Make use of Eq. A4.23, and express the electric field in terms of its scalar potential.)

**Problem 4.20.** Show that the results of Prob. 4.18 are valid for *any* distribution of current within and on the sphere of radius $R$ that gives rise to a magnetic-dipole field of moment $\boldsymbol{m}$ outside the sphere. (*Hint:* Make use of Eq. A4.25, and express the magnetic field in terms of its vector potential.)

# CHAPTER FIVE

# Fields and Matter

This chapter is devoted to the study of electromagnetic fields in the presence of material bodies. Matter, under certain conditions, is known to produce electromagnetic fields, even in the absence of the types of sources considered in the preceding chapters. For instance, a magnetic field is produced by a permanently magnetized piece of iron, and an electric field is produced by certain crystals, such as quartz, when subjected to mechanical stresses. In general, a great many materials become active as electromagnetic sources under the influence of externally applied electromagnetic fields. This type of interaction between fields and matter can be divided, for the purposes of our study, into two separate parts: the action of an electromagnetic field in changing the state of matter as a field source, and the action of activated matter in producing an electromagnetic field. We shall devote our attention almost exclusively to the second type of action. The first type of action involves the detailed study of the atomic structure of matter, and as such is outside the scope of our macroscopic study of electromagnetic phenomena.

Matter is known to be an aggregate of particles, some of which possess electric charges, and some of which act also as magnetic dipoles. This suggests that the presence of material bodies might be taken into account macroscopically by means of appropriate distributions of sources, acting as if they were in free space. This expectation is actually fulfilled. However, we shall see that the properties of the particles do not specify in an unique manner the types of sources to be used in such a macroscopic representation. In the end, the decision as to the appropriate types of sources will follow from the requirement that the resulting theory of electromagnetic fields in matter be self-consistent and in agreement with macroscopic experimental evidence.

Because of the presence in matter of charged particles, and of particles acting as magnetic dipoles, the electromagnetic field within matter is extremely complex. In dealing with large-scale electromagnetic phenomena, however, we can disregard such a fine structure and focus our attention on the smoothed fields obtained by averaging the actual fields over volumes large compared with atomic dimensions, yet small compared with the dimensions of the material bodies under consideration. We shall use the adjective "macroscopic" in referring to these smoothed fields, and the adjective "microscopic" in referring to the actual fields.

The use of average values in the description of electromagnetic fields does not occur in the present chapter for the first time. The theory of electromagnetic fields produced by charges and currents in free space already involved such averages. In fact, the discreteness of the elementary charges was disregarded from the beginning by using in the definition of charge density (see Sec. 1.1) a volume large enough to contain a great many elementary charges, yet small enough to be negligible compared with the dimensions of the system under consideration and with those of the measuring instruments used in connection with it. The same approach was used in the definition of current density. When densities defined in this manner are used in Maxwell's equations, the resulting fields do not and cannot involve the microscopic space variations resulting from the discreteness of the elementary charges, but are instead the smoothed fields resulting from the corresponding averaging process. We did not emphasize these averaging processes in our study of electromagnetic fields in free space, partly because no conceptual difficulties were involved, and partly because the nature of such averaging processes could not be properly understood without some previous experience with solutions of Maxwell's equations.

The macroscopic theory of electromagnetic fields in matter presented in this chapter starts from the experimental fact that two field vectors (the electric field $\boldsymbol{E}$ and the magnetic field $\boldsymbol{H}$) are necessary and sufficient to express the force acting on a moving charge in free space. Since matter is an aggregate of particles, it is reasonable to expect that the same two field vectors be sufficient as well as necessary to represent the electromagnetic force exerted on each particle. Furthermore, it seems reasonable to expect that the vector fields involved in a macroscopic theory of electromagnetism be appropriate averages of the microscopic electric field and of the microscopic magnetic field in matter, defined as in free space. The postulate that macroscopic electromagnetic phenomena in matter be representable in terms of two fields only (in addition to other quantities representing field sources and the electromagnetic state of matter) is the cardinal point of deviation of the theory presented here from that usually presented in textbooks. We shall see that the definition of the macroscopic electric field is unequivocal and does not lead to any deviation from the conventional theory. On the other hand, we shall have to choose between two possible definitions of the macroscopic field corresponding to the microscopic magnetic field. These two possible definitions are associated with two different models of the magnetic dipole exhibited by an electron, and correspond to the two magnetic vectors $\boldsymbol{H}$ and $\boldsymbol{B}$ of the conventional theory. We shall deviate from the conventional theory in the choice of $\boldsymbol{H}$ as the fundamental macroscopic magnetic vector. This deviation is required by energy considerations, discussed in Chapter 7. We shall see there that only by choosing $\boldsymbol{H}$ as the second macroscopic field vector it is possible to develop a macroscopic theory based on only two field vectors, which is both self-consistent and in agreement with experimental evidence. It turns out that this same choice also removes certain difficulties previously encountered in extending the theory to macroscopic bodies in relative motion. As a matter of fact, it is just such difficulties that led one of the authors (L. J. Chu) to reformulate the theory of electromagnetic fields in matter as presented below.

After a more detailed discussion of averaging processes for fields and sources, we shall study the roles of polarized matter and magnetized matter as distributions of electric dipoles and of magnetic dipoles, represented by their moment densities $\boldsymbol{P}$ and $\boldsymbol{M}$. We shall see that a charge distribution is associated with the space variation of $\boldsymbol{P}$, and that a current distribution is associated with its time variation. We shall show that distributions of magnetic charge and of magnetic current can be associated in a similar manner with space and time variations of $\boldsymbol{M}$. Maxwell's equations for macroscopic fields in matter will then result from inserting these source densities into the corresponding free-space equations discussed in Chapter 3. This will establish the role of matter as a source of electromagnetic fields.

The action of electromagnetic fields in polarizing and magnetizing matter will be considered from a macroscopic point of view only by discussing typical functional relations between $\boldsymbol{P}$ and $\boldsymbol{E}$ and between $\boldsymbol{M}$ and $\boldsymbol{H}$. Finally the over-all interaction of fields and matter will be illustrated by means of specific examples, and by a more detailed discussion of magnetic circuits, which play such an important role in engineering practice.

## 5.1 Microscopic and Macroscopic Fields

Matter consists of atoms, each of which, in turn, consists of a positively charged nucleus surrounded by negatively charged electrons. The electrons move about the nuclei; the spacings between nuclei are always much greater than the dimensions of the nuclei, so that most of the space in matter is occupied by the moving electrons. On the other hand, we know from quantum physics that it is incorrect to think of the moving electrons as charged particles that possess at any instant a definite position and velocity. Instead it is more proper to think of each electron as if it were a "cloud" with a total charge equal to that of the electron, but extending over a region of space comparable with the size of the atom. This charge "cloud" represents, for each electron, the spatial probability distribution of its position. Each orbiting electron, because of its motion, constitutes a current, which, in turn, produces a magnetic field. In addition, each electron, regardless of its motion, acts as a magnetic dipole, with respect to both the magnetic field produced by it and the force exerted on the electron by an external magnetic field. The magnetic-dipole moment of the electron was originally postulated in order to explain certain spectroscopic results. Later on, however, this dipole moment was found to be primarily responsible for the three magnetization phenomena in matter known as ferromagnetism, ferrimagnetism, and paramagnetism. The phenomenon known as diamagnetism, on the other hand, results from the motion of the electrons. This last phenomenon can be neglected for most practical purposes.

This brief discussion of the particles constituting matter should not give the erroneous impression that the structure of matter must be known in detail before a macroscopic theory of electromagnetism can be developed. To the contrary, it is perfectly possible to develop such a theory on the basis of classical (as opposed to quantum mechanical) reasoning, using macroscopic experiments on matter as a guide. It is helpful, however, to relate our macroscopic theory to at least the simplest, rudimentary notions about the structure of matter.

The microscopic fields in matter are very inhomogeneous in the neighborhood of each particle. However, as stated above, we are only interested in the macroscopic characteristics of such fields. More precisely, we are interested in their average values, evaluated over volumes of matter large enough to contain a great many atoms, yet negligibly small compared with all macroscopically significant dimensions. In a basically inhomogeneous material, additional precautions must be observed to obtain macroscopically meaningful averages. Thus, for example, many materials of practical interest consist of very small crystals, more or less randomly oriented. Since each of these crystals contains many atoms, the atomistic fields would be smoothed by averages evaluated over the volume of each crystal. However, average values obtained over adjacent crystals might be entirely different because of different orientations of the crystals. Thus, to obtain macroscopically meaningful averages, we must use volumes large enough to contain many such crystals, yet still negligibly small compared with all significant dimensions of the system. We shall use the word "grain" to indicate a volume of material suitable for averaging purposes, and regard its physical characteristics as representative of the macroscopic characteristics of the material.

## 5.2 The Macroscopic Model of Polarized Matter

Charged particles in matter can be divided into two groups, on the basis of their behavior under the influence of an external electric field. The particles of the first group are relatively free to move, as, for instance, certain atomic electrons in metals and ions in electrolytic solutions. The particles of the second group, on the other hand, are bound to the atomic structure by such strong forces so that they can be displaced only very small distances. Charged particles of the first group will be referred to as free charges. Their drift, under the influence of an external electric field, constitutes a macroscopic conduction current, which is found to depend at each point on the local electric-field intensity and on the local structure of matter.

We shall be concerned in this section with charged particles of the second type, which are held by such strong forces that only small changes of their mean positions can result from the action of an external electric field. In a solid, these charge particles are the nuclei that experience only relatively small displacements with respect to each other, and the so-called bound electrons that move about the nuclei. We shall now study how the nuclei and the bound electrons can give rise to a macroscopic charge distribution.

It is sufficient for our purpose to think of the nuclei and of the bound electrons moving about them as two smooth charge distributions of equal and opposite densities $\rho_0$ and $-\rho_0$. These distributions are essentially uniform over a grain of matter. Under normal conditions, the two charge distributions neutralize each other (with the exception of so-called permanently polarized bodies). On the other hand, when an electric field is present, charges of opposite polarities are displaced relatively to each other by the electric forces exerted on them. The magnitude of the relative displacement is limited by the restoring forces which increase with increasing displacement. In general, the two charge distributions do not neutralize each other after such a displacement.

Let us evaluate the net charge produced in a given volume by such a displacement. Suppose that the two charge distributions $\rho_0$ and $-\rho_0$ are displaced with respect to each other on the average by a small distance represented by a vector $\boldsymbol{d}$. The average displacement $\boldsymbol{d}$ is of the order of the atomic dimensions and may vary from grain to grain. In studying the relative displacement of the two charge distributions, it is convenient to consider the negative charge distribution as fixed and the positive charge distribution as displaced with respect to the negative one by the displacement $\boldsymbol{d}$. Since $\boldsymbol{d}$ is very small, this arbitrary convention has no effect upon the computations of the macroscopic fields.

Consider now an element of area $da$. When the positive charge is displaced with respect to the negative charge, a net charge $\rho_0 \boldsymbol{d} \cdot \boldsymbol{n}\, da$ crosses the surface element $da$ in the direction of the unit vector $\boldsymbol{n}$ normal to it. If $S$ is any closed surface, the net charge that crosses it in the outward direction is given by

$$Q = \oint_S \rho_0 \boldsymbol{d} \cdot \boldsymbol{n}\, da \tag{5.1}$$

where the unit vector $\boldsymbol{n}$ is outwardly directed. On the other hand, since the net charge in the volume $V$ enclosed by $S$ was originally equal to zero, the departure of the charge $Q$ from $V$ must leave in $V$ a net charge

$$Q_p = -\oint_S \rho_0 \boldsymbol{d} \cdot \boldsymbol{n}\, da = -\oint_S \boldsymbol{P} \cdot \boldsymbol{n}\, da \tag{5.2}$$

We refer to the charge $Q_p$ as the polarization charge, and to

$$\boldsymbol{P} = \rho_0 \boldsymbol{d} \tag{5.3}$$

as the polarization vector.

The physical significance of $\boldsymbol{P}$ can be brought out more clearly by studying the two mechanisms by which matter may become polarized:

(*a*) The externally applied field induces a dipole moment in molecules that have no dipole moment in the absence of an applied field; and

(*b*) the externally applied field reorients molecules that have permanent dipole moments.

In the case (*a*), the center of charge of the positively charged nuclei of a molecule and the center of charge of the associated electron cloud coincide in the absence of an applied field. If $q$ is the net charge of the nuclei making up a molecule, the charge of the electron cloud is equal to $-q$. The smoothed charge distribution $\rho_0$ defined above is then given by

$$\rho_0 = qN \tag{5.4}$$

where $N$ denotes the number of molecules per unit volume. In the presence of an applied electric field the center of charge of the electron cloud in a molecule is displaced with respect to the center of charge of the nuclei. The average of this displacement, taken over the molecules inside a grain can then be identified as the quantity $\boldsymbol{d}$ used above. Thus, in the presence of an applied field, each molecule forms a dipole of average moment

$$\boldsymbol{p} = q\boldsymbol{d} \tag{5.5}$$

Since there are $N$ molecules per unit volume, the sum of all dipole moments in a grain of matter divided by the volume $V$ of the grain yields,

$$\frac{1}{V}\sum_{i=1}^{NV}\boldsymbol{p}_i = N\boldsymbol{p} = Nq\boldsymbol{d} = \rho_0\boldsymbol{d} = \boldsymbol{P} \tag{5.6}$$

Thus, the polarization vector $\boldsymbol{P}$ can be interpreted as the dipole moment per unit volume, i.e., as the dipole-moment density in the material.

In matter that polarizes according to mechanism (*b*) the molecules possess a permanent dipole moment. In the absence of an applied field the orientations of these molecular dipoles are usually uniformly distributed over all directions in space because of the randomizing effect of thermal agitation. Thus the sum of all dipole moments in a grain of matter is, on the average, equal to zero. In the presence of an external field, however, the permanent dipoles become oriented preferentially in the direction of the field, with thermal agitation acting as a sort of restoring torque. The sum of all dipole moments over a grain of matter is no longer equal to zero. The resulting dipole-moment density is again given by

$$\boldsymbol{P} = \frac{1}{V}\sum_{i=1}^{NV}\boldsymbol{p}_i \tag{5.7}$$

where the summation is extended over all dipoles within a grain, and $V$ is the volume of the grain.

The vector $\boldsymbol{P}$ defined by Eq. 5.7 is the same as that defined by Eq. 5.3. The difference in appearance between the two definitions can be traced to the different methods of derivation. In deriving Eq. 5.3, the positive charges and the negative charges were smoothed out separately with $\boldsymbol{d}$ representing the average displacement between the two smoothed distributions. In deriving Eq. 5.7, on the other hand, the pairing of charges in the individual dipoles was preserved, and the average implied in $\boldsymbol{P}$ was carried out on the dipole distribution. Since the identity of the charges and of the dipoles is lost in a macroscopic average, it is clear that either approach has to lead to the same result.

Let us return now to the polarization charge $Q_p$, which was found to be present in a volume $V$ as a result of the relative displacement of positive and negative charges. The macroscopic density of such a charge is defined as the ratio

$$\rho_p = \frac{Q_p}{V} = -\frac{1}{V}\oint_S \boldsymbol{P}\cdot\boldsymbol{n}\,da \tag{5.8}$$

where $V$ is the volume of a grain of matter, i.e., a volume large enough for averaging purposes, yet much smaller than any of the significant dimensions of the system under consideration. On the other hand, the polarization vector $\boldsymbol{P}$ in Eq. 5.8 is already a smoothed macroscopic quantity obtained by dividing the sum of the moments of the dipoles within a grain by the volume of the grain. Thus, wherever the state of polarization of matter varies smoothly from grain to grain, $\boldsymbol{P}$ can be regarded from a mathematical standpoint as a differentiable function of position. It follows that the volume $V$ in Eq. 5.8 can be allowed to vanish, and $\rho_p$ can be defined mathematically as

$$\rho_p = -\lim_{V\to 0}\frac{1}{V}\oint_S \boldsymbol{P}\cdot\boldsymbol{n}\,da = -\operatorname{div}\boldsymbol{P} \tag{5.9}$$

When the polarization of a material body is a function of time, the motion of charge associated with the time variation of $\boldsymbol{P}$ constitutes a macroscopic current. The macroscopic density of such a current is readily obtained from the smoothed-charge model of polarization introduced at the beginning of this section. The average velocity of the charge density $\rho_0$ is the time derivative of its average displacement $\boldsymbol{d}$. It follows that the density of the resulting polarization current is

$$\boldsymbol{J}_p = \rho_0\frac{\partial \boldsymbol{d}}{\partial t} = \frac{\partial \boldsymbol{P}}{\partial t} \tag{5.10}$$

where $\rho_0$ is a characteristic of the material, independent of time. The same result is obtained by evaluating the macroscopic density of the current elements resulting from the time variation of the individual molecular dipoles. In fact, regardless of the mechanism of polarization, the time variation of each molecular dipole contributes a current element given in both magnitude and direction by the time derivative of its dipole moment. It follows that the macroscopic average of the current in a grain is given by

$$\boldsymbol{J}_p = \frac{1}{V}\sum_{i=1}^{NV}\frac{d\boldsymbol{p}_i}{dt} = \frac{\partial}{\partial t}\left(\frac{1}{V}\sum_{i=1}^{NV}\boldsymbol{p}_i\right) = \frac{\partial \boldsymbol{P}}{\partial t} \tag{5.11}$$

Equations 5.9 and 5.10 give the densities of the charges and currents resulting from polarization of matter. These polarization charges and polarization currents are entirely equivalent to free charges and free currents as sources of electric and magnetic fields. Thus, the charge density $\rho$ and the current density $\boldsymbol{J}$ appearing in Maxwell's equations must be regarded as sums of free components and polarization components,

$$\rho = \rho_f + \rho_p \tag{5.12}$$

$$\boldsymbol{J} = \boldsymbol{J}_f + \boldsymbol{J}_p \tag{5.13}$$

It is interesting to note that the law of conservation of charge is satisfied independently by each pair of charge density and current density. In fact, taking the divergence of Eq. 5.10 yields for $\rho_p$ and $\boldsymbol{J}_p$

$$\operatorname{div} \boldsymbol{J}_p = \operatorname{div}\frac{\partial \boldsymbol{P}}{\partial t} = \frac{\partial}{\partial t}\operatorname{div} \boldsymbol{P} = -\frac{\partial \rho_p}{\partial t} \tag{5.14}$$

Then, since the law of conservation of charge must be satisfied by the sums $\rho_f + \rho_p$ and $\boldsymbol{J}_f + \boldsymbol{J}_p$, it must also be satisfied by $\rho_f$ and $\boldsymbol{J}_f$.

Before concluding our discussion of polarization charge, it is important to stress that Eq. 5.9 becomes singular at any point at which $\boldsymbol{P}$ is discontinuous. More specifically, let $\Sigma$ be a surface over which $\boldsymbol{P}$ is discontinuous, and let $\boldsymbol{P}_1$ and $\boldsymbol{P}_2$ be the values assumed by $\boldsymbol{P}$ at points on opposite sides of $\Sigma$. We shall show that the volume charge density $\rho_p$ becomes singular on $\Sigma$, giving rise, thereby, to a surface polarization charge of density

$$\sigma_p = -(\boldsymbol{P}_1 - \boldsymbol{P}_2)\cdot\boldsymbol{n} \tag{5.15}$$

where the unit vector $\boldsymbol{n}$ is normal to $\Sigma$ and pointing from side 2 to side 1, as illustrated in Fig. 5.1. Let us consider, for this purpose the pillbox surface shown in Fig. 5.1, consisting of two open surfaces $S_1$ and $S_2$ parallel to each other and to $\Sigma$, and of the ribbonlike side surface nor-

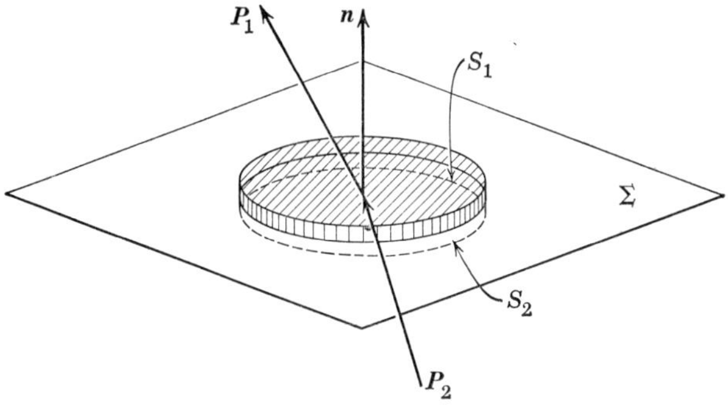


**Fig. 5.1.** Determination of surface polarization charge.

mal to $\Sigma$. If this pillbox surface is identified with $S$ in Eq. 5.2, the charge $Q_p$ will represent the surface charge on the part of $\Sigma$ enclosed by the pillbox. Then, let us divide $Q_p$ by the common area $a$ of $S_1$ and $S_2$, and evaluate the limit of this ratio when the area $a$ and the thickness of the pillbox approach zero simultaneously, and the pillbox shrinks to some internal point on $\Sigma$. The flux of $\boldsymbol{P}$ out of $S$ is the sum of the flux through $S_1$, the flux through $S_2$, and the flux through the ribbonlike side surface. The last component of the flux does not contribute to the limit in question because it vanishes faster than the area $a$. On the other hand, the sum of the components contributed by $S_1$ and $S_2$ yields

$$\lim_{a\to 0} \frac{1}{a}\left(\int_{S_1} \boldsymbol{P}\cdot\boldsymbol{n}\,da - \int_{S_2} \boldsymbol{P}\cdot\boldsymbol{n}\,da\right) = (\boldsymbol{P}_1 - \boldsymbol{P}_2)\cdot\boldsymbol{n} \qquad (5.16)$$

Thus, we obtain for the density of the surface polarization charge

$$\sigma_p = \lim_{a\to 0} \frac{Q_p}{a} = -(\boldsymbol{P}_1 - \boldsymbol{P}_2)\cdot\boldsymbol{n} \qquad (5.17)$$

Finally, we shall illustrate the above results with the aid of a simple example. A slab of thickness equal to $b$ is parallel to the $xy$-plane and is polarized in the direction of the $z$-axis, as shown in Fig. 5.2. The magnitude of the polarization is a sinusoidal function of time, and varies linearly with the $z$-coordinate,

$$\boldsymbol{P}(z, t) = \boldsymbol{i}_z P_0 \frac{z}{b} \sin \omega t \qquad (5.18)$$

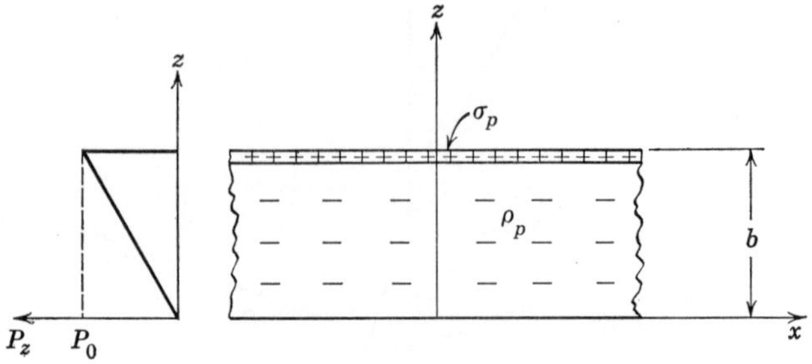


**Fig. 5.2.** Polarized slab with $\boldsymbol{P} = \boldsymbol{i}_z P_0(z/b) \sin \omega t$.

where $P_0$ is a constant. This linear space dependence can be visualized from a microscopic point of view in two different ways:

1. The molecules of the material have a uniform density, but the dipole moment of each molecule is proportional to $z$.
2. All the molecules have the same dipole moment, but the density of the molecules is proportional to $z$.

According to Eq. 5.9, a distribution of polarization charge of density

$$\rho_p = -\operatorname{div} \boldsymbol{P} = -\frac{P_0}{b} \sin \omega t \tag{5.19}$$

must be present in the slab. The origin of this polarization charge can be best visualized in terms of the second model, i.e., by assuming that a linear variation of the density of the molecules is entirely responsible for the linear variation of the polarization. This is equivalent to assuming that the density $\rho_0$ of the positive charges is proportional to $z$, while their displacement $\boldsymbol{d}$ is constant and parallel to the $z$-axis. Then, the positive charge in an element of volume $\delta v$ centered at a point on a plane $z = \zeta$ is displaced into an equal element of volume centered at a point on the plane $z = \zeta + d_z$. On the other hand, the negative charge, which has remained fixed, has a density $\rho_0(\zeta)$ on the plane $z = \zeta$, but a density

$$\rho_0(\zeta + d_z) = \rho_0(\zeta) + d_z \left(\frac{\partial \rho_0}{\partial z}\right)_{z=\zeta} \tag{5.20}$$

on the plane $\zeta + d_z$. It follows that the positive charge displaced from a volume element on the plane $z = \zeta$ does not neutralize the negative charge in the corresponding volume element on the plane $z = \zeta + d_z$.

The density of the resulting net charge is

$$\rho_0(\zeta) - \rho_0(\zeta + d_z) = -d_z\left(\frac{\partial \rho_0}{\partial z}\right)_{z=\zeta} = -\left(\frac{\partial P_z}{\partial z}\right)_{z=\zeta} \tag{5.21}$$

which checks with the polarization-charge density given by Eq. 5.19.

The normal component of $\boldsymbol{P}$ is discontinuous at the upper surface of the slab, which coincides with the plane $z = b$. Therefore, according to Eq. 5.15 a surface charge must be present on this plane with a density

$$\sigma_p = -(-P_z)_{z=b} = P_0 \sin \omega t \tag{5.22}$$

The origin of this surface charge can be visualized by noting that all the positive charge within a distance $d_z$ from the surface of the slab would normally be displaced into a layer of thickness $d_z$ on the upper side of the plane $z = b$. However, this is not possible because the charge must remain within the slab. It follows that all the positive charge within a distance $d_z$ from the upper surface of the slab accumulates on the surface, thereby giving rise to a surface charge of density

$$\sigma_p = \rho_0(b)\, d_z = P_z(b) \tag{5.23}$$

which checks with Eq. 5.22. No surface charge is present on the lower surface of the slab ($z = 0$) because $\boldsymbol{P}$ vanishes on it and, therefore, it is not discontinuous. It can be readily checked from Eqs. 5.19 and 5.22 that the total polarization charge within the slab is equal in magnitude and opposite in sign to the charge on the upper surface of the slab; this must be true because the slab, as a whole, is neutral.

The polarization current resulting from the time variation of $\boldsymbol{P}$ has, according to Eq. 5.10, a density

$$\boldsymbol{J}_p = \frac{\partial \boldsymbol{P}}{\partial t} = \boldsymbol{i}_z \omega P_0 \frac{z}{b} \cos \omega t \tag{5.24}$$

The phase of this current leads by $\pi/2$ the phase of $\boldsymbol{P}$; it is maximum when the polarization is equal to zero, and it is equal to zero when the polarization is maximum. The magnitude of this current is discontinuous at the upper surface of the slab because $\boldsymbol{P}$ vanishes outside the slab. On the other hand, $\boldsymbol{J}_p$ represents a flow of positive charge in the direction of the $z$-axis. It follows that the current density at $z = b$ must be equal to the time derivative of the surface charge density, i.e.,

$$J_z(b) = \omega P_0 \cos \omega t = \frac{\partial \sigma_p}{\partial t} \tag{5.25}$$

which agrees with Eq. 5.22.

## 5.3 Electric-Current and Magnetic-Charge Model of Magnetic Dipole

One observes experimentally that certain material bodies placed into a magnetic field react upon the field and modify it. The reaction of these material bodies upon the magnetic field is caused by the magnetization of the bodies. The material is then said to be magnetic or magnetizable. There are four basic types of magnetic materials: ferromagnetic, ferrimagnetic, paramagnetic, and diamagnetic. The magnetic effects in the first two types of materials are by far the largest. Paramagnetism and diamagnetism are small effects. In spite of this, paramagnetism has found an important application in the construction of the low-noise microwave device known as the Maser amplifier. The first three types of magnetization are known to be predominantly caused by the magnetic-dipole moments of the electrons. Only to a very small extent (a typical number is 1 per cent) are they attributable to the current produced by the motions of the electrons. Diamagnetism, on the other hand, results entirely from these motions. We shall be concerned primarily with the first three types of magnetic phenomena, and thus with the fields associated with the magnetic-dipole moments of electrons.

Paramagnetism is the magnetic analog of the electric polarization of materials whose molecules possess permanent electric-dipole moments. It consists of the orientation by an external magnetic field of the magnetic dipoles associated with the molecules of the material, against the randomizing effect of thermal agitation. In ferromagnetic and ferrimagnetic materials the mutual forces between neighboring molecular magnetic dipoles are so strong compared to the randomizing effect of thermal agitation that the dipoles orient one another in the same direction within small regions known as *domains*. The resulting net macroscopic magnetization depends on the relative sizes of these domains and on the orientation of the molecular dipoles within each of them. It may be different from zero even in the absence of an external magnetic field; this is the most striking macroscopic characteristic of ferromagnetic and ferrimagnetic materials. The domain structure can be modified by the application of an external magnetic field. The main effect of such an external field is to increase the sizes of the domains in which the molecular dipole moments have a component parallel to the field at the expense of the other domains. This change of domain structure increases the net macroscopic magnetization in the direction of the external field.

All ferromagnetic and ferrimagnetic materials exhibit to various extents the familiar hysteresis loop in their magnetization characteristics when subjected to an alternating magnetic field. The difference between ferromagnetic and ferrimagnetic materials lies in the structure of their molecules, which is beyond the scope of our discussion. It is important to stress, on the other hand, that a material which is ferromagnetic at normal temperatures becomes paramagnetic at sufficiently higher temperatures, as a result of the increased randomizing effect of thermal agitation which prevents the formation of domains. Conversely, a material which is paramagnetic at normal temperatures exhibits ferromagnetic characteristics at sufficiently low temperatures. The critical temperature which separates the two types of behavior is known as the *Curie temperature.*

An electron possesses, besides a charge and a mass, an angular momentum (spin) which may be crudely explained as being caused by a rotation of the electron around an axis. The magnetic-dipole moment of the electron is antiparallel to the angular momentum. Again, one may explain in a crude way the magnetic-dipole moment as resulting from the rotation of the negative charge of the electron. This picture at least gives the correct direction for the dipole moment.

In the theory of electromagnetic fields in free space we did not take into account the magnetic-dipole moment of the electron. This was done because, for electron densities realizable in free space, the effect of the electron dipole moment is quite negligible. Only very refined experiments can lead to its detection. In matter, however, much higher electron densities can be present; thus, the dipole moments of the electrons can give rise to macroscopic effects as pronounced as ferromagnetism.

Our primary objective is to develop a macroscopic representation of magnetized matter as a source of electromagnetic fields, just as we did in the preceding section for polarized matter. In the case of polarized matter, we regarded the electric-dipole moment of each molecule as resulting from the relative displacement of positive and negative charges. On the basis of this model we were able to show that a time-varying polarization is macroscopically equivalent, as a source of electromagnetic fields, to a charge distribution and a current distribution whose densities are functions of the macroscopic moment density of the molecular dipoles. To develop a similar macroscopic representation of magnetized matter, we must first postulate a suitable model for the magnetic-dipole moment associated with each electron. We shall consider in this section two possible models, namely, the amperian-current model and the magnetic-charge model. The magnetic-charge model will eventually be chosen; the reasons for this choice and the resulting representation of magnetized matter will be discussed in the next section.

We saw that the dipole moment and the angular momentum of an electron have opposite directions; their magnitudes are constants characteristic of the electron just as its charge. It would seem reasonable, therefore, to attribute the magnetic moment of the electron to the current resulting from the rotation of its charge. More precisely, let us think of the electron as a sphere of radius $R$ centered at the origin with charge uniformly distributed over its surface. Then a counterclockwise rotation of the electron around the $z$-axis would give rise to a surface current whose density can be expressed in spherical coordinates in the form

$$\boldsymbol{K} = \boldsymbol{i}_\varphi K_0 \sin\theta \tag{5.26}$$

where $K_0$ is a constant. This is just the type of surface current distribution used in the model of magnetic dipole discussed in Sec. 3.6. We saw there that the moment of the resulting dipole is related to $K_0$ by

$$\boldsymbol{m} = \boldsymbol{i}_z \tfrac{4}{3}\pi R^3 K_0 \tag{5.27}$$

and that the magnetic field produced by the current is given in spherical coordinates, by

$$\boldsymbol{H}_a = \frac{|\boldsymbol{m}|}{4\pi R^3}\begin{cases} 2(\boldsymbol{i}_r \cos\theta - \boldsymbol{i}_\theta \sin\theta) & r < R \\ \left(\dfrac{R}{r}\right)^3 (\boldsymbol{i}_r 2\cos\theta + \boldsymbol{i}_\theta \sin\theta) & r > R \end{cases} \tag{5.28}$$

We shall refer to this model as the amperian-current model of the magnetic dipole associated with the electron. Other models could be constructed by postulating different charge distributions within the sphere of radius $R$, and, therefore, different current distributions. Such models would yield the same magnetic field outside the sphere, although different fields inside the sphere. It can be shown that they are all equivalent from a macroscopic point of view.

Let us consider next the magnetic-charge model. We saw in Sec. 4.10 that the dipole field is a solution of Laplace's equation which is singular at the origin. This implies that in order for a dipole field to exist outside a sphere, an appropriate source must exist within the sphere or on its surface, i.e., either the curl or the divergence of the field must differ from zero somewhere inside the sphere, or on its surface. In the amperian-current model of the magnetic dipole, curl $\boldsymbol{H}$ differs from zero, whereas div $\boldsymbol{H}$ is equal to zero throughout the entire space. Clearly, an alternate model can be constructed by requiring curl $\boldsymbol{H}$ to vanish throughout the entire space and allowing div $\boldsymbol{H}$ to differ from zero within the sphere of radius $a$ and on its surface.

We observe, on the other hand, that Maxwell's equations in free space, as stated in Sec. 3.1, while permitting div $\boldsymbol{E}$ to differ from zero, require div $\boldsymbol{H}$ to vanish everywhere at all times. This asymmetry in the field equations reflects only the fact that no clear experimental evidence is available in support of the existence of isolated magnetic charges analogous to electric charges. At the same time, however, there is no experimental evidence that prevents us from picturing magnetic dipoles as neutral aggregates of magnetic charges. As a matter of fact, the theory of magnetism was originally developed in terms of magnetic charges analogous to electric charges, with the provision that isolated material bodies had to be magnetically neutral. Thus nothing prevents us from amending Eq. 3.17 to read

$$\text{div}\,\boldsymbol{H} = \frac{\rho^*}{\mu_0} \tag{5.29}$$

where $\rho^*$ is the density of magnetic charge, with the provision that such magnetic charge be present only in the form of neutral aggregates. When this is done, however, mathematical consistency requires us to amend at the same time Eq. 3.7 to read

$$\text{curl}\,\boldsymbol{E} + \mu_0 \frac{\partial \boldsymbol{H}}{\partial t} = -\boldsymbol{J}^* \tag{5.30}$$

where $\boldsymbol{J}^*$ is the density of the magnetic current resulting from the motion of magnetic charge, and is related to $\rho^*$ by the conservation law

$$\text{div}\,\boldsymbol{J}^* = -\frac{\partial \rho^*}{\partial t} \tag{5.31}$$

In fact, taking the divergence of Eq. 5.30 yields

$$\begin{aligned} -\,\text{div curl}\,\boldsymbol{E} &= \text{div}\,\boldsymbol{J}^* + \mu_0 \frac{\partial}{\partial t}\,\text{div}\,\boldsymbol{H} \\ &= \frac{\partial}{\partial t}\,(\mu_0\,\text{div}\,\boldsymbol{H} - \rho^*) = 0 \end{aligned} \tag{5.32}$$

A magnetic-charge model of a magnetic dipole can be constructed by analogy with the electric-charge model of electric dipole discussed in Sec. 3.5, in view of the fact that the equations for the static magnetic field produced by magnetic charges are identical in form to the equations for the static electric field produced by electric charges. Let us consider then a distribution of magnetic charge on the surface of a sphere of radius $R$, represented by a surface density

$$\sigma^* = \sigma_0^* \cos\theta \tag{5.33}$$

where $\sigma_0^*$ is a constant. By analogy with Eq. 3.66, the dipole moment of this distribution is related to $\sigma_0^*$ by

$$\mu_0 \boldsymbol{m} = \boldsymbol{i}_z \tfrac{4}{3}\pi R^3 \sigma_0^* \tag{5.34}$$

The constant $\mu_0$ appears on the left-hand side of this equation because, by tradition, the dimensions of the magnetic moment are not analogous to the dimensions of the electric moment. On the other hand, the dimensions of the magnetic charge have been made analogous to the dimensions of the electric charge by dividing the right-hand side of Eq. 5.29 by $\mu_0$.

The magnetic field produced by the charge distribution given by Eq. 5.33 is, by analogy with Eqs. 3.63 and 3.65,

$$\boldsymbol{H}_m = \frac{|\boldsymbol{m}|}{4\pi R^3} \begin{cases} (-1)(\boldsymbol{i}_r \cos\theta - \boldsymbol{i}_\theta \sin\theta) & r < R \\ \left(\dfrac{R}{r}\right)^3 (\boldsymbol{i}_r 2\cos\theta + \boldsymbol{i}_\theta \sin\theta) & r > R \end{cases} \tag{5.35}$$

We observe that this field is identical, outside the sphere of radius $R$, to that of the amperian-current model of magnetic dipole, given by Eq. 5.28. The field inside the sphere is uniform for both models and parallel to the $z$-axis. However, the field associated with the amperian-current model is in the direction of the $z$-axis, whereas the field associated with the magnetic-charge model is in the opposite direction. Furthermore, the magnitude of the former is twice that of the latter. Thus the integral over the entire space of their difference is

$$\oint (\boldsymbol{H}_a - \boldsymbol{H}_m)\, dv = \frac{\boldsymbol{m}}{4\pi R^3}[2 - (-1)]\frac{4}{3}\pi R^3 = \boldsymbol{m} \tag{5.36}$$

It can be shown with the help of Eqs. 2.122 and 2.126 that this result is independent of how electric currents and magnetic charges are distributed inside the sphere, as long as they produce the same magnetic field outside the sphere. In other words, it depends only on the fact that in one model the field is produced by electric currents, while in the other model it is produced by magnetic charges. This result will be used in Sec. 5.5 in connection with the distinction between the magnetic vectors $\boldsymbol{H}$ and $\boldsymbol{B}$.

## 5.4 The Macroscopic Model of Magnetized Matter

We mentioned in the preceding section that three of the four possible magnetization phenomena, namely, ferromagnetism, ferrimagnetism, and paramagnetism result from the magnetic moments of the electrons. Only diamagnetism, which is as yet of negligible engineering importance, results from the orbital motions of the electrons. Two possible models for the magnetic moment of an electron have been considered in the preceding section. One model was based on circulating electric currents, the other on magnetic charges. These two models cannot be distinguished by any external field measurement because, by assumption, they produce the same dipole field. We shall see in Chapter 7 that they cannot be distinguished either by external force measurements. Thus, in order to decide which model we must use in developing our macroscopic theory, we must look deeper into the theoretical consequences of the two possible choices and compare them with available experimental evidence. Unfortunately, however, the critical consequences that lead to the choice of the magnetic-charge model as opposed to the amperian-current model concern the flow, storage, and dissipation of energy which we are not ready to discuss at this time. Thus, to avoid having to develop our theory in two directions simultaneously, we shall postulate here the choice of the magnetic-charge model and defer to Chapter 7 any detailed discussion of the reasons for this choice.

It is desirable, nevertheless, to mention briefly at this point one disturbing characteristic of the macroscopic representation of magnetized matter that results from the amperian-current model of magnetic dipole. It can be shown [1, Sec. 7.11] that, if this model is postulated, the amperian currents associated with each electron give rise to a macroscopic current distribution of density

$$\boldsymbol{J}_m = \text{curl}\,\boldsymbol{M} \tag{5.37}$$

The vector $\boldsymbol{M}$ represents the macroscopic density of the magnetic moments of the electrons, evaluated over a suitably defined grain of matter; it is analogous to the vector $\boldsymbol{P}$ which represents the macroscopic density of the electric-dipole moments in polarized matter. Now, if we accept such a macroscopic representation of magnetized matter, we cannot avoid ascribing to the current associated with it all the properties that we usually ascribe to the current resulting from the motion of electric charges. In particular, if a steady current flow takes place in the presence of a static electric field, energy must be continuously supplied to the current by external forces wherever the current flows in a direction opposite to that of the electric field. Conversely, energy must be continuously dissipated locally or absorbed by external forces wherever the current flows in the direction of the electric field. Thus, for instance, if a permanent magnet is placed in a static electric field, energy must be continuously supplied by some parts of the magnet, and continuously absorbed by other parts. The presence of such a steady flow of energy is not supported by any experimental evidence; as a matter of fact, it can be reconciled with experimental evidence only by regarding it as a "virtual energy flow," i.e., by refusing to attach to it any physical significance.

If we accept the magnetic-charge model of magnetic dipole, the macroscopic representation of magnetized matter becomes entirely analogous to the macroscopic representation of polarized matter. The macroscopic density of magnetic moments is defined as the sum of the magnetic moments $\boldsymbol{m}_i$ within a grain of matter, divided by the volume of the grain,

$$\boldsymbol{M} = \frac{1}{V} \sum_i \boldsymbol{m}_i \tag{5.38}$$

The magnetic charges of the individual dipoles, when taken together, give rise to a distribution of magnetic charge. By analogy with Eq. 5.9, its macroscopic density is related to $\boldsymbol{M}$ by

$$\rho_m^* = -\operatorname{div} \mu_0 \boldsymbol{M} \tag{5.39}$$

Correspondingly, magnetic charge is present on any surface $\Sigma$ on which the normal component of $\boldsymbol{M}$ is discontinuous. By analogy with Eq. 5.15 we have for the surface density of this charge

$$\sigma_m^* = -(\mu_0 \boldsymbol{M}_1 - \mu_0 \boldsymbol{M}_2) \cdot \boldsymbol{n} \tag{5.40}$$

where $\boldsymbol{M}_1$ and $\boldsymbol{M}_2$ are the values assumed by $\boldsymbol{M}$ on opposite sides of $\Sigma$, and the unit vector $\boldsymbol{n}$ is normal to $\Sigma$ and directed from side 2 to side 1.

Magnetic currents, analogous to polarization currents are present whenever $\boldsymbol{M}$ varies with time. By analogy with Eq. 5.11, we have for the macroscopic magnetic-current density

$$\boldsymbol{J}_m^* = \mu_0 \frac{\partial \boldsymbol{M}}{\partial t} \tag{5.41}$$

This current density and the charge density given by Eq. 5.39 satisfy the conservation law

$$\operatorname{div} \boldsymbol{J}_m^* = \frac{\partial}{\partial t} \operatorname{div} \mu_0 \boldsymbol{M} = -\frac{\partial \rho_m^*}{\partial t} \tag{5.42}$$

which becomes, over a discontinuity surface,

$$(\boldsymbol{J}_{m1}^* - \boldsymbol{J}_{m2}^*) \cdot \boldsymbol{n} = \frac{\partial}{\partial t} (\mu_0 \boldsymbol{M}_1 - \mu_0 \boldsymbol{M}_2) \cdot \boldsymbol{n} = -\frac{\partial \sigma_m^*}{\partial t} \tag{5.43}$$

## 5.5 Macroscopic Maxwell's Equations in Matter

In Sec. 5.2 we recognized that polarization of matter leads to the presence of polarization charges and polarization currents. It is one of our basic assumptions that these charges and currents act upon the macroscopic electric and magnetic fields just like free charges and free currents. It is therefore easy to take the effects of polarization into account in Maxwell's equations. The free charge, which acts as a source of divergence of the electric field, has to be supplemented by the polarization charge; the free current, which acts as a source of curl of the magnetic field, must be supplemented by the polarization current. Starting with the integral form of Maxwell's equations, we have with the help of Eqs. 5.2 and 5.10

$$\oint_C \boldsymbol{H} \cdot d\boldsymbol{s} - \int_S \epsilon_0 \frac{\partial \boldsymbol{E}}{\partial t} \cdot \boldsymbol{n}\, da = \int_S \left( \boldsymbol{J}_f + \frac{\partial \boldsymbol{P}}{\partial t} \right) \cdot \boldsymbol{n}\, da \tag{5.44}$$

$$\oint_S \epsilon_0 \boldsymbol{E} \cdot \boldsymbol{n}\, da = \int_V \rho_f\, dv - \oint_S \boldsymbol{P} \cdot \boldsymbol{n}\, da \tag{5.45}$$

where $\rho_f$ represents the free-charge density and $\boldsymbol{J}_f$ represents the free-current density. The surface $S$ in Eq. 5.44 is, as usual, any two-sided surface bounded by the contour $C$, and the surface $S$ in Eq. 5.45 is the closed surface enclosing the volume $V$.

When discussing Maxwell's equations in free space, we did not make provisions for the presence of magnetic charges and magnetic currents, analogous to electric charges and currents, because there is no evidence in support of the existence of isolated magnetic charges. On the other hand, as pointed out in Sec. 5.3, it is not inconsistent with macroscopic experimental evidence to regard magnetic dipoles as neutral aggregates of magnetic charges, and to make provisions for such charges and for the magnetic currents resulting from their motion, by amending the free-space Maxwell's equations as indicated in Eqs. 5.29 and 5.30.

Gauss' law for magnetic fields becomes then

$$\oint_S \mu_0 \boldsymbol{H} \cdot \boldsymbol{n}\, da = \int_V \rho^* \, dv = Q^* \tag{5.46}$$

and can be taken as a definition of the magnetic charge $Q^*$ and of its density $\rho^*$. The magnetic-current density $\boldsymbol{J}^*$ is defined as the macroscopic density of the currents resulting from the motion of magnetic charges. It is related to the macroscopic charge density $\rho^*$ by the conservation law

$$\oint_S \boldsymbol{J}^* \cdot \boldsymbol{n}\, da = -\frac{dQ^*}{dt} = -\int_V \frac{\partial \rho^*}{\partial t} dv \tag{5.47}$$

Finally, mathematical consistency requires adding a magnetic-current term to the right-hand side of Faraday's induction law, which becomes then

$$\oint_C \boldsymbol{E} \cdot d\boldsymbol{s} + \int_S \mu_0 \frac{\partial \boldsymbol{H}}{\partial t} \cdot \boldsymbol{n}\, da = -\int_S \boldsymbol{J}^* \cdot \boldsymbol{n}\, da \tag{5.48}$$

We recognized in the preceding section, by analogy with polarized matter, that magnetized matter leads to the presence of macroscopic distributions of magnetic charge and of magnetic current, whose densities are related to the magnetic-moment density $\boldsymbol{M}$ by Eqs. 5.39 and 5.41. Substitution of these densities for $\rho^*$ and $\boldsymbol{J}^*$ in Eqs. 5.46 and 5.48 yields for the integral form of Maxwell's equations in magnetized matter

$$\oint_C \boldsymbol{E} \cdot d\boldsymbol{s} + \int_S \mu_0 \frac{\partial \boldsymbol{H}}{\partial t} \cdot \boldsymbol{n}\, da = -\int_S \mu_0 \frac{\partial \boldsymbol{M}}{\partial t} \cdot \boldsymbol{n}\, da \tag{5.49}$$

$$\oint_S \mu_0 \boldsymbol{H} \cdot \boldsymbol{n}\, da = -\oint_S \mu_0 \boldsymbol{M} \cdot \boldsymbol{n}\, da \tag{5.50}$$

These two equations together with Eqs. 5.44 and 5.45 are the laws governing the behavior of macroscopic electromagnetic fields in matter. The corresponding differential laws are derived from these integral laws, as in Sec. 3.1. We obtain

$$\text{curl}\, \boldsymbol{E} + \mu_0 \frac{\partial \boldsymbol{H}}{\partial t} = -\mu_0 \frac{\partial \boldsymbol{M}}{\partial t} = -\boldsymbol{J}_m{}^* \tag{5.51}$$

$$\text{curl}\, \boldsymbol{H} - \epsilon_0 \frac{\partial \boldsymbol{E}}{\partial t} = \boldsymbol{J}_f + \frac{\partial \boldsymbol{P}}{\partial t} = \boldsymbol{J}_f + \boldsymbol{J}_p \tag{5.52}$$

$$\text{div}\, \epsilon_0 \boldsymbol{E} = \rho_f - \text{div}\, \boldsymbol{P} = \rho_f + \rho_p \tag{5.53}$$

$$\text{div}\, \mu_0 \boldsymbol{H} = -\,\text{div}\, \mu_0 \boldsymbol{M} = \rho_m{}^* \tag{5.54}$$

The left-hand sides of these equations involve only field quantities, the right-hand sides only source quantities. Thus we may regard them as expressing the macroscopic electromagnetic field in terms of its sources, whether free or arising from polarized and magnetized matter.

There is another, purely formal, way of writing the macroscopic field laws, which often serves as the starting point of useful mathematical analogies. We note that $\boldsymbol{P}$ appears always together with $\epsilon_0\boldsymbol{E}$ and under the same differential operator. Similarly, $\mu_0\boldsymbol{M}$ appears always together with $\mu_0\boldsymbol{H}$ and under the same differential operator. It follows that the form of the field laws can be simplified by introducing the vectors

$$\boldsymbol{D} = \epsilon_0\boldsymbol{E} + \boldsymbol{P} \tag{5.55}$$

$$\boldsymbol{B} = \mu_0(\boldsymbol{H} + \boldsymbol{M}) \tag{5.56}$$

The vector $\boldsymbol{D}$ is referred to as the electric-flux density and also, somewhat misleadingly, as the electric displacement. The vector $\boldsymbol{B}$ is referred to as the magnetic-flux density, or the magnetic induction. With the aid of these two vectors, Eqs. 5.51, 5.52, 5.53, and 5.54 become

$$\text{curl}\ \boldsymbol{E} = -\frac{\partial \boldsymbol{B}}{\partial t} \tag{5.57}$$

$$\text{curl}\ \boldsymbol{H} = \boldsymbol{J}_f + \frac{\partial \boldsymbol{D}}{\partial t} \tag{5.58}$$

$$\text{div}\ \boldsymbol{D} = \rho_f \tag{5.59}$$

$$\text{div}\ \boldsymbol{B} = 0 \tag{5.60}$$

The striking feature of Eqs. 5.57 and 5.60 is their resemblance to Maxwell's equations in free space. Also, a symmetry is brought out between magnetic and electric fields in the absence of free charge and current. Often, one can take advantage of these resemblances and symmetries in forming analogies between fields in free space on one hand, and fields in matter on the other hand; or between field solutions involving magnetizable bodies and those involving polarizable bodies. The reason for the definition of the vectors $\boldsymbol{D}$ and $\boldsymbol{B}$ lies in the mathematical advantages gained through their use. In the macroscopic theory of electromagnetism discussed in this chapter, in which a clear separation is made between field vectors ($\boldsymbol{E}$, $\boldsymbol{H}$) and the source quantities ($\rho_f$, $\boldsymbol{J}_f$, $\boldsymbol{P}$, and $\boldsymbol{M}$), the vectors $\boldsymbol{D}$ and $\boldsymbol{B}$ have no basic physical significance. $\boldsymbol{D}$ and $\boldsymbol{B}$ are "mixed" vectors, being sums of field quantities and quantities characterizing the state of matter.

The macroscopic fields that appear on the left-hand sides of Eqs. 5.51, 5.52, 5.53, and 5.54 are the fields that would be produced by the macroscopic sources that appear on the right-hand sides of the same equations, in accordance with the free-space Maxwell's equations (amended to take into account magnetic charges and magnetic currents). The macroscopic sources were defined as averages of the microscopic sources over each grain of matter, with the intuitive expectation that the corresponding macroscopic fields could be interpreted similarly as average values of the microscopic fields. This is actually the case. We shall show below that, if the macroscopic sources and the macroscopic fields are defined independently, as suitable averages of the corresponding microscopic quantities, the macroscopic Maxwell's equations in the presence of matter follow directly from Maxwell's equations in free space.

Let us assume that the detailed microscopic distributions of field sources in matter as well as the corresponding microscopic fields are known (within the limitations imposed by quantum mechanics). We shall denote the microscopic fields by $\boldsymbol{e}$ and $\boldsymbol{h}$, to distinguish them from the corresponding macroscopic fields; the microscopic sources, on the other hand, will be indicated by the subscript $\mu$. The microscopic fields and the microscopic sources must satisfy the free-space Maxwell's equations, as amended to take into account magnetic charges and currents. A typical microscopic equation would be

$$\operatorname{div} \epsilon_0 \boldsymbol{e} = \rho_\mu \tag{5.61}$$

Now suppose that, at each point $(x_0, y_0, z_0)$, we average both sides of this equation by integrating them over a sphere centered at the point, and dividing by the volume of the sphere. If the size of the sphere is properly selected, the right-hand side of Eq. 5.61 becomes, by definition, the macroscopic density of free charges and polarization charges together, which can then be identified with $\rho_f + \rho_p$. The left-hand side involves the integral over a sphere of a sum of space derivatives. It can be shown that the process of integration can be interchanged, in this case, with the process of differentiation. Thus we obtain

$$\operatorname{div} \epsilon_0 \langle \boldsymbol{e} \rangle = \rho_f + \rho_p = \rho \tag{5.62}$$

where $\langle \boldsymbol{e} \rangle$ represents the average value of $\boldsymbol{e}$. It must be clearly understood that the values of $\langle \boldsymbol{e} \rangle$ and $\rho_f + \rho_p$ at any particular point are the averages $\boldsymbol{e}$ and $\rho_\mu$ over a sphere centered at that point; thus, whereas $\boldsymbol{e}$ and $\rho_\mu$ are functions of $x$, $y$, $z$, $\langle \boldsymbol{e} \rangle$ and $\rho_f + \rho_p$ are functions of $x_0$, $y_0$, $z_0$, the coordinates of the center of the sphere. Similarly, the divergence in Eq. 5.61 is evaluated with respect to $x$, $y$, $z$, and in Eq. 5.62 it is evaluated with respect to $x_0$, $y_0$, $z_0$.

The same averaging operation can be performed on the other free-space equations satisfied by the microscopic fields and the microscopic source densities. In each case, the microscopic source densities are transformed into the corresponding macroscopic source densities, and the microscopic field vectors, after interchanging differentiation with integration, are transformed into their average values $\langle \boldsymbol{e} \rangle$ and $\langle \boldsymbol{h} \rangle$. We obtain then

$$\text{curl}\, \langle \boldsymbol{e} \rangle + \mu_0 \frac{\partial \langle \boldsymbol{h} \rangle}{\partial t} = -\boldsymbol{J}^* \tag{5.63}$$

$$\text{curl}\, \langle \boldsymbol{h} \rangle - \epsilon_0 \frac{\partial \langle \boldsymbol{e} \rangle}{\partial t} = \boldsymbol{J} \tag{5.64}$$

$$\text{div}\, \mu_0 \langle \boldsymbol{h} \rangle = \rho^* \tag{5.65}$$

It is clear that, if we identify $\langle \boldsymbol{e} \rangle$ and $\langle \boldsymbol{h} \rangle$ with the macroscopic fields $\boldsymbol{E}$ and $\boldsymbol{H}$, Eqs. 5.62, 5.63, 5.64, and 5.65 become identical to Eqs. 5.51, 5.52, 5.53, 5.54.

It is interesting to note that the value of $\boldsymbol{h}$ as well as those of the macroscopic source distributions resulting from magnetized matter depend on whether the amperian-current model or the magnetic-charge model is used to represent magnetic dipoles. Indeed, if we denote the microscopic magnetic field corresponding to the amperian-current model by $\boldsymbol{h}_a$ and that corresponding to the magnetic-charge model by $\boldsymbol{h}_m$, we obtain from Eq. 5.36

$$\langle \boldsymbol{h}_a \rangle - \langle \boldsymbol{h}_m \rangle = \frac{1}{V} \sum_i \boldsymbol{m}_i = \boldsymbol{M} \tag{5.66}$$

where $V$ is the volume of the sphere used in the averaging process and the $\boldsymbol{m}_i$ are the moments of the magnetic dipoles inside the sphere. Thus, if we identify $\langle \boldsymbol{h}_m \rangle$ with the macroscopic $\boldsymbol{H}$ when the magnetic-charge model is used, the same averaging process must yield

$$\langle \boldsymbol{h}_a \rangle = \boldsymbol{H} + \boldsymbol{M} = \frac{\boldsymbol{B}}{\mu_0} \tag{5.67}$$

when the amperian-current model is used.

We are now in a position to relate the formulation of the macroscopic field laws presented in this text to the formulation based on the amperian-current model which is presented in most other texts. We stated in Sec. 5.4 that, when the amperian-current model is used, magnetized matter gives rise to a distribution of electric currents whose density $\boldsymbol{J}_m$ is related to the macroscopic moment density by Eq. 5.37. Of course, no magnetic-charge or magnetic-current distribution arises when this model is used. Thus the current density $\boldsymbol{J}_m$ must be included as part of $\boldsymbol{J}$ in Eq. 5.64, and $\rho^*$ and $\boldsymbol{J}^*$ must be set equal to zero. Then, if the average value of the microscopic magnetic field is identified with $\boldsymbol{B}/\mu_0$ as required by Eq. 5.67, we obtain from Eqs. 5.63, 5.64, and 5.65

$$\operatorname{curl} \boldsymbol{E} + \frac{\partial \boldsymbol{B}}{\partial t} = 0 \tag{5.68}$$

$$\operatorname{curl} \frac{\boldsymbol{B}}{\mu_0} - \epsilon_0 \frac{\partial \boldsymbol{E}}{\partial t} = \boldsymbol{J}_f + \frac{\partial \boldsymbol{P}}{\partial t} + \operatorname{curl} \boldsymbol{M} \tag{5.69}$$

$$\operatorname{div} \boldsymbol{B} = 0 \tag{5.70}$$

It can be readily checked that these equations reduce to Eqs. 5.51, 5.52, and 5.54 when $\boldsymbol{B}$ is expressed in terms of $\boldsymbol{H}$ and $\boldsymbol{M}$ with the help of Eq. 5.56. Thus the two formulations yield exactly the same macroscopic field laws, at least for stationary matter. It is shown in Appendix 1 that, in the presence of moving matter, the two formulations can be made to agree only by using different definitions for the macroscopic fields.

## 5.6 Boundary Conditions

We saw in Sec. 3.3 that, in the presence of a surface distribution of electric charge, the component of $\epsilon_0 \boldsymbol{E}$ normal to the surface suffers a discontinuity equal to the surface charge density. On the other hand, we saw in Sec. 5.2 that surface polarization charges are present on any surface at which the normal component of $\boldsymbol{P}$ is discontinuous. Since polarization charges are entirely equivalent to free charge with respect to the electric field, the surface charge density resulting from polarization must be included in Eq. 3.24, as part of $\sigma$. We obtain then from Eq. 5.15,

$$\epsilon_0(\boldsymbol{E}_1 - \boldsymbol{E}_2)\cdot\boldsymbol{n} = \sigma_f + \sigma_p = \sigma_f - (\boldsymbol{P}_1 - \boldsymbol{P}_2)\cdot\boldsymbol{n} \tag{5.71}$$

where the subscripts 1 and 2 correspond to the two sides of the surface, and the unit vector $\boldsymbol{n}$ is normal to the surface and directed from side 2 to side 1.

In Sec. 3.3 we did not contemplate a corresponding discontinuity of the normal component of $\boldsymbol{H}$ because the presence of magnetic charges was not taken into account in the free-space Maxwell's equations. Now, however, we know that surface distributions of magnetic charges as well as volume distributions can arise from magnetized matter. Since

Gauss' law for the magnetic field, expressed by Eq. 5.46 is analogous to Gauss' law for the electric field, we can write, directly from Eq. 5.71 and Eq. 5.40

$$\mu_0(\boldsymbol{H}_1 - \boldsymbol{H}_2)\cdot\boldsymbol{n} = \sigma_m{}^* = -\mu_0(\boldsymbol{M}_1 - \boldsymbol{M}_2)\cdot\boldsymbol{n} \tag{5.72}$$

Thus the magnetic field suffers a discontinuity equal in magnitude and opposite in sign to that suffered by the magnetization vector.

Let us turn our attention next to the surface discontinuities of the tangential components of $\boldsymbol{H}$ and $\boldsymbol{E}$. We saw in Sec. 3.3 that the tangential component of $\boldsymbol{H}$ suffers a discontinuity given by Eq. 3.31, in the presence of a surface current of density $\boldsymbol{K}$. If any surface polarization current were present, its density would have to be included in $\boldsymbol{K}$. Although no surface polarization currents can be present in stationary matter, we shall see in Chapter 9 that such currents may arise from the motion of polarized bodies. Similarly, surface magnetic currents can result only from the motion of magnetized bodies. Thus, Eqs. 3.28 and 3.31 are unaffected by the presence of stationary matter. These equations are repeated here for convenience of reference.

$$\boldsymbol{n} \times (\boldsymbol{E}_1 - \boldsymbol{E}_2) = 0 \tag{5.73}$$

$$\boldsymbol{n} \times (\boldsymbol{H}_1 - \boldsymbol{H}_2) = \boldsymbol{K}_f \tag{5.74}$$

We note that the discontinuity of the vector $\boldsymbol{P}$ appears in Eq. 5.71 together with the corresponding discontinuity of the vector $\epsilon_0\boldsymbol{E}$. Similarly, the discontinuity of $\boldsymbol{M}$ in Eq. 5.72 appears together with the discontinuity of the vector $\boldsymbol{H}$. Thus, again, we can simplify the form of these equations by expressing them in terms of the vectors $\boldsymbol{D}$ and $\boldsymbol{B}$, defined by Eqs. 5.55 and 5.56. We have

$$(\boldsymbol{D}_1 - \boldsymbol{D}_2)\cdot\boldsymbol{n} = \sigma_f \tag{5.75}$$

$$(\boldsymbol{B}_1 - \boldsymbol{B}_2)\cdot\boldsymbol{n} = 0 \tag{5.76}$$

Thus, we can conclude that the normal component of $\boldsymbol{B}$ is always continuous at the surface of any magnetized body, whereas the normal component of $\boldsymbol{D}$ is discontinuous at the surface of a polarized body only when free charge is distributed over the same surface. We shall see in the following sections how these boundary conditions are used in dealing with specific problems.

## 5.7 The Constituent Relations

The macroscopic field laws, developed in Sec. 5.5 express the curl and the divergence of $\boldsymbol{E}$ and $\boldsymbol{H}$ in terms of the time derivatives of the same vectors, on the one hand, and the source quantities $\rho_f$, $\boldsymbol{J}_f$, $\boldsymbol{P}$, and $\boldsymbol{M}$, on the other hand. These field laws, together with the associated boundary conditions discussed in Sec. 5.6 are sufficient to specify uniquely the fields when $\rho_f$, $\boldsymbol{J}_f$, $\boldsymbol{P}$, and $\boldsymbol{M}$ are given. In most physical problems, however, these source quantities are not known *a priori;* rather, they are themselves functions of the fields. Thus, the functional relation between these source quantities and the fields, often referred to as the *constituent relations,* must be known before the field can be determined.

The free current density $\boldsymbol{J}_f$ may depend on $\boldsymbol{E}$ and $\boldsymbol{H}$ in various ways. In material bodies, the case of a free current resulting from isotropic conduction is the most important. In this case, the current density is, at any given temperature, a single-valued function of the electric field of the form

$$\boldsymbol{J} = \sigma \boldsymbol{E} \tag{5.77}$$

where $\sigma$, the conductivity, is a parameter of the material that can be determined experimentally. In general, $\sigma$ may be a function of $|\boldsymbol{E}|$. In the special, but very common case, in which $\sigma$ is independent of $|\boldsymbol{E}|$, as in metals and in electrolytic solutions, $\boldsymbol{J}_f$ is simply proportional to $\boldsymbol{E}$, and the material is said to be linear. The free-charge density $\rho_f$ is related to $\boldsymbol{J}_f$ by the law of conservation of charge,

$$\frac{\partial \rho_f}{\partial t} = - \operatorname{div} \boldsymbol{J}_f \tag{5.78}$$

Thus, $\rho_f$ can always be expressed in terms of $\boldsymbol{J}_f$ and of its initial value.

Next, let us turn our attention to $\boldsymbol{P}$ and $\boldsymbol{M}$. The simplest situation occurs when $\boldsymbol{P}$ and $\boldsymbol{M}$ are vector functions of position, independent of the electromagnetic field, in which case they are equivalent to prescribed source distributions. This situation is approximated in practice by certain permanently magnetized and permanently polarized materials. The magnetization of high-quality permanent magnets is closely independent of the magnetic field inside the magnet over a reasonably large range of values. There are materials with analogous polarization properties. These materials, called ferroelectrics, are less well known than ferromagnetic materials, but they have found important application in the relative short time since their discovery.

When properly treated, their polarization is almost independent of the electric field inside the material.

A case of greater practical importance is that in which the magnetization $\boldsymbol{M}$ and the polarization $\boldsymbol{P}$ are functions of the field inside the material. The polarization $\boldsymbol{P}$, because of its electric origin, is then a function of the electric field inside the material; the magnetization $\boldsymbol{M}$ is a function of the magnetic field. Consider first, the process of electric polarization. In general, an applied electric field displaces the charge distribution due to the nuclei and that due to the electrons, with respect to each other. The spatial range of the forces that hold these charges together is of the order of interatomic distances. The range is, therefore, very small compared to the range of any macroscopic variation of the field. Consequently, the spatial variation of the macroscopic field can be neglected when considering its interaction with the charge distribution. We can conclude, therefore, that the polarization density $\boldsymbol{P}$ within matter must be a function of the point value of the macroscopic field only and should not depend upon its spatial derivatives. This is indeed observed experimentally. We may, therefore, write

$$\boldsymbol{P} = \boldsymbol{P}(\boldsymbol{E}) \tag{5.79}$$

This relation between the polarization and the electric field encompasses a great variety of physical situations. Here, we shall briefly classify the various functional dependences found experimentally. We shall concentrate then on the simplest special case, yet the one most often encountered in practice.

Although in all macroscopically homogeneous materials the polarization $\boldsymbol{P}$ of a particular grain is a function of the macroscopic field in the grain, the value of $\boldsymbol{P}$ at any particular instant of time is not necessarily uniquely determined by the value of $\boldsymbol{E}$ at the same instant of time. For instance, $\boldsymbol{P}$ may be a function of the value of $\boldsymbol{E}$ at previous times. An important phenomenon in which $\boldsymbol{P}$ in a grain is a function of the "history" of $\boldsymbol{E}$ in the same grain is known under the name of *hysteresis*. An example of hysteresis will be studied in greater detail after we have investigated the implications of isotropy in a material. Another important example of materials in which $\boldsymbol{P}$ is a function of the past values of $\boldsymbol{E}$ is provided by gyroelectric materials. In such materials, under proper biasing conditions, Eq. 5.79 assumes the form of a linear differential equation involving time derivatives. Finally, when $\boldsymbol{P}$ is independent of the past history of $\boldsymbol{E}$, it must be, by necessity, a single-valued function of $\boldsymbol{E}$, which assigns to each particular, instantaneous value of $\boldsymbol{E}$ a unique instantaneous value of $\boldsymbol{P}$.

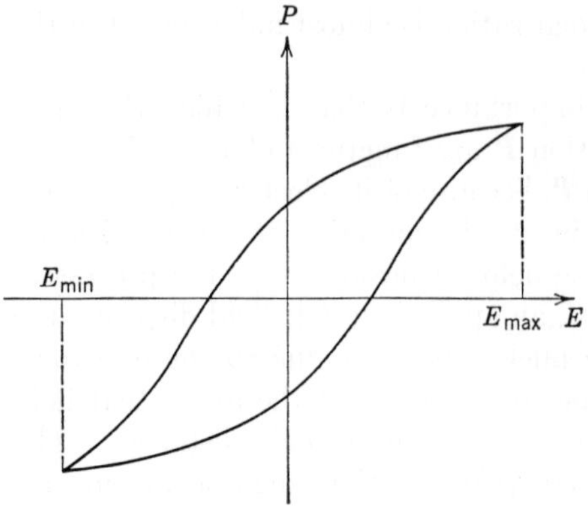


**Fig. 5.3.** Constituent relation exhibiting hysteresis.

All materials described above may be subdivided into two groups: isotropic and anisotropic. An isotropic material is one in which the relation between $\boldsymbol{P}$ and $\boldsymbol{E}$ is independent of the orientation of $\boldsymbol{E}$ relative to the material. In anisotropic materials, the orientations of $\boldsymbol{P}$ and $\boldsymbol{E}$ do not usually coincide. Such materials often possess anisotropic mechanical stress characteristics. Single crystals are examples of anisotropic materials. Isotropic materials can usually be characterized by a scalar relation, or graph, expressing the dependence of the magnitude of $\boldsymbol{P}$ upon the magnitude of $\boldsymbol{E}$ for one particular orientation of $\boldsymbol{E}$. This implies that the directions of $\boldsymbol{E}$ and $\boldsymbol{P}$ coincide. A graph for an isotropic material exhibiting hysteresis is shown in Fig. 5.3. In that figure it is assumed that the $\boldsymbol{E}$ field is a periodic function of time with only one maximum and one minimum of equal magnitudes and opposite signs. For different periodic variations different hysteresis curves have to be plotted. Clearly, the study of materials exhibiting hysteresis is not a simple one, and usually appropriate idealizations are intro-

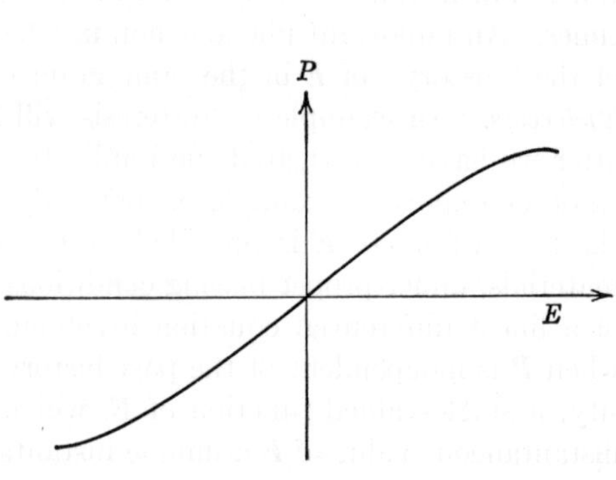


**Fig. 5.4.** Single-valued constituent relation.

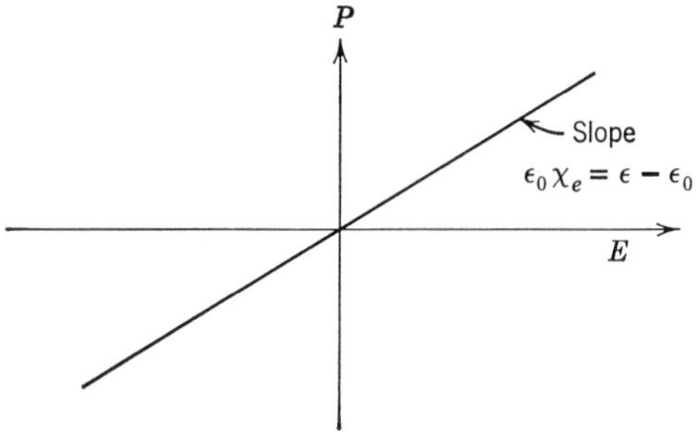


**Fig. 5.5.** Linear constituent relation.

duced to make an analysis of such cases possible. Figure 5.4 illustrates the behavior of a nonlinear isotropic material with a single-valued relation between $\boldsymbol{P}$ and $\boldsymbol{E}$.

The simplest material from the analytic point of view is the isotropic linear material. It is characterized by a straight-line relation between $\boldsymbol{P}$ and $\boldsymbol{E}$, as shown in Fig. 5.5. This straight-line relation is conveniently expressed analytically as

$$\boldsymbol{P} = \epsilon_0 \chi_e \boldsymbol{E} \tag{5.80}$$

where $\chi_e$ is the *electric susceptibility* of the material. A corresponding linear relation can be written for the electric flux density $\boldsymbol{D}$; combining Eqs. 5.55 and 5.80 yields

$$\boldsymbol{D} = \epsilon_0(1 + \chi_e)\boldsymbol{E} = \epsilon \boldsymbol{E} \tag{5.81}$$

where

$$\epsilon = \epsilon_0(1 + \chi_e) \tag{5.82}$$

The quantity $\epsilon$ is the *dielectric permittivity* (dielectric constant).

Magnetic materials can be categorized in an entirely analogous manner. Again, we can conclude from the model of interaction between macroscopic fields and the magnetic dipoles that the net magnetization $\boldsymbol{M}$ at a particular point in matter must be solely a function of the magnetic field at the same point and not of its spatial derivatives,

$$\boldsymbol{M} = \boldsymbol{M}(\boldsymbol{H}) \tag{5.83}$$

Again, materials for which the magnetization $\boldsymbol{M}$ depends upon the past history of the magnetization may exhibit hysteresis, or, they may be gyromagnetic materials. Again, one distinguishes isotropic and anisotropic materials. The graphs of Figs. 5.3, 5.4, and 5.5 can be taken to describe magnetic characteristics of isotropic magnetic materials by substituting $\boldsymbol{M}$ for $\boldsymbol{P}$ and $\boldsymbol{H}$ for $\boldsymbol{E}$. Linear isotropic materials can be represented by the simple relation

$$\boldsymbol{M} = \chi_m \boldsymbol{H} \tag{5.84}$$

where $\chi_m$ is the *magnetic susceptibility* of the material. A corresponding linear relation can be written for the magnetic flux density $\boldsymbol{B}$. Combining Eqs. 5.56 and 5.84 yields

$$\boldsymbol{B} = \mu_0(1 + \chi_m)\boldsymbol{H} = \mu \boldsymbol{H} \tag{5.85}$$

where

$$\mu = \mu_0(1 + \chi_m) \tag{5.86}$$

is the *permeability* of the material.

## 5.8 Example of a Field Produced by a Permanently Polarized Body

Let us consider the electric field produced by a permanently polarized sphere with a uniform constant polarization of magnitude $P_0$. The radius of the sphere is denoted by $R$.

The field is found by solving Maxwell's equations subject to the appropriate boundary conditions. Since there is no time dependence, Eqs. 5.51 and 5.53 reduce to

$$\text{curl } \boldsymbol{E} = 0 \tag{5.87}$$

$$\text{div } \epsilon_0 \boldsymbol{E} = -\text{ div } \boldsymbol{P} \tag{5.88}$$

and the other field equations do not concern us. Since the polarization is uniform inside the sphere and zero outside the sphere, we have,

$$\text{div } \boldsymbol{P} = 0 \tag{5.89}$$

both inside and outside. Thus, the only way the polarization can affect the field is through its discontinuity on the interface between the polarized sphere and the outside space.

Because of Eq. 5.87, the field is derivable from a scalar potential $\phi$, both inside and outside the sphere,

$$\boldsymbol{E} = -\text{ grad } \phi \tag{5.90}$$

Introducing this expression into Eq. 5.88 results in

$$\Delta\phi = 0 \tag{5.91}$$

both inside and outside the sphere. On the surface of the sphere, $\boldsymbol{E}$ must satisfy the boundary condition imposed by Eq. 5.71. The vector

$\boldsymbol{n}$ in this equation coincides in our case with the unit vector $\boldsymbol{i}_r$ of a system of spherical coordinates concentric with the polarized sphere. Taking the $z$-axis of the coordinate system in the direction of the polarization yields

$$\boldsymbol{P}_1 = 0 \qquad \boldsymbol{P}_2 = \boldsymbol{i}_z P_0 = (\boldsymbol{i}_r \cos\theta - \boldsymbol{i}_\theta \sin\theta)P_0 \tag{5.92}$$

where the subscript 1 refers to the space outside the sphere and the subscript 2 to the space inside the sphere. Thus, on the surface of the sphere,

$$\epsilon_0(E_{r1} - E_{r2}) = P_0 \cos\theta = \sigma_p \tag{5.93}$$

where $\sigma_p$ is the density of the surface polarization charge.

Equations 5.91 and 5.93 indicate that we are faced with a familiar problem. We must find solutions of Laplace's equations inside and outside the sphere for which the potential is continuous through the surface of the sphere while the normal component of the electric field has a prescribed discontinuity. Since the discontinuity is proportional to $\cos\theta$, we must look for solutions of Laplace's equations proportional to $\cos\theta$. There are two such solutions: the solution associated with the field of a dipole of moment parallel to the $z$-axis, and the solution associated with a uniform field also parallel to the $z$-axis. The first solution which is singular at the origin and vanishes at infinity can represent the field outside the sphere; the second solution can represent the field inside the sphere. When the condition stated by Eq. 5.93 is imposed on these two solutions, together with the requirement that the potential be continuous through the surface of the sphere, we obtain

$$\boldsymbol{E} = \frac{P_0}{3\epsilon_0}\begin{cases}(-\boldsymbol{i}_r \cos\theta + \boldsymbol{i}_\theta \sin\theta) & r < R \\ \left(\dfrac{R}{r}\right)^3 (\boldsymbol{i}_r 2\cos\theta + \boldsymbol{i}_\theta \sin\theta) & r > R\end{cases} \tag{5.94}$$

This is exactly the type of field discussed in Sec. 3.5 and illustrated in Fig. 3.5. Comparison of Eq. 5.94 with Eqs. 3.63 and 3.65 indicates that the magnitude of the dipole moment associated with the field is related to $P_0$ by

$$p = \tfrac{4}{3}\pi R^3 P_0 \tag{5.95}$$

Thus, the dipole moment of the field is equal to the total dipole moment of the polarized sphere, as expected.

## 5.9 Fields in Linear Dielectric and Magnetic Materials

The special case of linear dielectric and magnetic materials is of particular importance because the constituent relations of many materials of practical interest are closely linear. Furthermore, very often we are forced to assume that such relations are linear, even if they are actually appreciably nonlinear, in order to keep the mathematical complexity of a problem from becoming unmanageable.

When the linear constituent relations given by Eqs. 5.81 and 5.85 are introduced in the macroscopic field laws, the latter assume the simpler form

$$\text{curl}\, \boldsymbol{E} = -\mu \frac{\partial \boldsymbol{H}}{\partial t} \tag{5.96}$$

$$\text{curl}\, \boldsymbol{H} = \boldsymbol{J}_f + \epsilon \frac{\partial \boldsymbol{E}}{\partial t} \tag{5.97}$$

$$\text{div}\, \epsilon \boldsymbol{E} = \rho_f \tag{5.98}$$

$$\text{div}\, \mu \boldsymbol{H} = 0 \tag{5.99}$$

These equations are identical to the free-space equations except for the fact that $\epsilon$ has been substituted for $\epsilon_0$ and $\mu$ for $\mu_0$. It must be remembered, on the other hand, that $\epsilon$ and $\mu$ may still be functions of position, although they are, by assumption, independent of time and of the electromagnetic field. In particular, $\epsilon$ and $\mu$ are, in general, discontinuous at any surface at which the material changes abruptly. At any such surface, the tangential components of the fields must be continuous in the absence of surface currents, as required by Eqs. 5.73 and 5.74. However, their normal components may be discontinuous; we obtain from Eqs. 5.75 and 5.76 the boundary conditions

$$(\epsilon_1 \boldsymbol{E}_1 - \epsilon_2 \boldsymbol{E}_2) \cdot \boldsymbol{n} = \sigma_f \tag{5.100}$$

$$(\mu_1 \boldsymbol{H}_1 - \mu_2 \boldsymbol{H}_2) \cdot \boldsymbol{n} = 0 \tag{5.101}$$

where the subscript 1 is attached to a quantity measured on one side of the surface, and the subscript 2 indicates a quantity measured at the corresponding point on the opposite side of the surface; the unit vector $\boldsymbol{n}$ is directed from side 2 to side 1.

If the material is homogeneous, as well as linear, it is important to note that the problem of solving the macroscopic field equations becomes mathematically identical to the problem of solving the free-space equations. Thus, in particular, the methods developed in Chapter 4 are applicable to static fields in homogeneous, linear materials. It is interesting to note also that no magnetic charges can be present within a linear, homogeneous magnetic material, and no polarization charges can be present within a linear, homogeneous dielectric material unless free charges are also present. In fact, in such cases we obtain from Eq. 5.99

$$\rho_m{}^* = -\operatorname{div} \mu_0 \boldsymbol{M} = -\operatorname{div} (\mu - \mu_0)\boldsymbol{H}$$
$$= -\left(1 - \frac{\mu_0}{\mu}\right) \operatorname{div} \mu \boldsymbol{H} = 0 \tag{5.102}$$

and from Eq. 5.98

$$\rho_p = -\operatorname{div} \boldsymbol{P} = -\operatorname{div} (\epsilon - \epsilon_0)\boldsymbol{E}$$
$$= -\left(1 - \frac{\epsilon_0}{\epsilon}\right) \operatorname{div} \epsilon \boldsymbol{E} = -\rho_f \left(1 - \frac{\epsilon_0}{\epsilon}\right) \tag{5.103}$$

Of course, magnetic charges and polarization charges may be present on the boundaries between homogeneous materials with different values of $\epsilon$ and $\mu$.

The boundary conditions expressed by Eqs. 5.100 and 5.101, together with those expressed by Eqs. 5.73 and 5.74, have an interesting geometric interpretation concerning the changes of direction suffered by $\boldsymbol{E}$ and $\boldsymbol{H}$ in passing through a surface free of charges and currents. With reference to Fig. 5.6, let $\theta_1$ and $\theta_2$ be the angles between the normal to the surface and the vectors $\boldsymbol{E}_1$ and $\boldsymbol{E}_2$ representing the values of $\boldsymbol{E}$ on the two sides of the surface. If we indicate the tangential and normal components with the subscripts $t$ and $n$, we have

$$\tan \theta_1 = \frac{E_{1t}}{E_{1n}} \tag{5.104}$$

$$\tan \theta_2 = \frac{E_{2t}}{E_{2n}} \tag{5.105}$$

On the other hand, we have, from Eqs. 5.73 and 5.100,

$$E_{1t} = E_{2t} \tag{5.106}$$

$$\epsilon_1 E_{1n} = \epsilon_2 E_{2n} \tag{5.107}$$

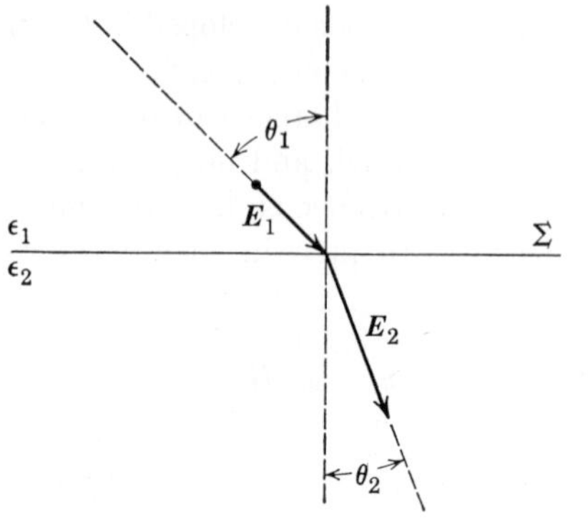


**Fig. 5.6.** Refraction of the electric field at the boundary between different materials.

where $\epsilon_1$ and $\epsilon_2$ are the values of the permittivity on the two sides of the surface. It follows that

$$\frac{\tan \theta_1}{\tan \theta_2} = \frac{\epsilon_1}{\epsilon_2} \tag{5.108}$$

This is the well-known law of refraction of the electric field at the boundary between different dielectric media. The same analysis can be carried out for $\boldsymbol{H}$ with the help of Eqs. 5.74 and 5.101. With the angles $\theta_1$ and $\theta_2$ defined in a similar manner, we obtain

$$\frac{\tan \theta_1}{\tan \theta_2} = \frac{\mu_1}{\mu_2} \tag{5.109}$$

where $\mu_1$ and $\mu_2$ are the permeabilities of the materials on the two sides of the surface.

As an illustration of how the methods developed in Chapter 4 can be applied to static fields in linear, homogeneous materials, we shall discuss the problem of a circular, dielectric rod of infinite length immersed in a uniform static electric field normal to its axis. Because of the symmetry of the problem, it is convenient to represent the field in circular-cylindrical coordinates, with the $z$-axis coinciding with the axis of the rod. Thus, we are in effect dealing with a two-dimensional problem in polar coordinates.

Since $\epsilon$ is constant within the rod, and no free charges are present, we have from Eq. 5.98

$$\operatorname{div} \boldsymbol{E} = 0 \tag{5.110}$$

both inside and outside the rod. It follows that the potential associated with the electric field must satisfy Laplace's equation everywhere except on the surface of the rod and, therefore, it must be expressible as a linear combination of the solutions found in Sec. 4.8, both inside and outside the rod.

Since the field was uniform before the rod was immersed in it, the potential associated with the field outside the rod must include a component representing the original uniform field and a component representing the field produced by the polarization of the rod. Let the angular coordinate $\varphi$ be measured from the direction of the uniform field. Then the potential associated with the uniform field becomes

$$\phi_0 = -E_0 r \cos \varphi \tag{5.111}$$

where $E_0$ is the intensity of the field. On the other hand, this potential in conjunction with the potentials produced inside the rod and outside the rod by its polarization must satisfy boundary conditions on the surface of the rod. It follows that only solutions of Laplace's equations proportional to $\cos \varphi$ can be involved.

We saw in Sec. 4.8 that the only solution proportional to $\cos \varphi$, besides that representing a uniform field, is the one representing the field of a dipole and given by

$$\phi_1 = \frac{A}{r} \cos \varphi \tag{5.112}$$

where $A$ is a constant. Thus, the potential outside the rod must be of the form

$$\phi = \left( -E_0 r + \frac{A}{r} \right) \cos \varphi \qquad r > a \tag{5.113}$$

where $a$ is the radius of the rod. Furthermore, since the dipole field is singular at the origin, the potential inside the sphere cannot include a dipole component. Therefore it must be of the form

$$\phi = Br \cos \varphi \qquad r < a \tag{5.114}$$

where $B$ is a constant to be determined.

The requirement that the tangential component of the field be continuous through the surface of the rod implies that the potential must be continuous. Equating the potentials given by Eqs. 5.113 and 5.114 for $r = a$ yields

$$-E_0 a + \frac{A}{a} = Ba \tag{5.115}$$

which reduces to

$$A = a^2(E_0 + B) \tag{5.116}$$

On the other hand, the normal components of the electric fields on the two sides of the surface of the rod, obtained by differentiating

Eqs. 5.113 and 5.114 with respect to $r$, must satisfy Eq. 5.100. We have

$$\epsilon_0 \left( E_0 + \frac{A}{a^2} \right) + \epsilon B = 0 \tag{5.117}$$

which reduces to

$$\epsilon_0 A = -a^2(\epsilon_0 E_0 + \epsilon B) \tag{5.118}$$

Finally, solving Eqs. 5.116 and 5.118 yields

$$A = a^2 E_0 \frac{\epsilon - \epsilon_0}{\epsilon + \epsilon_0} \tag{5.119}$$

$$B = -E_0 \frac{2\epsilon_0}{\epsilon + \epsilon_0} \tag{5.120}$$

Thus,

$$\phi = -E_0 \cos \varphi \begin{cases} \dfrac{2\epsilon_0 r}{\epsilon + \epsilon_0} & r < a \\ \left( r - a^2 \dfrac{\epsilon - \epsilon_0}{\epsilon + \epsilon_0} \dfrac{1}{r} \right) & r > a \end{cases} \tag{5.121}$$

and

$$\boldsymbol{E} = -\operatorname{grad} \phi = E_0 \begin{cases} \dfrac{2\epsilon_0}{\epsilon + \epsilon_0} (\boldsymbol{i}_r \cos \varphi - \boldsymbol{i}_\varphi \sin \varphi) & r < a \\ \boldsymbol{i}_r \left[ 1 + \dfrac{\epsilon - \epsilon_0}{\epsilon + \epsilon_0} \left( \dfrac{a}{r} \right)^2 \right] \cos \varphi & \\ -\boldsymbol{i}_\varphi \left[ 1 - \dfrac{\epsilon - \epsilon_0}{\epsilon + \epsilon_0} \left( \dfrac{a}{r} \right)^2 \right] \sin \varphi & r > a \end{cases} \tag{5.122}$$

The lines of force of the electric field and the traces of the equipotential surfaces are illustrated in Fig. 5.7.

The polarization in the rod is uniform and parallel to the electric field; its magnitude is given by

$$|\boldsymbol{P}| = (\epsilon - \epsilon_0)|\boldsymbol{E}| = 2\epsilon_0 E_0 \frac{\epsilon - \epsilon_0}{\epsilon + \epsilon_0} \tag{5.123}$$

and the density of the polarization charge on the surface of the rod is

$$\sigma_p = \boldsymbol{i}_r \cdot \boldsymbol{P} = 2\epsilon_0 E_0 \frac{\epsilon - \epsilon_0}{\epsilon + \epsilon_0} \cos \varphi \tag{5.124}$$

It is interesting to study how these results vary with the permittivity of the rod. For $\epsilon = \epsilon_0$, the dipole component of the field outside the rod vanishes, and the intensity of the uniform field inside the rod becomes equal to that of the uniform field outside the rod. This, of

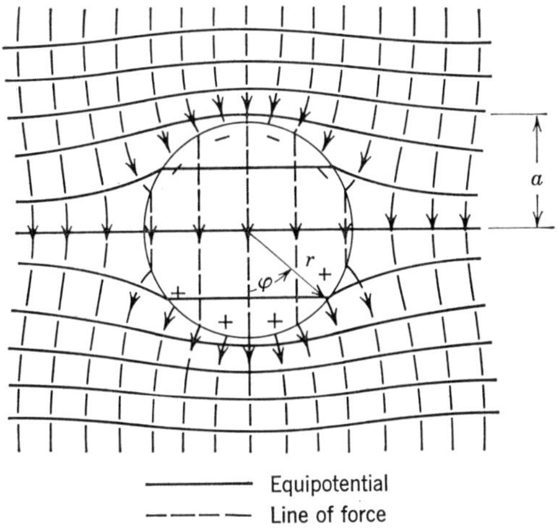


**Fig. 5.7.** A dielectric rod in a uniform electric field.

course, should be expected because, in this case, the rod is made of nonpolarizable material. For $\epsilon > \epsilon_0$, the electric field inside the rod is always weaker than the original uniform field. This can be attributed to the shielding effect of the polarization charge that accumulates on the surface of the rod; in fact, the charge polarity is such as to intercept some of the external field lines, thereby preventing them from entering the rod, as shown in Fig. 5.7. The higher the permittivity of the rod, the more the lines of force converge toward the rod. In the limit of infinite permittivity, the lines of force become normal to the surface of the rod and the electric field inside the rod vanishes completely. Accordingly, the electric field becomes the same as the field that would exist if the dielectric rod were replaced by a conducting rod. In general, a material with an infinite permittivity acts upon an external static electric field as if it were a conductor; this fact is often the basis of helpful analogies.

## 5.10 Magnetic Circuits

Many magnetic systems of practical interest consist of ferromagnetic cores around which are wound current-carrying wires. Electromagnets, transformers, and rotating machines are typical examples. Because of the wide use of such magnetic systems, their analysis is of great practical importance. The analysis is also of theoretical interest since it provides an example of the use of analogies in the solution of field problems.

We shall start with a study of the static magnetic field produced by a single turn of a current-carrying wire in a medium of permeability $\mu$. The permeability may be a function of position with discontinuities over a finite number of surfaces. A simple example, shown in Fig. 5.8, consists of a magnetic ring of constant permeability $\mu$ surrounded by air and interrupted by an air gap (permeability $\mu_0$). The turn of wire around the core carries a direct current $I_s$ and may be regarded as a current filament of negligibly small cross section. The equations pertinent to such a system are

$$\text{curl}\, \boldsymbol{H} = \boldsymbol{J} \tag{5.125}$$

$$\text{div}\, \boldsymbol{B} = 0 \tag{5.126}$$

$$\boldsymbol{B} = \mu \boldsymbol{H} \tag{5.127}$$

In addition, the following boundary conditions must be satisfied on all surfaces at which the permeability is discontinuous

$$\boldsymbol{n} \times (\boldsymbol{H}_1 - \boldsymbol{H}_2) = 0 \tag{5.128}$$

$$\boldsymbol{n} \cdot (\boldsymbol{B}_1 - \boldsymbol{B}_2) = 0 \tag{5.129}$$

In Eq. 5.128 we have assumed that no surface currents are present.

The current density $\boldsymbol{J}$ on the right-hand side of Eq. 5.125 is zero throughout the entire space except within the wire. Therefore, $\boldsymbol{H}$ can be expressed as the negative gradient of a scalar potential at all points outside the region occupied by the wire.

$$\boldsymbol{H} = -\,\text{grad}\, \phi \tag{5.130}$$

The definition of the potential $\phi$ encounters certain difficulties to which we now turn. It follows from Eq. 5.125 and Stokes' theorem that the line integral of the magnetic field over any closed path that does not encircle the wire is equal to zero. This is the very fact that enables us to express $\boldsymbol{H}$ as the gradient of a scalar potential. On the other hand, the line integral of $\boldsymbol{H}$ over a closed path that does encircle the wire, as shown in Fig. 5.8, is not equal to zero, but is equal to the current $I_s$ carried by the wire. This argument shows that, although $\boldsymbol{H}$ can be written as the gradient of a scalar potential in the space free of current, this potential is not single-valued. If the point of observation is moved around a closed path linking the wire, the potential will increase (or decrease) by $I_s$ each time the point completes a turn around

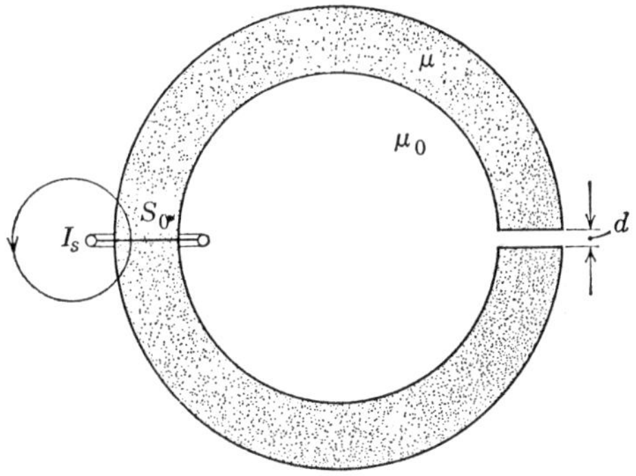


**Fig. 5.8.** Magnetic circuit excited by current loop.

the closed path. Thus, the potential at each point on the path can assume an infinite number of values which differ from one another by an integral multiple of $I_s$.

To resolve the difficulty associated with the multiple-valuedness of the potential, it is helpful to introduce the geometric concept of a simply connected region. A region of space $V$, enclosed by a surface $S$, is said to be simply connected when all closed paths within the region can be shrunk to a point by a continuous deformation process without ever cutting through the surface $S$. A region of space that does not satisfy the above requirement is said to be multiply connected. For instance, the space inside a doughnut-shaped surface is a multiply connected region.

We shall now interpret the multiple-valuedness of the potential in the present problem in the light of the concept of a multiply connected region. Let us study the nature of the region of space within which the curl of $\boldsymbol{H}$ vanishes. This region includes the whole space except the region occupied by the current-carrying wire. It is obvious that a closed path linking the wire cannot be shrunk to a point without cutting through the wire, i.e., without leaving the space within which the curl of $\boldsymbol{H}$ is equal to zero. Accordingly, the region where curl $\boldsymbol{H}$ is equal to zero is multiply connected. This very fact accounts for the multiple-valuedness of the potential associated with $\boldsymbol{H}$.

The space external to the wire can be made simply connected through the artifice of cutting the region of space within which curl $\boldsymbol{H} = 0$ by means of a surface bounded by the wire and indicated by $S_0$ in Fig. 5.8. If we divide the space in this manner, thereby preventing any path of integration from passing through $S_0$, the region thus defined is simply connected. It is clear that within this newly defined region the potential must be single-valued. It is, also, clear that the potential suffers

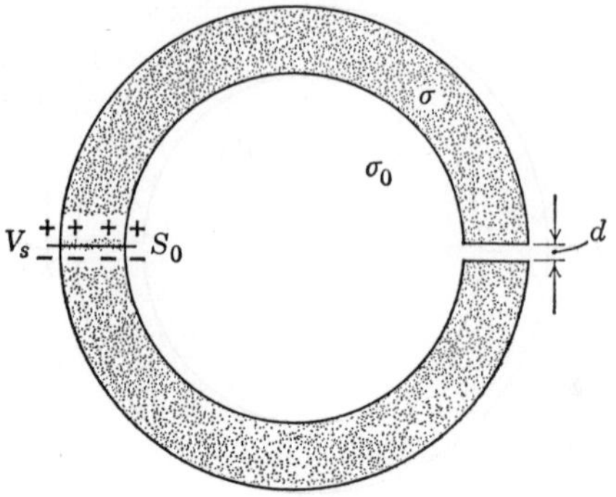


**Fig. 5.9.** Electric circuit analogous to the magnetic circuit of Fig. 5.8.

a discontinuity equal to $I_s$ over the artificial surface $S_0$. We must keep in mind that $S_0$ is chosen arbitrarily except for the fact that it must be bounded by the wire, and that the potential difference between the two sides of the surface has no direct physical significance. However, this potential difference serves as a guide in constructing a useful analog for our magnetic problem.

We shall now turn to the construction of the analog. Consider the structure shown in Fig. 5.9. It consists of a conducting ring of conductivity $\sigma$ surrounded by a medium of conductivity $\sigma_0$ that also extends into the gap of the ring. The geometry of the conducting ring is identical to that of the magnetic ring shown in Fig. 5.8. The ring is cut over the surface $S_0$, as indicated in Fig. 5.9, and an ideal voltage source is inserted in the resulting infinitesimal gap. The equations pertinent to this conduction problem are

$$\text{curl } \boldsymbol{E} = 0 \tag{5.131}$$

$$\text{div } \boldsymbol{J} = 0 \tag{5.132}$$

$$\boldsymbol{J} = \sigma \boldsymbol{E} \tag{5.133}$$

Furthermore, the following boundary conditions must be satisfied over the surface separating the two conducting media.

$$\boldsymbol{n} \times (\boldsymbol{E}_1 - \boldsymbol{E}_2) = 0 \tag{5.134}$$

and

$$\boldsymbol{n} \cdot (\boldsymbol{J}_1 - \boldsymbol{J}_2) = 0 \tag{5.135}$$

It is obvious at a glance that Eqs. 5.125 through 5.129 become identical to Eqs. 5.131 through 5.135, when $\boldsymbol{E}$, $\boldsymbol{J}$, and $\sigma$ are substituted for $\boldsymbol{H}$, $\boldsymbol{B}$, and $\mu$. We further note that the electric field in Eq. 5.131 can be expressed as the negative gradient of a scalar potential that experiences a discontinuity of magnitude $V_s$ on the surface $S_0$ where the ideal voltage source is located. We conclude that the equations and boundary conditions pertinent to the current flow problem are identical with those pertinent to the magnetic problem, except in the region occupied by the current-carrying wire in the magnetic problem which, however, is very small by assumption. Accordingly, both problems must lead to mathematically identical solutions. To facilitate the transformation from one problem to the other, we summarize the analogies in Table 5.1. The analogy developed above brings our ex-

**TABLE 5.1. Analogies**

| Magnetostatic Problem | | Conduction Problem | |
|---|---|---|---|
| Magnetic field | $\boldsymbol{H}$ | Electric field | $\boldsymbol{E}$ |
| Magnetic-flux density | $\boldsymbol{B}$ | Current density | $\mathbf{J}$ |
| Permeability | $\mu$ | Conductivity | $\sigma$ |
| Magnetic potential | $\phi$ | Electric potential | $\phi$ |
| Loop current | $I_s$ | Source voltage | $V_s$ |

perience with conduction problems to bear directly on the less familiar magnetostatic problems. There is another circumstance which makes this analogy very useful. Magnetic materials usually employed in magnetic systems have a permeability that is very much larger (by a factor of 1000 or more) than that of the surrounding space (air). This implies for the conduction analog that the conductivity must be higher in the region where the permeability is high in the magnetic system and correspondingly small in the surrounding space. On the other hand, in problems involving current flow in highly conducting media surrounded by media of low conductivity, it is often possible to find simple approximate solutions. Thus, for instance, let us consider the conducting ring of Fig. 5.9, which is analogous to the magnetostatic system of Fig. 5.8. Because of the high conductivity of the ring, the current flows mainly within the ring except in the very neighborhood of the gap. Further, if the average length $l$ of the ring is much larger than its thickness, and if its cross-sectional area $A$ is constant, the current distribution within the ring is essentially uniform. Finally, if the length $d$ of the gap is small, the current density in the gap is essentially uniform, except for fringing near the edges of the gap. To a first approximation we may neglect the fringing and assume that the current distribution is also uniform in the gap. Under these conditions, the net current forced through the ring by the voltage source can be readily computed. We can then treat the ring and the air gap as a *circuit problem* involving a series connection of a resistor representing the resistance of the ring, and a resistor representing the resistance of the air gap. We have

$$I = \frac{V_s}{R} \tag{5.136}$$

where the resistance $R$ is found in the usual way as the sum of the resistances of the ring and of the gap,

$$R = \frac{l}{\sigma A} + \frac{d}{\sigma_0 A} \tag{5.137}$$

Finally, the magnitude of the current density in the gap and in the ring is equal to $I$ divided by the cross-sectional area of the ring

$$J = \frac{V_s}{AR} \tag{5.138}$$

This result can be translated directly into the corresponding result for the magnetostatic problem. For this purpose, it is only necessary to add a few more entries to Table 5.1. (See Table 5.2.)

**TABLE 5.2**

| Magnetostatic Problem | Conduction Problem |
|---|---|
| $\Phi = \int \boldsymbol{B} \cdot \boldsymbol{n}\, da$ | $I = \int \boldsymbol{J} \cdot \boldsymbol{n}\, da$ |
| $\Phi = \dfrac{\mathfrak{F}}{\mathfrak{R}}$ | $I = \dfrac{V_s}{R}$ |
| $\mathfrak{R} = \dfrac{l}{\mu A} + \dfrac{d}{\mu_0 A}$ | $R = \dfrac{l}{\sigma A} + \dfrac{d}{\sigma_0 A}$ |

We note, first of all, that the current $I$ given by Eq. 5.136 is the surface integral of the current density over the cross section of the ring. The magnetic analog of the current density $\boldsymbol{J}$ is the magnetic-flux density $\boldsymbol{B}$, the analog of the conduction current $I$ is the magnetic flux $\Phi$. The name "magnetic circuit" is used to denote the system shown in Fig. 5.8 because of the analogy with the electric circuit. We refer to the quantity $\mathfrak{R}$ as the "reluctance" of the magnetic circuit; it is analogous to the resistance $R$ of the corresponding electric circuit. The analogy between the source voltage $V_s$ (the electromotive force) in the conduction problem, and the winding current $I_s$ in the magnetic problem is often emphasized by referring to the latter as the "magnetomotive force" indicated by the symbol $\mathfrak{F}$. Thus, in Table 5.2

$$\mathfrak{F} = I_s \tag{5.139}$$

So far we have been concerned only with magnetostatic systems involving a single turn of wire that could be regarded as a current filament of negligibly small cross section. We saw that such a current filament is equivalent, as a field source, to a discontinuity of the magnetic potential across an arbitrarily selected surface bounded by the filament. This discontinuity could then be visualized, in the analogous conduction problem, as an ideal voltage source maintaining a fixed potential difference between points on opposite sides of the surface. It must be stressed that the equivalence between the potential discontinuity and the closed current filament and the analogy between the potential discontinuity and the ideal voltage source do not depend on the relative permeability of the magnetic material, and hold as well for a current filament in free space. The assumption of a high relative permeability was used only in obtaining a solution for the field.

In practice, however, magnetic circuits are excited by coils consisting of many turns of wire with small but nonnegligible cross section. We shall show that such a coil still can be regarded as approximately equivalent to a potential discontinuity, provided the relative permeability of the magnetic circuit is large, and the air gap in the circuit is small compared with the cross-sectional dimensions. Let us assume that the coil is wound of thin wire so as to be essentially a current filament of negligibly small cross section. Then, the fact that the coil consists of $N$ turns simply means that the surface $S_0$ bounded by the filament must cut the magnetic circuit $N$ times instead of just once. Thus, there are $N$ discontinuities of magnetic potential along the magnetic circuit, each of magnitude $I_s$. In the analogous electric circuit there will be $N$ identical voltage sources of magnitude $V_s$ inserted at $N$ different cross sections of the conducting ring. Now, if the conductivity of the ring is much greater than the conductivity of the surrounding medium, it does not make much difference where the voltage sources are inserted; they can be lumped together into a single voltage source of magnitude $NV_s$. Analogously, the $N$ discontinuities of the magnetic potential can be lumped together into a single discontinuity of magnitude $NI_s$, representing the total magnetomotive force in the circuit. Thus, the presence of $N$ turns instead of just one requires only using for the magnetomotive force in Table 5.2 the value

$$\mathfrak{F} = NI_s \tag{5.140}$$

instead of the value given by Eq. 5.139. Finally, the fact that the wire forming the coil has a nonnegligible cross section does not matter if we are interested only in the magnetic field within the magnetic ring and in the air gap. In fact, under the assumed conditions, this field depends, for all practical purposes, only on the characteristics of the magnetic circuit and on the total magnetomotive force provided by the coil.

The preceding analysis can be extended with minor modifications to magnetic systems involving permanent magnets instead of exciting coils. Any magnetic material whose characteristics exhibit an hysteresis loop, as illustrated in Fig. 5.10, can be permanently magnetized by subjecting it temporarily to the action of an external magnetic field. When the external exciting field is removed, the position assumed on the hysteresis loop by the point representing the state of the material depends on the magnetic field produced by the magnetization, and, therefore on the geometry of the entire magnetic system.

Let us consider first a homogeneous magnetic ring, similar to that shown in Fig. 5.8, but without any air gap. Let us suppose, further, that the ring has been permanently magnetized by sending a current through an exciting coil for a brief period. Because of the circular symmetry of the system, the lines of $\boldsymbol{M}$ and those of $\boldsymbol{H}$ will form circles concentric with the ring and their magnitudes must be constant over such circles. Furthermore, because of the absence of any exciting current, the line integral of $\boldsymbol{H}$ over any closed path must be equal to zero. It follows that $\boldsymbol{H}$ must be equal to zero everywhere, and that, within the ring,

$$\boldsymbol{B} = \mu_0 \boldsymbol{M}_0 \tag{5.141}$$

where the magnitude of $\boldsymbol{M}_0$ is the value assumed by the magnetization for $H = 0$ in Fig. 5.10, at the point indicated with an ×. Thus, for this particular geometry, the material is permanently magnetized but no magnetic field results from the magnetization.

Next, let us reintroduce the air gap shown in Fig. 5.8, and assume again that the ring has been permanently magnetized by sending a current through the exciting coil for a brief period. Now, because of the presence of the air gap, the system has no longer a circular symmetry, and a magnetic field will be present both inside and outside the ring. In order to determine it, we shall assume that its magnitude is sufficiently small so that the hysteresis loop of Fig. 5.10 can be approximated in the neighborhood of $M = M_0$ by the tangent to the loop. In other words, we assume that

$$\boldsymbol{M} = \boldsymbol{M}_0 + \left(\frac{\mu_i}{\mu_0} - 1\right)\boldsymbol{H} \tag{5.142}$$

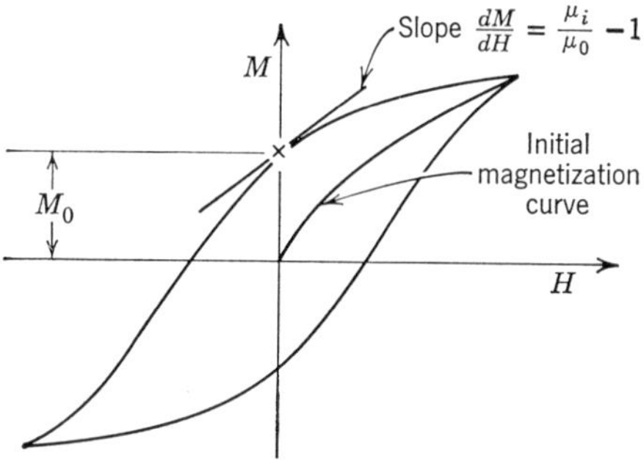


**Fig. 5.10.** Hysteresis loop.

The slope of the tangent is equal to $(\mu_i/\mu_0) - 1$, where $\mu_i$ is the incremental permeability of the permanently magnetized material. Correspondingly

$$\boldsymbol{B} = \mu_0(\boldsymbol{M} + \boldsymbol{H}) = \mu_0\boldsymbol{M}_0 + \mu_i\boldsymbol{H} \tag{5.143}$$

It is again convenient to relate the present magnetic problem to an analogous conduction problem. The same fundamental equations and the same boundary conditions apply as before. However, $\boldsymbol{B}$ as given by Eq. 5.143, although still linearly related to $\boldsymbol{H}$, contains an additional term independent of $\boldsymbol{H}$. If we substitute $\boldsymbol{J}$ for $\boldsymbol{B}$, $\boldsymbol{E}$ for $\boldsymbol{H}$, and $\sigma_i$ for $\mu_i$, we obtain for the equation analogous to Eq. 5.143

$$\boldsymbol{J} = \sigma_i(\boldsymbol{E}_0 + \boldsymbol{E}) \tag{5.144}$$

where the term $\boldsymbol{E}_0$ plays a role analogous to that of $(\mu_0/\mu_i)\boldsymbol{M}_0$.

We recognize from Eq. 5.144 that the conducting system now contains a field source of magnitude $E_0$ distributed throughout the conducting material. This distributed source along any closed path produces a net electromotive force given by

$$V = \oint \boldsymbol{E}_0 \cdot d\boldsymbol{s} \tag{5.145}$$

Thus, if the thickness of the ring and the length of the gap are small compared with the length of the ring, the current in the conducting ring is

$$I = \frac{V}{R} = \frac{E_0 l}{R} \tag{5.146}$$

Thus, by analogy, $M_0(\mu_0/\mu_i)$ acts as a distributed source of magnetomotive force. The total equivalent magnetomotive force around any closed path $C$ is

$$\mathfrak{F} = \frac{\mu_0}{\mu_i} \oint \boldsymbol{M}_0 \cdot d\boldsymbol{s} \tag{5.147}$$

and the magnetic flux in the ring is given by

$$\Phi = \frac{\mathfrak{F}}{\mathfrak{R}} = \frac{\mu_0 M_0 l}{\mu_i \mathfrak{R}} \tag{5.148}$$

where $\mathfrak{R}$ is the reluctance of the magnetic circuit defined in Table 5.2, with $\mu_i$ substituted for $\mu$. Finally, dividing the flux by the cross-sectional area yields the flux density $\boldsymbol{B}$, from which the magnetic field is obtained with the help of Eq. 5.143. It is important to note that although $\boldsymbol{H}$ and $\boldsymbol{B}$ are in the same direction in the air gap, they are in opposite directions within the magnetized material. This follows from the fact that the line integral of $\boldsymbol{H}$ around any closed path must be equal to zero in the absence of exciting currents; clearly, in order for this to be possible, the direction of $\boldsymbol{H}$ in the magnetized material must be opposite to that in the air gap.

## ► 5.11 Examples of Field Synthesis

A type of problem with which engineers are confronted in practice is that of designing either an electric or a magnetic structure that generates a static field with prescribed properties. Problems of this type can be solved sometimes by first finding a solution of Laplace's equation which has the specified behavior in the desired region of space, and then designing a structure that fits the field on the surface of the region.

In this section we shall illustrate this procedure with examples of the design of magnetic systems. Magnetic systems rather than electric systems were chosen for illustration, partly because problems of this type are encountered more frequently in practice, and partly because in this connection a property of magnetic systems will be brought out which has not yet been emphasized. We have already pointed out the analogy between magnetic systems and battery-driven conduction systems. Use was made of the fact that magnetic materials of high permeability are often used in practice, and simple relations between the flux and the magnetomotive force were obtained. In the examples to be discussed here, another analogy will be emphasized, namely, the analogy between an electrostatic system containing (perfect) conductors and magnetic systems containing materials of high permeability.

Suppose, first, that we wish to generate a uniform magnetic field within a sphere of radius $R$ in free space. If we represent the vector $\boldsymbol{H}$ in terms of a scalar magnetic potential,

$$\boldsymbol{H} = -\operatorname{grad} \phi \tag{5.149}$$

the potential corresponding to a uniform field of unit magnitude is

$$\phi_1 = -r \cos \theta \tag{5.150}$$

where $\theta$ is the angle relative to the direction of the field. We observe next that, if a tightly wound single-layer coil is used to produce this field, the current in the coil is approximately equivalent to a current sheet. For instance, a coil tightly wound on the surface of the sphere is approximately equivalent to a uniform surface current around the sphere. On the other hand, we know that the normal component of $\boldsymbol{H}$ is continuous through a current sheet, and the tangential component has a discontinuity equal to the surface current density. It follows that we must find a solution of Laplace's equation outside the sphere for which the normal component of the corresponding field on the surface of the sphere is equal to the normal component of the uniform field. The discontinuity of the tangential component will then give the required surface current density. The expression for the uniform field in spherical coordinates is

$$\boldsymbol{H}_i = -A \operatorname{grad} \phi_1 = A(\boldsymbol{i}_r \cos \theta - \boldsymbol{i}_\theta \sin \theta) \tag{5.151}$$

where $A$ is an arbitrary constant. Thus we must look for a solution of Laplace's equation for which the radial component of the gradient is also proportional to $\cos \theta$. The solution associated with a dipole has this property, so that we have for the field outside the sphere

$$\boldsymbol{H}_o = -C \operatorname{grad} \frac{\cos \theta}{r^2} = \boldsymbol{i}_r \frac{2C \cos \theta}{r^3} + \boldsymbol{i}_\theta \frac{C \sin \theta}{r^3} \tag{5.152}$$

where $C$ is a constant related to $A$. Equating the radial components of $\boldsymbol{H}_i$ and $\boldsymbol{H}_o$ for $r = R$, yields

$$C = \tfrac{1}{2}AR^3 \tag{5.153}$$

and

$$\boldsymbol{H}_o = AR^3 \left( \boldsymbol{i}_r \frac{\cos \theta}{r^3} + \boldsymbol{i}_\theta \frac{\sin \theta}{2r^3} \right) \tag{5.154}$$

The density of the required surface current on the sphere of radius $R$ corresponding to the discontinuity of the tangential component of the magnetic field is then given by

$$\boldsymbol{i}_r \times (\boldsymbol{H}_o - \boldsymbol{H}_i)_{r=R} = \boldsymbol{i}_\varphi A \frac{3 \sin \theta}{2} \tag{5.155}$$

This surface current, being proportional to $\sin \theta$, can be realized by means of a coil tightly wound on the surface of the sphere and with a constant number of turns per unit length along the axis parallel to the desired field, as illustrated in Fig. 3.6. The resulting field on a meridian plane is shown in the same figure. The proper density of field lines in three dimensions can be constructed from the plot in Fig. 3.6 by repeating the plot on several meridian planes. When these planes are distributed at equal angular intervals around the $z$-axis, the proper three-dimensional field is obtained.

Next, suppose that the sphere is filled with a linear, homogeneous, isotropic magnetic material. The same types of fields are involved. Now, however, it is the normal component of $\boldsymbol{B}$ rather than that of $\boldsymbol{H}$ that must be continuous at the surface of the sphere. We have, then, from Eqs. 5.151 and 5.152

$$\mu A \cos \theta = 2C\mu_0 \frac{\cos \theta}{R^3} \tag{5.156}$$

from which we obtain

$$A = \frac{2\mu_0}{\mu} \frac{C}{R^3} \tag{5.157}$$

and

$$\boldsymbol{H}_i = \frac{C}{R^3} \frac{2\mu_0}{\mu} (\boldsymbol{i}_r \cos \theta - \boldsymbol{i}_\theta \sin \theta) \tag{5.158}$$

The tangential ($\theta$) component of the magnetic field just outside the surface of the magnetic sphere is thus

$$H_{o\theta} = \frac{C}{R^3} \sin \theta$$

The same component just inside the sphere is

$$H_{i\theta} = -\frac{C}{R^3} \frac{2\mu_0}{\mu}$$

Thus the surface current density corresponding to this discontinuity is

$$\begin{aligned} \boldsymbol{K} = \boldsymbol{i}_r \times (\boldsymbol{H}_o - \boldsymbol{H}_i)_{r=R} &= \boldsymbol{i}_\varphi (H_{o\theta} - H_{i\theta})_{r=R} \\ &= \boldsymbol{i}_\varphi \frac{C}{R^3} \sin \theta \left(1 + \frac{2\mu_0}{\mu}\right) \end{aligned} \tag{5.159}$$

If the permeability of the sphere is large, the discontinuity of the tangential field is approximately equal to $H_{0\theta}$, and the surface current needed to provide the discontinuity is

$$\boldsymbol{K} \simeq \boldsymbol{i}_\varphi \frac{C}{R^3} \sin\theta \tag{5.160}$$

The above equations show that the discontinuity of the tangential component of $\boldsymbol{H}$ is equal, for all practical purposes, to the tangential component of the field outside the sphere. This implies that the tangential component of $\boldsymbol{H}$ can be assumed to vanish at $r = R$ and inside the magnetic sphere. In other words, the scalar magnetic potential can be assumed to be constant inside the highly permeable sphere and on its surface. This is actually a general property of magnetic bodies having a permeability much greater than that of the surrounding medium. Its origin becomes evident in the limit of infinitely permeable bodies. Thus, consider an interface between a body with infinite permeability and free space in the absence of any surface current. Then, if the tangential component of the magnetic field $\boldsymbol{H}$ just outside the body were finite, the tangential component of $\boldsymbol{B}$ would have to be infinite inside the body since the tangential component of $\boldsymbol{H} = \boldsymbol{B}/\mu$ is continuous. We conclude, therefore, that the tangential component of $\boldsymbol{H}$ just outside the infinitely permeable body must vanish. Therefore any line integral $\int \boldsymbol{H} \cdot d\boldsymbol{s}$ on the surface of the body has to vanish; *the surface of a body with an infinite permeability is an equipotential surface.* This argument shows that an infinitely permeable magnetic body has a behavior in a magnetostatic field analogous to that of a conductor in an electrostatic field.

Now, let us connect these considerations with Eq. 5.160. For this purpose it is advantageous to introduce a very thin gap between the surface of the magnetic sphere, now assumed to be infinitely permeable, and the surface on which the current $\boldsymbol{K}$ flows. Then, it is clear from the preceding argument that the tangential magnetic field in the thin gap just outside the sphere must be zero. Accordingly, the tangential component of the magnetic field just outside the current-carrying surface uniquely specifies the surface current density. This argument explains why in Eq. 5.160 the field inside the highly permeable sphere could be disregarded.

We shall study next the design of magnetic structures suitable for rotating electric machines. Such magnetic structures consist of a stationary outer cylinder, the stator, and of an inner rotating cylinder, the rotor. A coil is wound either on the surface of the stator or on that of the rotor. We shall assume at first that the coil is wound on the rotor and that the inner surface of the stator and the outer surface of the rotor are coaxial circular cylinders, as illustrated in Fig. 5.11. The case of a salient-pole rotor will be considered later.

The primary objective in the design of the magnetic structure for a rotating machine is to obtain a radial magnetic field that varies sinusoidally over the surface of the stator. Because of the cylindrical symmetry of the system, the field can be assumed to be independent of the coordinate in the axial direction, i.e., it can be assumed to be two-dimensional. We know that for each particular number $n$ of spatial cycles of the field ($\varphi$-dependence), there are two solutions of Laplace's equation that meet the above requirement; thus the desired magnetic potential must be of the form

$$\phi = (A_1 r^n - A_2 r^{-n}) \cos n\varphi \tag{5.161}$$

where $A_1$ and $A_2$ are constants to be determined and $n$ is the number of cycles in the sinusoidal variation of the field. For the sake of simplicity, we shall take $n$ equal to one; the case of $n$ different from one can be treated analogously.

Assuming that the permeability of the stator is high, the inner surface of the stator can be treated as a magnetic equipotential surface on the basis of the preceding argument. On the other hand, we know from Sec. 4.8 that the above solution of Laplace's equation has a circular equipotential surface corresponding to zero potential. Thus, if $a$ is the radius of the stator, the constants $A_1$ and $A_2$ must satisfy the equation

$$A_1 a - A_2 a^{-1} = 0 \tag{5.162}$$

from which it follows that

$$a = \sqrt{\frac{A_2}{A_1}} \tag{5.163}$$

and

$$\phi = -C\left(\frac{r}{a} - \frac{a}{r}\right) \cos \varphi \tag{5.164}$$

where $C$ is a constant.

Let us consider next the field at the surface of the rotor. If $b$ is the radius of the rotor, the magnetic field at the surface just outside the rotor is given by

$$\boldsymbol{H}_{r=b} = \frac{C}{b}\left[\boldsymbol{i}_r\left(\frac{b}{a} + \frac{a}{b}\right)\cos\varphi - \boldsymbol{i}_\varphi\left(\frac{b}{a} - \frac{a}{b}\right)\sin\varphi\right] \tag{5.165}$$

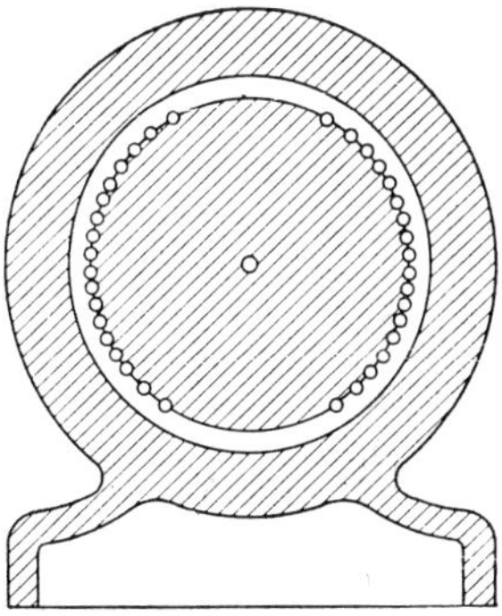

**Fig. 5.11.** Stator and rotor with circular cylindrical surfaces.

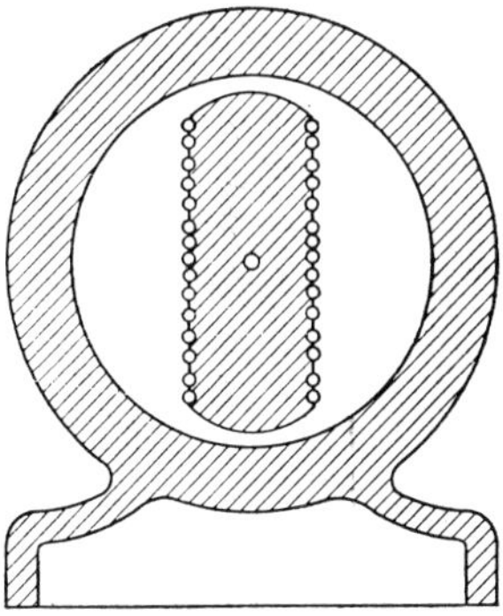

**Fig. 5.12.** Schematic diagram of a salient-pole rotor.

Since $H_\varphi = 0$ at the surface just inside a highly permeable rotor, it follows that the surface current on the rotor must have a density

$$\boldsymbol{K} = \boldsymbol{i}_r \times (-\boldsymbol{H})_{r=b} = \boldsymbol{i}_z \frac{C}{b}\left(\frac{b}{a} - \frac{a}{b}\right) \sin \varphi \tag{5.166}$$

where $\boldsymbol{i}_z$ is a unit vector parallel to the axis of the system. The surface current density is proportional to the sine of the angle, and, therefore, can be obtained by means of conductors on the surface of the rotor, equally spaced in a direction parallel to a diameter of the rotor, as indicated in Fig. 5.11.

A salient-pole rotor can be designed in a similar manner. We note first that the potential given by Eq. 5.164 is, apart from a change of scale, that illustrated in Fig. 4.16, with the zero-potential circle corresponding to the inner surface of the stator. Then we can select for pole faces any two equipotential circular segments symmetrically located, as illustrated in Fig. 5.12. The sides of the poles can be any two arbitrary lines joining the edges of the faces, for instance, straight lines, as indicated in the same figure. A coil must then be wound around the poles to form a current sheet of density equal to the tangential component of the magnetic field. The difference of potential between the two pole faces is the number of ampere-turns that must be supplied by the coil on the assumption that the iron is infinitely permeable.

## 5.12 Summary and Conclusions

This chapter has been devoted to the development of macroscopic models for polarized and magnetized matter and to the extension of the field laws to macroscopic fields in matter. The point of view taken in our discussion was that electrically polarized bodies are equivalent, as far as the macroscopic electromagnetic field is concerned, to appropriate distributions of polarization charges and polarization currents having the same properties as free charges and free currents. In the case of magnetized matter, two alternate representations were considered, one involving electric currents, and one involving magnetic charges and magnetic currents. The second type of representation, analogous to that used for polarized matter, was chosen for reasons that will be discussed more fully in Chapter 7. Thus we were led to think of the electromagnetic field as being always in free space, with polarized and magnetized matter being taken into account by appropriate source distributions. The macroscopic field laws in matter were then obtained by inserting the densities of these source distributions into the free-space laws.

The source distributions representing the macroscopic effects of polarized and magnetized matter were found to be expressible in terms of the density $\boldsymbol{P}$ of the electric-dipole moments, and the density $\boldsymbol{M}$ of the magnetic-dipole moments. In turn, these macroscopic densities were found to depend on the local state of matter only; in particular, they were found to be independent of the macroscopic space and time variations of the state of matter. Thus the macroscopic field laws became relations between the space and time derivatives of the fields on the one hand, and the space and time derivatives of $\boldsymbol{P}$ and $\boldsymbol{M}$ (representing the local electromagnetic characteristics of matter) together with the densities of free charges and free currents on the other hand.

We turned our attention next to the action of the electromagnetic field in forcing changes in the state of matter and corresponding changes in the macroscopic densities $\boldsymbol{P}$ and $\boldsymbol{M}$. This question was discussed only at the empirical, macroscopic level, except for a brief rudimentary survey of the major phenomena responsible for polarization and magnetization. The detailed microscopic study of these phenomena has received an increasing amount of attention in the last decade, and is fast becoming a separate, major branch of engineering physics. For this reason we purposely limited our discussion to a consideration of representative types of constituent relations between $\boldsymbol{P}$ and $\boldsymbol{M}$ on the one hand, and $\boldsymbol{E}$ and $\boldsymbol{H}$ on the other.

The last three sections of this chapter have been devoted to illustrative examples of interactions between fields and matter, indicating how the analytical techniques developed in Chapter 4 can be used to deal with such situations. Most of our discussion in the following chapters will be limited to systems involving only linear materials, because only linear systems lend themselves to quantitative analysis of any generality.

## 5.13 Selected References

1. W. K. H. Panofsky and M. Phillips, *Classical Electricity and Magnetism*, Addison-Wesley, Cambridge, Mass., 1955, Chapter 2, Secs. 7.10 and 7.11, 8.1 to 8.4.
2. J. A. Stratton, *Electromagnetic Theory*, McGraw-Hill, New York, 1941, Secs. 1.1 to 1.8 and 1.13.
3. J. C. Slater and N. H. Frank, *Electromagnetism*, McGraw-Hill, New York, 1947, Secs. 4.1 to 4.4 and 6.1 to 6.3, 7.3 and 7.4.
4. A. Sommerfeld, *Electrodynamics*, Academic Press, New York, 1952, Secs. 11 to 14.

## PROBLEMS

**Problem 5.1.** A capacitor with parallel conducting plates at $x = 0$ and at $x = d$ is filled with a material whose dielectric permittivity varies with position as

$$\epsilon = \epsilon_0 \frac{2d}{x + d}$$

A direct-voltage source $V_0$ is connected to the plates of the capacitor. Find the electric field and potential distribution between the plates, neglecting fringing. Find the polarization $\boldsymbol{P}$ and the surface polarization-charge density $\sigma_p$ at $x = 0$ and $x = d$.

**Problem 5.2.** A slab of conducting material of thickness $d$ with a uniform dielectric permittivity $\epsilon$ is placed between two perfectly conducting plates separated by a distance $d$. The conductivity of the material is

$$\sigma = \sigma_0 \frac{2d}{x + d}$$

where the $x$-axis is normal to the plates.

(a) Find the electric field and the polarization in the slab when a direct voltage $V_0$ is applied between the plates. Neglect fringing.
(b) Find the distributions of polarization charge and of free charge.

**Problem 5.3.** A slab of dielectric material partially fills the space between the plates of a parallel-plate capacitor, leaving an air gap equal to $\frac{1}{10}$ of the distance between the plates. The constituent relation for the dielectric material is:

$$\boldsymbol{P} = P_0 \frac{\boldsymbol{E}}{|\boldsymbol{E}|}$$

where $P_0$ is a constant. Find the electric field and the distribution of polarization changes as functions of the voltage between the plates.

**Problem 5.4.** A dielectric sphere with a uniform permittivity $\epsilon$ is immersed in an electric field which is uniform at large distances from the sphere. Find the potential, the electric field, and the distribution of polarization charges.

**Problem 5.5.** A permanent magnet in the form of a circular rod of radius $R$ and length $L$ has a magnetization

$$\boldsymbol{M} = \boldsymbol{i}_z(R - r)M_0$$

where $M_0$ is a constant, $\boldsymbol{i}_z$ is a unit vector along the axis of the rod, and $r$ is the radial distance from the axis of the rod. Find the equivalent distribution of magnetic charges. Calculate and sketch the equivalent amperian current distribution.

**Problem 5.6.** A spherical ball is uniformly magnetized ($\boldsymbol{M}$ = constant). Determine the equivalent distribution of magnetic charges, and the magnetic field inside and outside the sphere.

**Problem 5.7.** A magnetic rod of infinite length and uniform permeability $\mu$ is immersed in a magnetic field which lies in a plane normal to the rod and is uniform at large distances from the rod. Find the magnetic field both inside and outside the rod.

**Problem 5.8.** A magnetic circuit consists of a ring with a rectangular cross section, half of which has a uniform permeability $\mu_1$, and half a uniform permeability $\mu_2$. A coil with $N$ turns is wound on the ring. Express the magnetic flux in the ring in terms of the physical and geometric characteristics of the ring and of the current in the coil.

# CHAPTER SIX

# Time-Varying Fields

Our discussion of electromagnetism began with the formulation of Maxwell's equations for time-varying fields; yet, so far we have dealt in detail only with static fields, i.e., with fields that are independent of time. This was done partly because the analysis of static fields is relatively simple, but partly, also, because many important time-varying fields can be dealt with by a process of successive approximations which involves mathematical steps developed in the study of static fields. This method of analyzing time-varying fields is particularly useful in the study of the electromagnetic phenomena associated with electric circuits, i.e., in the study of fields whose time variations are relatively slow. Above all, this method places in evidence the relationship between field theory and circuit theory and points out the approximations involved in the use of the latter theory.

The first part of this chapter is devoted to the development of the method of successive approximations for analyzing time-varying fields. This method of analysis will then be used in the second part of the chapter to study the relation between circuit theory and field theory. The study of this relation will continue in the next chapter, which is devoted to a discussion of energy relations in time-varying fields, and will be concluded in Chapter 8 where we shall analyze in some detail the behavior of representative circuit elements in the sinusoidal steady state. Thus, this chapter and the following two chapters form a closely connected sequence in which the same broad class of electromagnetic systems is discussed from various points of view. The major purpose of this chapter is to introduce the conceptual framework and the mathematical formalism needed in the following two chapters.

## 6.1 Static and Time-Varying Fields

It is helpful, as an introduction, to reconsider the structure of Maxwell's equations by focusing our attention, in particular, on the manner in which the electric field and the magnetic field are coupled to each other. The form of Maxwell's equations most convenient for our present purposes is

$$\text{curl}\,\boldsymbol{E} = -\frac{\partial \boldsymbol{B}}{\partial t} \tag{6.1}$$

$$\text{curl}\,\boldsymbol{H} = \boldsymbol{J}_f + \frac{\partial \boldsymbol{D}}{\partial t} \tag{6.2}$$

$$\text{div}\,\boldsymbol{D} = \rho_f \tag{6.3}$$

$$\text{div}\,\boldsymbol{B} = 0 \tag{6.4}$$

$$\text{div}\,\boldsymbol{J}_f = -\frac{\partial \rho_f}{\partial t} \tag{6.5}$$

where

$$\boldsymbol{D} = \epsilon_0 \boldsymbol{E} + \boldsymbol{P} \tag{6.6}$$

and

$$\boldsymbol{B} = \mu_0(\boldsymbol{H} + \boldsymbol{M}) \tag{6.7}$$

The reason for writing Maxwell's equations in this particular form is that we shall be concerned mostly with linear systems, i.e., with systems in which at any particular point $\boldsymbol{P}$ is proportional to $\boldsymbol{E}$, $\boldsymbol{M}$ is proportional to $\boldsymbol{H}$, and the free current density $\boldsymbol{J}_f$ is proportional to $\boldsymbol{E}$. Furthermore, as we shall see shortly, the manner in which $\boldsymbol{E}$ and $\boldsymbol{H}$ are mutually coupled is most conveniently expressed in terms of $\boldsymbol{D}$, $\boldsymbol{B}$, and $\boldsymbol{J}_f$.

The main characteristic of Maxwell's equations is that the electric field depends on the magnetic field through the time variation of $\boldsymbol{B}$, and that the magnetic field depends on the electric field through the time variation of $\boldsymbol{D}$, as indicated by Eqs. 6.1 and 6.2. This particular form of coupling between electric and magnetic fields disappears when the fields are time-invariant; the two fields can then be determined, independently of each other, from the free-charge distribution, the free-current distribution, and the properties of whatever matter is present in the system. This is the reason why static-field problems are relatively simple.

On the other hand, there is another type of coupling between electric field and magnetic field which may be present even when the fields are time-independent. This type of coupling arises from conduction currents, and is, therefore, associated with dissipation. Let us suppose, for instance, that the electromagnetic field is time-independent and that current is present in a linear conducting material of finite conductivity $\sigma$. Then within such a material,

$$\boldsymbol{J} = \sigma \boldsymbol{E} \tag{6.8}$$

and Eq. 6.2 becomes

$$\text{curl } \boldsymbol{H} = \sigma \boldsymbol{E} \tag{6.9}$$

so that the magnetic field depends on the electric field. On the other hand, we have from Eqs. 6.1, 6.5, and 6.8

$$\text{curl } \boldsymbol{E} = 0 \tag{6.10}$$

$$\text{div } \sigma \boldsymbol{E} = \sigma \text{ div } \boldsymbol{E} + \boldsymbol{E} \cdot \text{grad } \sigma = 0 \tag{6.11}$$

Thus, whereas the sources of the magnetic field depend on the electric field, the sources of the electric field are independent of the magnetic field. In other words, the coupling resulting from conduction currents is "unidirectional." It follows that the determination of the electromagnetic field can be broken into two successive parts: the determination of the electric field from Eqs. 6.10 and 6.11, and the determination of the magnetic field from the known conduction current $\sigma\boldsymbol{E}$, with the help of Eqs. 6.4 and 6.9 together with the constituent relation between $\boldsymbol{B}$ and $\boldsymbol{H}$. In other words, the conduction current is evaluated first, independently of the magnetic field, with the magnetic field being evaluated, in turn, from the known current distribution.

The situation is quite different with respect to the coupling resulting from time variations of $\boldsymbol{D}$ and $\boldsymbol{B}$. In this case, the time derivative of $\boldsymbol{D}$ acts as a source of $\boldsymbol{H}$ and the time derivative of $\boldsymbol{B}$ acts as a source of $\boldsymbol{E}$, so that the coupling between electric field and magnetic field becomes bilateral. Thus, Maxwell's equations must be solved simultaneously in the case of time-varying fields, a fact which increases considerably the difficulty of the problem.

The method of successive approximations developed below can be regarded as an attempt to circumvent the simultaneous solution of Maxwell's equations by substituting an infinite series of unidirectional couplings for the bilateral coupling resulting from the time derivatives of $\boldsymbol{D}$ and $\boldsymbol{B}$. Roughly speaking, at first the coupling is disregarded and $\boldsymbol{E}$ and $\boldsymbol{H}$ are determined as if they were static fields. Then, the time derivative of the statically determined $\boldsymbol{B}$ is used to compute a correction term for $\boldsymbol{E}$, and, separately, the time derivative of the statically determined $\boldsymbol{D}$ is used to compute a corresponding correction term for $\boldsymbol{H}$. Next, the time derivatives of the first-order correction terms for $\boldsymbol{B}$ and $\boldsymbol{D}$ are used to compute second-order terms for $\boldsymbol{E}$ and $\boldsymbol{H}$, from which, in turn, third-order correction terms are computed, and so forth. Such a procedure turns out to be valid in many situations. On the other hand, one has to pay a price for avoiding in this manner the simultaneous solution of Maxwell's equations: the fields are determined as infinite series, which may or may not converge sufficiently fast for practical purposes. We shall see that relatively fast convergence can be expected only when the dimensions of the electromagnetic system under consideration are smaller than the wave length corresponding to the highest frequency of operation.

## 6.2 The Time-Rate Parameter

In the study of physical systems, it is often advantageous to enlarge artificially the scope of the problem under consideration, even at the risk of apparently complicating it. Thus, for instance, in dealing with electric circuits in the sinusoidal steady state, it is convenient to consider the frequency of excitation as a variable, even though it may be precisely specified in advance. As a matter of fact, it is very helpful to enlarge the scope of the problem even further by regarding the frequency as a complex variable, i.e., by considering not only sinusoidal excitations of constant amplitude but also exponentially damped or growing excitations. Such an enlargement of the scope of the problem makes it possible to describe the operation of the circuit in terms of the location of poles and zeros in the complex-frequency plane, a description which not only facilitates the numerical evaluation of the steady-state performance of the circuit but also relates it to its transient behavior.

In the study of a particular, time-varying electromagnetic field, it is also helpful to enlarge the scope of the problem, although this is done for a different reason than when dealing with electric circuits. Instead of the particular field under study, one considers an entire family of fields. In the special case of sinusoidal time variations, the desired family is that generated by varying the frequency of excitation, just as in connection with circuit problems. In general, we would like to consider the family of fields generated by changing the time scale of the excitation, i.e., by increasing and decreasing its time rate of change. Thus, for instance, if the independent source of the field is a charge density $\rho(x, y, z, t)$, we would like to consider the family of electromagnetic fields corresponding to a charge density $\rho(x, y, z, \alpha t)$, where $\alpha$ is a parameter describing the family. Since the time rate of

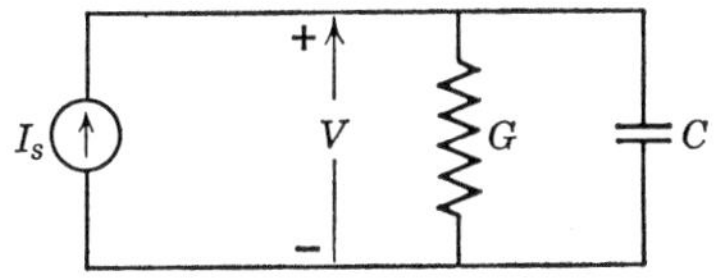


**Fig. 6.1.** Circuit used for illustrative purposes.

change of the charge density is proportional to $\alpha$, we shall refer to $\alpha$ as the *time-rate parameter*. It is clear that in the particular case of sinusoidal excitations, substituting $\alpha t$ for $t$ is equivalent to substituting $\alpha\omega$ for the angular frequency $\omega$. Thus, varying the value of $\alpha$ is equivalent to varying the frequency of excitation.

The idea of constructing a family of solutions to a physical problem by varying the scale of the excitation applies to electric circuits as well as to general electromagnetic systems; as a matter of fact, an electric circuit is an idealization of a particular type of electromagnetic system. For the sake of simplicity, let us then use the parallel $RC$ circuit, shown in Fig. 6.1, to illustrate this basic idea. The current source, $I_s(t)$, consists of two unit current impulses of opposite polarities, separated by a time interval $T$, which are shown in Fig. 6.2$a$ as two very narrow pulses. The resulting voltage $V(t)$ must satisfy the differential equation

$$C\frac{dV}{dt} + GV = I_s(t) \tag{6.12}$$

and the initial condition

$$V(t) = 0 \qquad t < 0 \tag{6.13}$$

We have then,

$$V(t) = \frac{1}{C}\begin{cases} (e^{-(G/C)t}) & 0 < t < T \\ (e^{-(G/C)t} - e^{-(G/C)(t-T)}) & T < t \end{cases} \tag{6.14}$$

as illustrated in Fig. 6.2$a$.

Let us now generate a family of solutions by varying the time scale of the current source, i.e., by making the source current equal to $I_s(\alpha t)$, where the time-rate parameter $\alpha$ can assume all possible values. Clearly, the time interval between the two impulses is inversely proportional to $\alpha$, as illustrated in Figs. 6.2$b$ and 6.2$c$ for $\alpha = 2$ and $\alpha = \frac{1}{2}$. Furthermore, the width of the two impulses is also inversely proportional to $\alpha$, and, therefore, the charge fed to the capacitor by each impulse, i.e., the value of the impulse becomes equal to $1/\alpha$. Clearly, the "shape" of the source current as a function of time is the same for all members of the family; only the time scale is changed,

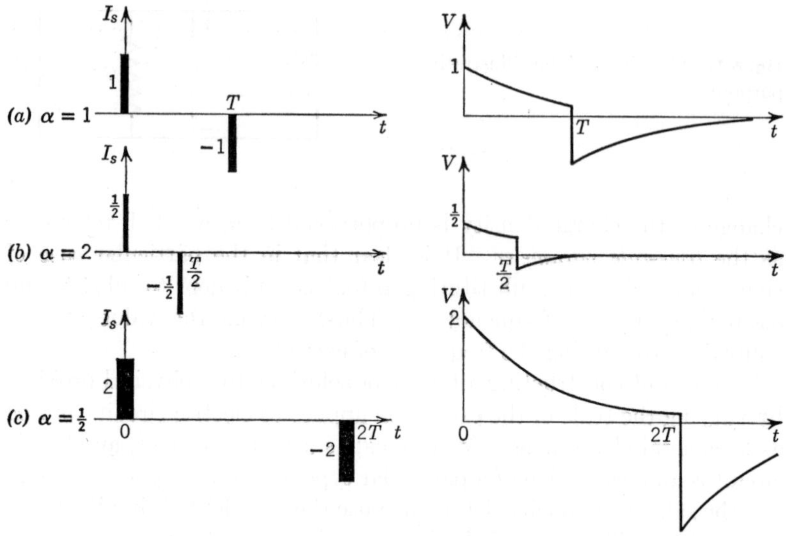


**Fig. 6.2.** Excitations and responses of circuit of Fig. 6.1.

i.e., the function is stretched when $\alpha < 1$, and compressed when $\alpha > 1$. To stress this constancy of the "shape" of the excitation, we write the source current as a function $I_s(\tau)$ of a new time variable

$$\tau = \alpha t \tag{6.15}$$

which coincides with the real time when $\alpha = 1$. We shall refer to $\tau$ as the *family time*. It is also convenient to rewrite the differential Eq. 6.12 in terms of this new variable. Since

$$\frac{dV}{dt} = \frac{dV}{d\tau}\frac{d\tau}{dt} = \alpha\frac{dV}{d\tau} \tag{6.16}$$

we obtain

$$\alpha C\frac{dV}{d\tau} + GV = I_s(\tau)$$

The resulting voltage is then given by

$$V(\alpha, \tau) = \frac{1}{\alpha C}\begin{cases}(e^{-(G/\alpha C)\tau}) & 0 < \tau < T\\ (e^{-(G/\alpha C)\tau} - e^{-(G/\alpha C)(\tau - T)}) & T < \tau\end{cases} \tag{6.17}$$

The behavior of this voltage as a function of real time can be obtained by substituting $\alpha t$ for $\tau$, and is illustrated in Figs. 6.2*b* and 6.2*c* for $\alpha = 2$ and $\alpha = ½$. It is important to note that the voltage depends on $\alpha$ directly, as well as through $\tau$, as evidenced by the fact that the "shape" of its dependence on time varies with $\alpha$. Thus, whereas the excitation $I_s(\tau)$ can be represented as a function of a single variable, the response $V(\alpha, \tau)$ is necessarily a function of the two variables $\alpha$ and $\tau$. It is also interesting to note that the differential equation controlling the behavior of the voltage becomes a function of $\alpha$ when written in terms of $\tau$ rather than $t$. Thus, the family of voltages can be thought to consist of the solutions of a family of differential equations in $\tau$, involving a parameter $\alpha$, with a driving force $I_s(\tau)$, independent of $\alpha$.

In general, if a circuit contains many branches and many independent voltage sources and current sources, all the source voltages and all the source currents are functions of the family time $\tau$ alone, and do not depend directly on the time-rate parameter $\alpha$. On the other hand, each branch voltage and each branch current is, in general, a function of both $\tau$ and $\alpha$. This is a direct generalization of the situation encountered in the sinusoidal steady state, where all independent sources are sinusoidal functions of $\omega t$ with constant amplitudes and phases, and the branch voltages and the branch currents have amplitudes and phases that depend on $\omega$, in addition to being sinusoidal functions of $\omega t$.

Returning now to electromagnetic fields, we note that the quantities that act in a given system as independent sources of the electromagnetic field are functions of $\tau$, the family time defined by Eq. 6.15, and, of course, of the space coordinates. For instance, if the independent source of the field is a charge distribution of density $\rho(x, y, z, t)$, the family of charge distributions generated by varying the time scale is represented by the charge density $\rho(x, y, z, \tau)$. In other words, the family of excitations is obtained by substituting the family time $\tau$ for the real time $t$. The resulting electric field, on the other hand, is a vector function $\boldsymbol{E}(x, y, z, \alpha, \tau)$ which depends on the time-rate parameter $\alpha$, as well as on the family time $\tau$ and the space coordinates. Thus the family of electric fields, just like the family of voltages in the circuit illustration, involves explicitly $\alpha$, and cannot be generated from the actual field (corresponding to $\alpha = 1$) by simply substituting $\tau$ for $t$. Thus, the space dependence of the electric field as well as its time dependence is changed when the time scale of the excitation is changed. The same is true for the family of magnetic fields, represented by the function $\boldsymbol{H}(x, y, z, \alpha, \tau)$, and for all other electromagnetic quantities that are not independently controlled by external forces.

Let us now write Maxwell's equations in terms of the family time $\tau$ and the time-rate parameter $\alpha$, just like it was done in the circuit illustration for the differential equation governing the behavior of the voltage. With the introduction of the family time $\tau$, the time derivative of $\boldsymbol{B}$ can be written in the form

$$\frac{\partial \boldsymbol{B}}{\partial t} = \frac{\partial \boldsymbol{B}}{\partial \tau}\frac{d\tau}{dt} = \alpha\frac{\partial \boldsymbol{B}}{\partial \tau} \tag{6.18}$$

and the other time derivatives can be expressed in a similar manner. From Eqs. 6.1, 6.2, and 6.5, we obtain

$$\text{curl } \boldsymbol{E} = -\alpha\frac{\partial \boldsymbol{B}}{\partial \tau} \tag{6.19}$$

$$\text{curl } \boldsymbol{H} = \boldsymbol{J}_f + \alpha\frac{\partial \boldsymbol{D}}{\partial \tau} \tag{6.20}$$

$$\text{div } \boldsymbol{J}_f = -\alpha\frac{\partial \rho_f}{\partial \tau} \tag{6.21}$$

The remaining equations, namely, Eqs. 6.3 and 6.4 stay unchanged because they do not involve time derivatives. Thus the family of electromagnetic fields can also be regarded in the $\tau$ domain as being generated by a family of differential equations involving the time-rate parameter $\alpha$, with driving forces independent of $\alpha$.

Up to this point we have been thinking of a family as being generated by varying the time scale of the excitation while maintaining fixed the "shape" of its functional dependence on time, i.e., by assuming that the excitation is a function of $\tau$ but not of $\alpha$. Actually, this restriction is totally unnecessary, and sometimes inconvenient. Thus, for instance, there is no reason why, in studying the frequency behavior of a circuit, we should keep fixed the amplitude of the driving voltage while changing its frequency. Obviously, the amplitude of the driving voltage can be varied with frequency in any desired manner, although, of course, the family of responses will depend on the particular frequency variation used. On the other hand, it is usually convenient to keep fixed as a reference the amplitude of some branch voltage or branch current. This means, from an experimental point of view, that we must vary the amplitude of the source voltage each time we change its frequency in such a way as to maintain fixed the indication of the voltmeter or ammeter connected to the reference branch. Thus, the frequency dependence of the source voltage for any given circuit is specified by the particular branch voltage or branch current whose amplitude is kept constant as a reference. In other words, the amplitude of any voltage or current, whether of a source or of a branch, can be kept constant as a reference. In the more general terminology used here, any one voltage or current can be required to be a function of $\tau$, independent of $\alpha$, thereby maintaining fixed the "shape" of its time dependence over the entire family. It is entirely a matter of convenience which voltage or current is used as a reference.

The same considerations apply to electromagnetic fields. Any electromagnetic quantity can be used as a reference, and required to be a function of $\tau$ alone, provided, of course, that the constraint introduced by this requirement is consistent with the laws of electromagnetism. This question of consistency and, therefore, the choice of a reference quantity cannot be discussed profitably in general terms. We shall return to this question in later sections, in connection with specific illustrations.

## 6.3 The Power Series in the Time-Rate Parameter

We saw in the preceding section how a family of electromagnetic fields can be defined, for any given system, by changing the time scale with the help of an independent time-rate parameter $\alpha$. We saw also that, in such a family of electromagnetic fields, each electromagnetic quantity is a function of the parameter $\alpha$, of the family time $\tau$, as well as of the space coordinates. Such quantities must satisfy the laws of electromagnetism, as expressed in particular by Eqs. 6.19, 6.20, and 6.21.

Let us consider these equations from the point of view of coupling between electric and magnetic field, as discussed in Sec. 6.1. The two derivatives of $\boldsymbol{B}$ and $\boldsymbol{D}$ with respect to $\tau$ are multiplied by $\alpha$, so that the coupling resulting from them is small for small values of $\alpha$. In the limit, when $\alpha$ approaches zero, the coupling disappears entirely, and the equations reduce to those of static fields. This makes good physical sense because, in such a limiting case, all electromagnetic quantities vary at an infinitely slow rate, and, therefore, they must obey the static laws. It follows that, for $\alpha = 0$, the electric field can be evaluated independently of the magnetic field, as discussed in Sec. 6.1.

For $\alpha$ small, although different from zero, the coupling introduced by the derivatives with respect to $\tau$ is correspondingly small. Then, since $\boldsymbol{E}$ and $\boldsymbol{H}$ can be expected to be continuous functions of $\alpha$, they cannot differ much from their values for $\alpha = 0$. As a matter of fact, we have approximately, for small values of $\alpha$,

$$\boldsymbol{E} = (\boldsymbol{E})_0 + \alpha \left(\frac{\partial \boldsymbol{E}}{\partial \alpha}\right)_0 \tag{6.22}$$

$$\boldsymbol{H} = (\boldsymbol{H})_0 + \alpha \left(\frac{\partial \boldsymbol{H}}{\partial \alpha}\right)_0 \tag{6.23}$$

where the subscript 0 indicates that the quantity in parentheses is evaluated for $\alpha = 0$. These two equations are valid at each point in space and for each value of $\tau$; thus the values of $\boldsymbol{E}$ and $\boldsymbol{H}$ evaluated for $\alpha = 0$, and their derivatives with respect to $\alpha$, also evaluated for $\alpha = 0$, are all functions of $x$, $y$, $z$, and $\tau$.

The derivatives with respect to $\alpha$ in Eqs. 6.22 and 6.23 can be evaluated directly from the field laws. In fact, differentiating Eqs. 6.19, 6.20, and 6.21 with respect to $\alpha$, and setting $\alpha$ equal to zero yields,

$$\text{curl} \left(\frac{\partial \boldsymbol{E}}{\partial \alpha}\right)_0 = -\frac{\partial}{\partial \tau} (\boldsymbol{B})_0 \tag{6.24}$$

$$\text{curl} \left(\frac{\partial \boldsymbol{H}}{\partial \alpha}\right)_0 = \left(\frac{\partial \boldsymbol{J}_f}{\partial \alpha}\right)_0 + \frac{\partial}{\partial \tau} (\boldsymbol{D})_0 \tag{6.25}$$

$$\text{div} \left(\frac{\partial \boldsymbol{J}_f}{\partial \alpha}\right)_0 = -\frac{\partial}{\partial \tau} (\rho_f)_0 \tag{6.26}$$

The quantities that are differentiated with respect to $\tau$ on the right-hand side of these equations can be obtained from the static solutions and, therefore, can be considered as known. It follows that $(\partial \boldsymbol{E}/\partial \alpha)_0$ and $(\partial \boldsymbol{H}/\partial \alpha)_0$ can be determined independently in succession just like static fields. Thus, both terms on the right-hand side of Eq. 6.22 and 6.23 can be evaluated without having to solve the field equations simultaneously.

If the linear approximations given by Eqs. 6.22 and 6.23 are not satisfactory, square terms in $\alpha$ can be added, proportional to the second derivatives of $\boldsymbol{E}$ and $\boldsymbol{H}$ with respect to $\alpha$, evaluated for $\alpha = 0$. Next, cubic terms can be added, proportional to the third derivatives, and so forth. The equations that the successive derivatives with respect to $\alpha$ must satisfy are more readily derived by approaching the problem more directly, as shown below.

Since the electric field and the magnetic field are functions of the parameter $\alpha$ as well as functions of $x$, $y$, $z$, and $\tau$, they can be expressed as power series in $\alpha$,

$$\boldsymbol{E}(x, y, z, \tau, \alpha) = \boldsymbol{E}_0(x, y, z, \tau) + \alpha \boldsymbol{E}_1(x, y, z, \tau) + \alpha^2 \boldsymbol{E}_2(x, y, z, \tau) + \cdots \tag{6.27}$$

$$\boldsymbol{H}(x, y, z, \tau, \alpha) = \boldsymbol{H}_0(x, y, z, \tau) + \alpha \boldsymbol{H}_1(x, y, z, \tau) + \alpha^2 \boldsymbol{H}_2(x, y, z, \tau) + \cdots \tag{6.28}$$

where

$$\boldsymbol{E}_0(x, y, z, \tau) = [\boldsymbol{E}(x, y, z, \tau, \alpha)]_{\alpha=0} \tag{6.29}$$

$$\boldsymbol{E}_1(x, y, z, \tau) = \left[\frac{\partial \boldsymbol{E}(x, y, z, \tau, \alpha)}{\partial \alpha}\right]_{\alpha=0} \tag{6.30}$$

$$\boldsymbol{E}_k(x, y, z, \tau) = \frac{1}{k!}\left[\frac{\partial^k \boldsymbol{E}(x, y, z, \tau, \alpha)}{\partial \alpha^k}\right]_{\alpha=0} \tag{6.31}$$

and $\boldsymbol{H}_0$, $\boldsymbol{H}_1$, $\boldsymbol{H}_k$ are defined in a similar manner. All the other electromagnetic quantities can be expressed, similarly, as power series in $\alpha$.

These expressions are then introduced into Eqs. 6.19, 6.20, and 6.21. It is assumed in this regard that all series can be differentiated term by term with respect to the independent variables $x$, $y$, $z$, and $\tau$, so that, for instance,

$$\text{curl } \boldsymbol{E} = \text{curl } \boldsymbol{E}_0 + \alpha \text{ curl } \boldsymbol{E}_1 + \alpha^2 \text{ curl } \boldsymbol{E}_2 + \cdots$$

Then, if all terms in each equation are combined on one side, Eqs. 6.19, 6.20, and 6.21 take the form of power series in $\alpha$ equated to zero. For instance, Eq. 6.19 becomes

$$\text{curl } \boldsymbol{E}_0 + \alpha\left(\text{curl } \boldsymbol{E}_1 + \frac{\partial \boldsymbol{B}_0}{\partial \tau}\right) + \alpha^2\left(\text{curl } \boldsymbol{E}_2 + \frac{\partial \boldsymbol{B}_1}{\partial \tau}\right) + \cdots = 0 \tag{6.32}$$

This equation must be satisfied for all values of $\alpha$; i.e., the infinite sum of the terms on the left-hand side must be equal to zero for all values of $\alpha$. This condition can be met only if the coefficients of all the powers of $\alpha$ are separately equal to zero. The same is true for the corresponding equations obtained from Eqs. 6.20 and 6.21. It follows that each of these equations separates into a series of equations. We obtain for the zero-order set

$$\text{curl } \boldsymbol{E}_0 = 0 \tag{6.33}$$

$$\text{curl } \boldsymbol{H}_0 = \boldsymbol{J}_{f0} \tag{6.34}$$

$$\text{div } \boldsymbol{J}_{f0} = 0 \tag{6.35}$$

for the first-order set

$$\operatorname{curl} \boldsymbol{E}_1 = -\frac{\partial \boldsymbol{B}_0}{\partial \tau} \tag{6.36}$$

$$\operatorname{curl} \boldsymbol{H}_1 = \boldsymbol{J}_{f1} + \frac{\partial \boldsymbol{D}_0}{\partial \tau} \tag{6.37}$$

$$\operatorname{div} \boldsymbol{J}_{f1} = -\frac{\partial \rho_{f0}}{\partial \tau} \tag{6.38}$$

and, in general, for the $k$th-order set,

$$\operatorname{curl} \boldsymbol{E}_k = -\frac{\partial}{\partial \tau} \boldsymbol{B}_{k-1} \tag{6.39}$$

$$\operatorname{curl} \boldsymbol{H}_k = \boldsymbol{J}_{fk} + \frac{\partial}{\partial \tau} \boldsymbol{D}_{k-1} \tag{6.40}$$

$$\operatorname{div} \boldsymbol{J}_{fk} = -\frac{\partial}{\partial \tau} \rho_{f(k-1)} \tag{6.41}$$

where all quantities involved are, in general, functions of $x$, $y$, $z$, and $\tau$.

The other two field equations, namely, Eqs. 6.3 and 6.4, do not involve explicitly the parameter $\alpha$, and therefore yield series of equations involving only terms of the same order. We have in general

$$\operatorname{div} \boldsymbol{D}_k = \rho_{fk} \tag{6.42}$$

$$\operatorname{div} \boldsymbol{B}_k = 0 \tag{6.43}$$

The same is true for the constituent relations, as long as they depend only on the space coordinates.

The zero-order equations (Eqs. 6.33 to 6.35) are clearly of the static type, as expected. Thus $\boldsymbol{E}_0$ and $\boldsymbol{H}_0$ can be determined independently as static fields, although they are both functions of the family time $\tau$. They can be regarded, from a physical point of view, as slowly varying static fields. The first-order equations are also solvable by static-field methods because the derivatives with respect to $\tau$ of $\boldsymbol{B}_0$, $\boldsymbol{D}_0$, and $\rho_{f0}$ can be obtained from the zero-order fields. The $k$th-order equations are similarly solvable by static-field methods because the quantities that are differentiated with respect to $\tau$ can be obtained from the fields of order $k - 1$. Thus, all the terms in the series expansions of $\boldsymbol{E}$ and $\boldsymbol{H}$ can be evaluated in succession by solving only equations of the static type.

The actual electromagnetic field of interest is the member of the family of fields corresponding to $\alpha = 1$. Thus, for instance, the actual electric field and the actual magnetic field are given by the sums of the coefficients of the powers of $\alpha$ in Eqs. 6.27 and 6.28, with $t$ substituted for $\tau$. The number of terms in each series that must be evaluated in order to obtain a satisfactory approximation depends, of course, on the particular problem considered. Similarly, little can be said in general about the convergence of the series involved. Therefore these questions will be dealt with, when necessary, in connection with specific physical problems.

In concluding, let us summarize the basic ideas involved in the method of successive approximations developed above. To start with, we enlarged the scope of the problem under consideration by considering a family of electromagnetic fields generated from the desired field by changing the time scale of its sources. This was done, formally, by substituting a family time $\tau = \alpha t$ for the real time $t$, where $\alpha$ was a time-rate parameter describing the resulting family of electromagnetic fields. Thus, a value of $\alpha$ larger than one corresponded to compressing the time scale, i.e., to speeding up the electromagnetic phenomenon in question. Conversely, a value of $\alpha$ smaller than one corresponded to stretching the time scale, i.e., to slowing down the electromagnetic phenomenon in question. The advantage resulting from the definition of such a family of electromagnetic fields was that each electromagnetic quantity became a function of the parameter $\alpha$ as well as a function of the space coordinates and of the family time. This gave us the opportunity to start from static field solutions corresponding to $\alpha = 0$, and work our way toward the desired electromagnetic field along the path provided by the new variable $\alpha$; this was accomplished by computing successive corrections to the original static fields as the value of $\alpha$ was increased. The intuitive idea of working our way from $\alpha = 0$ to $\alpha = 1$ in successive steps was then identified with the mathematical process of representing all electromagnetic quantities as power series in $\alpha$. The coefficients of these series, being proportional to successive derivatives with respect to $\alpha$, evaluated for $\alpha = 0$, were found to satisfy field equations of the static type. Thus, the entire process turned out to involve only determinations of static fields. The details of the process are illustrated in the next section.

## 6.4 Example of Power Series Solution

The power series method developed in the preceding sections is illustrated below by applying it to the determination of an electromagnetic

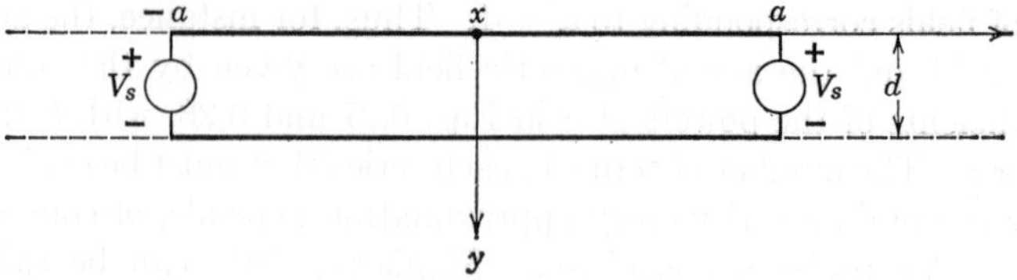


**Fig. 6.3.** Parallel-plate system analyzed in Sec. 6.4.

field of the simplest possible type, namely, a field which depends on a single Cartesian coordinate. Fields of this type can be generated, in principle, by connecting idealized voltage sources between parallel, perfectly conducting sheets, and can be approximated in practice by connecting physical sources between the terminals of parallel-plate transmission lines. The particular example on which we shall focus our attention is illustrated schematically in Fig. 6.3. Two parallel conducting plates, normal to the $y$-axis are fed symmetrically by voltage sources connected between their edges at $z = a$ and $z = -a$. The length $2a$ is very much greater than the spacing $d$ between the two plates, and the width of the plates in the direction of the $x$-axis is also appreciably greater than $d$. Furthermore the plates have such a high conductivity that they act as infinitely conducting sheets, at least for the purposes of our analysis. Under these conditions, the electromagnetic field between the plates is, for all practical purposes, independent of $x$ and $y$, except near the edges of the plates. We shall idealize this situation in such a way as to make the field exactly independent of $x$ and $y$, by making the plates infinite in both the $x$ and $y$ directions and by regarding the voltage sources as devices that force the electric field to be uniform and parallel to the $y$-axis over the planes $z = a$ and $z = -a$; we shall confine our attention hereafter to the space between these planes.

We wish to determine the electromagnetic field between the conducting sheets in general terms, without specifying the time dependence of the voltage sources, except for the fact that the two voltage sources at opposite ends of the plates are identical. Because of the symmetry of the system, it is convenient to use as a reference the electric field on the plane $z = 0$, i.e., on the plane of symmetry, rather than the source voltage. Thus, we shall characterize the family of electromagnetic fields by requiring the electric field on the plane $z = 0$ to be a function of the family time, independent of the time-rate parameter. More precisely, since the electric field is, by assumption, uniform and parallel to the $y$-axis, we set

$$(\boldsymbol{E})_{z=0} = \boldsymbol{i}_y \frac{V_0(\tau)}{d} \tag{6.44}$$

where $V_0(\tau)$, a function of the family time alone, represents the voltage between the plates on the plane of symmetry of the system. This implies that, when the electric field is expressed as a power series in $\alpha$, the zero-order term must assume the value given by Eq. 6.44 for $z = 0$, and all higher order terms must vanish for $z = 0$. This follows from the fact that the electric field is, by assumption, independent of $\alpha$ for $z = 0$.

The zero-order electric field must satisfy the static-field equations

$$\text{curl } \boldsymbol{E}_0 = 0 \tag{6.45}$$

$$\text{div } \boldsymbol{E}_0 = 0 \tag{6.46}$$

must be normal to the perfectly conducting plates, and must assume the value given by Eq. 6.44 for $z = 0$. It follows that the zero-order electric field is uniform and parallel to the $y$-axis throughout the space between the conducting sheets,

$$\boldsymbol{E}_0 = \boldsymbol{i}_y \frac{V_0(\tau)}{d} = \boldsymbol{i}_y E_{0y}(\tau) \tag{6.47}$$

where $E_{0y}(\tau)$ is a scalar function of the variable $\tau$ alone. The zero-order surface charge on the upper conducting plate has, correspondingly, a density

$$\sigma_0 = \epsilon_0 E_{0y}(\tau) \tag{6.48}$$

and, therefore, is uniformly distributed over the plate. The charge on the lower plate has the same magnitude and opposite sign. The subscript $f$ indicating free charge or free current is dropped in this example to simplify the notations in view of the absence of polarized matter.

The current flow in the system is restricted to the conducting plates, and, therefore, can be represented by a surface current density $\boldsymbol{K}$. The zero-order component of this current density, because of Eq. 6.35, must satisfy the two-dimensional divergence equation, defined in Sec. 3.2,

$$\text{div}_\Sigma \, \boldsymbol{K}_0 = 0 \tag{6.49}$$

and, therefore, it must be constant. On the other hand, the symmetry of the system requires the current density to be an odd function of $z$. It follows that the zero-order current is equal to zero, as expected in view of the static character of the field.

The zero-order magnetic field must satisfy the static equations

$$\text{curl}\,\boldsymbol{H}_0 = \boldsymbol{J}_0 \tag{6.50}$$

$$\text{div}\,\boldsymbol{H}_0 = 0 \tag{6.51}$$

On the other hand, no zero-order currents are present anywhere. It follows that the zero-order magnetic field vanishes everywhere.

The first-order electric field must satisfy Eqs. 6.36 and 6.42, which, in view of the absence of any zero-order magnetic field, reduce to

$$\text{curl}\,\boldsymbol{E}_1 = 0 \tag{6.52}$$

$$\text{div}\,\boldsymbol{E}_1 = 0 \tag{6.53}$$

Again, only a uniform field, parallel to the $y$-axis, can satisfy these equations and be normal to the conducting plates. The first-order electric field must vanish for $z = 0$, as stated above. It follows that this field must vanish everywhere, and, as a consequence, there cannot be any first-order charge on the plates.

The first-order current on the plates must satisfy Eq. 6.38, which reduces to the two-dimensional equation

$$\text{div}_\Sigma\,\boldsymbol{K}_1 = -\frac{\partial\sigma_0}{\partial\tau} \tag{6.54}$$

However, because of the one-dimensional character of the system, current can flow only in the $z$ direction. It follows that this equation reduces to

$$\frac{\partial K_{1z}}{\partial z} = \mp\epsilon_0\frac{dE_{0y}(\tau)}{d\tau} \tag{6.55}$$

where the minus sign applies to the upper plate ($y = 0$) and the plus sign applies to the lower plate ($y = d$). Thus, we obtain by integration

$$K_{1z} = \mp\epsilon_0 z\frac{dE_{0y}(\tau)}{d\tau} \tag{6.56}$$

where the constant of integration has been set equal to zero in view of the symmetry of the system.

The first-order magnetic field must satisfy Eqs. 6.37 and 6.43. In the space between the two conducting plates, these equations reduce to

$$\text{curl}\,\boldsymbol{H}_1 = -\boldsymbol{i}_x\frac{\partial H_{1y}}{\partial z} + \boldsymbol{i}_y\frac{\partial H_{1x}}{\partial z} = \boldsymbol{i}_y\epsilon_0\frac{dE_{0y}(\tau)}{d\tau} \tag{6.57}$$

$$\text{div}\,\boldsymbol{H}_1 = \frac{\partial H_{1z}}{\partial z} = 0 \tag{6.58}$$

in view of the one-dimensional character of the field. Integration with respect to $z$ yields then

$$H_{1x} = \epsilon_0 z \frac{dE_{0y}(\tau)}{d\tau} \tag{6.59}$$

$$H_{1y} = H_{1z} = 0 \tag{6.60}$$

where the integration constants have again been set equal to zero because of the symmetry of the system and because of the absence of currents that can generate uniform fields in the $y$ and $z$ directions. Thus, the first-order magnetic field in the space between the plates is parallel to the $x$-axis, and varies linearly as an odd function of $z$. Its magnitude is just equal to the magnitude of the surface current density on the plates, given by Eq. 6.56. Thus, in accordance with Eq. 3.31, the $x$ component of the first-order magnetic field is discontinuous at the two plates and vanishes in the space outside the plates.

Let us proceed next to the evaluation of the second-order terms. The electric field must satisfy Eqs. 6.39 and 6.42, for $k = 2$. In the space between the two plates, these equations reduce to

$$\text{curl } \boldsymbol{E}_2 = -\boldsymbol{i}_x \frac{\partial E_{2y}}{\partial z} + \boldsymbol{i}_y \frac{\partial E_{2x}}{\partial z} = -\boldsymbol{i}_x \mu_0 \frac{\partial H_{1x}}{\partial \tau} \tag{6.61}$$

$$\text{div } \boldsymbol{E}_2 = \frac{\partial E_{2z}}{\partial z} = 0 \tag{6.62}$$

in view of the one-dimensional character of the field. We obtain then, by integration, and with the help of Eq. 6.59,

$$E_{2y} = \epsilon_0 \mu_0 \frac{z^2}{2} \frac{d^2 E_{0y}(\tau)}{d\tau^2} \tag{6.63}$$

$$E_{2x} = E_{2z} = 0$$

where the integration constants have been set again equal to zero because $E_{2y}$ must vanish for $z = 0$ and because the entire electric field must be normal to the conducting plates. Thus the second-order electric field is parallel to the $y$-axis, and proportional to $z^2$.

The second-order charge on the plates has a density

$$\sigma_2 = \pm {\epsilon_0}^2 \mu_0 \frac{z^2}{2} \frac{d^2 E_{0y}(\tau)}{d\tau^2} \tag{6.64}$$

where the plus sign applies to the upper plate ($y = 0$), and the minus sign to the lower plate ($y = d$). The second-order current, on the other hand, is equal to zero, because the first-order charge is equal to zero. Similarly, the second-order magnetic field is equal to zero because the first-order electric field and the second-order current are equal to zero. In fact, for $k = 2$, the right-hand side of Eq. 6.40, which includes all the sources of $\boldsymbol{H}_2$ vanishes everywhere.

The pattern of the successive terms should be clear by now. We have in general

$$\boldsymbol{E}_k = \begin{cases} 0 & k \text{ odd} \\ \boldsymbol{i}_y c^{-k} \dfrac{z^k}{k!} \dfrac{d^k E_{0y}(\tau)}{d\tau^k} & k \text{ even} \end{cases} \tag{6.65}$$

$$\boldsymbol{H}_k = \begin{cases} \boldsymbol{i}_x \sqrt{\dfrac{\epsilon_0}{\mu_0}}\, c^{-k} \dfrac{z^k}{k!} \dfrac{d^k E_{0y}(\tau)}{d\tau^k} & k \text{ odd} \\ 0 & k \text{ even} \end{cases} \tag{6.66}$$

$$\sigma_k = \pm \epsilon_0 E_{ky} \tag{6.67}$$

$$K_{kz} = \mp H_{kx} \tag{6.68}$$

where

$$c = \frac{1}{\sqrt{\epsilon_0 \mu_0}} \tag{6.69}$$

is the velocity of light in free space; the upper signs in Eqs. 6.67 and 6.68 apply to the upper plate ($y = 0$), and the lower signs to the lower plate ($y = d$). Thus, the desired power-series expressions for the families of electric fields and of magnetic fields are

$$\boldsymbol{E}(\alpha, \tau, z) = \boldsymbol{i}_y \sum_{k \text{ even}} \frac{1}{k!} \left(\frac{\alpha z}{c}\right)^k \frac{d^k E_{0y}(\tau)}{d\tau^k} \tag{6.70}$$

$$\boldsymbol{H}(\alpha, \tau, z) = \boldsymbol{i}_x \sqrt{\frac{\epsilon_0}{\mu_0}} \sum_{k \text{ odd}} \frac{1}{k!} \left(\frac{\alpha z}{c}\right)^k \frac{d^k E_{0y}(\tau)}{d\tau^k} \tag{6.71}$$

The corresponding family of source voltages is given by

$$V_s(\alpha, \tau) = [E_y(\alpha, \tau, z)]_{z=a} d \tag{6.72}$$

As expected, the source voltages are functions of $\alpha$ as well as of $\tau$ because the electric field on the plane $z = 0$ has been used as a reference by making it independent of $\alpha$.

Let us suppose, more specifically, that the system is sinusoidally excited in such a way that the electric field on the plane $z = 0$ is

$$[\boldsymbol{E}(t)]_{z=0} = \boldsymbol{i}_y A \cos \omega t \tag{6.73}$$

where $A$ is a constant, and $\omega$ is the angular frequency. We have, then, by substituting $\tau$ for $t$,

$$E_{0y} = A \cos \omega\tau \tag{6.74}$$

from which we obtain

$$\frac{d^k E_{0y}(\tau)}{d\tau^k} = \begin{cases} (-1)^{(k+1)/2} A\omega^k \sin \omega\tau & k \text{ odd} \\ (-1)^{k/2} A\omega^k \cos \omega\tau & k \text{ even} \end{cases} \tag{6.75}$$

Substitution of these expressions in Eqs. 6.70 and 6.71 yields for the family of electromagnetic fields

$$\begin{aligned} \boldsymbol{E}(\alpha, \tau, z) &= \boldsymbol{i}_y \left[ \sum_{k \text{ even}} (-1)^{k/2} \frac{1}{k!} \left( \frac{\alpha\omega z}{c} \right)^k \right] A \cos \omega\tau \\ &= \boldsymbol{i}_y A \cos \frac{\alpha\omega z}{c} \cos \omega\tau \end{aligned} \tag{6.76}$$

$$\begin{aligned} \boldsymbol{H}(\alpha, \tau, z) &= \boldsymbol{i}_x \sqrt{\frac{\epsilon_0}{\mu_0}} \left[ \sum_{k \text{ odd}} (-1)^{(k+1)/2} \frac{1}{k!} \left( \frac{\alpha\omega z}{c} \right)^k \right] A \sin \omega\tau \\ &= -\boldsymbol{i}_x A \sqrt{\frac{\epsilon_0}{\mu_0}} \sin \frac{\alpha\omega z}{c} \sin \omega\tau \end{aligned} \tag{6.77}$$

The desired member of this family is then obtained by substituting $\alpha t$ for $\tau$, and setting $\alpha = 1$, which is equivalent to making the frequency equal to $\omega$. Thus

$$\boldsymbol{E}(t, z) = \boldsymbol{i}_y A \cos \frac{\omega z}{c} \cos \omega t \tag{6.78}$$

$$\boldsymbol{H}(t, z) = -\boldsymbol{i}_x A \sqrt{\frac{\epsilon_0}{\mu_0}} \sin \frac{\omega z}{c} \sin \omega t \tag{6.79}$$

Plots of $E_y$ and $H_x$ at times corresponding to $\omega t$ equal to 0, $\pi/4$, and $\pi/2$, are shown in Fig. 6.4. The phase of the time variation of the electric field is the same at all points; so is the phase of the time variation of the magnetic field. On the other hand, the phase of $H_x$ and that of $E_y$ differ by $\pi/2$. The electric field has its largest amplitude on the plane of symmetry of the system ($z = 0$), and is an even, cosinusoidal function of $z$ with a period

$$\lambda = \frac{2\pi}{\omega} c = \frac{2\pi}{\omega\sqrt{\epsilon_0\mu_0}} \tag{6.80}$$

We refer to this period as the wave length. The higher the frequency,

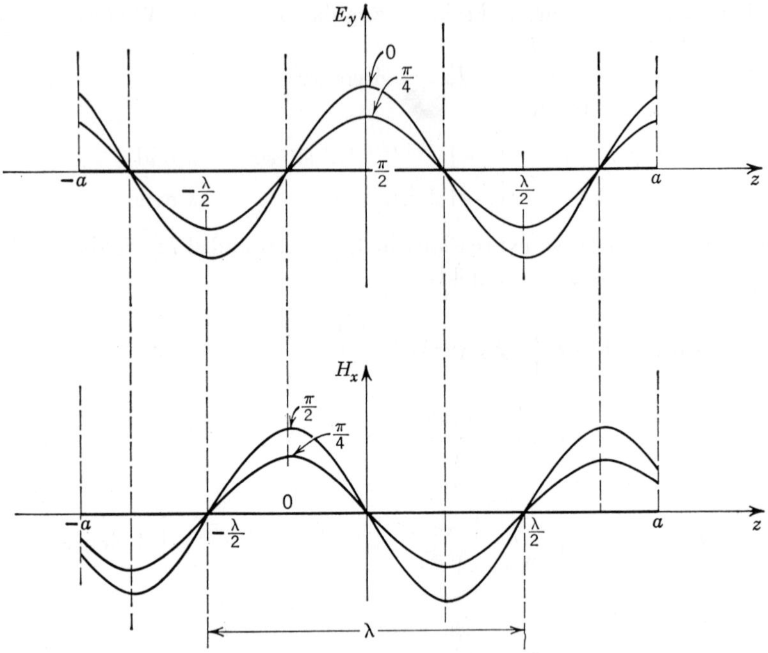


**Fig. 6.4.** Plots of $E_y$ and $H_x$ in system of Fig. 6.3 for $\omega t = 0, \pi/4, \pi/2$.

the more periods fit in the length $2a$ between the sources. The magnetic field, on the other hand, is an odd sinusoidal function of $z$, with the same period $\lambda$ and, therefore, it is equal to zero on the plane of symmetry of the system.

The study of the general properties of the electromagnetic field given by Eqs. 6.78 and 6.79 is beyond the scope of the present discussion; it constitutes one of the major topics treated in a separate book by the same authors.[1] The main objective of the above derivation is to illustrate the power-series method of analysis in a case in which all the terms of the series can be readily evaluated and summed. As a matter of fact, Eqs. 6.78 and 6.79 could be derived more directly as simultaneous solutions of Maxwell's equations. The power-series method becomes useful when the simultaneous solution of Maxwell's equations is not feasible, yet the first two or three terms of the series provide a sufficiently accurate answer.

[1] R. B. Adler, L. J. Chu, R. M. Fano, *Electromagnetic Energy Transmission and Radiation*, John Wiley & Sons, New York, 1960.

Let us suppose, for instance, that the frequency of excitation is so low that only a small fraction of a period $\lambda$ fits in the length $2a$ between the voltage sources, i.e.,

$$\frac{2a}{\lambda} = \frac{2a\omega\sqrt{\epsilon_0\mu_0}}{2\pi} \ll 1 \tag{6.81}$$

Equations 6.78 and 6.79 indicate that in such a case the amplitude of the electric field is approximately $z$-independent in the space between the sources, and the amplitude of the magnetic field varies linearly with $z$, as illustrated in Fig. 6.5. This is just the behavior given by the zero-order and first-order terms in the series on the right-hand sides of Eqs. 6.76 and 6.77. In fact,

$$\boldsymbol{E}_0 + \alpha\boldsymbol{E}_1 = \boldsymbol{i}_y A \cos \omega\tau \tag{6.82}$$

$$\boldsymbol{H}_0 + \alpha\boldsymbol{H}_1 = -\boldsymbol{i}_x A\,\epsilon_0\alpha\omega z \sin \omega\tau \tag{6.83}$$

Substituting $\alpha t$ for $\tau$ and setting $\alpha = 1$, yields the approximate expressions

$$\boldsymbol{E} = \boldsymbol{i}_y A \cos \omega t \tag{6.84}$$

$$\boldsymbol{H} = -\boldsymbol{i}_x A\omega\epsilon_0 z \sin \omega t \tag{6.85}$$

The higher order terms can be safely neglected if

$$\frac{\omega z}{c} = 2\pi\frac{z}{\lambda} \ll 1 \tag{6.86}$$

a limitation equivalent to that expressed by Eq. 6.81. Under these conditions, the voltage between the two plates is given approximately by

$$V = Ad \cos \omega t = |V_s| \cos \omega t \tag{6.87}$$

where $|V_s|$ is the amplitude of the source voltage. The charge density

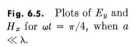

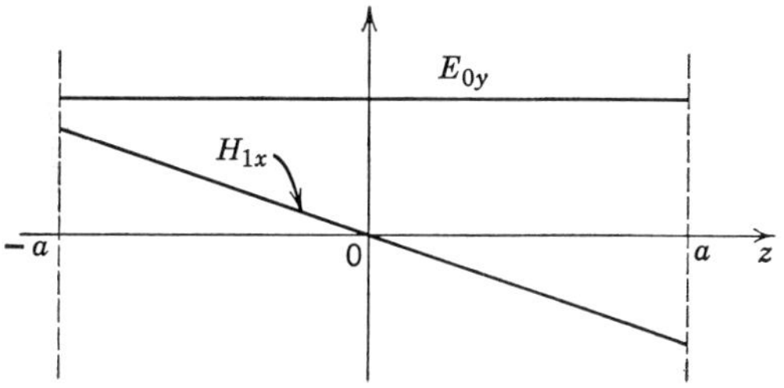


**Fig. 6.5.** Plots of $E_y$ and $H_x$ for $\omega t = \pi/4$, when $a \ll \lambda$.

on the upper plate is

$$\sigma = \epsilon_0 \frac{|V_s|}{d} \cos \omega t \tag{6.88}$$

and the current density, also on the upper plate is

$$K_z = -H_x = \omega\epsilon_0 \frac{|V_s|}{d} z \sin \omega t \tag{6.89}$$

In particular, the amplitude of each source current (per unit width in the $x$ direction) is given by

$$|K_z|_{z=a} = \omega \frac{\epsilon_0 a}{d} |V_s| = \omega C |V_s| \tag{6.90}$$

where $C$ is the capacitance (per unit width in the $x$ direction) of the capacitor formed by the plates on each side of the plane of symmetry. Thus, as expected, the system behaves like a parallel-plate capacitor at sufficiently low frequencies.

The usefulness of the power-series approach lies in the fact that the zero-order and first-order fields are sufficient to describe the behavior of systems at low frequencies, i.e., when the dimensions of the system are small compared to the wave length, as illustrated above. We shall see in the following sections that, when such approximations are valid, complex electromagnetic systems can usually be divided into component parts, corresponding to circuit elements, with the result that their over-all behavior can then be studied by means of circuit theory. Thus, with the help of the power-series method of analysis, we shall be able to appreciate in detail the relation between circuit theory and field theory.

## 6.5 Circuit Theory as a Quasi-Static Approximation

Since the phenomena described by circuit theory are clearly of electromagnetic nature, the concepts and laws of circuit theory should be derivable from Maxwell's equations. On the other hand, there are electromagnetic phenomena, such as radiation, that are adequately described by Maxwell's equations but not by circuit laws. Thus, circuit theory can be regarded as describing a restricted class of solutions of Maxwell's equations.

The concepts and laws of circuit theory are much older than Maxwell's equations, and date back to the days when experimental investigation was limited to relatively slow electromagnetic phenomena.

Correspondingly, the class of solutions of Maxwell's equations that are adequately described by circuit theory are characterized by slow time variations. The rest of this chapter is devoted to a detailed study of this class of solutions with the objective of establishing a clear connection between circuit theory and field theory.

The power-series formalism developed in the preceding sections provides us with the tool appropriate for this endeavor. In fact, in any family of electromagnetic fields, the number of power-series terms necessary to represent with adequate accuracy a particular member of the family increases with the value of $\alpha$ corresponding to the particular member. The time rate of change of each member field, in turn, is proportional to the value of $\alpha$, which, for this reason, has been referred to as the time-rate parameter. Thus, in the limit of vanishingly small time rates, i.e., when $\alpha$ approaches zero, the zero-order terms alone provide an adequate representation. On the other hand, for small but finite time rates of change, the first-order terms must also be taken into account. More precisely, for every power-series representation of a family of electromagnetic fields there exists a range of values of the parameter $\alpha$ for which sufficient accuracy can be obtained by disregarding all terms of order higher than the first one. In other words, each family of electromagnetic fields includes members with sufficiently slow time variations so that they can be represented solely by zero-order and first-order terms. We shall refer to any such member field as *quasi-static*, and show that this class of fields includes the solutions of Maxwell's equations that are adequately described by circuit theory.

The time-rate parameter $\alpha$ was introduced in our discussion for the purpose of justifying the power-series expansions of electromagnetic fields and of emphasizing the relation between the successive terms of the series and the time rate of change of the electromagnetic field. Now, after having achieved these objectives, the parameter $\alpha$ can be eliminated from our discussion by setting its value equal to one, and $\tau$ equal to $t$. In fact, any member of a family of fields generated by varying the value of $\alpha$ is a physically realizable field, regardless of the value of $\alpha$ corresponding to it. Any member of the family can be regarded as the original field from which the family was obtained, i.e., as the member of the family corresponding to $\alpha = 1$. It should be remembered in this regard that $\alpha$ is only a relative measure of the time rate of change, not an absolute measure; thus the value corresponding to a particular field can be changed arbitrarily by appropriately modifying the time dependence of the driving forces. We can conclude, therefore, that no loss of generality will result in the following discussion of quasi-static fields from assuming that the field under consideration corresponds to $\alpha = 1$. With this assumption, Eqs. 6.27 and 6.28 yield for quasi-static fields,

$$\boldsymbol{E} = \boldsymbol{E}_0 + \boldsymbol{E}_1 \tag{6.91}$$

$$\boldsymbol{H} = \boldsymbol{H}_0 + \boldsymbol{H}_1 \tag{6.92}$$

Since the main objective of the following discussion is to relate the concepts of field theory to those of circuit theory, we shall assume for the sake of simplicity that all materials in the system under consideration are linear and isotropic. Thus the constituent relations become simply

$$\boldsymbol{D} = \epsilon \boldsymbol{E} \tag{6.93}$$

$$\boldsymbol{B} = \mu \boldsymbol{H} \tag{6.94}$$

$$\boldsymbol{J}_f = \sigma \boldsymbol{E} \tag{6.95}$$

The zero-order equations can then be rewritten in the simpler form

$$\text{curl } \boldsymbol{E}_0 = 0 \tag{6.96}$$

$$\text{curl } \boldsymbol{H}_0 = \boldsymbol{J}_{f0} \tag{6.97}$$

$$\text{div } \epsilon \boldsymbol{E}_0 = \rho_{f0} \tag{6.98}$$

$$\text{div } \mu \boldsymbol{H}_0 = 0 \tag{6.99}$$

$$\text{div } \boldsymbol{J}_{f0} = 0 \tag{6.100}$$

and the first-order equations in the corresponding form

$$\text{curl } \boldsymbol{E}_1 = -\mu \frac{\partial \boldsymbol{H}_0}{\partial t} \tag{6.101}$$

$$\text{curl } \boldsymbol{H}_1 = \epsilon \frac{\partial \boldsymbol{E}_0}{\partial t} + \boldsymbol{J}_{f1} \tag{6.102}$$

$$\text{div } \epsilon \boldsymbol{E}_1 = \rho_{f1} \tag{6.103}$$

$$\text{div } \mu \boldsymbol{H}_1 = 0 \tag{6.104}$$

$$\text{div } \boldsymbol{J}_{f1} = -\frac{\partial \rho_{f0}}{\partial t} \tag{6.105}$$

where all the electromagnetic quantities are functions of $t$ and of the space coordinates. The current density is still written directly as $\boldsymbol{J}_f$ rather than as $\sigma \boldsymbol{E}$, because we will want to assume, in some cases, that the conductivity is infinite.

Inspection of the above equations indicates that there exist three basic types of quasi-static fields, which can be classified according to the character of their zero-order terms. It is apparent from Eqs. 6.95 and 6.97 that, in the absence of conduction current, or when the conductivity is infinite, no coupling exists between the zero-order electric field and the zero-order magnetic field. In any such case the zero-order electric field and the zero-order magnetic field are independent of each other and, therefore, can be dealt with separately. Therefore, we can classify the resulting solutions of the zero-order equations into two basic types:

1. Solutions of the electric type, characterized by the absence of a zero-order magnetic field;
2. solutions of the magnetic type, characterized by the absence of a zero-order electric field.

Solutions of these two basic types may, of course, coexist in the same region of space as well as in different regions. The important fact to remember is that they are totally independent. Thus, for instance, the electric field associated with a lossless capacitor and the magnetic field associated with a lossless coil are totally independent even if they exist in the same region of space.

The third basic type of zero-order solutions is associated with the presence of currents that depend on the electric field. Although convection currents as well as conduction currents in finitely conducting media can give rise to such solutions, we shall limit our discussion to the latter type of currents. In accordance with Eq. 6.95, we have for the conduction-current density

$$\boldsymbol{J}_{0f} = \sigma \boldsymbol{E}_{0f} \tag{6.106}$$

so that Eq. 6.97 becomes

$$\operatorname{curl} \boldsymbol{H} = \sigma \boldsymbol{E}_0 \tag{6.107}$$

thereby introducing a one-directional coupling between the zero-order electric field and the zero-order magnetic field. Clearly, because of the one-directional character of the coupling, the electric field can be evaluated first, independently of the magnetic field. The magnetic field can be evaluated next, once the right-hand side of Eq. 6.107 has become a known quantity. Thus, we have for the third type of solutions of the zero-order equations:

3. Solutions characterized by a zero-order electric field and a zero-order magnetic field coupled by currents in a finitely conducting material.

We shall show presently that the three basic circuit elements, namely, capacitance, inductance, and resistance are associated with these three types of solutions.

Let us review, for this purpose, the circuit definitions of the three basic elements. Each branch of a network is characterized by two variables, namely, the branch voltage $V(t)$, and the branch current $I(t)$. Three possible types of linear relations can exist between these branch variables that involve, at most, their first time derivatives:

1. The branch current is proportional to the time derivative of the voltage

$$I = C\frac{dV}{dt} \tag{6.108}$$

where the proportionality constant $C$ is, by definition, the branch capacitance.

2. The branch voltage is proportional to the time derivative of the current

$$V = L\frac{dI}{dt} \tag{6.109}$$

where the proportionality constant $L$ is, by definition, the branch inductance.

3. The branch voltage is proportional to the current

$$V = RI \tag{6.110}$$

where the proportionality constant $R$ is, by definition, the branch resistance and its reciprocal $G$ is the branch conductance.

Thus, we may regard a capacitance as an element that couples a current to the time derivative of a voltage, an inductance as an element that couples a voltage to the time derivative of a current, and a resistance as an element that provides mutual coupling between voltage and current.

Let us now return our attention to the three types of quasi-static fields. A zero-order electric field of type 1 gives rise, because of Eq. 6.102, to a first-order magnetic field proportional to its time derivative. Correspondingly, the time derivative of the zero-order charge, associated with the zero-order electric field, gives rise, because of Eq. 6.105, to a first-order current associated with the first-order magnetic field. On the other hand, the zero-order electric field is conservative and, therefore, can be represented by a scalar potential. We can conclude, therefore, that the first-order current can be regarded as caused by the time derivative of the zero-order potential. This is just the type of functional relation characteristic of capacitances. The details of the reduction of the field quantities to branch currents and voltages are discussed in Sec. 6.7.

A zero-order magnetic field of type 2 gives rise, because of Eq. 6.101, to a first-order electric field proportional to its derivative. This electric field, however, is not conservative and, therefore, in general, it cannot be represented by a scalar potential. On the other hand, we shall show in Sec. 6.8 that nonconservative fields of this type can still be represented by suitably defined voltages, at least in connection with circuit components of practical interest. We can conclude, therefore, that the first-order electric field and any voltage associated with it can be regarded as caused by the time derivative of the current associated with the zero-order magnetic field. This is just the type of functional relation characteristic of inductances. The details of the reduction of the field quantities to branch currents and voltages are discussed in Secs. 6.8 and 6.9.

In the case of type-3 solutions, the zero-order electric field gives rise, because of Eq. 6.102, to a first-order magnetic field, while the zero-order magnetic field gives rise, because of Eq. 6.101, to a first-order electric field. The intensity of each first-order field may be either negligible or not negligible when compared to the intensity of the zero-order field of the same type. Thus, we have four different special cases:

3(*a*). Both first-order fields are negligible when compared to the zero-order fields, so that the electromagnetic field is adequately represented by the zero-order terms alone.

3(*b*). The first-order electric field is negligible when compared to the zero-order electric field.

3(*c*). The first-order magnetic field is negligible when compared to the zero-order magnetic field.

3(*d*). Neither one of the first-order fields can be neglected.

In case 3*a* the coupling between electric field and current density does not involve any time derivative; furthermore, the electric field is conservative and, therefore, can be represented by a scalar potential. It follows that the current density can be expressed in terms of the scalar potential, independently of any time derivative. This is just the type of functional relation characteristic of resistances. The details of the reduction of field quantities to branch voltages and currents are discussed in Sec. 6.6.

In case 3*b* the quasi-static magnetic field is the sum of a zero-order term and a first-order term. The zero-order term is produced by the zero-order electric field through the zero-order conduction current, just as in case 3*a*. The first-order term, on the other hand, is produced by the time derivative of the zero-order electric field, just as in the case of fields of type 1. Correspondingly, there is a first-order current, associated with the first-order magnetic field, and produced by the time derivative of the zero-order charge associated with the electric field, in accordance with Eq. 6.105. Furthermore, the electric field is conservative and can be represented by a scalar potential. We can conclude, therefore, that the current is the sum of two terms, of which the zero-order one can be regarded as caused directly by the potential, and the first-order one as caused by the time derivative of the potential. This situation corresponds, in circuit theory, to a functional relation of the type

$$I = GV + C\frac{dV}{dt} \tag{6.111}$$

and, therefore, to a parallel combination of a resistance and a capacitance.

In case 3*c* the quasi-static electric field is the sum of a zero-order term, and a first-order term. If we regard the zero-order current as the driving force of the system, the zero-order electric field is caused directly by the conduction current, and the first-order field is caused by the time-derivative of the same current, through the time derivative of the zero-order magnetic field associated with it, just as in the case of fields of type 2. Let us assume again that both electric fields can be represented by suitably defined voltages, in spite of the fact that the first-order field is not conservative. Then, we can conclude that each voltage consists of a zero-order component, caused by the zero-order current, and a first-order component caused by the time derivative of the same current. In circuit theory, this situation corresponds to a functional relation of the type

$$V = RI + L\frac{dI}{dt} \tag{6.112}$$

and, therefore, to a series combination of a resistance and an inductance.

In case 3*d* both zero-order fields, and both first-order fields must be taken into account. This results into four different couplings being involved simultaneously: the coupling between zero-order fields introduced by the zero-order conduction currents; the coupling between the first-order magnetic field and the time derivative of the zero-order electric field; the coupling between the first-order electric field and the time derivative of the zero-order magnetic field; the coupling between the two first-order fields introduced by the first-order conduction current. No corresponding situation exists in circuit theory.

The above discussion can be summarized as follows. The possible relations between voltages and currents in circuit theory correspond to relations between quasi-static electric fields and quasi-static magnetic fields. The three basic circuit elements correspond to the three possible combinations of one electric-field term and one magnetic-field term with the provision that at least one be of zero order. Consequently, the relations defining the three basic circuit elements correspond to the couplings between the fields of each of these three pairs, namely:

1. The capacitive coupling between first-order magnetic field and time derivative of the zero-order electric field.

2. The inductive coupling between first-order electric field and time derivative of the zero-order magnetic field.

3(*a*). The resistive coupling between zero-order electric field and zero-order magnetic field.

The two possible types of quasi-static fields in which one of the first-order fields can be neglected correspond to combinations of a resistance with one of the two other elements. Such fields involve, therefore, one of the following two pairs of couplings:

3(*b*). The pair formed by the capacitive coupling between first-order magnetic field and time derivative of the zero-order electric field in conjunction with the resistive coupling between zero-order fields. This pair of couplings corresponds to the parallel combination of a capacitance and a resistance.

3(*c*). The pair formed by the inductive coupling between first-order electric field and time derivative of the zero-order magnetic field, in conjunction with the resistive coupling between zero-order fields. This pair of couplings corresponds to the series combination of an inductance and a resistance.

Quasi-static fields involving both first-order fields fall outside the scope of circuit theory.

The first three types of quasi-static fields are discussed in greater detail in the following sections.

## ► 6.6 Multiterminal Conductors

We shall begin our detailed study of the quasi-static fields corresponding to circuit elements by considering the resistive fields of type

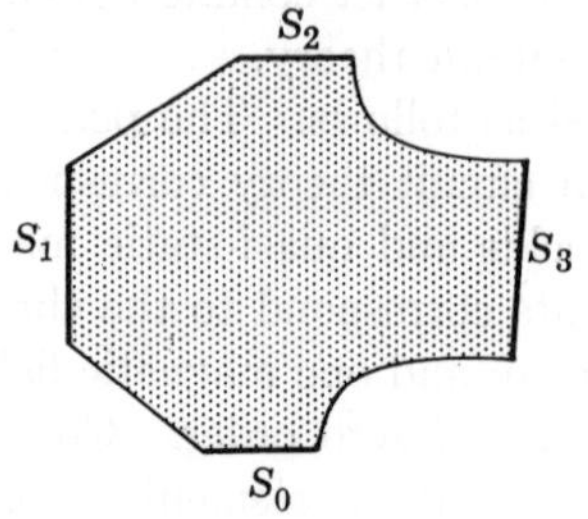


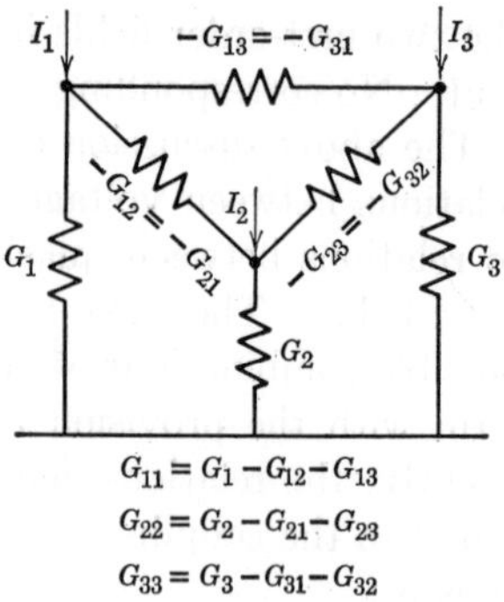


**Fig. 6.6.** Representation of a linear multiterminal conductor.

3*a*, which involve only zero-order terms. We observe, first of all, that, because of Eq. 6.96, the zero-order electric field is conservative and, therefore, it can be expressed as the negative gradient of a scalar potential $\phi_0$,

$$\boldsymbol{E}_0 = -\operatorname{grad} \phi_0 \tag{6.113}$$

The conduction current density can be expressed, correspondingly, in the form

$$\boldsymbol{J}_{f0} = \sigma \boldsymbol{E}_0 = -\sigma \operatorname{grad} \phi_0 \tag{6.114}$$

where the conductivity $\sigma$ is a function of the space coordinates alone.

Our objective is to reduce Eq. 6.114 to a circuit relation between suitably defined voltages and currents. In order for this to be possible, the system under consideration must possess terminals at which voltages and currents can be measured. In the model of a multiterminal conductor illustrated in Fig. 6.6*a* the surfaces $S_0$, $S_1$, $S_2$, and $S_3$ play the role of terminals. It is assumed that each of these surfaces is connected to a voltage source which forces the potential $\phi_0$ to assume the same value at all points of the surface. Thus, taking the surface $S_0$ as a zero-potential reference, each surface $S_k$ is assumed to be part of an equipotential surface characterized by a voltage $V_k$ measured with respect to $S_0$. An example of a multiterminal conductor is a block of graphite of the shape illustrated in Fig. 6.6*a*, plated with copper over the separate surfaces $S_0$, $S_1$, $S_2$, and $S_3$. Because of the great difference in conductivity between copper and graphite, the potential remains constant, for all practical purposes, over each of the four plated surfaces, regardless of the manner in which these surfaces are connected to voltage sources or to the terminals of other devices.

The current flowing through each of the terminal surfaces into the conducting medium is related to the current density and to the gradient of $\phi_0$ by integral expressions of the form

$$I_j = \int_{S_j} \boldsymbol{J}_{f0} \cdot \boldsymbol{n} \, da = -\int_{S_j} \sigma \boldsymbol{n} \cdot \text{grad } \phi_0 \, da \tag{6.115}$$

where the unit vector $\boldsymbol{n}$ is normal to the surface $S_j$, and inwardly directed. We shall refer to $I_j$ as the terminal current associated with the $j$th terminal and to $V_k$ as the voltage associated with the $k$th terminal, measured with respect to $S_0$.

The electric field $\boldsymbol{E}_0$ must satisfy Eq. 6.98, and the current density $\boldsymbol{J}_{0f}$ must satisfy Eq. 6.100. The latter equation becomes with the help of Eqs. 6.113 and 6.114,

$$-\text{div } \boldsymbol{J}_{0f} = \text{div } (\sigma \text{ grad } \phi_0) = \sigma \, \Delta\phi_0 + \text{grad } \sigma \cdot \text{grad } \phi_0 = 0 \tag{6.116}$$

which, in the particular case of an homogeneous conductor, reduces to

$$\Delta\phi_0 = 0 \tag{6.117}$$

i.e., to Laplace's equation. In addition, $\phi_0$ must be constant over each terminal surface and its normal derivative must vanish over the rest of the surface of the conductor. This follows from the fact that the normal component of the current density must be equal to zero wherever the surface of the conductor is insulated. The differential Eq. 6.116 together with these boundary conditions is sufficient to specify uniquely $\phi_0$ for given values of the terminal voltages.

Because of the linearity of all the equations involved, we expect the terminal currents to be expressible as linear functions of the terminal voltages, thereby yielding the set of equations

$$\begin{aligned}
I_1 &= G_{11}V_1 + G_{12}V_2 + \cdots + G_{1k}V_k + \cdots + G_{1n}V_n \\
I_2 &= G_{21}V_1 + G_{22}V_2 + \cdots + G_{2k}V_k + \cdots + G_{2n}V_n \\
&\cdots\cdots\cdots\cdots\cdots\cdots\cdots\cdots\cdots \\
I_j &= G_{j1}V_1 + G_{j2}V_2 + \cdots + G_{jk}V_k + \cdots + G_{jn}V_n \\
&\cdots\cdots\cdots\cdots\cdots\cdots\cdots\cdots\cdots \\
I_n &= G_{n1}V_1 + G_{n2}V_2 + \cdots + G_{nk}V_k + \cdots + G_{nn}V_n
\end{aligned} \tag{6.118}$$

where the coefficients $G_{jk}$ are constants of the system, independent of the terminal voltages and terminal currents. Furthermore, the sum of the currents entering the conductor through terminals $1, 2, \cdots, j, \cdots, n$ must be equal to the current leaving the conductor through the reference terminal $S_0$. This follows from the fact that, because of Eq. 6.116, charge cannot accumulate within the conductor.

The validity of the above equations can be demonstrated as follows. Let us consider the special case in which all terminal voltages are equal to zero with the exception of the voltage on terminal 1, which is equal to one, and represent the resulting potential function by $\varphi_1$. Because of the linearity of Eq. 6.116, any function proportional to $\varphi_1$ is a physically realizable potential which vanishes over all terminal surfaces with the exception of the first one. In particular, the function $V_1\varphi_1$ assumes the value $V_1$ on the first terminal surface, and is equal to zero on all other terminal surfaces. The corresponding terminal currents can be obtained by substituting $V_1\varphi_1$ for $\phi_0$ in Eq. 6.115. Let $I_{j1}$ be the value assumed by $I_j$ when all terminal voltages are equal to zero except for $V_1$. We have then

$$I_{j1} = G_{j1}V_1 \tag{6.119}$$

where

$$G_{j1} = -\int_{S_j} \sigma \boldsymbol{n} \cdot \text{grad } \varphi_1 \, da \tag{6.120}$$

Similar expressions are obtained by setting all terminal voltages equal to zero except for $V_k$. If $\varphi_k$ is the potential corresponding to $V_k = 1$, we have in general

$$I_{jk} = G_{jk}V_k \tag{6.121}$$

where

$$G_{jk} = -\int_{S_j} \sigma \boldsymbol{n} \cdot \text{grad } \varphi_k \, da \tag{6.122}$$

Let us consider now the linear combination

$$\phi_0 = V_1\varphi_1 + V_2\varphi_2 + \cdots + V_k\varphi_k + \cdots + V_n\varphi_n \tag{6.123}$$

This function, being a linear combination of functions that satisfy Eq. 6.116, will also satisfy Eq. 6.116. Furthermore, its normal derivative will vanish over the insulated part of the surface of the conductor because all its component terms satisfy this requirement. Finally, $\phi_0$ assumes the value $V_k$ on the $k$th terminal surface because $\varphi_k$ is equal to one on that surface and all other $\varphi$ are equal to zero. Thus $\phi_0$ is the potential function corresponding to arbitrary values $V_1, V_2, \cdots, V_k, \cdots, V_n$ of the terminal voltages. The corresponding terminal currents are obtained by inserting Eq. 6.123 into Eq. 6.115. Term-by-term integration yields the expression for $I_j$ given by Eq. 6.118.

It is clear that the coefficient $G_{kk}$ is the ratio of $I_k$ to $V_k$ when all the other terminal voltages are equal to zero. We refer to $G_{kk}$ as the self-conductance of the $k$th terminal. Similarly, $G_{jk}$ is the ratio of $I_j$ to $V_k$ when all terminal voltages are equal to zero except for $V_k$. We refer to $G_{jk}$ as the mutual conductance between the $j$th terminal and the $k$th terminal. We shall show in Sec. 7.8 that

$$G_{jk} = G_{kj} \leq 0 \tag{6.124}$$

$$G_{kk} \geq 0 \tag{6.125}$$

These properties of the conductance coefficients are associated with the dissipation of power in the conductor. The resulting circuit representation of a multiterminal conductor is illustrated in Fig. 6.6*b*. A second illustration is provided by Fig. 7.6. It must be stressed, in this regard, that such a circuit representation would not be possible without the reciprocity property expressed by Eq. 6.124. The terminal properties of the conductor can be represented also by expressing the terminal voltages as linear functions of the terminal currents. The coefficients in these expressions can be obtained by solving the set of Eqs. 6.118 for the terminal voltages.

The above analysis has dealt only with the zero-order electric field and the zero-order current density because only these two vector fields are involved in the circuit representation of a multiterminal conductor. The zero-order magnetic field can be evaluated from the zero-order current, if desired. Its space distribution, however, does not influence at all the circuit representation. As a matter of fact, the circuit representation is also independent of the electric field in the space outside the conductor. In fact, when solving the conduction problem inside the conductor, we make use of the boundary conditions imposed on the current flow on the surface of the conductor, and we do not need any information about the electric field in the surrounding space. Thus, in effect, the electric field inside the conductor is insulated from the electric field outside the conductor by the boundary conditions on the surface of the conductor.

A final comment is in order, concerning the time dependence of the terminal voltages and currents. Their time dependence did not enter our discussion because only zero-order fields had to be considered, which obey static-field equations. Yet, no limitation is placed on their time dependence other than those implied by the assumption that the first-order fields can be neglected. Thus, for instance, in the case of sinusoidal excitation, the frequency must be sufficiently small for inductive and capacitive effects to be negligible. On the other hand, we shall see in Chapter 8 that the frequency must be very small in order for the higher order magnetic fields to be negligible. The phenomenon associated with such higher order fields is known as *skin effect* and it lies completely outside the scope of circuit theory.

## ► 6.7 Multiconductor Capacitive Systems

Let us consider next the capacitive fields classified as type 1 in Sec. 6.5. These fields are characterized by a zero-order electric term and a first-order magnetic term. We shall focus our attention on the electric field because it can be evaluated independently of the magnetic field.

A zero-order electric field obeys static equations and, therefore, must be associated with charges which, in the case of circuit components, must be located on the surfaces of conducting bodies. Thus, we can use, as a model of capacitive system, a set of insulated conductors, such as the one illustrated in Fig. 6.7*a*. When a system of this type is used as a circuit component, the conductors are connected to voltage sources or to other circuit components that specify the potential of each conductor of the system with respect to a reference conductor which is usually the ground. Of course, the surfaces of the conductors are equipotential surfaces of the zero-order field. We shall assume in the following that the wires connecting the conductors to

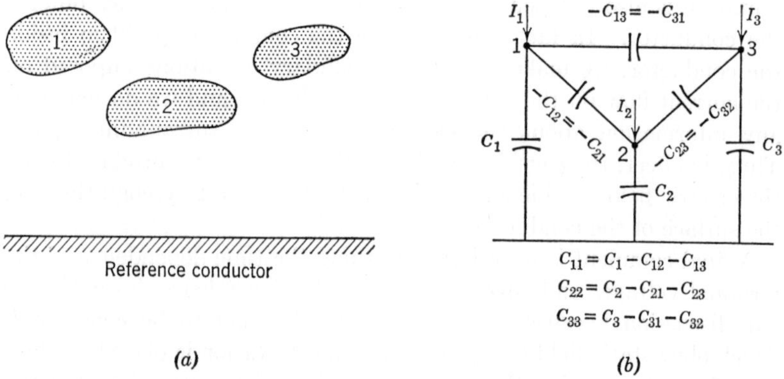


**Fig. 6.7.** Representation of a system of conductors embedded in a linear dielectric medium.

other circuit components have a negligible effect on such zero-order field.

The terminals of a capacitive system are the equipotential surfaces of the conductors forming the system. Thus, if we represent the zero-order electric field as the negative gradient of a potential $\phi_0$,

$$\boldsymbol{E}_0 = -\operatorname{grad} \phi_0 \tag{6.126}$$

the terminal voltage $V_k$ is the difference between the values assumed by $\phi_0$ on the $k$th conductor and on the reference conductor.

The total charge on the $j$th conductor can be obtained by integrating over its surface the normal component of $\epsilon \boldsymbol{E}_0$. We have, in terms of the potential

$$Q_j = -\int_{S_j} \epsilon \boldsymbol{n} \cdot \operatorname{grad} \phi_0 \, da \tag{6.127}$$

where $\epsilon$, in general a function of position, is the permittivity of the medium between the conductors, and the unit vector $\boldsymbol{n}$ is normal to the surface $S_j$ of the $j$th conductor and outwardly directed from the conductor.

The zero-order electric field must satisfy Eq. 6.98, which, in the medium between the conductors reduces to

$$-\operatorname{div} \epsilon \boldsymbol{E}_0 = \operatorname{div} (\epsilon \operatorname{grad} \phi_0) = \epsilon \, \Delta\phi_0 + \operatorname{grad} \epsilon \cdot \operatorname{grad} \phi_0 = 0 \tag{6.128}$$

In the particular case of an homogeneous medium, this equation reduces further to

$$\Delta\phi_0 = 0 \tag{6.129}$$

i.e., to Laplace's equation. In addition, $\phi_0$ must be constant on the surface of each conductor and must vanish at infinity. These conditions are sufficient to specify uniquely $\phi_0$ for given values of the terminal voltages.

The differential equation to be satisfied by $\phi_0$ is identical in form to Eq. 6.116. Similarly, Eq. 6.127 expressing the charge on the $j$th conductor is identical in form to Eq. 6.115 expressing the current through the $j$th terminal surface of a multiterminal conducting body. It follows that each terminal charge $Q_j$ can be expressed as a linear function of the terminal voltages, just as, in the preceding section, we were able to express each terminal current $I_j$ as a linear function of the terminal voltages. Thus, without any further proof, we can write the set of equations

$$
\begin{aligned}
Q_1 &= C_{11}V_1 + C_{12}V_2 + \cdots + C_{1k}V_k + \cdots + C_{1n}V_n \\
Q_2 &= C_{21}V_1 + C_{22}V_2 + \cdots + C_{2k}V_k + \cdots + C_{2n}V_n \\
&\cdots\cdots\cdots\cdots\cdots\cdots\cdots\cdots\cdots \\
Q_j &= C_{j1}V_1 + C_{j2}V_2 + \cdots + C_{jk}V_k + \cdots + C_{jn}V_n \\
&\cdots\cdots\cdots\cdots\cdots\cdots\cdots\cdots\cdots \\
Q_n &= C_{n1}V_1 + C_{n2}V_2 + \cdots + C_{nk}V_k + \cdots + C_{nn}V_n
\end{aligned}
\tag{6.130}
$$

where the coefficients $C_{jk}$ are constants of the system, independent of the $V$ and the $Q$. Of course, similar relations could be written expressing the $V$ as functions of the $Q$ by solving the above set of equations. The coefficient $C_{kk}$ is the ratio of $Q_k$ to $V_k$ when all the other terminal voltages are equal to zero. We refer to $C_{kk}$ as the self-capacitance of the $k$th terminal; it is the capacitance of the $k$th conductor with respect to all the other conductors held at the reference potential. Similarly, $C_{jk}$ is the ratio of $Q_j$ to $V_k$ when all terminal voltages are equal to zero except for $V_k$. We refer to $C_{jk}$ as the mutual capacitance between the $j$th terminal and the $k$th terminal. We shall show in Sec. 7.7 that

$$C_{jk} = C_{kj} \leq 0 \tag{6.131}$$

$$C_{kk} \geq 0 \tag{6.132}$$

These properties of the capacitance coefficients are associated with the storage of energy in the medium in which the conductors are immersed. The circuit representation of a multiconductor system resulting from the zero-order electric field is illustrated in Fig. 6.7*b*. A second illustration is provided by Fig. 7.5. Again, as in the case of multiterminal conductors, such a circuit representation would not be possible without the reciprocity property expressed by Eq. 6.131.

Let us turn our attention next to the first-order terms. The first-order magnetic field can be evaluated, if desired, from the zero-order electric field. However, it is the first-order current rather than the first-order magnetic field that is directly involved in the circuit representation of a capacitive system. As pointed out in Sec. 6.5, the first-order current is related to the zero-order charge by Eq. 6.105. In the particular class of systems under consideration, zero-order charge is present only on the conductor surfaces and, therefore, first-order currents can be present only in the conductors and in the wires connecting the conductors to other circuit components. On the other hand, for the purposes of our circuit representation, we are only interested in the terminal currents, i.e., in the current entering each conductor. By the law of conservation of charge, expressed in differential form by Eq. 6.105, the first-order current $I_j$ *entering* the $j$th conductor must be equal to the time derivative of the zero-order charge on the conductor, i.e.,

$$I_j = \frac{dQ_j}{dt} \tag{6.133}$$

It follows that the terminal currents are related to the terminal voltages by the set of equations

$$\begin{aligned}
I_1 &= C_{11}\frac{dV_1}{dt} + C_{12}\frac{dV_2}{dt} + \cdots + C_{1k}\frac{dV_k}{dt} + \cdots + C_{1n}\frac{dV_n}{dt} \\
I_2 &= C_{21}\frac{dV_1}{dt} + C_{22}\frac{dV_2}{dt} + \cdots + C_{2k}\frac{dV_k}{dt} + \cdots + C_{2n}\frac{dV_n}{dt} \\
&\cdots\cdots\cdots\cdots\cdots\cdots\cdots\cdots \\
I_j &= C_{j1}\frac{dV_1}{dt} + C_{j2}\frac{dV_2}{dt} + \cdots + C_{jk}\frac{dV_k}{dt} + \cdots + C_{jn}\frac{dV_n}{dt} \\
&\cdots\cdots\cdots\cdots\cdots\cdots\cdots\cdots \\
I_n &= C_{n1}\frac{dV_1}{dt} + C_{n2}\frac{dV_2}{dt} + \cdots + C_{nk}\frac{dV_k}{dt} + \cdots + C_{nn}\frac{dV_n}{dt}
\end{aligned} \tag{6.134}$$

Furthermore, the sum of the $n$ terminal currents entering the $n$ conductors must be equal to the terminal current leaving the reference conductor because the charge on the reference conductor is equal in magnitude and opposite in sign to the sum of the charges on the $n$ conductors.

An important result of our analysis to be emphasized is that a capacitive system is completely represented by electrostatic coefficients, in spite of the fact that first-order quantities and, therefore, time derivatives are involved in its operation. This is one of the reasons why electrostatics play such an important part in the practical use of field theory.

## 6.8 Examples of Inductive Fields

The next type of quasi-static field to be discussed is the inductive field, classified as type 2 in Sec. 6.5. Quasi-static fields of this type are characterized by a first-order electric field which, because of Eq.

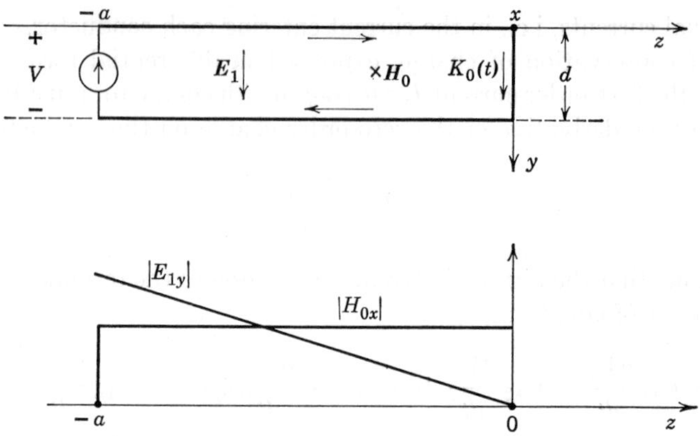


**Fig. 6.8.** Single-turn coil consisting of two parallel conducting plates, short-circuited at one end.

6.101, is not conservative and, therefore, cannot be represented as the negative gradient of a scalar potential. This fact raises a difficulty with regard to the definition of the terminal voltages to be used in connection with the circuit representation of inductive devices. This difficulty must be overcome before inductive fields can be discussed in their full generality. We shall consider in this section two illustrative examples of inductive fields that will clarify this point.

Let us consider first the single-turn coil, illustrated in Fig. 6.8, consisting of two parallel infinitely conducting sheets, separated by a distance $d$, and joined (short-circuited) at one end by a third infinitely conducting sheet. The system is fed by a current source located at a distance $a$ from the short circuit. If the width of the two parallel sheets is considerably larger than their spacing $d$, and their length $a$ is considerably larger than their width, the electromagnetic field between the two sheets is approximately independent of the $x$ and $y$ coordinates, just as in the example discussed in Sec. 6.4. We shall idealize this situation, as we did in Sec. 6.4, in such a way as to make the field exactly independent of $x$ and $y$ by making the parallel sheets infinite in both the $x$ and $y$ directions, and by regarding the current source as a uniform current sheet on the plane $z = -a$. Furthermore, we shall use as a reference the surface-current density on the short-circuiting sheet, i.e., on the plane $z = 0$. This implies that such a surface current density possesses only a zero-order term parallel to the $y$-axis; we shall set its magnitude equal to an arbitrary time function $K_0(t)$, as indicated in Fig. 6.8.

Because of the solenoidal character of the zero-order current field, the zero-order surface current has the same density $K_0$ on all conducting sheets and in the source located on the plane $z = -a$; its direction is indicated in Fig. 6.8. The corresponding zero-order magnetic field is uniform and given by

$$\boldsymbol{H}_0 = -\boldsymbol{i}_x K_0(t) \tag{6.135}$$

in the space bounded by the parallel sheets, the short-circuiting sheet, and the plane of the current source. No zero-order electric field is present because all conducting sheets have, by assumption, infinite conductivity.

The first-order electric field must satisfy Eqs. 6.101 and 6.103. In our particular case, these equations reduce to

$$\text{curl}\,\boldsymbol{E}_1 = -\boldsymbol{i}_x \frac{\partial E_{1y}}{\partial z} + \boldsymbol{i}_y \frac{\partial E_{1x}}{\partial z} = \boldsymbol{i}_x \mu_0 \frac{dK_0(t)}{dt} \tag{6.136}$$

$$\text{div}\,\boldsymbol{E}_1 = \frac{\partial E_{1z}}{\partial z} = 0 \tag{6.137}$$

in view of the one-dimensional character of the field. Integration with respect to $z$ yields

$$E_{1y} = -\mu_0 z \frac{dK_0(t)}{dt} \tag{6.138}$$

$$E_{1x} = E_{1z} = 0 \tag{6.139}$$

where the integration constants have been set equal to zero because the tangential component of the field must vanish on the three infinitely conducting sheets.

The behavior of $E_{1y}$ as a function of $z$ is shown in Fig. 6.8. Its time dependence, on the other hand, is the same as that of the time derivative of $K_0(t)$, for all values of $z$. This electric field is not conservative and, therefore, cannot be represented by means of a scalar potential. It follows that the voltage between the terminals of the current source is not uniquely defined. For instance, if we define this voltage as the line integral of the electric field along a line parallel to the $y$-axis, we obtain

$$V = \int_0^d (E_{1y})_{z=-a}\,dy = \mu_0 a d \frac{dK_0(t)}{dt} \tag{6.140}$$

As a matter of fact, the same result is obtained for any path of integration lying on the plane $z = -a$. On the other hand, a different result is obtained when the path of the integration does not lie on such a plane; for instance the line integral of $\boldsymbol{E}_1$ between the terminals of the source becomes equal to zero if the path of integration lies entirely on the conducting sheets because the tangential component of the field is equal to zero on them.

In view of the fact that the current source is located on the plane $z = -a$, it seems reasonable to define the terminal voltage, in this particular case, as the line integral of $E_{1y}$ along a path lying on the plane of the source. Then, using this definition, we obtain from Eq. 6.140

$$V = L\frac{dK_0(t)}{dt} \tag{6.141}$$

where

$$L = \mu_0 ad \tag{6.142}$$

Since $K_0$ is the source current per unit width in the $x$ direction, the constant $L$ is recognized as the inductance of a unit width of the one-turn coil formed by the conducting sheets.

In the particular case of sinusoidal excitation, with

$$K_0(t) = A \sin \omega t \tag{6.143}$$

where $A$ is an arbitrary constant, Eq. 6.141 becomes,

$$V = A\omega L \cos \omega t \tag{6.144}$$

Evaluation of the second-order fields shows that the limits of validity of the quasi-static approximation for the single-turn coil of Fig. 6.8 are exactly the same as for the parallel-plate system illustrated in Fig. 6.3 and discussed in Sec. 6.4. As a matter of fact, evaluation of the entire series yields

$$\boldsymbol{H} = -\boldsymbol{i}_x A \cos\frac{\omega z}{c}\sin \omega t \tag{6.145}$$

$$\boldsymbol{E} = -\boldsymbol{i}_y A \sqrt{\frac{\mu_0}{\epsilon_0}}\sin\frac{\omega z}{c}\cos \omega t \tag{6.146}$$

These expressions are very similar in character to Eqs. 6.78 and 6.79 and can be approximated by quasi-static fields when the length $a$ of the system is much smaller than the wave length $\lambda$, defined by Eq. 6.80.

Let us turn our attention next to the inductive system illustrated in Fig. 6.9, as a more realistic example of the type of coil that might be used in an electric circuit. The coil consists of $N$ closely spaced turns of a flat conductor whose width is much larger than its thickness but

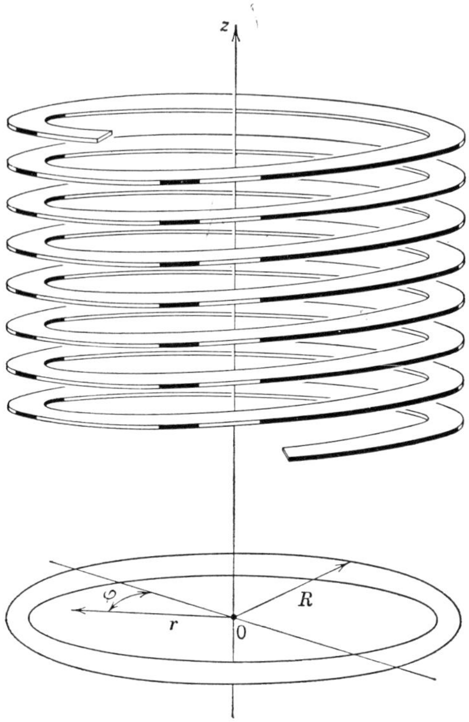


**Fig. 6.9.** Geometry of a coil.

much smaller than the radius of the coil. We shall assume, to start with, that the coil is open-circuited and immersed in a uniform magnetic field produced by a separate coaxial coil. More precisely, we shall assume that the zero-order magnetic field, a function of time, is given by

$$\boldsymbol{H}_0 = \boldsymbol{i}_z H_{0z}(t) \tag{6.147}$$

in the space occupied by the coil, and that the $z$-axis coincides with the axis of the coil, as illustrated in Fig. 6.9.

The first-order electric field must satisfy Eq. 6.101 and appropriate boundary conditions on the surface of the conductor forming the coil. Let us consider, first, the character of the electric field that would exist *in the absence of the coil.* The knowledge that the magnetic field is uniform in the space occupied by the coil is not sufficient for our purposes because the first-order electric field depends on the zero-order magnetic field in the entire space. However, the electric field becomes uniquely specified in the region where the magnetic field is uniform if we assume, in addition, that the entire magnetic field has circular symmetry about

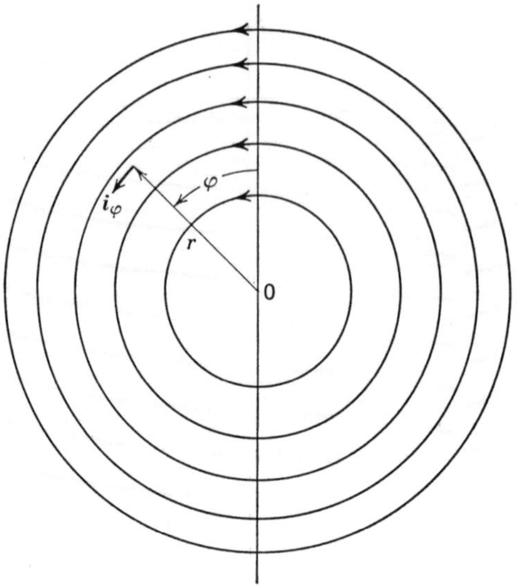


**Fig. 6.10.** First-order electric field produced by a uniform magnetic field normal to the paper and possessing circular symmetry.

the $z$-axis, i.e., that the field is independent of the $\varphi$ coordinate when expressed in circular cylindrical coordinates. Then, because of this circular symmetry, the first-order electric field must be of the form

$$\boldsymbol{E}_1 = \boldsymbol{i}_\varphi E_{1\varphi} \tag{6.148}$$

and, therefore, its lines of force must be circles centered on the $z$-axis and lying on planes normal to it, as illustrated in Fig. 6.10.

The component $E_{1\varphi}$, in the absence of the coil, is most readily computed by evaluating the line integral of $\boldsymbol{E}_1$ over circular paths formed by the lines of force. We have from Eq. 6.101, with the help of Stokes' theorem,

$$\oint_C \boldsymbol{E}_1 \cdot d\boldsymbol{s} = 2\pi r E_{1\varphi} = -\pi r^2 \mu_0 \frac{dH_{0z}(t)}{dt} \tag{6.149}$$

where $C$ is any one of such circular paths and $r$ is its radius. Thus, we obtain, in the space where $\boldsymbol{H}_0$ is uniform,

$$E_{1\varphi} = -\mu_0 \frac{r}{2} \frac{dH_{0z}(t)}{dt} \tag{6.150}$$

Next, let us consider a closed path $C_0$ consisting of a helix with $N$ turns together with a return path joining the terminal points $P_1$ and $P_2$ and lying in a plane parallel to the $z$-axis, as illustrated in Fig. 6.11. The helix represents the position to be assumed by the coil when introduced into the field. If the helix consists of $N$ turns, the complete flux of the zero-order magnetic field through any two-sided surface bounded by $C_0$ is equal to $N$ times the flux through a circle of the same radius $R$ as the helix on a plane normal to the $z$-axis. The selection of a particular path joining the terminals of the helix does not affect the flux, as long as the path is on a plane parallel to the $z$-axis, because $\boldsymbol{H}_0$ has only a $z$ component. Thus, the flux through any two-sided surface $S$ bounded by $C_0$ is given by

$$\int_S \mu_0 \boldsymbol{H}_0 \cdot \boldsymbol{n}\, da = \Phi_0 = \pi R^2 N \mu_0 H_{0z}(t) \tag{6.151}$$

On the other hand, we have from Eq. 6.101, with the help of Stokes' theorem

$$\int_{C_0} \boldsymbol{E}_1 \cdot d\boldsymbol{s} = -\frac{d\Phi_0}{dt} = -\pi R^2 N \mu_0 \frac{dH_{0z}(t)}{dt} \tag{6.152}$$

Clearly, since $\boldsymbol{E}_1$ has only a $\varphi$ component, the line integral is contributed entirely by the helix, with no contribution resulting from the return path joining the terminals of the helix. As a matter of fact, the right-hand side of Eq. 6.152 can be obtained directly from Eq. 6.149 as $N$ times the integral of $\boldsymbol{E}_1$ over the same circular path used in the evaluation of $\Phi_0$.

The introduction of the coil does not change the zero-order magnetic field but changes radically the first-order electric field. This situation is similar to that encountered in electrostatics when a conducting body

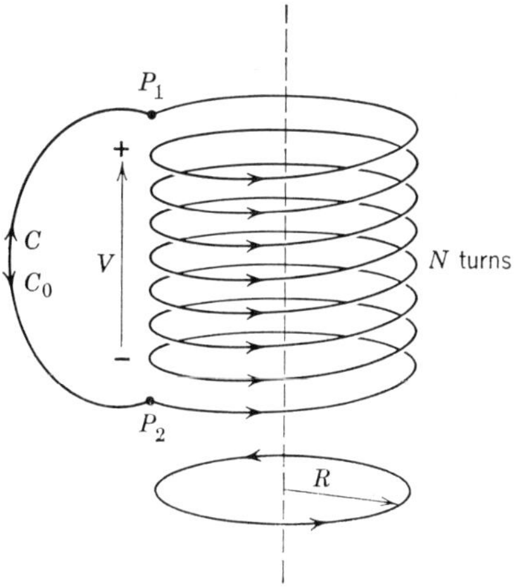


**Fig. 6.11.** Closed path in the form of helix with $N$ turns.

is introduced in the field of fixed charges. The charges induced on the surface of the conductor forming the coil produce an additional electric field $\boldsymbol{E}_1'$ that cancels $\boldsymbol{E}_1$ within the conductor. Thus, the total first-order electric field

$$\boldsymbol{E}_{t1} = \boldsymbol{E}_1 + \boldsymbol{E}_1' \tag{6.153}$$

becomes normal to the surface of the conductor. On the other hand, since $\boldsymbol{E}_1$ satisfies Eq. 6.101, $\boldsymbol{E}_1'$ must be a conservative field, representable as the negative gradient of a scalar potential

$$\boldsymbol{E}_1' = -\operatorname{grad} \phi_1' \tag{6.154}$$

It follows that the line integral of $\boldsymbol{E}_{t1}$ over the closed path $C_0$, illustrated in Fig. 6.11, is still equal to the line integral of $\boldsymbol{E}_1$ given by Eq. 6.152, because no net contribution results from the conservative field $\boldsymbol{E}_1'$. In other words,

$$\oint_{C_0} \boldsymbol{E}_{t1} \cdot d\boldsymbol{s} = \oint_{C_0} \boldsymbol{E}_1 \cdot d\boldsymbol{s} = -\pi R^2 N \mu_0 \frac{dH_{0z}(t)}{dt} \tag{6.155}$$

The presence of the conservative field $\boldsymbol{E}_1'$, however, affects very significantly the relative contributions to the line integral over $C_0$ of the helix and of the return path. In fact, the helical part of $C_0$ lies now within the conductor forming the coil or on its surface and, therefore, the tangential component of $\boldsymbol{E}_{t1}$ vanishes over it. Thus, the helical part of $C_0$ makes no contribution to the line integral of $\boldsymbol{E}_{t1}$, with the result that

$$\oint_{C_0} \boldsymbol{E}_{t1} \cdot d\boldsymbol{s} = \int_{P_1}^{P_2} \boldsymbol{E}_{t1} \cdot d\boldsymbol{s} = \int_{P_1}^{P_2} \boldsymbol{E}_1' \cdot d\boldsymbol{s} = \phi_1'(P_1) - \phi_1'(P_2) \tag{6.156}$$

In other words, the line integral over $C_0$ becomes equal to the difference between the values assumed by the potential $\phi_1'$ at the terminals $P_1$ and $P_2$ of the coil. This difference of potential can be taken as the terminal voltage of the coil and is equal to the line integral of the total first-order electric field over any path joining the terminals of the coil, with the only provision that the path must lie on a plane parallel to the zero-order magnetic field. Then, combining Eqs. 6.155 and 6.156 yields for this terminal voltage

$$V = \phi_1'(P_1) - \phi_1'(P_2) = -\frac{d\Phi_0}{dt} = -\pi R^2 N \mu_0 \frac{dH_{0z}(t)}{dt} \tag{6.157}$$

The problem of determining the electric field $\boldsymbol{E}_1'$ produced by the charges induced on a coil is in general very difficult. However, the main characteristics of $\boldsymbol{E}_1'$ can be estimated in the case of the coil

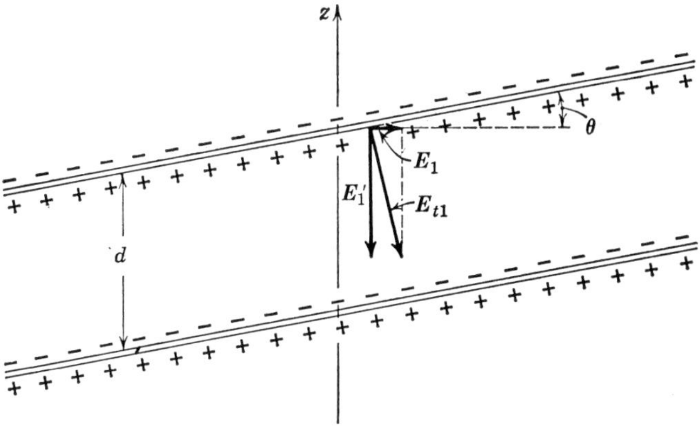


**Fig. 6.12.** The electric field $E_1'$ produced by charges on the conductor.

illustrated in Fig. 6.9 because of the flatness of the conducting wire. The geometry of the coil suggests that, between adjacent turns, $E_1'$ should be approximately uniform and parallel to the axis of the coil. In fact if we add an $E_1'$ to $E_1$, as illustrated in Fig. 6.12, the magnitude of $E_1'$ can be adjusted relative to that of $E_1$ to make the resultant $E_{t1}$ normal to the surfaces of the adjacent turns of the conductor. It is clear from Fig. 6.12 that

$$E_{1z}' = -E_{1\varphi} \operatorname{cotan} \theta \tag{6.158}$$

On the other hand, we have, from the geometry of the coil

$$\operatorname{cotan} \theta = \frac{2\pi R}{d} \tag{6.159}$$

where $d$ is the spacing between successive turns in the direction of the $z$-axis. Thus

$$E_{z1}' = -\frac{2\pi R}{d} E_{1\varphi} \tag{6.160}$$

The charge associated with this conservative electric field is indicated schematically in Fig. 6.12. The terminal voltage is given by

$$V = \int_{\frac{1}{2}Nd}^{-\frac{1}{2}Nd} E_{1z}\, dz = -\pi R^2 N \mu_0 \frac{dH_{0z}(t)}{dt} \tag{6.161}$$

which checks with the right-hand side of Eq. 6.157.

Equation 6.160 indicates that the intensity of the conservative field produced by the charges on the coil is much greater than the intensity of the field produced directly by the time derivative of $\boldsymbol{H}_0$ when the radius of the coil is much larger than the spacing between turns. When this is the case, the line integral of the electric field between the terminals of the coil is approximately independent of the path of integration even if the path does not lie on a plane parallel to the $z$-axis, provided only that the path be much shorter than the length of the conductor forming the coil. This result is actually very general, because the order of magnitude of the intensity of $\boldsymbol{E}_1'$ is given by the time derivative of the magnetic flux $\Phi_0$ divided by the length $Nd$ of the coil, whereas the order of magnitude of the intensity of $\boldsymbol{E}_1$ is given by the time derivative of $\Phi_0$ divided by $N$ and by $2\pi R$ which is approximately the length of a turn. Thus, the ratio of the two intensities is of the order of magnitude of $2\pi R/d$.

The main conclusion that we can draw from the above discussion is that the first-order electric field existing in the region around an open-circuited coil with closely spaced turns is produced primarily by the charges on the conductor forming the coil rather than directly by the time derivative of the zero-order magnetic field. The time derivative of $\boldsymbol{H}_0$ produces $\boldsymbol{E}_1$, which induces charges on the coil, which in turn produce $\boldsymbol{E}_1'$. The possibility of defining a terminal voltage for a coil in a reasonably unique manner rests just on the fact that $\boldsymbol{E}_1'$, the field produced by the charges, is conservative and, in practical cases, much larger than $\boldsymbol{E}_1$. The terminal voltage is then the difference between the values assumed at the terminals by the potential associated with the conservative field. Conversely, no generally satisfactory definition of the terminal voltage can be given when $\boldsymbol{E}_1'$ is of the same order of magnitude as $\boldsymbol{E}_1$.

Let us suppose, next, that the zero-order magnetic field is produced by a current $I_0(t)$ flowing in the same coil, the conductivity of which we shall now assume to be infinite; the reference direction of the current is opposite to that of $C_0$. The zero-order magnetic field, although no longer uniform, is representable by the product of the current in the coil and a vector function of the space coordinates,

$$\boldsymbol{H}_0 = \boldsymbol{h}(x, y, z)I_0(t) \tag{6.162}$$

where $\boldsymbol{h}(x, y, z)$ represents the magnetic field produced by a direct current of unit magnitude. Then, the flux of the zero-order magnetic field through the closed path $C$, shown in Fig. 6.11 (coinciding with

$C_0$ but with opposite direction), can be expressed in the form

$$\Phi_0 = LI_0(t) \tag{6.163}$$

where

$$L = \int_S \mu_0 \boldsymbol{h}(x, y, z) \cdot \boldsymbol{n}\, da \tag{6.164}$$

$S$ is any two-sided surface bounded by $C$, and $\boldsymbol{n}$ is a unit vector normal to it, and directed according to the right-handed-screw rule relative to the direction of $C$. Then, proceeding as in the case of the open-circuited coil, and remembering that the reference direction of the $\Phi_0$ given by Eq. 6.163 is opposite to that of the $\Phi_0$ in Eq. 6.157, we obtain for the terminal voltage

$$V = L\frac{dI_0(t)}{dt} \tag{6.165}$$

which is the circuit relation defining the inductance $L$. Similarly, if the current $I_0(t)$ were flowing in a different coil from that at whose terminals $V$ is measured, we would obtain

$$V = M\frac{dI_0(t)}{dt} \tag{6.166}$$

The mutual inductance $M$ is equal to the flux of $\mu_0 \boldsymbol{h}(x, y, z)$ through the closed contour $C$ associated with the coil at whose terminals $V$ is measured, and $\boldsymbol{h}(x, y, z)$ represents now the magnetic field produced by a unit current flowing in the other coil. We can conclude, therefore, that the concepts of self-inductance and mutual inductance are geometric characteristics of static magnetic fields. These results are extended to multiwinding systems in the following section.

## ► 6.9 Multiwinding Systems

We wish to generalize the results of the preceding section to a system consisting of an arbitrary number $n$ of current-carrying coils interacting with one another in the presence of linear magnetic materials. We shall at first assume that the cross sections of the conductors forming the coils are sufficiently small that we may disregard at this point the question of how each current is distributed through the cross section of the conductor in which it flows. We shall discuss this question later in this section.

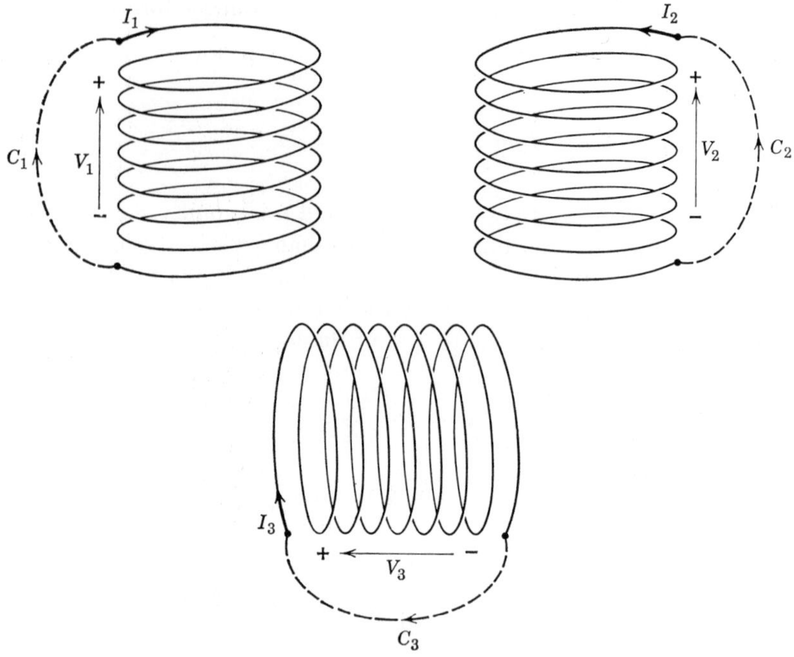


**Fig. 6.13.** Multiwinding system.

With reference to Fig. 6.13, let us represent the geometry of each coil by means of a closed contour which coincides with the coil except for a short return path indicated by a dotted line and joining the terminals of the coil. We shall represent by $C_k$, $I_k$, and $V_k$ the contour, the current, and the terminal voltage associated with the $k$th coil of the system. The reference directions are indicated in Fig. 6.13; attention is called to the fact that the reference direction of $C_k$ is the same as that of the current and opposite to that of the contour used in the definition of $V_k$.

The zero-order magnetic field must satisfy Eqs. 6.97 and 6.99; the first of these equations is inherently linear, the second one is linear because of the assumption that all magnetic materials have linear constituent relations. It follows that $\boldsymbol{H}_0$ can be regarded as the superposition of the fields produced separately by each current. Furthermore, the field produced by each current is, for the same reason, proportional to the current itself. Let $\boldsymbol{h}_k$, a function of the space coordinates alone, represent the static magnetic field produced by a unit current in the $k$th coil, with all other currents equal to zero. Then, the zero-order magnetic field can be expressed in the form

$$\boldsymbol{H}_0 = I_1\boldsymbol{h}_1 + I_2\boldsymbol{h}_2 + \cdots + I_k\boldsymbol{h}_k + \cdots + I_n\boldsymbol{h}_n \tag{6.167}$$

where the currents are arbitrary functions of time, except for the requirement that their time derivatives be small enough to justify the quasi-static approximation used in our analysis. The flux of $\mu\boldsymbol{H}_0$ through the contour associated with each coil can now be expressed as the sum of the contributions of each separate current; we obtain the set of equations

$$\begin{aligned}
\Phi_1 &= L_{11}I_1 + L_{12}I_2 + \cdots + L_{1k}I_k + \cdots + L_{1n}I_n \\
\Phi_2 &= L_{21}I_1 + L_{22}I_2 + \cdots + L_{2k}I_k + \cdots + L_{2n}I_n \\
&\cdots\cdots\cdots\cdots\cdots\cdots\cdots\cdots \\
\Phi_j &= L_{j1}I_1 + L_{j2}I_2 + \cdots + L_{jk}I_k + \cdots + L_{jn}I_n \\
&\cdots\cdots\cdots\cdots\cdots\cdots\cdots\cdots \\
\Phi_n &= L_{n1}I_1 + L_{n2}I_2 + \cdots + L_{nk}I_k + \cdots + L_{nn}I_n
\end{aligned} \tag{6.168}$$

where

$$L_{jj} = \int_{S_j} \mu\boldsymbol{h}_j\cdot\boldsymbol{n}\,da \tag{6.169}$$

$$L_{jk} = \int_{S_j} \mu\boldsymbol{h}_k\cdot\boldsymbol{n}\,da \tag{6.170}$$

and $S_j$ is any two-sided surface bounded by $C_j$. The flux $\Phi_j$ is a zero-order quantity associated with the $j$th coil, which plays a role analogous to that of the charge $Q_j$ in the multiconductor system discussed in Sec. 6.7.

We saw in the preceding section that for any coil consisting of closely spaced turns a terminal voltage $V_j$ can be defined as the line integral of the first-order electric field over a closed path identical to the path $C_j$ associated with the coil, but with opposite reference direction. On the other hand, applying Stokes' theorem to Eq. 6.101 yields for such a line integral

$$-\oint_{C_j} \boldsymbol{E}_1\cdot d\boldsymbol{s} = -\int_{S_j} \mu\frac{\partial\boldsymbol{H}_0}{\partial t}\cdot\boldsymbol{n}\,da = -\frac{d\Phi_j}{dt} \tag{6.171}$$

It follows that the terminal voltages can be expressed as linear functions of the terminal currents by means of equations of the form

$$V_j = L_{j1}\frac{dI_1}{dt} + L_{j2}\frac{dI_2}{dt} + \cdots + L_{jj}\frac{dI_j}{dt} + \cdots + L_{jn}\frac{dI_n}{dt} \tag{6.172}$$

The coefficient $L_{jj}$ is the self-inductance of the $j$th coil, defined by Eq. 6.169, and $L_{jk}$ is the mutual inductance between the $j$th coil and the $k$th coil. We shall show in Sec. 7.9 that

$$L_{jk} = L_{kj} \tag{6.173}$$

$$L_{jj} \geq 0 \tag{6.174}$$

These two properties of the inductance coefficients are related to the storage of magnetic energy in the medium surrounding the coils.

Let us consider now the case of coils formed by conductors of non-negligible cross section. The difficulty that arises in connection with such coils is that the current distribution within each conductor cannot be specified *a priori* in a consistent manner as a zero-order current density. More precisely, the description of the current density within the conductor involves in any case of practical interest terms of order higher than the first one, and therefore it lies outside the scope of our quasi-static approximation. We shall see in Sec. 8.8 that, even for relatively slow time variations, the current is crowded near the surface of the conductor because of the phenomenon known as *skin effect.* We shall see also that, in the limit of infinite conductivity, current can flow only on the surface of a conductor and must be distributed in such a way as to make the electromagnetic field vanish inside the conductor. The reason why this must be so can be readily appreciated by noting that, if any electric field existed inside a perfect conductor, the conduction current associated with it would have to have an infinite density; in turn, no time-varying magnetic field can exist in a region in which the electric field is identically equal to zero.

The requirement that the current density and the magnetic field vanish inside a perfect conductor implies that the magnetic field outside the conductor must be tangent to the surface of the conductor and equal in magnitude to the surface current density. In fact, the normal component of $\mu\boldsymbol{H}$ must be continuous through the surface of the conductor, and the tangential component of $\boldsymbol{H}$ must suffer a discontinuity equal in magnitude to the surface current density. In particular, if the electromagnetic field outside the conductor is a quasi-static field of type 2, the zero-order magnetic field must be tangent to the surface of the conductor. It can be shown that this boundary condition is sufficient to specify uniquely $\boldsymbol{H}_0$ when the total current flowing in each coil is given. This situation is analogous to that of the zero-order field studied in Sec. 6.7, which is uniquely specified by the net charge on each isolated conductor and by the requirement that it be normal to the surfaces of all conductors.

Let us reconsider next the steps involved in the evaluation of the terminal voltage of each coil from the zero-order magnetic field produced by the given currents. Since the cross section of each conductor was assumed to be negligibly small, the flux linking the $j$th coil could be identified with the flux through any two-sided surface bounded by $C_j$. A little thought will show that this identification is still correct as long as $C_j$ lies within the conductor or on its surface. This follows from the fact that the flux is independent of the path chosen as long as $C_j$ lies inside the conductor because of the absence of magnetic field within the conductor. Furthermore, since each of the magnetic fields produced separately by unit currents must satisfy the above boundary conditions, the total magnetic field can still be expressed as a linear function of the currents, in the form given by Eq. 6.167. Thus, the definitions of the self-inductances $L_{jj}$ and of the mutual inductances $L_{jk}$ are still valid for perfect conductors of nonnegligible cross section, and so is Eq. 6.172 expressing the $j$th terminal voltage as a linear function of the time derivatives of the currents.

## 6.10 The Concept of Voltage and Kirchhoff's Laws

The field approach to electromagnetic problems is by far more general and powerful than the circuit approach. We shall see in the next chapter, for instance, that a few simple transformations are sufficient to derive from Maxwell's equations the laws governing the flow of energy in electromagnetic systems; the derivation from Kirchhoff's laws of the corresponding network relations is considerably more involved and leads, in addition, to more restricted results. On the other hand, when we wish to analyze in complete detail a given electromagnetic system, the mathematical difficulties arising from the field approach are so great that they can be overcome only in a very limited number of special cases. The circuit approach, although restricted in its applicability, is considerably simpler mathematically, and therefore it is better suited to detailed analysis and synthesis problems.

The relative mathematical simplicity of the circuit approach stems from the assumption that the given system consists of components whose individual behavior and mutual interactions can be completely specified in terms of their terminal voltages and currents. This assumption eliminates from the problem all the geometric characteristics of the system but for the manner in which the component's terminals are interconnected. Two interrelated questions arise in this connection. First of all, how are the terminal voltages and currents related to the electromagnetic field? Second, under what conditions are the assumptions inherent to the circuit approach justifiable? These two questions have been partly answered in the preceding sections. We saw there how the circuit definitions of resistance, capacitance, and inductance are associated with three basic types of quasi-static fields, thereby establishing a relation between circuit theory and field theory at the individual circuit element level. In this section we shall consider further the relation between circuit theory and field theory with regard to the laws governing the interaction of circuit elements.

The interrelations among branch currents and among branch voltages in a network are governed by Kirchhoff's laws. Kirchhoff's current law states that the sum of the currents flowing out of a node must be equal to zero. The relation of this law to the law of conservation of charge in field theory is rather obvious. In field theory, the surface integral of the current density over a closed surface must be equal to zero if no charge accumulates inside the surface. Since a node in circuit theory is a theoretical abstraction of a physical interconnection of wires to which no capacitance is assigned, no charge can accumulate on a node, and the sum of the currents leaving a node must be equal to zero.

Kirchhoff's voltage law states that the sum of the branch voltages along any closed path in the circuit (measured in the same direction) must be equal to zero. This law is the circuit equivalent of Maxwell's first equation, i.e., of Faraday's induction law. This equivalence, however, is not as directly evident as the relation between Kirchhoff's current law and the law of conservation of charge. Indeed, the voltage law depends on how the branch voltages are defined in terms of the electromagnetic field. Although the concept of voltage has already been discussed in Sec. 6.8 in connection with inductive fields, it deserves some further, careful consideration in view of its key role in circuit theory.

To obtain a better feeling for what is involved in the circuit concept of voltage, it is helpful to consider its definition from an experimental point of view. A little thought will make it obvious that all voltmeters are designed to measure the line integral of the electric field along the path formed by the connecting leads. This is evident in the case of the electrostatic voltmeters whose operation depends directly on the forces exerted by the electric field. Other more common instruments measure actually the current through a resistor of known value (including the leads); the current density in any such resistor is proportional, by Ohm's law, to the electric field and, therefore, the total current is proportional to the line integral of the electric field between the terminals of the resistor. On the other hand, there are implicit limitations on the use of voltmeters. For instance, nobody in his right mind would wrap the leads of a voltmeter around the core of a transformer in determining the voltage between two points in a circuit. Furthermore, it is understood that the leads of a voltmeter should be kept *reasonably short*, and that little meaning should be attached to an indication which depends appreciably on the exact position of the leads.

These limitations on the use of voltmeters indicate that the voltage between two points has a meaning only when the line integral of the electric field between the two points is closely independent of the path of integration for all reasonably short paths. In mathematical terms, this amounts to saying that a voltage can be defined only between points of a region in which there exists a scalar potential whose negative gradient is closely equal to the electric field. Thus the concept of voltage in the presence of time-varying currents is strictly an extension of the concept of voltage as defined in electrostatic systems; this extension is valid only when the path of integration used in the computation of the voltage is contained in a region of space in which the electric field behaves approximately as an electrostatic field.

We saw in the preceding sections that no difficulty arises with the definition of terminal voltage in connection with resistive and capacitive fields because the electric field involved is of order zero and, therefore, conservative. In the inductive case, however, the electric field is not conservative because its curl is proportional to the time derivative of the zero-order magnetic field. We also saw that, in the case of coils of practical interest, the conservative electric field associated with the charges induced on the coil is usually considerably more intense than the electric field produced directly by the time derivative of the magnetic field. In any such case, the line integral of the electric field between the terminals of the coil is closely independent of the path of integration, as long as the path is short and reasonably selected. Thus the conclusions reached in connection with purely inductive fields are in agreement with those reached in this section, from an experimental point of view.

With the voltage between the terminals of a circuit component defined as the line integral of the electric field, the sum of the voltages around a closed loop in a circuit becomes the line integral of the electric field around a closed path, as illustrated in Fig. 6.14. It will be noted

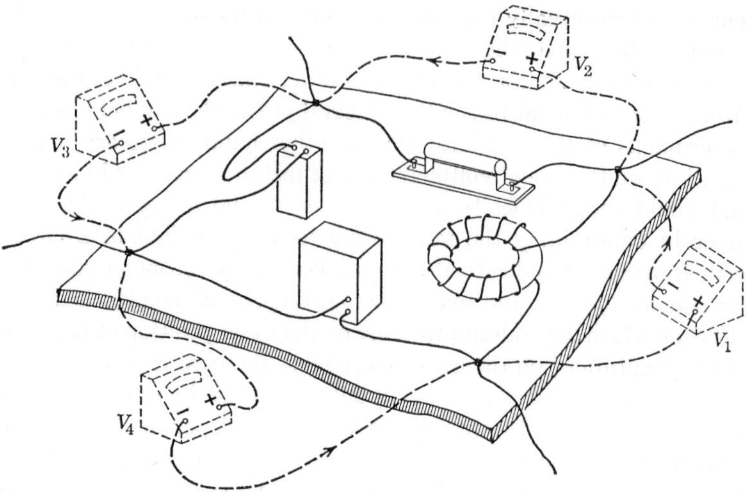


**Fig. 6.14.** The voltmeter leads form suitable paths along which the electric field may be integrated in computing the branch voltages.

that the closed path around which the electric field must be integrated is not the path of the wire, especially not where the wire is wound to form an inductor; rather, the path of integration follows the voltmeter leads that might be used in the actual measurement of branch voltages. The electric field involved in this integration is, by assumption, equal (or approximately so) to the negative gradient of a scalar potential, and therefore its line integral around a closed path must vanish. Consequently, the sum of the branch voltages around the closed path must vanish, as required by Kirchhoff's voltage law.

The definition of voltage will be discussed once more in the next chapter for the purpose of relating the flow of power in a circuit to the flow of power in an electromagnetic field. We shall see that, in order for the two definitions of power to agree, the voltages involved in the circuit expression for the power must be defined in the manner and with the restrictions discussed above.

## 6.11 Summary and Conclusions

This chapter has been devoted entirely to the study of quasi-static fields, and to the power-series representation of electromagnetic fields which provides the appropriate analytical tool. We saw that the terms of such power series become significant in succession as the speed of an electromagnetic phenomenon is increased. For this reason the quasi-static approximation, consisting of the zero-order and first-order terms alone, was found to describe adequately the relatively slow field phenomena characteristic of electric circuits. In particular, we saw that the three ideal circuit elements—resistance, capacitance, and inductance—correspond to three specific types of quasi-static field, each involving one electric term and one magnetic term. The two types of quasi-static fields involving both electric terms or both magnetic terms were found to correspond to circuit components that can be represented by a resistance in series with an inductance or by a resistance in parallel with a capacitance. These two, more complex types of fields will be discussed in greater detail in Chapter 8, together with the type of quasi-static field that involves both electric and magnetic terms, and which does not correspond to any combination of circuit elements. Last, but not least, we saw how, and under what conditions, the concept of voltage can be defined for time-varying fields, and how Kirchhoff's two laws can be related to Maxwell's equations.

The reason for devoting so much attention to quasi-static fields is that, unless the relation between circuit theory and field theory is clearly understood, it is very difficult to deal effectively with systems whose mode of operation lies on the border line between that of electric circuits and that of transmission lines, and which partake of the characteristics of both. Such systems have gained in importance in the last decade with the increasing use of frequencies in the hundreds of megacycles; their study can be greatly aided by the power-series method of analysis.

We have discussed in this chapter only one aspect of quasi-static fields, namely, the relation between electric and magnetic fields, on the one hand, and currents and voltages on the other. The other aspect, involving the storage and flow of energy, will be discussed in the next chapter.

## PROBLEMS

**Problem 6.1.** Two parallel, perfectly conducting plates, normal to the $y$-axis, are fed symmetrically by two voltage sources, as shown in Fig. 6.3. A thin resistive sheet on the plane $z = 0$ is connected between the plates. The field can be regarded as independent of $x$ and $y$.

(a) Find the differential equations for the quasi-static fields in terms of the voltage $V_0(t)$ between the plates at $z = 0$.

(b) Find the quasi-static fields when $V_0(t)$ is proportional to $t$.

**Problem 6.2.** Find the quasi-static field produced by an electric dipole of moment $\boldsymbol{p}(t)$ proportional to $t$. Compare the first-order magnetic field with that given by

Biot-Savart's law for a differential current element (see Eq. 4.70). Is the curl of the first-order field equal to zero? Is the curl of the field produced by a current element equal to zero? Explain!

**Problem 6.3.** A slot of width $a$, depth $b$, and infinite length is cut in a slab of perfectly conducting material. A time-varying potential

$$\phi(x, t) = V_0 \cos \omega t \sin \frac{2\pi}{a} x \qquad 0 < x < a$$

is generated at the mouth of the slot by an appropriate voltage source.

(a) Find the zero-order electric field within the slot.
(b) Find the first-order magnetic field within the slot.

**Problem 6.4.** Two parallel, perfectly conducting circular disks in free space, spaced a distance $d$ apart, are connected by a thin, perfectly conducting tube of radius $a$ at their center. The structure is fed by a current generator producing a circularly symmetrical current density flowing radially towards the tube on one plate and away from it on the other plate. Defining the family of fields as all the fields with current $I_0(\tau)$ in the center tube:

(a) Evaluate the zero-order and first-order fields in terms of the current $I_0(\tau)$ in the tube.
(b) Find a reasonable definition for the inductance of the structure at a radius $r = b \gg a$, and compute its value.
(c) Find the charge distributions on the plates up to first order.

**Problem 6.5.** A two-terminal conductor consists of two concentric, perfectly conducting spherical shells imbedded in an infinite medium of conductivity $\sigma$. The potentials are referred to infinity. (The spherical surface at infinity is thus the reference surface.)

(a) Find the functions $\varphi_1$ and $\varphi_2$ defined in Sec. 6.6.
(b) Find the conductances $G_{11}$, $G_{12}$, $G_{21}$, and $G_{22}$.

**Problem 6.6.** A two-conductor capacitive system consists of three coaxial perfectly conducting circular cylinders of negligibly small thickness. The outside cylinder is regarded as the reference conductor.

(a) Find the capacitances (defined per unit length) $C_{11}$, $C_{12}$, $C_{21}$, and $C_{22}$.
(b) Find the functions $\varphi_1$ and $\varphi_2$, defined in Sec. 6.6.
(c) Repeat (a) and (b) using the inner cylinder as reference conductor.

**Problem 6.7.** Three coaxial cylindrical conductors are short-circuited to one another at one end by a perfectly conducting plate normal to their common axis. The conductors and the short-circuiting plate have infinite conductivity and negligibly small thickness, and they can be regarded as perfectly conducting sheets. Two current sources are connected between the inner conductor and the two other conductors. Assuming that the resulting field has circular symmetry:

(a) Find the vector functions $\boldsymbol{h}_1$ and $\boldsymbol{h}_2$ defined in Sec. 6.9.
(b) Find the self- and mutual inductances at the current-source terminals.

**Problem 6.8.** Find the mutual inductance $M$ between two circular loops of radius $a$. The loops lie on the same plane (so that the loop axes are parallel). The centers of the loops are a distance $d \gg a$ apart. What is $M$ when the axis of the two loops form an angle $\theta$ different from zero?

# CHAPTER SEVEN

# Electromagnetic Energy and Power

The objective of this chapter is to introduce the energy point of view into the study of electromagnetic fields. This point of view is of great importance to us on two counts at least. In the first place, many devices of interest to electrical engineers are designed to transmit electric energy or convert electric energy into some other form of energy, and vice versa. In the second place, the energy point of view is a very powerful help in arriving at important general properties of fields: for instance, it provides a direct link between the impedance concept of circuit theory and field quantities even when it is not possible to subdivide the system under consideration into parts directly identifiable as inductors, capicitors, and resistors.

Experimental evidence indicates that, in all cases, the creation of an electromagnetic field requires the expenditure of mechanical energy or of some other form of energy and that, conversely, energy is made available when the field is destroyed. Our faith in the validity of the law of conservation of energy suggests that it should be possible to define energy functions for electromagnetic fields expressing the energy supplied to a field or delivered by it.

The concept of electromagnetic field was developed originally, as discussed in Sec. 1.1, for the purpose of correlating experimental evidence on the mutual forces between electrically or magnetically active matter. More precisely, the electromagnetic field was intended to play the role of a conceptual connection between the source of a force and its object; thus, for instance, the Coulomb force between two charged particles came to be regarded as exerted on one particle by the electric field produced by the other particle. On the other hand, the field concept proved so useful in interpreting later experimental evidence not involving directly macroscopic forces, that it assumed the status of a primary physical concept. As a matter of fact, after having defined initially the electric field and the magnetic field in terms of the force exerted on a moving charge, we have hardly mentioned again any force in our treatment of electromagnetic phenomena.

In spite of the cardinal role played by the electromagnetic field as a physical concept, we must not lose sight of the fact that its presence becomes evident only through the forces it exerts on matter, be they directly observable macroscopic forces, or microscopic forces acting on the elementary particles constituting matter. It is just through these forces that energy functions can be associated with electromagnetic fields.

We shall begin our discussion of electromagnetic energy by evaluating the forces exerted by electric and magnetic fields on electric dipoles and magnetic dipoles, in the light of the Lorentz force on a moving charge used in the original definition of these fields. We shall see that, if we wish to consider magnetic dipoles as neutral aggregates of magnetic charges, consistency in our definitions requires us to postulate the existence of a force on moving magnetic charges, analogous to the Lorentz force on moving electric charges. These two types of forces are sufficient to establish a connection between mechanical energy and electromagnetic energy. In this chapter we shall be concerned only with the energy exchanges resulting from the motion of free charges and from the relative motion of the electric charges and of the magnetic charges associated with the polarization and the magnetization of stationary matter. The macroscopic forces on material bodies and the energy exchanges resulting from their motion will be discussed in Chapter 10.

Next, with the help of Maxwell's equations, we shall evaluate the power expended by external forces through the motion of electric and magnetic charges. The resulting expression, known as Poynting's theorem, will form the basis for our discussion of the energy associated with electromagnetic fields. Most of the chapter will be devoted to a detailed discussion of the various terms appearing in Poynting's theorem. Finally, we shall relate the energy and power concepts of circuit theory to the corresponding concepts of field theory.

## 7.1 Electromagnetic Forces

The first task in our study of electromagnetic energy is to identify the forces exerted by the electromagnetic field on distributions of electric charges, electric currents, magnetic charges, and magnetic currents.

Our starting point must be the expression for the Lorentz force on an electric charge $q$, moving with a velocity $\boldsymbol{v}$,

$$\boldsymbol{F} = q(\boldsymbol{E} + \boldsymbol{v} \times \mu_0 \boldsymbol{H}) \tag{7.1}$$

in terms of which $\boldsymbol{E}$ and $\boldsymbol{H}$ were originally defined. Its generalization to a distributed charge of density $\rho$, moving with a velocity $\boldsymbol{v}$ follows immediately. We have for the force density acting on the distributed charge

$$\boldsymbol{f} = \rho(\boldsymbol{E} + \boldsymbol{v} \times \mu_0 \boldsymbol{H}) = \rho \boldsymbol{E} + \boldsymbol{J} \times \mu_0 \boldsymbol{H} \tag{7.2}$$

where

$$\boldsymbol{J} = \rho \boldsymbol{v} \tag{7.3}$$

is the current density resulting from the motion of the charge.

The derivation of the analogous expression for the force density acting on magnetic charges and magnetic currents is more involved because we cannot experiment directly on isolated magnetic charges. We shall show, on the other hand, that this force density follows as well from the Lorentz force on a moving electric charge, although in a somewhat devious way. Let us outline first the logical steps involved in the derivation of this second type of force density.

We recall, first of all, that magnetic charges were introduced in our discussion for the purpose of providing an alternate model of magnetic dipole and, through it, a more satisfactory representation of magnetized matter. Magnetic currents had to be introduced simultaneously with magnetic charges in order to preserve the mathematical consistency of Faraday's induction law, expressed by Eq. 5.48. We observe, next, that the introduction of magnetic charges and magnetic currents completes the symmetry between electric quantities and magnetic quantities in the field laws. In fact, the three field equations

$$\operatorname{curl} \boldsymbol{E} + \mu_0 \frac{\partial \boldsymbol{H}}{\partial t} = -\boldsymbol{J}^* \tag{7.4}$$

$$\operatorname{div} \mu_0 \boldsymbol{H} = \rho^* \tag{7.5}$$

$$\operatorname{div} \boldsymbol{J}^* = -\frac{\partial \rho^*}{\partial t} \tag{7.6}$$

are identical in form to the other three field equations

$$\operatorname{curl} \boldsymbol{H} - \epsilon_0 \frac{\partial \boldsymbol{E}}{\partial t} = \boldsymbol{J} \tag{7.7}$$

$$\operatorname{div} \epsilon_0 \boldsymbol{E} = \rho \tag{7.8}$$

$$\operatorname{div} \boldsymbol{J} = -\frac{\partial \rho}{\partial t} \tag{7.9}$$

except for the difference in sign between $\boldsymbol{J}$ and the time derivative of $\boldsymbol{E}$ on the one hand, and $\boldsymbol{J}^*$ and the time derivative of $\boldsymbol{H}$ on the other. This symmetry in the field laws was exploited in Sec. 5.3 in constructing a magnetic-charge model of magnetic dipole analogous to the electric-charge model of electric dipole discussed in Sec. 3.5. We can exploit it further by constructing a magnetic-current model of electric dipole, analogous to the electric-current model of magnetic dipole discussed in Sec. 3.6; here, however, the magnetic-current density $\boldsymbol{K}^*$ must be opposite in sign to the electric-current density $\boldsymbol{K}$ given by Eq. 3.80, in order for $\boldsymbol{E}$ and $\boldsymbol{p}$ to be analogous to $\boldsymbol{H}$ and $\mu_0\boldsymbol{m}$ respectively. Thus we have two alternate models of electric dipole as well as two alternate models of magnetic dipole.

The next step in our reasoning is to show that, if we regard the above models of dipoles as rigid structures, the torque exerted by a static electric field on an electric dipole must be independent of whether the dipole consists of electric charges or magnetic currents. Similarly the torque exerted by a static magnetic field on a magnetic dipole can be shown to be independent of whether the dipole consists of magnetic charges or of electric currents.

The final step in our reasoning is to show that, in order for the torques on different models of dipoles to be equal, there must exist a force on moving magnetic charges given by

$$F^* = q^*(\boldsymbol{H} - \boldsymbol{v} \times \epsilon_0\boldsymbol{E}) \tag{7.10}$$

where $q^*$ is the magnetic charge and $\boldsymbol{v}$ is its velocity, and a corresponding force density

$$f^* = \rho^*(\boldsymbol{H} - \boldsymbol{v} \times \epsilon_0\boldsymbol{E}) = \rho^*\boldsymbol{H} - \boldsymbol{J}^* \times \epsilon_0\boldsymbol{E} \tag{7.11}$$

where $\rho^*$ is the magnetic-charge density and

$$\boldsymbol{J}^* = \rho^*\boldsymbol{v} \tag{7.12}$$

is the magnetic-current density.

Let us now prove the individual steps of our reasoning. The proof that the torque exerted on an electric dipole by a static electric field is independent of the type of sources that constitutes the dipole follows from the well-known mechanical principle of action and reaction. The total torque exerted by an electric dipole on the charges producing the external electric field depends on the electric field produced by the dipole in the region occupied by such charges, but not on the type of sources that constitutes the dipole. On the other hand, the torque exerted by the external field on the dipole must be equal in magnitude and opposite in sign to the torque exerted by the dipole field on the charges that produce the external field. It follows that the torque on the dipole as well must be independent of the type of sources constituting the dipole. The same argument can be made for the fact that the torque on a magnetic dipole is independent of whether the dipole consists of magnetic charges or electric currents.

The proof of the last step hinges on the fact that Eq. 7.2 yields analogous expressions for the torque exerted by a uniform electric field on an electric dipole consisting of electric charges, and by a uniform magnetic field on a magnetic dipole consisting of electric currents, namely,

$$\boldsymbol{T} = \boldsymbol{p} \times \boldsymbol{E} \tag{7.13}$$

$$\boldsymbol{T}^* = \mu_0 \boldsymbol{m} \times \boldsymbol{H} \tag{7.14}$$

Let us prove Eq. 7.13 by evaluating the torque on the model of electric dipole, discussed in Sec. 3.5, consisting of charges distributed over a spherical surface of radius $R$. Using a system of spherical coordinates with the origin at the center of the sphere, and the $z$-axis parallel to the dipole moment $\boldsymbol{p}$, the density of the surface charge constituting the dipole is, from Eq. 3.66,

$$\sigma = \frac{3|\boldsymbol{p}|}{4\pi R^3} \cos\theta \tag{7.15}$$

Then, according to Eq. 7.2, the torque on the dipole is given by

$$\boldsymbol{T} = \oint_S (\boldsymbol{i}_r R \times \sigma \boldsymbol{E})\, da = -\boldsymbol{E} \times \oint_S \boldsymbol{i}_r R\sigma\, da \tag{7.16}$$

where $S$ is the surface of the sphere of radius $R$. The force density exerted by the electric field produced by the dipole charges themselves is not included in the computation because the mutual forces between such charges cannot yield any net torque.

The integral on the right-hand side of Eq. 7.16 can be recognized, from Eq. 4.27, as the dipole moment $\boldsymbol{p}$ of the charge distribution. This can be readily checked by direct evaluation of the surface integral. Because of the circular symmetry of the charge distribution, the integral must be a vector parallel to the $z$-axis of the spherical system of coordinates. Thus

$$\oint_S \boldsymbol{i}_r R\sigma\, da = \boldsymbol{i}_z \frac{3|\boldsymbol{p}|}{2R^2} \int_0^\pi R^2 \cos^2\theta \sin\theta\, d\theta = \boldsymbol{i}_z |\boldsymbol{p}| = \boldsymbol{p} \tag{7.17}$$

It follows that the torque is given by Eq. 7.13.

Let us evaluate next the torque exerted by a static magnetic field on the electric-current model of magnetic dipole, discussed in Sec. 3.6, and characterized by a surface current of density

$$\boldsymbol{K} = \boldsymbol{i}_\varphi \frac{3|\boldsymbol{m}|\sin\theta}{4\pi R^3} \tag{7.18}$$

distributed over the surface of a sphere of radius $R$. Again the sphere is centered at the origin, and the dipole moment $\boldsymbol{m}$ is parallel to the $z$-axis of the spherical system of coordinates. Then, according to Eq. 7.2, the torque on the magnetic dipole is given by

$$\boldsymbol{T}^* = \oint_S \boldsymbol{i}_r R \times (\boldsymbol{K} \times \mu_0 \boldsymbol{H})\, da = \oint_S \mu_0 R \boldsymbol{K}(\boldsymbol{i}_r \cdot \boldsymbol{H})\, da \tag{7.19}$$

where use has been made of Eq. 2.22 and of the fact that $\boldsymbol{K}$ is normal to $\boldsymbol{i}_r$. Again, the force density exerted by the magnetic field produced by the dipole currents themselves has been disregarded because the net torque contributed by it must be equal to zero.

To evaluate the integral on the right-hand side of Eq. 7.19, it is convenient to express $\boldsymbol{i}_r$ and $\boldsymbol{K}$ in terms of their Cartesian components, i.e., in the form

$$\boldsymbol{i}_r = \boldsymbol{i}_x \sin\theta\cos\varphi + \boldsymbol{i}_y \sin\theta\sin\varphi + \boldsymbol{i}_z \cos\theta \tag{7.20}$$

$$\boldsymbol{K} = \frac{3|\boldsymbol{m}|\sin\theta}{4\pi R^3}(-\boldsymbol{i}_x \sin\varphi + \boldsymbol{i}_y \cos\varphi) \tag{7.21}$$

where the angle $\varphi$ is measured from the $x$-axis. The surface integral can then be evaluated by computing its Cartesian components one at a time. We obtain

$$\boldsymbol{T}^* = \mu_0|\boldsymbol{m}|(-\boldsymbol{i}_x H_y + \boldsymbol{i}_y H_x) = \mu_0 \boldsymbol{m} \times \boldsymbol{H} \tag{7.22}$$

which proves Eq. 7.14.

Let us return now to Eqs. 7.13 and 7.14. These two equations are analogous with respect to electric and magnetic quantities in the same sense as the field laws. Furthermore, they must be valid regardless of the types of sources that constitute the dipoles. It follows that the electric field and the magnetic field must exert forces on magnetic charges and magnetic currents analogous to the forces exerted by the same two fields on electric charges and electric currents. By analogy with Eq. 7.1, the force on a moving magnetic charge must be that given by Eq. 7.10. We refer to this force as the magnetic analog of the Lorentz force. Similarly, by analogy with Eq. 7.2, the force density on a distribution of magnetic charges and magnetic currents must be that given by Eq. 7.11.

In conclusion, we have shown that, if magnetic charges and magnetic currents are introduced in our macroscopic theory, the Lorentz force on a moving electric charge implies the existence of an analogous force on a moving magnetic charge. In other words, Eqs. 7.10 and 7.11 do not involve any additional postulate; rather they are required by the internal consistency of the theory.

## 7.2 Poynting's Theorem

Because of the forces exerted by the electromagnetic field on moving electric charges and moving magnetic charges, energy must be exchanged between the electromagnetic field and the external forces that maintain such charges in dynamic equilibrium. The power delivered (absorbed if negative) by the electromagnetic field is given by the scalar product of the force acting on each charge and the velocity of the charge. We have, from Eq. 7.1, for an electric charge moving with velocity $\boldsymbol{v}_e$

$$P_e = \boldsymbol{v}_e \cdot q(\boldsymbol{E} + \boldsymbol{v}_e \times \mu_0 \boldsymbol{H}) = q\boldsymbol{v}_e \cdot \boldsymbol{E} \tag{7.23}$$

and for a magnetic charge moving with velocity $\boldsymbol{v}_m$

$$P_m = \boldsymbol{v}_m \cdot q^*(\boldsymbol{H} - \boldsymbol{v}_m \times \mu_0 \boldsymbol{E}) = q^* \boldsymbol{v}_m \cdot \boldsymbol{H} \tag{7.24}$$

It follows, that the density of the total power delivered by the electromagnetic field because of the motion of electric charges and of magnetic charges is

$$p = p_e + p_m = \boldsymbol{J} \cdot \boldsymbol{E} + \boldsymbol{J}^* \cdot \boldsymbol{H} \tag{7.25}$$

where $\boldsymbol{J}$ and $\boldsymbol{J}^*$ are the macroscopic densities of the resulting electric and magnetic currents.

The right-hand side of Eq. 7.25 can be expressed in terms of the electromagnetic field alone, with the help of Maxwell's equations. We obtain from Eqs. 7.4 and 7.7,

$$\begin{aligned} p &= \boldsymbol{J} \cdot \boldsymbol{E} + \boldsymbol{J}^* \cdot \boldsymbol{H} \\ &= \boldsymbol{E} \cdot \operatorname{curl} \boldsymbol{H} - \epsilon_0 \boldsymbol{E} \cdot \frac{\partial \boldsymbol{E}}{\partial t} - \boldsymbol{H} \cdot \operatorname{curl} \boldsymbol{E} - \mu_0 \boldsymbol{H} \cdot \frac{\partial \boldsymbol{H}}{\partial t} \end{aligned} \tag{7.26}$$

On the other hand, we have from Eq. A4.16 of Appendix 4,

$$\operatorname{div} (\boldsymbol{E} \times \boldsymbol{H}) = \boldsymbol{H} \cdot \operatorname{curl} \boldsymbol{E} - \boldsymbol{E} \cdot \operatorname{curl} \boldsymbol{H} \tag{7.27}$$

Thus,

$$\operatorname{div} (\boldsymbol{E} \times \boldsymbol{H}) + \epsilon_0 \boldsymbol{E} \cdot \frac{\partial \boldsymbol{E}}{\partial t} + \mu_0 \boldsymbol{H} \cdot \frac{\partial \boldsymbol{H}}{\partial t} = -(\boldsymbol{J} \cdot \boldsymbol{E} + \boldsymbol{J}^* \cdot \boldsymbol{H}) \tag{7.28}$$

This last relation, known as Poynting's theorem, is a direct consequence of Maxwell's equations; its right-hand side represents the density of the power absorbed by the electromagnetic field, which is, of course, the negative of the power delivered by the field. The form of this relation can be simplified by introducing two new quantities: a vector quantity

$$\boldsymbol{S} = \boldsymbol{E} \times \boldsymbol{H} \tag{7.29}$$

known as Poynting's vector, and a scalar quantity

$$w = \tfrac{1}{2}(\epsilon_0 \boldsymbol{E}\cdot\boldsymbol{E} + \mu_0 \boldsymbol{H}\cdot\boldsymbol{H}) = \tfrac{1}{2}(\epsilon_0 |\boldsymbol{E}|^2 + \mu_0 |\boldsymbol{H}|^2) \tag{7.30}$$

In terms of these two quantities, Poynting's theorem takes the form

$$\operatorname{div} \boldsymbol{S} + \frac{\partial w}{\partial t} = -(\boldsymbol{J}\cdot\boldsymbol{E} + \boldsymbol{J}^*\cdot\boldsymbol{H}) = -p \tag{7.31}$$

The corresponding integral form is obtained by integrating over an arbitrary volume $V$, enclosed by a surface $S$

$$\oint_S \boldsymbol{S}\cdot\boldsymbol{n}\, da + \frac{d}{dt}\int_V w\, dv = -\int_V (\boldsymbol{J}\cdot\boldsymbol{E} + \boldsymbol{J}^*\cdot\boldsymbol{H})\, dv \tag{7.32}$$

Gauss' theorem has been used in transforming the first term on the left-hand side into a surface integral, and the sign of total derivative has been substituted for that of partial derivative because the volume $V$ is not a function of time.

The left-hand side of Eq. 7.31 involves only the fields $\boldsymbol{E}$ and $\boldsymbol{H}$ and their time and space derivatives. The right-hand side, on the other hand, was obtained from the forces exerted on electric and magnetic charges, and represents the power supplied by the external forces that maintain the charges in dynamic equilibrium. This power must, somehow, be absorbed by the electromagnetic field either at the point at which it is supplied or elsewhere. We observe, in this regard, that the left-hand side of Eq. 7.31 consists of two terms. The first term is the divergence of a vector which has the dimensions of power per unit area. The second term is the time derivative of a scalar quantity which has the dimensions of energy per unit volume. This suggests that the second term be regarded as the density with which power is absorbed locally by the electromagnetic field, in which case $w$ can be interpreted as the density of the energy stored by the field. The first term, on the other hand, is the source density of the vector field $\boldsymbol{S}$, and, as such, it can be regarded as the density of the power that flows away from the place at which it is supplied. Thus $\boldsymbol{S}$ can be interpreted as the density of electromagnetic power flow. Correspondingly, the first term on the left-hand side of Eq. 7.32 represents the electromagnetic power flowing out of the volume $V$ through the surface $S$, and the second term represents the time rate of change of the energy stored by the electromagnetic field within $V$.

It is important to stress that the above interpretations of $\boldsymbol{S}$ and $w$ are possible because these two quantities are strictly electromagnetic, in the sense that they are independent of the sources of the electromagnetic field, whether free or associated with matter. It is this fact that permits us to separate the electromagnetic energy from the other forms of energy that might be present simultaneously.

The density $w$ of the energy stored in the electromagnetic field can be further separated, according to Eq. 7.30, into a component

$$w_E = \tfrac{1}{2}\epsilon_0 \boldsymbol{E}\cdot\boldsymbol{E} = \tfrac{1}{2}\epsilon_0|\boldsymbol{E}|^2 \tag{7.33}$$

associated with the electric field, and a component

$$w_H = \tfrac{1}{2}\mu_0 \boldsymbol{H}\cdot\boldsymbol{H} = \tfrac{1}{2}\mu_0|\boldsymbol{H}|^2 \tag{7.34}$$

associated with the magnetic field. On the other hand, the power flow density $\boldsymbol{S}$ results from the interaction of electric field and magnetic field, and, for this reason, it cannot be separated into components associated with $w_E$ and $w_H$. This fact suggests that $w_E$ and $w_H$ must be intimately related in spite of their apparent mutual independence.

Next, let us consider in more detail the right-hand side of Eq. 7.31. We saw that the entire term represents power supplied by external forces (if positive) or absorbed by external forces (if negative), regardless of the origin of the current densities involved. Magnetic current can result only from a time-varying magnetization

$$\boldsymbol{J}^* = \mu_0\frac{\partial \boldsymbol{M}}{\partial t} \tag{7.35}$$

Thus,

$$p_M = \boldsymbol{H}\cdot\mu_0\frac{\partial \boldsymbol{M}}{\partial t} \tag{7.36}$$

must represent the density of the power supplied by the electromagnetic field to matter when its magnetization changes with time. On the other hand, the electric-current density consists of a polarization component

$$\boldsymbol{J}_p = \frac{\partial \boldsymbol{P}}{\partial t} \tag{7.37}$$

and a free component $\boldsymbol{J}_f$. The polarization component gives rise to a power-density component

$$p_P = \boldsymbol{E} \cdot \frac{\partial \boldsymbol{P}}{\partial t} \tag{7.38}$$

which must represent power supplied by the electromagnetic field to matter when its polarization changes with time.

The power-density component resulting from free currents may be associated with different physical phenomena, depending on the character of the external forces that, together with the electromagnetic forces, keep the charges in dynamic equilibrium. If the free current results purely from conduction in matter, the forces exerted by the electric field are balanced by frictionlike forces depending on the drift velocity of the charges. In this case, the power supplied by the electromagnetic field is dissipated into heat. The density of the power dissipated in a linear conductor is

$$\boldsymbol{J}_f \cdot \boldsymbol{E} = \sigma \boldsymbol{E} \cdot \boldsymbol{E} = \sigma |\boldsymbol{E}|^2 \tag{7.39}$$

In general

$$\boldsymbol{J}_f \cdot \boldsymbol{E} \tag{7.40}$$

represents electromagnetic power converted into some other form of energy (if positive), or vice versa (if negative).

The various terms in Eq. 7.31 can be elucidated further by considering quasi-static situations in which only two of the terms are different from zero. For this reason, and also as a preparation for a later discussion of the energy aspects of electric circuits, we shall show that, when the fields are expressed as power series in the time-rate parameter $\alpha$, Poynting's theorem breaks into a series of separate equations. The first two equations of the series are

$$\text{div} (\boldsymbol{E}_0 \times \boldsymbol{H}_0) = -\boldsymbol{J}_{f0} \cdot \boldsymbol{E}_0 \tag{7.41}$$

$$\text{div} (\boldsymbol{E}_0 \times \boldsymbol{H}_1 + \boldsymbol{E}_1 \times \boldsymbol{H}_0) + \frac{\partial}{\partial t} \frac{1}{2} (\epsilon_0 |\boldsymbol{E}_0|^2 + \mu_0 |\boldsymbol{H}_0|^2)$$

$$= -\boldsymbol{E}_0 \cdot \frac{\partial \boldsymbol{P}_0}{\partial t} - \boldsymbol{H}_0 \cdot \mu_0 \frac{\partial \boldsymbol{M}_0}{\partial t} - (\boldsymbol{J}_{f0} \cdot \boldsymbol{E}_1 + \boldsymbol{J}_{f1} \cdot \boldsymbol{E}_0) \tag{7.42}$$

where the subscripts indicate the order of the fields, in accordance with the notations introduced in Sec. 6.3. Integral relations corresponding to Eq. 7.32 can be obtained by integrating Eqs. 7.41 and 7.42 over an arbitrary volume, with the help of Gauss' theorem.

The derivation of Eqs. 7.41 and 7.42 is similar to the derivation of Maxwell's equations for quasi-static fields. The main difference is that we are now dealing with products of electromagnetic quantities. Substituting for $\boldsymbol{E}$ and $\boldsymbol{H}$ in Eqs. 7.29 and 7.30 the series expressions given by Eqs. 6.27 and 6.28 yields,

$$\boldsymbol{S} = \boldsymbol{S}_0 + \alpha \boldsymbol{S}_1 + \cdots = \boldsymbol{E}_0 \times \boldsymbol{H}_0 + \alpha(\boldsymbol{E}_0 \times \boldsymbol{H}_1 + \boldsymbol{E}_1 \times \boldsymbol{H}_0) + \cdots \tag{7.43}$$

$$w = w_0 + \alpha w_1 + \cdots = \tfrac{1}{2}(\epsilon_0 |\boldsymbol{E}_0|^2 + \mu_0 |\boldsymbol{H}_0|^2) + \alpha(\epsilon_0 \boldsymbol{E}_0 \cdot \boldsymbol{E}_1 + \mu_0 \boldsymbol{H}_0 \cdot \boldsymbol{H}_1) + \cdots \tag{7.44}$$

Following the same procedure, we obtain from Eqs. 7.36, 7.38, and 7.40,

$$p = \boldsymbol{J} \cdot \boldsymbol{E} + \boldsymbol{J}^* \cdot \boldsymbol{H} = p_0 + \alpha p_1 + \cdots$$
$$= \boldsymbol{J}_{f0} \cdot \boldsymbol{E}_0 + \alpha \left( \boldsymbol{E}_0 \cdot \frac{\partial \boldsymbol{P}_0}{\partial \tau} + \boldsymbol{H}_0 \cdot \mu_0 \frac{\partial \boldsymbol{M}_0}{\partial \tau} + \boldsymbol{J}_{f0} \cdot \boldsymbol{E}_1 + \boldsymbol{J}_{f1} \cdot \boldsymbol{E}_0 \right) + \cdots \tag{7.45}$$

where $\tau$ is the family time defined in Sec. 6.2, and

$$\frac{\partial}{\partial t} = \alpha \frac{\partial}{\partial \tau} \tag{7.46}$$

Next we move the terms on the right-hand side of Eq. 7.31 to the left-hand side of the same equation and substitute for all terms the corresponding power-series expressions. Then, keeping in mind Eq. 7.46 and the fact that each series can be differentiated term by term, we obtain

$$\operatorname{div} \boldsymbol{S} + \frac{\partial w}{\partial t} + p = (\operatorname{div} \boldsymbol{S}_0 + p_0) + \alpha \left( \operatorname{div} \boldsymbol{S}_1 + \frac{\partial w_0}{\partial \tau} + p_1 \right) + \cdots = 0 \tag{7.47}$$

Since this equation must be valid for all values of $\alpha$, the individual coefficients of the series must be equal to zero,

$$\operatorname{div} \boldsymbol{S}_0 + p_0 = 0 \tag{7.48}$$

$$\operatorname{div} \boldsymbol{S}_1 + \frac{\partial w_0}{\partial \tau} + p_1 = 0 \tag{7.49}$$

Finally, we can always assume that the member of the family of electromagnetic fields generated by the parameter $\alpha$ corresponds to $\alpha = 1$, as discussed in Sec. 6.5, in which case the real time $t$ coincides with the family time $\tau$. With this identification, Eqs. 7.41 and 7.42 follow immediately from Eqs. 7.48 and 7.49.

The next three sections are intended to provide further insight in the interpretations of $\boldsymbol{S}$, $w_E$, and $w_H$ introduced above, and a more detailed discussion of how energy is absorbed by matter when its polarization and magnetization vary with time. It is convenient for these purposes to focus our attention on special cases in which as few as possible of the quantities to be interpreted differ from zero. Suitable special cases are the quasi-static fields discussed in Sec. 6.5, and referred to as types 1, 2, and $3a$.

The fields of type 1 are characterized by the absence of zero-order magnetic field, first-order electric field, and zero-order power dissipation; they will allow us to focus our attention on the energy associated with the electric field and with polarized matter. The fields of type 2 are characterized by the absence of zero-order electric field, first-order magnetic field, and zero-order power dissipation; they will allow us to focus our attention on the energy associated with the magnetic field and with magnetized matter. Finally, the fields of type $3a$ are characterized by negligibly small first-order fields; they will allow us to focus our attention on the zero-order power flow, which, in a passive system, is related only to the zero-order power dissipation.

## 7.3 Electric Energy and Polarization Energy

Let us consider a system consisting of electric charges, isolated conductors, and dielectric bodies located within a finite distance from the origin, in which the charge density varies with time at a sufficiently slow rate for the quasi-static approximation to be valid. The zero-order current and zero-order magnetic field are equal to zero in any such system. The zero-order electric field is the static field corresponding to the zero-order charge density existing at any given time. Under these conditions, both terms in Eq. 7.41 vanish and Eq. 7.42 reduces to

$$\operatorname{div}\,(\boldsymbol{E}_0 \times \boldsymbol{H}_1) + \frac{\partial}{\partial t}\left(\frac{1}{2}\,\epsilon_0 |\boldsymbol{E}_0|^2\right) = -\boldsymbol{E}_0 \cdot \frac{\partial \boldsymbol{P}_0}{\partial t} - \boldsymbol{J}_{f1}\cdot\boldsymbol{E}_0 \quad (7.50)$$

It is convenient for our purposes to consider the integral form of this equation when the volume includes the entire space. We shall show first that the volume integral over the entire space of the first term on the left-hand side is equal to zero. For this purpose, we integrate this term over a sphere of radius $r$, centered at the origin. We obtain, with the help of Gauss' theorem

$$\int_V \text{div}\,(\boldsymbol{E}_0 \times \boldsymbol{H}_1)\,dv = \oint_S (\boldsymbol{E}_0 \times \boldsymbol{H}_1)\cdot\boldsymbol{n}\,da \tag{7.51}$$

where $V$ is the volume of the sphere and $S$ is its surface. On the other hand, $\boldsymbol{E}_0$ is a static field produced by charges located within a finite distance from the origin. Therefore $\boldsymbol{E}_0$ must vanish at infinity at least as fast as the field of a point charge, i.e., at least as fast as $r^{-2}$. Furthermore, because of Eq. 6.37, curl $\boldsymbol{H}_1$ must vanish at infinity in the same manner as $\boldsymbol{E}_0$, and, as a result, $\boldsymbol{H}_1$ must vanish at least as fast as $r^{-1}$ (see Eq. A3.7, App. 3). It follows that the integrand on the right-hand side of Eq. 7.51 vanishes at least as fast as $r^{-3}$. Since the surface of the sphere is proportional to $r^2$, we can conclude that the right-hand side of Eq. 7.51 vanishes when the radius of the sphere approaches infinity.

Next we shall show that the volume integral over the entire space of the last term on the right-hand side of Eq. 7.50 can be written in the form

$$-\oint (\boldsymbol{J}_{f1}\cdot\boldsymbol{E}_0)\,dv = \oint \phi_0 \frac{\partial \rho_{f0}}{\partial t}\,dv \tag{7.52}$$

where $\rho_{f0}$ is the zero-order charge density and $\phi_0$ is the potential associated with the zero-order electric field,

$$\boldsymbol{E}_0 = -\,\text{grad}\,\phi_0 \tag{7.53}$$

We observe first that the integrand on the left-hand side of Eq. 7.52 can be rewritten with the help of Eq. 7.53 and of Eq. A4.14, Appendix 4, in the form

$$-\boldsymbol{J}_{f1}\cdot\boldsymbol{E}_0 = \boldsymbol{J}_{f1}\cdot\text{grad}\,\phi_0 = \text{div}\,(\phi_0\boldsymbol{J}_{f1}) - \phi_0\,\text{div}\,\boldsymbol{J}_{f1} \tag{7.54}$$

The integral over a sphere of radius $r$ of the first term on the right-hand side of this equation can be transformed into a surface integral with the help of Gauss' theorem. This surface integral vanishes when $r$ approaches infinity because $\boldsymbol{J}_{f1}$ can differ from zero only within a finite distance from the origin. Finally, the right-hand side of Eq. 7.52 is obtained from the last term on the right-hand side of Eq. 7.54 with the help of Eq. 6.38 with $\tau = t$.

In conclusion, integration of Eq. 7.50 over the entire space yields

$$\frac{d}{dt}\oint \frac{1}{2}\epsilon_0|\boldsymbol{E}_0|^2\,dv = \oint \phi_0\frac{\partial \rho_{f0}}{\partial t}\,dv - \oint \left(\boldsymbol{E}_0\cdot\frac{\partial \boldsymbol{P}_0}{\partial t}\right)dv \tag{7.55}$$

The first term on the right-hand side of this equation represents the total power supplied by external forces as a result of the motion of charges constituting the first-order current $\boldsymbol{J}_{f1}$. The second integral on the same side represents the total power absorbed by matter because of its changing state of polarization. Since there are no other sources or sinks of power in the system, the left-hand side of Eq. 7.55 must represent the time rate of change of the total energy associated with the zero-order electric field.

The above result is in agreement with our interpretation of the quantity $w_E$ given by Eq. 7.33 as the density of the energy stored by the electric field. It should be noted, however, that Eq. 7.55 says nothing about how the energy associated with the electric field is distributed, although it is consistent with our considering the integrand on the left-hand side as the energy density.

Additional light can be thrown on the problem by considering the process of building up an electric field by transferring charge from one place to another. We may use as a simple example the process of charging a capacitor by transferring charge from one plate to the other. Clearly, such a process is quasi-static if the charges are moved sufficiently slowly. If all quantities are equal to zero at $t = 0$, integrating Eq. 7.55 with respect to $t$ yields for the total energy supplied by the external forces responsible for the transfer of the charges,

$$W_e = \oint \left( \int_0^{\rho_f} \phi \, d\rho_f \right) dv = \oint \frac{1}{2} \epsilon_0 |\boldsymbol{E}|^2 \, dv + \oint \left( \int_0^{\boldsymbol{P}} \boldsymbol{E} \cdot d\boldsymbol{P} \right) dv \quad (7.56)$$

where the zero-order subscripts have been dropped because the fields are no longer regarded as functions of time.

The first term on the right-hand side is the total energy stored in the electric field. The second term represents the total energy supplied to polarized matter. This polarization energy may be stored in the material in a recoverable form or not, depending on the characteristics of the material. If the material is isotropic, and the constituent relation between $\boldsymbol{P}$ and $\boldsymbol{E}$ is single-valued as in Fig. 5.4, the integral representing the polarization energy density is also a single-valued function of $\boldsymbol{E}$. In this particular case, the polarization energy can be thought of as being stored in the material with a density

$$w_P = \int_0^{\boldsymbol{P}} \boldsymbol{E} \cdot d\boldsymbol{P} \quad (7.57)$$

and the material is said to be conservative. This energy density is proportional to the shaded area on the upper side of the $E$-axis in Fig. 7.1$a$.

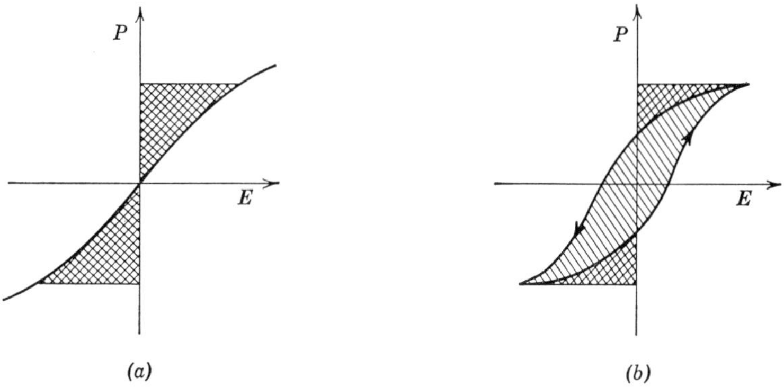


**Fig. 7.1.** Work per unit volume done by the external forces in changing the field from $E$ to $-E$ and back to $E$ (positive work \\\, negative work ///).

On the other hand, if the constituent relation exhibits hysteresis, as in Fig. 5.3, the integral is not a single-valued function of $\boldsymbol{E}$. We can see from Fig. 7.1*b* that the net energy supplied to the material when the field is changed from $E$ to $-E$ and back to $E$ is proportional to the area enclosed by the hysteresis loop; this energy is dissipated in the material.

It is sometimes convenient in the case of a conservative material to lump together the energy stored in the electric field with the energy stored in the material. We have then

$$w_e = w_E + w_P = \int_0^{\boldsymbol{E}} \boldsymbol{E}\cdot \epsilon_0 \, d\boldsymbol{E} + \int_0^{\boldsymbol{P}} \boldsymbol{E}\cdot d\boldsymbol{P} = \int_0^{\boldsymbol{D}} \boldsymbol{E}\cdot d\boldsymbol{D} \tag{7.58}$$

where $\boldsymbol{D}$ is the electric-flux density defined by Eq. 5.55. Finally, in the special case of a linear dielectric material, this total energy density becomes simply

$$w_e = \int_0^{\boldsymbol{E}} \epsilon \boldsymbol{E}\cdot d\boldsymbol{E} = \frac{1}{2}\,\epsilon |\boldsymbol{E}|^2 \tag{7.59}$$

where $\epsilon$ is the permittivity of the linear dielectric.

Let us suppose now that the entire system is linear, i.e., that only linear dielectric materials are involved. Then, the right-hand side of Eq. 7.56 reduces to

$$W_e = \oint \frac{1}{2}\,\epsilon |\boldsymbol{E}|^2 \, dv \tag{7.60}$$

This expression depends only on the electric field and on the dielectric characteristics of the system. It follows that the integral in Eq. 7.56 involving the potential and the charge density must be expressible in a similar manner. We observe in this regard that, because of the linearity of the system, if the charge density is multiplied at all points by a scale factor $\gamma$, the potential is multiplied at all points by the same scale factor. It follows that

$$\int_0^{\rho_f} \phi \, d\rho_f = \int_0^1 \phi\rho_f\gamma \, d\gamma = \frac{1}{2}\phi\rho_f \tag{7.61}$$

We can conclude that, for a linear system, Eq. 7.56 reduces to

$$W_e = \oint \frac{1}{2}\phi\rho_f \, dv = \oint \frac{1}{2}\epsilon|\boldsymbol{E}|^2 \, dv \tag{7.62}$$

As an illustration of the use of this equation, let us evaluate the electric energy stored in the field of the spherical model of electric dipole discussed in Sec. 3.5. Let $R$ indicate the radius of the sphere. Using spherical coordinates with the origin at the center of the sphere and the $z$-axis in the direction of the dipole moment $\boldsymbol{p}$, the surface-charge density, the electric field, and the potential are given by

$$\sigma_f = \frac{3|\boldsymbol{p}|}{4\pi R^3}\cos\theta \tag{7.63}$$

$$\boldsymbol{E} = \frac{|\boldsymbol{p}|}{4\pi\epsilon_0 R^3}\begin{cases} \left(\dfrac{R}{r}\right)^3(\boldsymbol{i}_r 2\cos\theta + \boldsymbol{i}_\theta \sin\theta) & r > R \\ (-\boldsymbol{i}_r\cos\theta + \boldsymbol{i}_\theta\sin\theta) & r < R \end{cases} \tag{7.64}$$

$$\phi = \frac{|\boldsymbol{p}|}{4\pi\epsilon_0 R^2}\begin{cases} \left(\dfrac{R}{r}\right)^2\cos\theta & r > R \\ \dfrac{r}{R}\cos\theta & r < R \end{cases} \tag{7.65}$$

The work done by external forces in building up such a field is

$$W_e = \frac{1}{2}\oint_S \phi\sigma_f \, da = \frac{3|\boldsymbol{p}|^2}{32\pi^2\epsilon_0 R^3}\int_0^{2\pi}\left(\int_0^\pi \cos^2\theta\sin\theta\,d\theta\right)d\varphi$$

$$= \frac{|\boldsymbol{p}|^2}{8\pi\epsilon_0 R^3} \tag{7.66}$$

where $S$ is the surface of the sphere. The same computation can be carried out by evaluating the right-hand side of Eq. 7.62. We have for the energy stored inside the spherical surface, where the electric field is uniform,

$$\frac{1}{2}\epsilon_0\int_{V_i}|\boldsymbol{E}|^2\,dv = \frac{1}{3}\frac{|\boldsymbol{p}|^2}{8\pi\epsilon_0 R^3} \tag{7.67}$$

and for the energy stored outside the spherical surface

$$\begin{aligned}\frac{1}{2}\epsilon_0\int_{V_0}|\boldsymbol{E}|^2\,dv &= \frac{1}{2}\epsilon_0\left(\frac{|\boldsymbol{p}|}{4\pi\epsilon_0 R^3}\right)^2\int_{V_0}\left(\frac{R}{r}\right)^6(4\cos^2\theta+\sin^2\theta)\,dv \\ &= \frac{|\boldsymbol{p}|^2}{16\pi\epsilon_0 R^6}\int_0^{\pi}\int_R^{\infty}\left(\frac{R}{r}\right)^6 \\ &\qquad\times(4\cos^2\theta+\sin^2\theta)r^2\sin\theta\,dr\,d\theta \\ &= \frac{2}{3}\frac{|\boldsymbol{p}|^2}{8\pi\epsilon_0 R^3}\end{aligned} \tag{7.68}$$

The sum of Eqs. 7.67 and 7.68 yields Eq. 7.66 as expected. It is interesting to note that for a fixed dipole moment the energy is inversely proportional to $R^3$, i.e., inversely proportional to the volume of the sphere.

## 7.4 Magnetic Energy and Magnetization Energy

Let us consider next a system consisting of electric currents and magnetizable bodies located within a finite distance from the origin, in which the current density varies with time at a sufficiently slow rate for the quasi-static approximation to be valid. We shall assume that the currents flow in perfect conductors and through ideal sources, so that the zero-order electric field can be equal to zero. The zero-order magnetic field is the static field corresponding to the zero-order current-density existing at any given time. Under these conditions, both terms in Eq. 7.41 vanish, and Eq. 7.42 reduces to

$$\operatorname{div}(\boldsymbol{E}_1\times\boldsymbol{H}_0)+\frac{\partial}{\partial t}\left(\frac{1}{2}\mu_0|\boldsymbol{H}|^2\right) = -\boldsymbol{H}_0\cdot\mu_0\frac{\partial\boldsymbol{M}_0}{\partial t}-\boldsymbol{J}_{f0}\cdot\boldsymbol{E}_1 \tag{7.69}$$

It is convenient for our purposes to consider again the integral form of this equation when the volume includes the entire space. The volume integral over the entire space of the first term on the left-hand side can be shown to be equal to zero, just as in the case of Eq. 7.50. The proof of this result is completely analogous to that given in the preceding section, and can be omitted. Thus, we obtain from Eq. 7.69

$$\frac{d}{dt}\oint \frac{1}{2}\mu_0 |\boldsymbol{H}_0|^2\, dv = \oint (-\boldsymbol{J}_{f0}\cdot\boldsymbol{E}_1)\, dv - \oint \boldsymbol{H}_0\cdot\mu_0 \frac{\partial \boldsymbol{M}_0}{\partial t}\, dv \qquad (7.70)$$

The first term on the right-hand side of this equation represents the power supplied by the external forces that maintain the current flow in the presence of the first-order electric field. The first-order electric field, in turn, is produced by the time variation of the zero-order magnetic field and of the zero-order magnetization. Let us suppose, for instance, that the current flows in a perfectly conducting winding, whose terminals are connected to a current source of magnitude $I_0$, a slowly varying function of time. Then, $\boldsymbol{E}_1$ vanishes in the conductor forming the winding but differs from zero within the current source, and the volume integral reduces to

$$\oint (-\boldsymbol{J}_{f0}\cdot\boldsymbol{E}_1)\, dv = I_0 \int_{P_2}^{P_1} (-\boldsymbol{E}_1)\cdot d\boldsymbol{s} = I_0 V_1 \qquad (7.71)$$

where $V_1$ is the voltage between the terminals $P_1$ and $P_2$ of the winding, defined as in Sec. 6.8. It is important to note that the source delivers power to the system only in the presence of a first-order electric field, i.e., only in the presence of a time-varying magnetic field.

The second volume integral on the right-hand side of Eq. 7.70 represents the power absorbed by matter because of its changing magnetization. Since there are no other sources or sinks of power, the left-hand side of Eq. 7.70 must represent the time rate of change of the energy stored in the magnetic field. This result agrees with the interpretation of $w_H$, given by Eq. 7.34, as the density of the energy stored by the magnetic field.

The volume integral representing the power supplied by external forces can be rewritten in a form which places in evidence its dependence on the time variation of the magnetic field and of the magnetization. We shall show presently that

$$-\oint (\boldsymbol{J}_{f0}\cdot\boldsymbol{E}_1)\, dv = \oint \left(\boldsymbol{J}_{f0}\cdot\frac{\partial \boldsymbol{A}_0}{\partial t}\right) dv \qquad (7.72)$$

where the vector potential $\boldsymbol{A}_0$ satisfies the equation

$$\text{curl}\, \boldsymbol{A}_0 = \mu_0(\boldsymbol{H}_0 + \boldsymbol{M}_0) = \boldsymbol{B}_0 \qquad (7.73)$$

Since the field of $\boldsymbol{B}_0$ is inherently solenoidal because of the absence of free magnetic charges, it is always possible to define a vector $\boldsymbol{A}_0$ satisfying Eq. 7.73, just as we did in Sec. 4.4 for free-space magnetic fields.

On the other hand, because of Eq. 6.36 (with $t = \tau$)

$$\operatorname{curl} \boldsymbol{E}_1 = -\operatorname{curl} \frac{\partial \boldsymbol{A}_0}{\partial t} \tag{7.74}$$

It follows that

$$\boldsymbol{E}_1 = -\frac{\partial \boldsymbol{A}_0}{\partial t} - \operatorname{grad} \phi_1 \tag{7.75}$$

where $\phi_1$ is a scalar function that plays a role similar to that of a constant of integration. In other words, $\boldsymbol{E}_1$ is specified by the time derivative of $\boldsymbol{A}_0$, except for an additive conservative field. The first term on the right-hand side of this equation yields the right-hand side of Eq. 7.72. Further, the volume integral over the entire space of the scalar product of the second term and $\boldsymbol{J}_{f0}$ is equal to zero, because of Theorem (*e*) of Sec. 2.8 and of Eq. 6.35. Thus, Eq. 7.70 can be rewritten in the form

$$\frac{d}{dt}\oint \frac{1}{2}\mu_0|\boldsymbol{H}_0|^2\,dv = \oint\left(\boldsymbol{J}_{f0}\cdot\frac{\partial \boldsymbol{A}_0}{\partial t}\right)dv - \oint\left(\boldsymbol{H}_0\cdot\mu_0\frac{\partial \boldsymbol{M}_0}{\partial t}\right)dv \tag{7.76}$$

Let us suppose, for instance, that the current distribution consists of a filament of intensity $I_0$ forming a closed path $C$. Then, the volume integral representing the power supplied by external forces reduces, with the help of Stokes' theorem, to

$$\oint\left(\boldsymbol{J}_{f0}\cdot\frac{\partial \boldsymbol{A}_0}{\partial t}\right)dv = I_0\oint_C \frac{\partial \boldsymbol{A}_0}{\partial t}\cdot d\boldsymbol{s} = I_0\frac{d}{dt}\int_S \boldsymbol{B}_0\cdot\boldsymbol{n}\,da \tag{7.77}$$

where $S$ is any two-sided surface bounded by $C$. In other words, the power supplied by external forces is equal to the product of the filament current and the time rate of change of the magnetic flux linking the filament. If the filament consists of a current source and a perfectly conducting winding, the time rate of change of the magnetic flux can be identified with the terminal voltage, and Eq. 7.77 reduces to Eq. 7.71.

It is interesting to note that Eqs. 7.55 and 7.76 are analogous except for the term representing the power supplied by external forces. In the electric case, it is the rate of change of the source density $\rho_{f0}$ that requires power from external forces, and the scalar potential $\phi_0$ plays the role of a multiplier. In the magnetic case, it is the rate of change of the vector potential $\boldsymbol{A}_0$ that requires power from the external forces, and the source density $\boldsymbol{J}_{f0}$ plays the role of multiplier. In the first case, the force acting on the electric charges are proportional to $\boldsymbol{E}_0$ and, therefore, are of the static type. In the second case, the forces acting on the moving charges forming the current are proportional to $\boldsymbol{E}_1$ and, therefore, are of the dynamic type, like the forces of inertia in mechanics. As a result, electric energy is, in a sense, analogous to potential energy, and magnetic energy is analogous to kinetic energy.

Let us consider now the process of building up a magnetic field by increasing the currents from zero to their final values, in the absence of permanently magnetized bodies. On the assumption that the currents are changing slowly enough for the quasi-static approximation to be valid, integration of Eq. 7.76 with respect to $t$ yields for the total energy supplied by external forces

$$W_m = \oint \left( \int_0^{A} \boldsymbol{J}_f \cdot d\boldsymbol{A} \right) dv = \oint \frac{1}{2} \mu_0 |\boldsymbol{H}|^2 \, dv + \oint \left[ \int_0^{M} \boldsymbol{H} \cdot d(\mu_0 \boldsymbol{M}) \right] dv \tag{7.78}$$

where the zero-order subscripts have been dropped because the fields are no longer regarded as functions of time.

The first term on the right-hand side of this equation is the total energy stored in the magnetic field. The second term represents the total energy supplied to magnetized matter. As in the analogous electric case, this magnetization energy may be stored in the material in a recoverable form, or not, depending on the characteristics of the material. If the material is isotropic, and the constituent relation between $\boldsymbol{M}$ and $\boldsymbol{H}$ is single-valued, the integral representing the magnetization energy is also a single-valued function of $\boldsymbol{H}$. In this particular case, the magnetization energy can be thought of as being stored in the material with a density

$$w_M = \mu_0 \int_0^{M} \boldsymbol{H} \cdot d\boldsymbol{M} \tag{7.79}$$

and the material is said to be conservative. In a plot of $\mu_0 M$ versus $H$, this energy density is proportional to the area between the curve and the $\mu_0 M$ axis, just as in the analogous polarization case, illustrated in Fig. 7.1*a*. Again, if the constituent relation exhibits hysteresis, the integral representing the magnetization energy density is not a single-valued function of $\boldsymbol{H}$. The net energy supplied to the material when the field is changed from $H$ to $-H$ and back to $H$ is proportional to the area enclosed by the hysteresis loop, as in the analogous polarization case, illustrated in Fig. 7.1*b*; this energy is dissipated in the material.

It is sometimes convenient in the case of a conservative material to lump together the energy stored in the magnetic field with the energy stored in the material. We have then

$$w_m = w_H + w_M = \int_0^H \boldsymbol{H}\cdot\mu_0\, d\boldsymbol{H} + \int_0^M \boldsymbol{H}\cdot\mu_0\, d\boldsymbol{M} = \int_0^B \boldsymbol{H}\cdot d\boldsymbol{B} \quad (7.80)$$

where $\boldsymbol{B}$ is the magnetic flux density defined by Eq. 5.56. Finally, in the special case of a linear magnetic material, this energy density becomes simply

$$w_m = \int_0^H \mu\boldsymbol{H}\cdot d\boldsymbol{H} = \frac{1}{2}\mu|\boldsymbol{H}|^2 \quad (7.81)$$

Let us consider now a linear magnetic system, i.e., a system involving only linear magnetic materials. Then, the right-hand side of Eq. 7.78 reduces to

$$W_m = \oint \frac{1}{2}\mu|\boldsymbol{H}|^2\, dv \quad (7.82)$$

This expression depends only on the magnetic field and on the magnetic characteristics of the system. It follows that the integral in Eq. 7.78 involving the vector potential and the current density must be expressible in a similar manner. We observe in this regard that, because of the linearity of the system, if the current density is multiplied at all points by a scale factor $\gamma$, the vector potential is multiplied at all points by the same scale factor. It follows that

$$\int_0^A \boldsymbol{J}_f\cdot d\boldsymbol{A} = \int_0^1 \boldsymbol{J}_f\cdot\boldsymbol{A}\gamma\, d\gamma = \frac{1}{2}\boldsymbol{J}_f\cdot\boldsymbol{A} \quad (7.83)$$

We can conclude that, for a linear system, Eq. 7.78 reduces to

$$W_m = \oint \frac{1}{2}\boldsymbol{J}_f\cdot\boldsymbol{A}\, dv = \oint \frac{1}{2}\mu|\boldsymbol{H}|^2\, dv \quad (7.84)$$

As an illustration of the use of this equation, let us evaluate the magnetic energy stored in the field of the spherical model of magnetic dipole discussed in Sec. 3.6. Let $R$ indicate the radius of the sphere. Using spherical coordinates with the origin at the center of the sphere and the $z$-axis in the direction of the dipole moment $\boldsymbol{m}$, the surface current density and the magnetic field are given by

$$\boldsymbol{K}_f = \boldsymbol{i}_\varphi \frac{3|\boldsymbol{m}|}{4\pi R^3}\sin\theta \quad (7.85)$$

$$\boldsymbol{H} = \frac{|\boldsymbol{m}|}{2\pi R^3}\begin{cases}\left(\dfrac{R}{r}\right)^3\left(\boldsymbol{i}_r\cos\theta + \boldsymbol{i}_\theta\dfrac{1}{2}\sin\theta\right) & r > R \\ (\boldsymbol{i}_r\cos\theta - \boldsymbol{i}_\theta\sin\theta) & r < R\end{cases} \quad (7.86)$$

The corresponding vector potential outside the sphere and on its surface is given by Eq. 4.82;

$$\boldsymbol{A} = \frac{\mu_0}{4\pi r^2}(\boldsymbol{m} \times \boldsymbol{i}_r) = \boldsymbol{i}_\varphi \frac{\mu_0|\boldsymbol{m}|}{4\pi r^2} \sin\theta \tag{7.87}$$

The work done by external forces in building up such a field is then from Eq. 7.84

$$W_m = \frac{1}{2}\oint_S \boldsymbol{K}_f \cdot \boldsymbol{A}\, da = \frac{3\mu_0|\boldsymbol{m}|^2}{32\pi^2R^3}\int_0^{2\pi}\left(\int_0^{\pi}\sin^3\theta\, d\theta\right) d\varphi = \frac{\mu_0|\boldsymbol{m}|^2}{4\pi R^3} \tag{7.88}$$

where $S$ is the surface of the sphere. The same computation can be carried out by evaluating the right-hand side of Eq. 7.84. We have for the energy stored inside the sphere where the magnetic field is uniform

$$\frac{1}{2}\mu_0\int_{V_i}|\boldsymbol{H}|^2\, dv = \frac{2}{3}\frac{\mu_0|\boldsymbol{m}|^2}{4\pi R^3} \tag{7.89}$$

The energy stored outside the sphere can be computed by analogy with Eq. 7.68; we obtain

$$\frac{1}{2}\mu_0\int_{V_0}|\boldsymbol{H}|^2\, dv = \frac{1}{3}\frac{\mu_0|\boldsymbol{m}|^2}{4\pi R^3} \tag{7.90}$$

The sum of Eq. 7.89 and 7.90 yields Eq. 7.88, as expected.

We saw in Sec. 3.6 that the current distribution given by Eq. 7.85 can be approximated by means of a coil wound on the spherical surface with a uniform axial-turn density. For a coil with $N$ turns the dipole moment is related to the current $I$ in the coil by (see Eq. 3.81)

$$|\boldsymbol{m}| = \tfrac{2}{3}\pi R^2 NI \tag{7.91}$$

Thus the total energy stored in the field is related to the current by

$$W_m = \tfrac{1}{9}\pi\mu_0 RN^2I^2 \tag{7.92}$$

Using the well-known fact, which will be demonstrated in Sec. 7.9, that the inductance of the coil is related to the energy by

$$W_m = \tfrac{1}{2}LI^2 \tag{7.93}$$

we obtain for the inductance of the coil

$$L = \tfrac{2}{9}\pi\mu_0 RN^2 \tag{7.94}$$

## 7.5 Power Flow and Dissipation in Conductors

Let us consider, as a third special case, a system of current-carrying conductors in which the currents vary at such a slow rate that all first-order fields can be neglected in comparison with the zero-order fields. For any such system only the zero-order power relation

$$\operatorname{div}\,(\boldsymbol{E}_0 \times \boldsymbol{H}_0) = -\boldsymbol{J}_{f0}\cdot\boldsymbol{E}_0 \tag{7.95}$$

needs to be considered. The corresponding integral relation is

$$\oint_S (\boldsymbol{E}_0 \times \boldsymbol{H}_0)\cdot\boldsymbol{n}\,da = \int_V (-\boldsymbol{J}_{f0}\cdot\boldsymbol{E}_0)\,dv \tag{7.96}$$

where $V$ is the volume enclosed by $S$, and the unit vector $\boldsymbol{n}$ is normal to $S$ and outwardly directed.

Let us suppose that the volume $V$ is free of electric power sources, and that all conductors are linear. Then, we obtain from Eq. 7.96

$$-\oint_S (\boldsymbol{E}_0 \times \boldsymbol{H}_0)\cdot\boldsymbol{n}\,da = \int_V \sigma|\boldsymbol{E}_0|^2\,dv \tag{7.97}$$

where the conductivity $\sigma$ may be a function of position. The right-hand side of this equation is the power dissipated in the conducting material within $V$. Therefore, the right-hand side must represent the electromagnetic power flowing into $V$ through the surface $S$. This result is in agreement with the interpretation of the zero-order Poynting's vector

$$\boldsymbol{S}_0 = \boldsymbol{E}_0 \times \boldsymbol{H}_0 \tag{7.98}$$

as the density of power flow in the zero-order electromagnetic field.

The following simple illustration will help us gain a better physical understanding of the flow of electromagnetic power. Let us consider a linear, homogenous, finitely conducting rod, connected between two parallel, infinitely conducting plates, as illustrated in Fig. 7.2. The entire system has circular symmetry, and a potential difference $V$ is maintained between the edges of the plates by means of appropriate voltage sources. Since the two plates have infinite conductivity, they are equipotential surfaces for the zero-order electric field; furthermore, the surface of the conducting rod is normal to the two plates. It follows that the electric field within the rod is uniform and normal to the plates. The same is true for the electric field outside the rod, except near the edges of the plates where fringing may be appreciable. Thus, if the $z$-axis coincides with the axis of the rod, we have

$$\boldsymbol{E}_0 = \boldsymbol{i}_z E_{z0} = \boldsymbol{i}_z \frac{V}{d} \tag{7.99}$$

where $d$ is the spacing between the plates. The current density in the conductor is

$$\boldsymbol{J}_{f0} = \sigma \boldsymbol{E}_0 = \boldsymbol{i}_z \sigma \frac{V}{d} \tag{7.100}$$

where $\sigma$ is the conductivity of the rod, and the total current in the rod is

$$I = \frac{\sigma \pi a^2}{d} V = GV \tag{7.101}$$

where $G$ is the conductance of the rod and $a$ is its radius.

The zero-order magnetic field has circular lines of force and is given, in cylindrical coordinates, by

$$\boldsymbol{H}_0 = \boldsymbol{i}_\varphi \frac{I}{2\pi a} \begin{cases} r/a & r < a \\ a/r & r \geq a \end{cases} \tag{7.102}$$

except near the edges of the plates. Thus, the zero-order Poynting's vector is

$$\boldsymbol{S}_0 = -\boldsymbol{i}_r \frac{VI}{2\pi a d} \begin{cases} r/a & r < a \\ a/r & r \geq a \end{cases} \tag{7.103}$$

The lines of force of the magnetic field and those of Poynting's vector are shown in Fig. 7.3. Clearly, the power flows in the space between

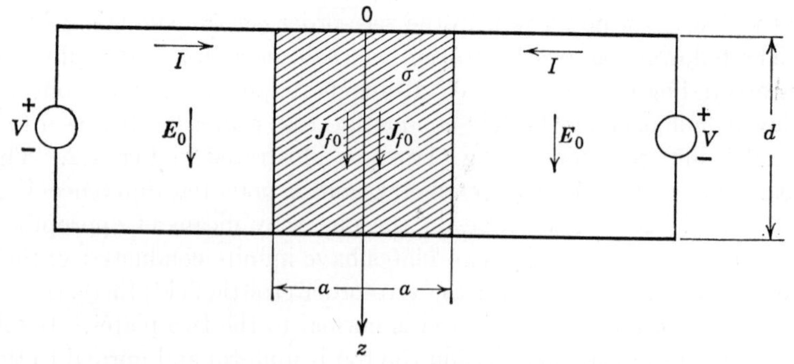


**Fig. 7.2.** Cross section of conducting rod inserted between circular, perfectly conducting plates.

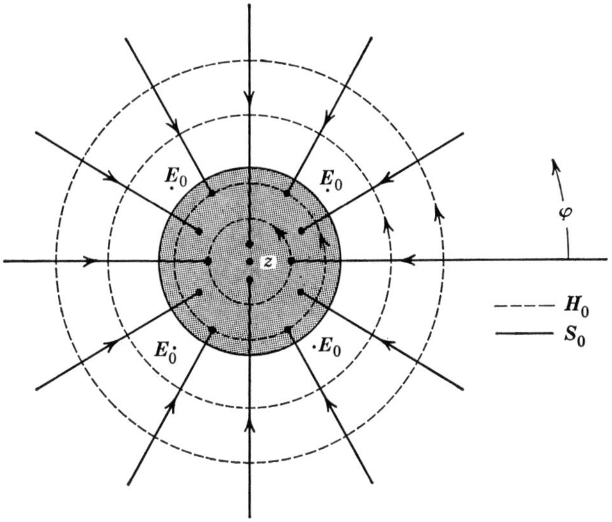


**Fig. 7.3.** Lines of force for $\boldsymbol{H}_0$ and $\boldsymbol{S}_0$ in system of Fig. 7.2.

the plates toward the rod. The total power crossing a cylindrical surface of radius $r$ in the inward direction is, for $r \geq a$,

$$P = -2\pi r d\, S_{r0} = VI = GV^2 \qquad r \geq a \tag{7.104}$$

This equals, of course, the total power dissipated in the rod, i.e.,

$$P_d = \int_V \sigma |\boldsymbol{E}_0|^2\, dv = \sigma \left(\frac{V}{d}\right)^2 \pi a^2 d = GV^2 \tag{7.105}$$

For $r < a$, i.e., for a cylindrical surface within the rod, the total power crossing such a surface must remain equal to the power dissipated in the volume within the surface. We have

$$P = -2\pi r d\, S_{r0} = VI \left(\frac{r}{a}\right)^2 = P_d \left(\frac{r}{a}\right)^2 \qquad r < a \tag{7.106}$$

It is important to note that, contrary to the conception of power flow that might be suggested by circuit theory, the power flow does not coincide in any way with the current flow. This, however, should not be surprising because, even in electric circuits, power can be transmitted from a source to a load without the two being connected by a wire through which current can flow. For instance, the source and the load may be inductively coupled by a pair of separate coils with a finite mutual inductance. We shall see in the next section how, and under what conditions, the field and circuit concepts of power flow can be reconciled.

## 7.6 The Circuit Concept of Power

Let us turn our attention next to the circuit-theory definition of power and its relation to Poynting's vector. With reference to Fig. 7.4, the power flowing out of a surface $S$ enclosing a portion of a circuit is defined, in circuit theory, as

$$P = I_1V_1 + I_2V_2 + \cdots = \sum_k I_kV_k \tag{7.107}$$

where the terminal voltages $V_k$ are measured with respect to an arbitrary reference node, and the currents are outwardly directed. On the other hand, the same power is defined in field theory as the flux of Poynting's vector, $\boldsymbol{S} = \boldsymbol{E} \times \boldsymbol{H}$, through the surface $S$ enclosing the portion of the circuit in question,

$$P = \oint_S (\boldsymbol{E} \times \boldsymbol{H}) \cdot \boldsymbol{n}\, da \tag{7.108}$$

where $\boldsymbol{n}$ is the usual unit vector normal to $S$ and outwardly directed. We shall show that these two expressions for the power flowing out of $S$ can be reconciled provided the terminal voltages $V_1$, $V_2$, $\cdots$ can be regarded as the values assumed by a scalar potential defined on $S$ at the points where the currents cross the surface $S$. In other words, we must assume that the line integral of the electric field intensity between any two points of $S$ is independent of the path of integration as long as the path lies on $S$. This restriction is substantially equivalent to that imposed on the definition of voltage in Sec. 6.10. We note also that this restriction implies that the normal component of $\partial \boldsymbol{B}/\partial t$ must vanish on $S$; in fact, if this were not the case, the line integral of $\boldsymbol{E}$ could not vanish for all closed paths on $S$.

Let us then assume that the component of $\boldsymbol{E}$ tangent to $S$ can be expressed as the negative gradient of a scalar potential $\phi$. Then, since only the tangential component of $\boldsymbol{E}$ contributes to the flux of Poynting's vector through $S$, Eq. 7.108 can be written in the form

$$P = -\oint_S (\text{grad}\,\phi \times \boldsymbol{H}) \cdot \boldsymbol{n}\, da = \int_V \text{div}\,(\boldsymbol{H} \times \text{grad}\,\phi)\, dv \tag{7.109}$$

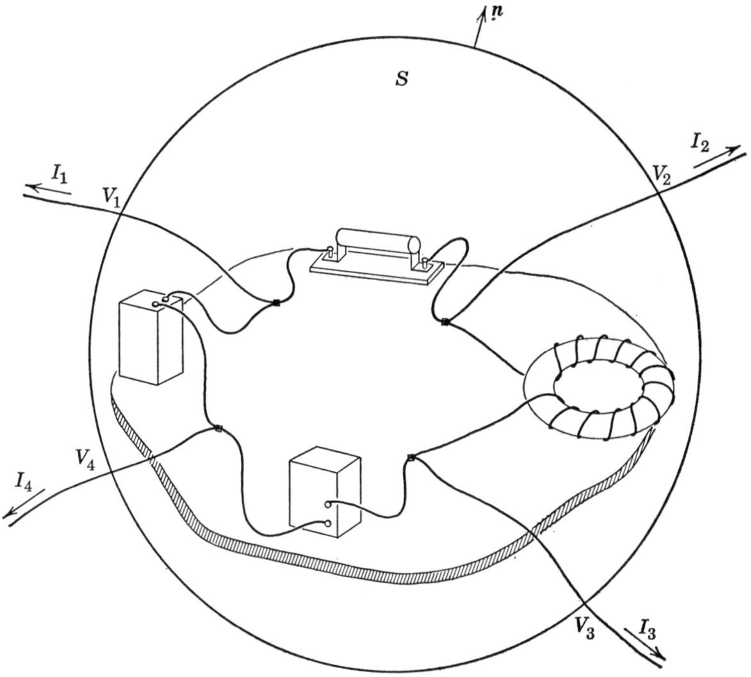


**Fig. 7.4.** Illustrating the computation of the power output from the portion of a circuit enclosed by a surface $S$.

On the other hand, because of Eqs. A4.12 and A4.14,

$$0 = \text{div curl } (\phi \boldsymbol{H}) = \text{div } (\phi \text{ curl } \boldsymbol{H}) - \text{div } (\boldsymbol{H} \times \text{grad } \phi) \qquad (7.110)$$

Thus,

$$P = \int_V \text{div } (\phi \text{ curl } \boldsymbol{H})\, dv = \oint_S (\phi \text{ curl } \boldsymbol{H}) \cdot \boldsymbol{n}\, da \qquad (7.111)$$

Finally, substituting for curl $\boldsymbol{H}$ from Eq. 6.2 yields,

$$P = \oint_S \phi \left( \boldsymbol{J}_f + \frac{\partial \boldsymbol{D}}{\partial t} \right) \cdot \boldsymbol{n}\, da \qquad (7.112)$$

The values assumed by the scalar potential $\phi$ at the points where the wires cross $S$ in Fig. 7.4 have been identified with the terminal voltages $V_1$, $V_2$, $\cdots$. Thus the term in Eq. 7.112 involving $\boldsymbol{J}_f$ reduces to the right-hand side of Eq. 7.107. The term involving $\partial \boldsymbol{D}/\partial t$ represents power associated with the flow of "displacement current" through

$S$. This term is negligible in practice unless the surface $S$ cuts through a capacitor, in which case the displacement current is equal to the terminal current of the capacitor. Thus the parenthesis in Eq. 7.112, when integrated over $S$, takes into account all currents flowing out of $V$. In conclusion, the network point of view and the field point of view can be reconciled whenever terminal voltages can be defined in a consistent manner, i.e., whenever the electromagnetic system in question can be treated as a circuit. Conversely, it can be shown that Eqs. 7.107 and 7.108 cannot be reconciled unless the electric field can be regarded as conservative over the surface $S$ enclosing the portion of the circuit in question.

## ► 7.7 Energy in Systems of Charged Conductors

We saw in Sec. 6.7 how the quasi-static behavior of a system of isolated conductors and linear dielectric materials can be represented in terms of an equivalent electric circuit consisting of capacitive branches. Furthermore, we saw in Sec. 7.3 that the power supplied by external forces to such a system must be equal to the time rate of change of the energy associated with the zero-order electric field and with the zero-order polarization; the density of the sum of these two energies is, for linear dielectric materials,

$$w_e = \tfrac{1}{2}\epsilon|\boldsymbol{E}|^2 \tag{7.113}$$

Our present objective is to establish a relation between the circuit point of view and the field point of view with respect to the storage of energy in the system.

The total energy supplied by external forces in charging the various conductors can be readily evaluated from the first integral in Eq. 7.62 with the help of the set of Eqs. 6.130. We obtain

$$\begin{aligned} W_e &= \frac{1}{2}(Q_1V_1 + Q_2V_2 + \cdots + Q_kV_k + \cdots + Q_nV_n) \\ &= \sum_{j=1}^{n}\sum_{k=1}^{n}\frac{1}{2}C_{jk}V_jV_k \end{aligned} \tag{7.114}$$

where $V_k$ is the value assumed on the $k$th conductor by the potential $\phi$ associated with the zero-order electric field, and $Q_k$ is the net zero-order charge on the $k$th conductor. If we indicate by $r$ the distance from the origin, $\phi$ vanishes at infinity as $r^{-2}$ when the sum of the charges on the conductors is equal to zero, and as $r^{-1}$ when it is different from zero, in which case an equal amount of charge of opposite polarity is located at infinity. In the latter, more general case, the spherical surface at infinity plays the role of reference conductor; in the former case, any one of the conductors may be taken as a reference by redefining accordingly the voltages $V_k$ and the capacitance coefficients. In any case, the sum of the charges on all conductors, including the one used as a reference, must be equal to zero. In the two-dimensional illustration shown in Fig. 7.5, the reference conductor encloses all the other conductors, and the sum of the charges on the three conductors is equal to zero. In this special case, the potential of the reference conductor is the same as the potential at infinity; the $C_{jk}$ are capacitances per unit length of the cylindrical system.

The total system energy given by Eq. 7.114 (energy per unit length in the system of Fig. 7.5) can also be evaluated from the right-hand side of Eq. 7.62, as the volume integral of the energy density given by Eq. 7.113. For this purpose, we recall that, because of the linearity of the system, the potential $\phi$ can be expressed as a linear combination of potentials

$$\phi = V_1\varphi_1 + V_2\varphi_2 + \cdots + V_k\varphi_k + \cdots + V_n\varphi_n \tag{7.115}$$

where $\varphi_k$ is the potential in the system when $V_k$ is equal to unity, and the voltages of all the other conductors are equal to zero, as illustrated in Fig. 7.5*c* and 7.5*d*. Substitution of $-\text{grad}\,\phi$ for $\boldsymbol{E}$ on the right-hand side of Eq. 7.62 yields

$$W_e = \sum_{j=1}^{n}\sum_{k=1}^{n}\frac{1}{2}V_kV_j\oint(\epsilon\,\text{grad}\,\varphi_k\cdot\text{grad}\,\varphi_j)\,dv \tag{7.116}$$

The right-hand sides of Eqs. 7.114 and 7.116 must be equal for all values of the conductor voltages. In particular, they must be equal when all voltages are equal to zero except for $V_k = 1$. It follows that

$$C_{kk} = \oint\epsilon|\text{grad}\,\varphi_k|^2\,dv \geq 0 \tag{7.117}$$

for all values of the integer $k$. On the other hand, if all the voltages are equal to zero except for $V_j = V_k = 1$, we obtain with the help of Eq. 7.114

$$\frac{1}{2}(C_{jk} + C_{kj}) = \oint(\epsilon\,\text{grad}\,\varphi_k\cdot\text{grad}\,\varphi_j)\,dv \tag{7.118}$$

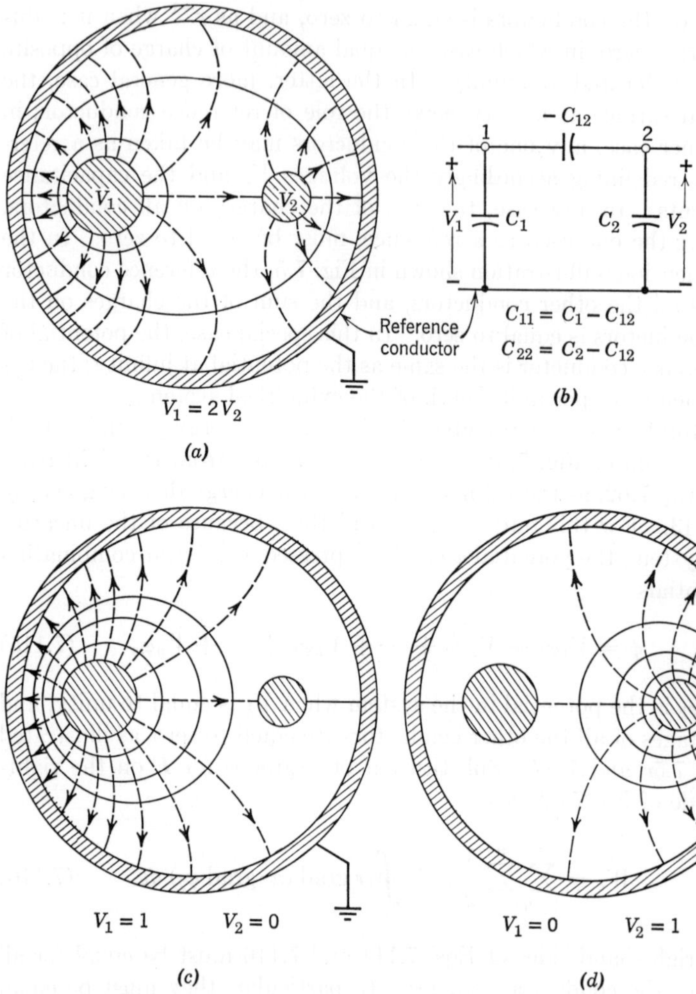


**Fig. 7.5.** Illustration of the unitary fields and of the equivalent circuit for system of cylindrical conductors.

Furthermore, since the total energy must be nonnegative for $V_j = V_k = 1$,

$$C_{kk} + C_{jj} + C_{jk} + C_{kj} \geq 0 \tag{7.119}$$

It follows from Eq. 7.117 that the capacitance $C_{kk}$ is equal to twice the energy associated with the unitary potential $\varphi_k$. Similarly, the sum of the mutual capacitances $C_{jk}$ and $C_{kj}$ is equal to four times the energy contributed by the interaction of the unitary potentials $\varphi_k$ and $\varphi_j$. We shall show presently that these two mutual capacitances are equal, and, therefore,

$$C_{jk} = C_{kj} = \oint (\epsilon \operatorname{grad} \varphi_k \cdot \operatorname{grad} \varphi_j)\, dv \tag{7.120}$$

For this purpose, let us rewrite the integrand in the form

$$\epsilon \operatorname{grad} \varphi_k \cdot \operatorname{grad} \varphi_j = -\boldsymbol{d}_k \cdot \operatorname{grad} \varphi_j = -\operatorname{div}(\varphi_j \boldsymbol{d}_k) \tag{7.121}$$

where $\boldsymbol{d}_k$ is the electric-flux density associated with $\varphi_k$. Use has been made of Eq. A4.14, Appendix 4, and of the fact that div $\boldsymbol{d}_k$ vanishes by assumption in the space between the conductors. We obtain, then, with the help of Gauss' theorem, for any volume $V$

$$\int_V (\epsilon \operatorname{grad} \varphi_k \cdot \operatorname{grad} \varphi_j)\, dv = -\oint_S (\varphi_j \boldsymbol{d}_k) \cdot \boldsymbol{n}\, da \tag{7.122}$$

where $\boldsymbol{n}$ is the usual unit vector normal to the surface $S$ enclosing $V$. Let us now take as the volume $V$ the entire space except for the regions occupied by the conductors. With this choice of $V$, the integral on the left-hand side of Eq. 7.122 is equal to the integral on the right-hand side of Eq. 7.120 because the potentials $\varphi_k$ and $\varphi_j$ are constant within all the conductors and on their surfaces. The surface $S$, on the other hand, consists of the surfaces of the conductors and the surface at infinity which may be regarded as a spherical surface of radius $r$, approaching infinity. The contribution of the surface at infinity to the right-hand side of Eq. 7.122 is equal to zero, because $\varphi_j$ must vanish at infinity at least as fast as $r^{-1}$, $\boldsymbol{d}_k$ must vanish at least as fast as $r^{-2}$, and the area of the spherical surface is proportional to $r^2$. Furthermore $\varphi_j$ is, by definition, equal to zero on all conductors except the $j$th one where it is equal to one. It follows that Eq. 7.122 reduces to

$$\oint (\epsilon \operatorname{grad} \varphi_k \cdot \operatorname{grad} \varphi_j)\, dv = -\oint_{S_j} \boldsymbol{d}_k \cdot \boldsymbol{n}\, da \tag{7.123}$$

where $S_j$ is the surface of the $j$th conductor and $\boldsymbol{n}$ is directed toward the conductor. The vector $\boldsymbol{d}_k$ represents the contribution to the vector $\boldsymbol{D}$ resulting from the potential $\varphi_k$. Thus, the right-hand side of Eq. 7.123 represents the charge on the $j$th conductor contributed by $\varphi_k$, which is equal to one on the $k$th conductor. Then, we can conclude on the basis of Eq. 6.130 that the right-hand side of Eq. 7.123 is equal to the mutual capacitance $C_{jk}$. Furthermore, since the integrand on the left-hand side of Eq. 7.123 is symmetrical with respect to $\varphi_k$ and $\varphi_j$, $C_{kj}$ must be equal to $C_{jk}$. This concludes the proof of Eq. 7.120.

The theorem that we have just proved is known as the *reciprocity theorem.* It states, in words, that the charge induced on the $j$th conductor by a voltage on the $k$th conductor is equal to the charge induced on the $k$th conductor by an equal voltage on the $j$th conductor. It is important to note that, because of this theorem, the number of independent capacitance coefficients necessary to represent a system of $n$ conductors (plus a reference conductor) is $n(n+1)/2$ rather than $n^2$. Thus the system can be represented by a network of capacitances, as illustrated in Fig. 7.5*b*, with as many nodes as there are conductors. It remains to be shown in this connection that all capacitances in the network are nonnegative.

With reference to Fig. 7.5*b*, the capacitance $C_{kk}$ is the sum of the capacitances of all the branches stemming from the $k$th node,

$$C_{kk} = C_k - C_{k1} - C_{k2} - \cdots - C_{kj} - \cdots - C_{kn} \qquad (7.124)$$

where $C_k$ is the capacitance of the branch joining the $k$th node to the reference node and $-C_{kj}$ is the capacitance of the branch joining the $k$th node to the $j$th node. With a unit voltage applied to the $k$th conductor and all the conductors at zero potential, the charge on the $k$th conductor is equal to $C_{kk}$, a positive quantity, while the charge on the reference conductor is $-C_k$, and that on the $j$th conductor is $C_{kj}$. We shall show presently that these last two charges are negative, and therefore

$$C_k \geq 0 \qquad -C_{kj} \geq 0 \qquad (7.125)$$

We saw in Sec. 4.6 that a scalar potential cannot have either a maximum or a minimum value within a region in which it satisfies Laplace's equation. The scalar potential associated with a static electric field, however, does not satisfy Laplace's equation within a nonhomogeneous, charge-free dielectric, but rather the equation

$$\operatorname{div}(\epsilon \operatorname{grad} \phi) = \epsilon\, \Delta\phi + \operatorname{grad} \epsilon \cdot \operatorname{grad} \phi = 0 \qquad (7.126)$$

On the other hand, at any point at which $\phi$ is either a maximum or a minimum, grad $\phi$ must be equal to zero, and, therefore, $\Delta\phi$ must also be equal to zero. This, however, cannot happen at a point at which $\phi$ is a maximum or a minimum because, at such a point, all second derivatives of $\phi$ would have to have the same sign. It follows that *the potential cannot have either a maximum or a minimum value in a charge-free region, even if the dielectric is inhomogeneous.*

If the $k$th conductor is held at unit potential, while all the other conductors are at zero potential, the potential in the dielectric must then assume intermediate values. It follows that

$$\boldsymbol{d}_k = -\epsilon \operatorname{grad} \varphi_k \tag{7.127}$$

must be outwardly directed on the surface of the $k$th conductor, and inwardly directed on the surfaces of all the other conductors, as illustrated in Fig. 7.5*c*. We can conclude, therefore, that the charge on the $k$th conductor is positive, while the charge on all the other conductors is negative. This completes the proof of Eq. 7.125.

It is worth stressing, with respect to the equivalent circuit of Fig. 7.5*b*, that the branch capacitances cannot be associated individually with different parts of the field, although their values can be expressed in terms of the unitary potentials $\varphi_k$. In other words, the circuit is equivalent to the system of conductors only with respect to the linear relationships between the charges on the conductors and their potentials. The equivalence with respect to the total energy results from the fact that the field energy depends only on the charges on the conductors and their potentials. In particular, the energy associated with each individual branch capacitance has no direct physical significance; it cannot be identified with the energy associated with any one of the unitary potentials or with the energy stored in any one region of space. However, it can be expressed in terms of the energies associated with the unitary potentials and with their interactions, as indicated by Eqs. 7.117, 7.118, and 7.124.

## ► 7.8 Power in a Multiterminal Conductor

We saw in Sec. 6.6 how the static behavior of a multiterminal, linear conductor can be represented in terms of an equivalent resistive circuit. Furthermore, we saw in Sec. 7.5 that the power input to the conductor must be equal to the volume integral of the power-dissipation density

$$p_d = \sigma |\boldsymbol{E}|^2 \tag{7.128}$$

where the conductivity $\sigma$ may be a function of position. Our present objective is to establish a relation between the circuit point of view and the field point of view with respect to the power dissipation in the conductor.

The total power supplied to the conductor can be readily expressed in terms of the terminal voltages with the help of the set of Eqs. 6.118.

We obtain

$$P_d = I_1V_1 + I_2V_2 + \cdots + I_kV_k + \cdots + I_nV_n$$

$$= \sum_{k=1}^{n} \sum_{j=1}^{n} G_{jk}V_jV_k \qquad (7.129)$$

where $V_k$ is the value assumed on the $k$th terminal by the potential $\phi$ associated with the zero-order electric field, and $I_k$ is the current flowing into the conductor from the same terminal, as illustrated in Fig. 7.6. The potential is equal to zero on the reference terminal. The sum of the currents flowing into the conductor from all the terminals must be equal to the current flowing out of the conductor from the reference terminal.

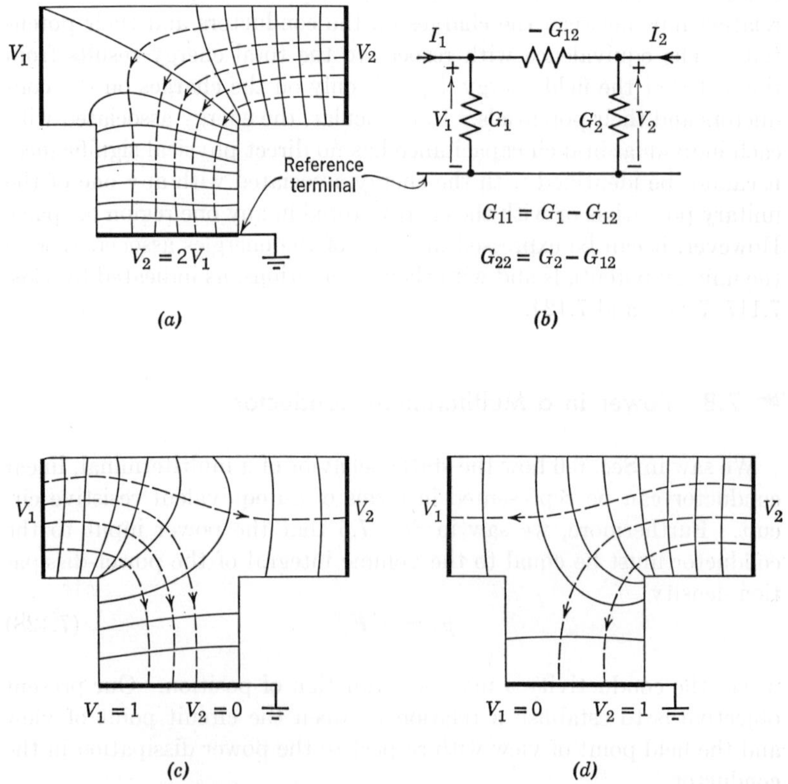


**Fig. 7.6.** Illustration of the unitary fields and of the equivalent circuit for a two-dimensional conductor.

The power input to the conductor may be evaluated also as the volume integral of the power-dissipation density given by Eq. 7.128. For this purpose, we recall that, because of the linearity of the system, the potential $\phi$ can be expressed as a linear combination of potentials

$$\phi = V_1\varphi_1 + V_2\varphi_2 + \cdots + V_k\varphi_k + \cdots + V_n\varphi_n \tag{7.130}$$

where $\varphi_k$ is the potential in the conductor when $V_k$ is equal to unity and all the other terminal voltages are equal to zero, as illustrated in Figs. 7.6*c* and 7.6*d*. Substitution of $-\text{grad}\,\phi$ for $\boldsymbol{E}$ on the right-hand side of Eq. 7.97 yields

$$P_d = \sum_{k=1}^{n} \sum_{j=1}^{n} V_k V_j \int_V (\sigma \,\text{grad}\, \varphi_k \cdot \text{grad}\, \varphi_j)\, dv \tag{7.131}$$

where $V$ is the volume occupied by the conductor.

The right-hand sides of Eqs. 7.129 and 7.131 must be equal for all values of the terminal voltages. Furthermore, these equations are identical in form to Eqs. 7.114 and 7.116 except for a factor of ½ and the substitution of $\sigma$ for $\epsilon$; integration over $V$ is equivalent to integration over the entire space because $\sigma$ is assumed to be equal to zero outside $V$. It follows that the properties of the capacitance coefficient $C_{jk}$, derived in the preceding section, can be translated directly into corresponding properties of the conductance coefficient $G_{jk}$. Thus,

$$G_{kk} = \int_V \sigma |\text{grad}\, \varphi_k|^2\, dv \geq 0 \tag{7.132}$$

$$G_{jk} = G_{kj} = \int_V (\sigma \,\text{grad}\, \varphi_k \cdot \text{grad}\, \varphi_j)\, dv \leq 0 \tag{7.133}$$

The equality of $G_{jk}$ and $G_{kj}$ follows from a reciprocity theorem analogous to that proved in the preceding section. This theorem states that the current forced through the $j$th terminal by the voltage applied to the $k$th terminal is equal to the current forced through the $k$th terminal by an equal voltage applied to the $j$th terminal. Again, because of this theorem, the number of independent conductance coefficients necessary to represent the multiterminal conductor is equal to $n(n+1)/2$ rather than $n^2$. Thus, the conductor can be represented by a network of conductances, as illustrated in Fig. 7.6*b*, with as many nodes as there are terminal surfaces on the conductor. The branch conductances are all positive, just as the branch capacitances in the capacitive system discussed in the preceding section.

We must stress that also in this case the branch conductances cannot be individually associated with different parts of the conductor although their values can be expressed in terms of the unitary potentials $\varphi_k$. In other words, the circuit is equivalent to the multiterminal conductor only with respect to the linear relationships between terminal voltages and terminal currents. The equivalence with respect to the total power dissipated follows from the fact that the power can be expressed in terms of terminal voltages and terminal currents. In particular, the power dissipated in each branch of the network has no direct physical significance; it cannot be identified with the power dissipated in any particular part of the conductor or with the power associated with any one unitary potential. On the other hand, it can be expressed in terms of the powers associated with the unitary potentials and with their interactions.

## ► 7.9 Energy in Multiwinding Systems

We saw in Sec. 6.9 how the quasi-static behavior of multiwinding systems in the presence of linear magnetic materials can be represented in terms of self-inductances and mutual inductances. Furthermore, we saw in Sec. 7.4 that the power supplied by external forces to such a system must be equal to the time rate of change of the energy associated with the zero-order magnetic field, and with the zero-order magnetization; the density of the sum of these two energies is, for linear magnetic materials,

$$w_m = \tfrac{1}{2}\mu|\boldsymbol{H}|^2 \tag{7.134}$$

where the permeability $\mu$ may be a function of position. Our present objective is to establish a relation between the circuit point of view and the field point of view with respect to the storage of energy in the system.

The total energy supplied by external forces in building up the currents in the separate windings can be readily evaluated from the left-hand side of Eq. 7.84,

$$W_e = W_1 + W_2 + \cdots + W_i + \cdots + W_n \tag{7.135}$$

where

$$W_i = \oint \frac{1}{2} \boldsymbol{J}_i \cdot \boldsymbol{A}\, dv \tag{7.136}$$

and $\boldsymbol{J}_i$ is the current density in the $i$th winding. Let us assume now that the space distribution of the current in each winding is independent of time, although the magnitude of the current density may vary with time; in other words, let us assume that

$$\boldsymbol{J}_i = I_i \boldsymbol{j}_i \tag{7.137}$$

and $\boldsymbol{j}_i$ is independent of time, and represents the current density in the $i$th winding when the total current flowing in the winding is equal to one; $I_i$ is the actual current in the winding, and, therefore, it may be a function of time, but not of position.

Under the above conditions, the current through the winding, and through the source connected to the winding can be divided into closed-current filaments of differential intensity, with the geometry of the filaments independent of time. It must be carefully noted that, whereas the division into current filaments requires only that the divergence of $\boldsymbol{J}_i$ be equal to zero, the time independence of the geometry of the filaments requires that $\boldsymbol{J}_i$ be expressible as in Eq. 7.137. Each current filament contributes a differential amount of energy

$$dW_i = \frac{1}{2}\, dI_i \oint_C \boldsymbol{A}\cdot d\boldsymbol{s} \tag{7.138}$$

where $dI_i$ is the filament current, $C$ is the closed path formed by the filament and $d\boldsymbol{s}$ is a differential element of $C$ in the reference direction of $I_i$. The total energy $W_m$ can then be evaluated by adding the contributions of the individual filaments.

The line integral on the right-hand side of Eq. 7.138 can be transformed into a surface integral with the help of Stokes' theorem. We obtain

$$\oint_C \boldsymbol{A}\cdot d\boldsymbol{s} = \int_S \boldsymbol{B}\cdot\boldsymbol{n}\, da = \int_S \mu\boldsymbol{H}\cdot\boldsymbol{n}\, da \tag{7.139}$$

where $S$ is any two-sided surface bounded by $C$. Since the surface integral represents the magnetic flux linking the closed path $C$, the quantity

$$\lambda_i = \frac{1}{I_i}\int_0^{I_i}\left(\oint_C \boldsymbol{A}\cdot d\boldsymbol{s}\right) dI_i = \oint \boldsymbol{j}_i\cdot\boldsymbol{A}\, dv \tag{7.140}$$

represents the mean flux linking the filaments that constitute the current $I_i$. The integration with respect to $I_i$ must be regarded as the limit of the summation over the current filaments of intensity $dI_i$. The quantity $\lambda_i$ is referred to as the *flux linkage* associated with $I_i$. It reduces to the flux $\Phi_i$ of Sec. 6.9, when the line integral in Eq. 7.140 has the same value for all current filaments, i.e., when all filaments are linked by the same flux. Thus, the energy associated with the current $I_i$ can be expressed in the form

$$W_i = \tfrac{1}{2} I_i \lambda_i \tag{7.141}$$

Because of the linearity of the system, the vector potential $\boldsymbol{A}$ can be expressed as a linear combination

$$\boldsymbol{A} = I_1 \boldsymbol{a}_1 + I_2 \boldsymbol{a}_2 + \cdots + I_k \boldsymbol{a}_k + \cdots + I_n \boldsymbol{a}_n \tag{7.142}$$

where $\boldsymbol{a}_k$ is the vector potential that results when $I_k = 1$, and all the other currents in the system are equal to zero. In other words, $\boldsymbol{a}_k$ is a unitary vector potential, analogous to the unitary scalar potential $\varphi_k$ of the preceding two sections. A magnetic flux density

$$\mu \boldsymbol{h}_k = \operatorname{curl} \boldsymbol{a}_k \tag{7.143}$$

is associated with each unitary vector potential, where $\boldsymbol{h}_k$ is the same unitary magnetic field defined in Sec. 6.9.

Substitution of the summation in Eq. 7.142 for $\boldsymbol{A}$ in Eq. 7.140 yields for the flux linkage associated with $I_i$,

$$\lambda_i = L_{i1} I_1 + L_{12} I_2 + \cdots + L_{ik} I_k + \cdots + L_{1n} I_n \tag{7.144}$$

where

$$L_{ik} = \oint \boldsymbol{j}_i \cdot \boldsymbol{a}_k \, dv \tag{7.145}$$

In view of Eq. 7.140, $L_{ik}$ represents the unitary flux linkage with the $i$th coil produced by a unit current in the $k$th coil, and it is a geometric characteristic of the two coils. Clearly, Eq. 7.144 is a generalization of the equations of the set 6.168. We must recall, in this regard, that, in Sec. 6.9, the current distribution in each coil was restricted in such a way that the same flux linked all the current filaments. For this restriction we have now substituted the less stringent requirement that the geometry of the current distribution be independent of time. The total energy supplied to the system by external forces can now be expressed in the form

$$W_m = \sum_{i=1}^{n} W_i = \sum_{i=1}^{n} \frac{1}{2} I_i \lambda_i = \sum_{i=1}^{n} \sum_{i=1}^{n} \frac{1}{2} L_{ik} I_i I_k \tag{7.146}$$

analogous to that of Eq. 7.114.

Proceeding as in Sec. 7.7, the energy supplied to the system can also be evaluated as the volume integral of the energy density stored in the system. Expressing the total magnetic field $\boldsymbol{H}$ as a linear combination of the unitary fields defined by Eq. 7.143 yields,

$$W_m = \oint \frac{1}{2} \mu |\boldsymbol{H}|^2 \, dv = \sum_{i=1}^{n} \sum_{k=1}^{n} \frac{1}{2} I_i I_k \oint \frac{1}{\mu} (\text{curl } \boldsymbol{a}_i \cdot \text{curl } \boldsymbol{a}_k) \, dv \quad (7.147)$$

The right-hand side of this equation must be equal to the right-hand side of Eq. 7.146 for all values of the currents. If $I_k = 1$ and all the other currents are equal to zero we obtain

$$L_{kk} = \oint \frac{1}{\mu} |\text{curl } \boldsymbol{a}_k|^2 \, dv = \oint \mu |\boldsymbol{h}_k|^2 \, dv \geq 0 \quad (7.148)$$

If, instead, $I_i = I_k = 1$, and all the other currents are equal to zero, we obtain, with the help of Eq. 7.148,

$$\frac{1}{2} (L_{ik} + L_{ki}) = \oint \frac{1}{\mu} (\text{curl } \boldsymbol{a}_i \cdot \text{curl } \boldsymbol{a}_k) \, dv = \oint \mu (\boldsymbol{h}_i \cdot \boldsymbol{h}_k) \, dv \quad (7.149)$$

It can be shown further that

$$L_{ik} = L_{ki} = \oint \mu (\boldsymbol{h}_i \cdot \boldsymbol{h}_k) \, dv \quad (7.150)$$

The proof of this reciprocity theorem is similar to that given in Sec. 7.7. First of all, with the help of Eq. A4.16, Appendix 4, we write the integrand on the right-hand side of Eq. 7.149 in the form,

$$\boldsymbol{h}_i \cdot \text{curl } \boldsymbol{a}_k = \text{div } (\boldsymbol{a}_k \times \boldsymbol{h}_i) + \boldsymbol{a}_k \cdot \text{curl } \boldsymbol{h}_i \quad (7.151)$$

The integral over the entire space of the first term on the right-hand side is equal to zero. In fact, integration over a sphere of radius $r$ centered at the origin yields, with the help of Gauss' theorem,

$$\int_V \text{div } (\boldsymbol{a}_k \times \boldsymbol{h}_i) \, dv = \oint_S (\boldsymbol{a}_k \times \boldsymbol{h}_i) \cdot \boldsymbol{n} \, dv \quad (7.152)$$

The surface integral vanishes when $r$ approaches infinity because $\boldsymbol{h}_i$ vanishes at least as fast as $r^{-3}$ and $\boldsymbol{a}_k$ vanishes at least as fast as $r^{-2}$, while the area of the surface is proportional to $r^2$. On the other hand, $\boldsymbol{h}_i$ is the static field produced by a unit current in the $i$th coil, and therefore

$$\text{curl } \boldsymbol{h}_i = \boldsymbol{j}_i \quad (7.153)$$

Thus, we obtain from Eqs. 7.145, 7.149 and 7.151

$$\frac{1}{2}(L_{ik} + L_{ki}) = \oint (\boldsymbol{h}_i \cdot \text{curl } \boldsymbol{a}_k)\, dv = \oint (\boldsymbol{a}_k \cdot \boldsymbol{j}_i)\, dv = L_{ik} \quad (7.154)$$

which completes the proof of the reciprocity theorem.

The usual circuit representation of a multiwinding system illustrated in Fig. 7.7*a*, hardly differs from its physical appearance because the self-inductance of a coil and the mutual inductance between separate coils are both recognized as circuit parameters. Thus the energy term

$$W_{kk} = \tfrac{1}{2} L_{kk} I_k^2 \quad (7.155)$$

can be identified by itself as the energy stored in the self-inductance of the $k$th coil, and the energy term

$$W_{ik} + W_{ki} = L_{ik} I_i I_k \quad (7.156)$$

as the energy associated with the mutual inductance between the $i$th coil and the $k$th coil. On the other hand, if we do not recognize mutual inductances as circuit parameters, and insist on a circuit representation consisting of self-inductances alone, we obtain the circuit illustrated in Fig. 7.7*b*. In this second circuit the energy terms $W_{kk}$ and $W_{ik} + W_{ki}$ cannot be associated with individual inductive branches, just as in Sec. 7.7 the analogous electric-energy terms could not be associated with individual capacitive branches.

As an illustration of the preceding analysis, we shall evaluate the energy stored in a system consisting of two coils with $N_1$ and $N_2$ turns

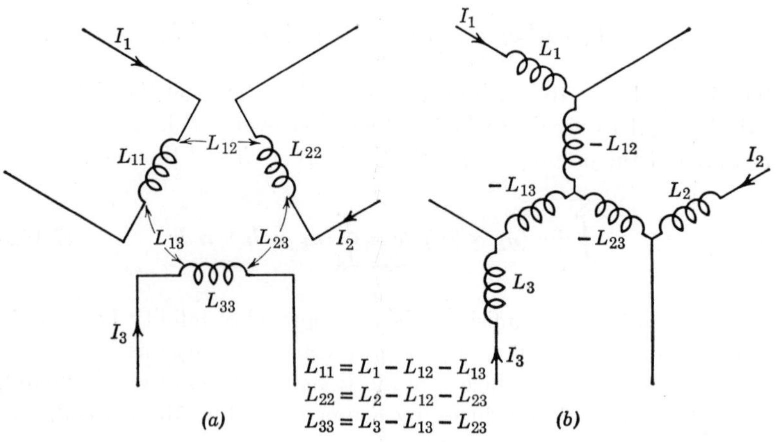


**Fig. 7.7.** Equivalent circuits for a three-winding system.

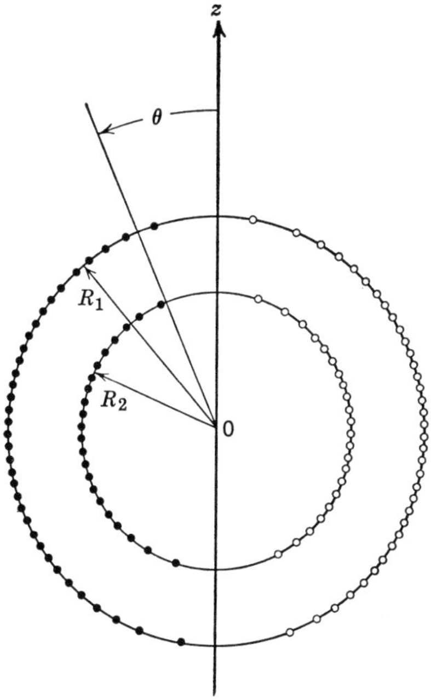


**Fig. 7.8.** Two concentric spherical coils.

wound on the surfaces of two concentric spheres of radii $R_1$ and $R_2$, as illustrated in Fig. 7.8. Both coils are wound with uniform turn density along their common axis, so that the current distribution on each sphere can be approximated by a surface current density of the type given by Eq. 7.85 for the single coil discussed in Sec. 7.4. Using a system of spherical coordinates with the origin at the center of the two spheres, and the $z$-axis coinciding with the axis of the two coils, we have for the two surface current densities

$$\boldsymbol{K}_{f1} = \boldsymbol{i}_\varphi \frac{3}{4\pi R_1{}^3} (\boldsymbol{m}_1 \cdot \boldsymbol{i}_z) \sin\theta \tag{7.157}$$

$$\boldsymbol{K}_{f2} = \boldsymbol{i}_\varphi \frac{3}{4\pi R_2{}^3} (\boldsymbol{m}_2 \cdot \boldsymbol{i}_z) \sin\theta \tag{7.158}$$

where, according to Eq. 7.91,

$$\boldsymbol{m}_1 = \boldsymbol{i}_z \tfrac{2}{3}\pi R_1{}^2 N_1 I_1 \tag{7.159}$$

$$\boldsymbol{m}_2 = \boldsymbol{i}_z \tfrac{2}{3}\pi R_2{}^2 N_2 I_2 \tag{7.160}$$

and $I_1$ and $I_2$ are the currents in the two coils.

The inductance of each coil can be evaluated as if the other coil were not present, and therefore it can be obtained directly from Eq. 7.94. Thus,

$$L_{11} = \tfrac{2}{9}\pi\mu_0 R_1 N_1^2 \tag{7.161}$$

$$L_{22} = \tfrac{2}{9}\pi\mu_0 R_2 N_2^2 \tag{7.162}$$

The mutual inductance $L_{12} = L_{21}$ is most readily evaluated from Eq. 7.145. We have

$$L_{12} = \oint \boldsymbol{j}_i \cdot \boldsymbol{a}_2 \, dv = \frac{1}{I_1 I_2} \oint_S \boldsymbol{K}_{f1} \cdot \boldsymbol{A}_2 \, da \tag{7.163}$$

where $S$ is the spherical surface of radius $R_1$ and $\boldsymbol{A}_2$ is the vector potential produced by the surface current $\boldsymbol{K}_{f2}$. If $R_1 > R_2$, this vector potential can be obtained from Eq. 7.87. We have,

$$\boldsymbol{A}_2 = \boldsymbol{i}_\varphi \frac{\mu_0}{4\pi r^2} (\boldsymbol{m}_2 \cdot \boldsymbol{i}_z) \sin\theta \qquad r > R_2 \tag{7.164}$$

Thus,

$$L_{12} = \frac{\boldsymbol{m}_1 \cdot \boldsymbol{m}_2}{I_1 I_2} \frac{3\mu_0}{8\pi R_1^3} \int_0^\pi \sin^3\theta \, d\theta = \frac{\mu_0(\boldsymbol{m}_1 \cdot \boldsymbol{m}_2)}{2\pi R_1^3 I_1 I_2} \tag{7.165}$$

and with the help of Eqs. 7.159 and 7.160

$$L_{12} = \frac{2}{9} \pi\mu_0 R_2 \frac{R_2}{R_1} N_1 N_2 \qquad R_1 \geq R_2 \tag{7.166}$$

which reduces to Eqs. 7.162 for $R_1 = R_2$ and $N_1 = N_2$, as expected. The same result is obtained by evaluating the volume integral on the right-hand side of Eq. 7.150.

In conclusion, the total energy in the system formed by the two coils is

$$\begin{aligned} W_m &= \tfrac{1}{2} L_{11} I_1^2 + \tfrac{1}{2} L_{22} I_{22}^2 + L_{12} I_1 I_2 \\ &= \frac{1}{9} \pi\mu_0 \left( R_1 N_1^2 I_1^2 + R_2 N_2^2 I_2^2 + 2R_2 \frac{R_2}{R_1} N_1 N_2 I_1 I_2 \right) \end{aligned} \tag{7.167}$$

The fields and the energies associated with the currents in the wires that connect the coils to their sources are usually negligible for large values of $N_1$ and $N_2$, and, for this reason, have been disregarded in the above computations.

## ► 7.10 Poynting's Theorem for the Amperian-Current Model

The derivation of Poynting's theorem for macroscopic fields, presented in Sec. 7.2, and its interpretation are based on the magnetic-charge model of magnetized matter. We wish to inquire now how this theorem and its interpretation would have to be modified if the amperian-current model of magnetized matter were to be adopted.

We saw in Sec. 5.4 that, if the amperian-current model is used, magnetized matter is represented macroscopically by an electric-current distribution of density

$$\boldsymbol{J}_m = \text{curl}\, \boldsymbol{M} \tag{7.168}$$

Furthermore, the macroscopic field obtained by averaging the microscopic magnetic field $\boldsymbol{h}$ is $\boldsymbol{B}/\mu_0$ rather than $\boldsymbol{H}$. The resulting macroscopic field equations are

$$\text{curl}\, \boldsymbol{E} + \frac{\partial \boldsymbol{B}}{\partial t} = 0$$

$$\text{curl}\, \frac{\boldsymbol{B}}{\mu_0} - \epsilon_0 \frac{\partial \boldsymbol{E}}{\partial t} = \boldsymbol{J} \tag{7.169}$$

where

$$\boldsymbol{J} = \boldsymbol{J}_f + \frac{\partial \boldsymbol{P}}{\partial t} + \text{curl}\, \boldsymbol{M} \tag{7.170}$$

Since no magnetic charges or magnetic currents are involved, the only electromagnetic force that may be present is the Lorentz force on moving electric charges, with the result that $\boldsymbol{E}\cdot\boldsymbol{J}$ by itself represents the density of the power supplied by external forces. Then, following the same procedure as in Sec. 7.2, we obtain for Poynting's theorem

$$\text{div}\left(\boldsymbol{E} \times \frac{\boldsymbol{B}}{\mu_0}\right) + \frac{\partial}{\partial t}\left(\frac{1}{2}\epsilon_0|\boldsymbol{E}|^2 + \frac{1}{2}\mu_0\left|\frac{\boldsymbol{B}}{\mu_0}\right|^2\right) = -\boldsymbol{E}\cdot\boldsymbol{J}$$

$$= -\left(\boldsymbol{E}\cdot\frac{\partial \boldsymbol{P}}{\partial t} + \boldsymbol{E}\cdot\text{curl}\, \boldsymbol{M} + \boldsymbol{E}\cdot\boldsymbol{J}_f\right) \tag{7.171}$$

Formally, this expression is entirely equivalent to that obtained in Sec. 7.2 and can be reduced to it by appropriate manipulations. However, the choice of the amperian-current model forces us to interpret the various terms in a radically different manner.

Since $-\boldsymbol{E}\cdot\boldsymbol{J}$ represents the density of the power supplied by external forces, the left-hand side of Eq. 7.171 must represent the density of the power absorbed by the electromagnetic field, and stored by it either at the point at which it is supplied or elsewhere. Thus, following the same line of reasoning as in Sec. 7.2 we are led to interpret $\boldsymbol{E} \times \boldsymbol{B}/\mu_0$ as the density of electromagnetic power flow, and $\frac{1}{2}(\epsilon_0|\boldsymbol{E}|^2 + \mu_0|\boldsymbol{B}/\mu_0|^2)$ as the density of the energy stored in the electromagnetic field.

The first term and the last term on the right-hand side of Eq. 7.171 can still be interpreted as in Sec. 7.2. The term $\boldsymbol{E}\cdot\text{curl}\,\boldsymbol{M}$ must now be interpreted as the density of the power supplied by the electromagnetic field to magnetized matter. In fact, consistency requires us to regard all electric currents as possessing the same macroscopic physical attributes, regardless of their microscopic origin. On the other hand, this interpretation is very disturbing for three reasons. In the first place, as already indicated in Sec. 5.4, different parts of a permanent magnet would appear to absorb or deliver power in the presence of a static electric field. Although it can be readily shown that the net power absorbed by the magnet would always be equal to zero, the continuous transfer of energy from one part of the magnet to another is unacceptable unless we can point to some other physical mechanism capable of transferring the same energy back. In the second place, Eq. 7.168 implies that a surface amperian current must be present on any surface at which the tangential component of $\boldsymbol{M}$ is discontinuous. This implies, in turn, that energy may be absorbed or delivered by a magnetized body right at its surface, with an infinite volume density. This second conclusion is also unacceptable from a physical standpoint. Finally, when energy is dissipated because of hysteresis in the constituent relation of the magnetic material, the space distribution of the energy dissipated as given by Eq. 7.171 does not agree with the space distribution of the heat generated, as determined by measurements.

The reasons against interpreting $\boldsymbol{E}\cdot\text{curl}\,\boldsymbol{M}$ as the density of the power absorbed by magnetized matter are so strong that this interpretation has never been seriously proposed. On the other hand, some textbooks present a macroscopic theory of electromagnetism based on the amperian-current model of magnetized matter, and avoid the above interpretation by introducing in the theory what appears to the authors of this book as a logical inconsistency. While $\boldsymbol{B}/\mu_0$ is taken as the fundamental magnetic vector, $\boldsymbol{E} \times \boldsymbol{H}$ rather than $(\boldsymbol{E} \times \boldsymbol{B}/)\mu_0$ is interpreted as representing the density of the electromagnetic power flow. This interpretation seems to us inconsistent for the following reason. When the amperian-current model is adopted, $\boldsymbol{H}$ becomes a "mixed" vector, involving the state of magnetization of matter as well as the magnetic part of the electromagnetic field. Thus, $\boldsymbol{E} \times \boldsymbol{H}$ cannot represent an inherent property of the electromagnetic field, which, by its very definition, must be independent of the state of matter. In effect, the amperian-current model is used in the derivation of the macroscopic field equations but, by implication at least, the magnetic-charge model is used in the interpretation of Poynting's theorem. The relation between the macroscopic theories based on the two different models is discussed further in Appendix 1.

## 7.11 Summary and Conclusions

The focal point of this chapter has been Poynting's theorem. As a mathematical relation, Poynting's theorem is a straightforward consequence of Maxwell's equations. It is its physical interpretation that is of cardinal importance. For this reason, it is well to summarize the line of reasoning that led to its interpretation.

Our point of departure was the Lorentz force on a moving electric charge, in terms of which the electric field and the magnetic field were originally defined. We showed next that Maxwell's equations, together with the mechanical principle of action and reaction, implied the existence of an analogous force on moving magnetic charges. We were able then to express the density of the total power supplied by external forces as $-(\boldsymbol{E}\cdot\boldsymbol{J} + \boldsymbol{H}\cdot\boldsymbol{J}^*)$ with $\boldsymbol{J}$ representing the total macroscopic electric current density (free or resulting from polarization of matter) and $\boldsymbol{J}^*$ representing the magnetic-current density resulting from the magnetization of matter.

After deriving formally Poynting's theorem from the macroscopic field laws, we observed that the density of the power supplied by external forces (including the power supplied by matter or vice versa) was equated to the sum of two terms involving only $\boldsymbol{E}$ and $\boldsymbol{H}$ together with their time and space derivatives. This suggested that the two terms represented inherent characteristics of the electromagnetic field, associated with the storage and flow of energy. Then, because of the mathematical form of the two terms, we were led to identify one of them as the divergence of the electromagnetic power flow and the other as the time rate of change of the energy density stored in the field. It is important to stress again that the bases for these identifications are:

1. The two terms must account for the process of absorption on the part of the electromagnetic field of the energy supplied by external forces.

2. The two terms involve only $\boldsymbol{E}$ and $\boldsymbol{H}$ together with their time and space derivatives, and therefore represent inherent properties of the electromagnetic field, independent of any other physical characteristics of the system under consideration.
3. The mathematical form of the two terms is such that one of them can represent the source density of a power-flow field, the other the time derivative of an energy density.

We turned next to the interpretation of the terms representing power supplied by external forces, including the forces within polarized and magnetized matter and the frictionlike forces opposing the drift of charges in conductors. The term resulting from magnetic currents was interpreted to represent the interchange of energy between electromagnetic field and matter caused by a time-varying magnetization. The term resulting from polarization currents was interpreted to represent the interchange of energy between electromagnetic field and matter caused by a time-varying polarization. Finally, the term resulting from free electric currents was interpreted to represent either energy dissipated in conductors or energy converted from electromagnetic form to some other form (or vice versa) because of the motion of free electric charges.

These interpretations of the various terms in Poynting's theorem were further investigated in three special cases of quasi-static fields, in which some of the terms disappeared, thereby giving us the opportunity to focus our attention on the remaining terms. We were able to conclude that, in the case of materials with single-valued constituent relations, the energy supplied to polarized and magnetized matter could be regarded as stored locally and, as such, could be lumped with the energy stored by the electromagnetic field. This procedure of lumping the polarization energy with the energy stored by the electric field and the magnetization energy with the energy stored by the magnetic field facilitates considerably the study of the energy properties of linear systems.

The last part of the chapter has been devoted to the energy properties of quasi-static systems, and to the relation between the field approach and the circuit approach to the storage of energy and to the flow of power. This study will continue in the next chapter as part of our discussion of the behavior of electromagnetic systems in the sinusoidal steady state.

We have dealt in this chapter only with the energy interchanges resulting from the polarization and magnetization of matter, the conduction of current, and the motion of free charges. Of course, there are many other ways in which electromagnetic energy can be transformed into other forms of energy, and vice versa. We shall discuss in Chapter 10 the electromechanical energy conversion that results from the relative motion of macroscopic bodies. Thermoelectric and other types of energy conversion are outside the scope of this volume.

## 7.12 Selected References


1. E. A. Guillemin, *Introductory Circuit Theory*, John Wiley and Sons, New York, 1953. Sections 3.9, 7.1, and the first half of Sec. 10.6 should be reviewed in connection with Secs. 7.6, 7.7, 7.8, and 7.9 of this chapter.
2. J. A. Stratton, *Electromagnetic Theory*, McGraw-Hill, New York, 1941. Sections 2.7, 2.8, 2.14, 2.16, discuss the electric energy and the magnetic energy from a static point of view and Sec. 2.19 discusses Poynting's theorem.
3. W. R. Symthe, *Static and Dynamic Electricity*, McGraw-Hill, New York, 1939. Sections 2.12 to 2.20 parallel Sec. 7.7 in this chapter.


## PROBLEMS

**Problem 7.1.** The space between the two perfectly conducting plates of Fig. 6.3 is filled with homogeneous, linear conducting material. Two direct-voltage sources are connected symmetrically to the plates, as shown in the same figure.

(a) Find the electric and magnetic fields between the plates.
(b) Find Poynting's vector and the density of power dissipation.
(c) Check that the results of part (b) satisfy Poynting's theorem.

**Problem 7.2.** The inner conductor of a coaxial cable is made of homogeneous, linear conducting material, while the outer conductor can be regarded as a perfectly conducting sheet. The cable is short-circuited at one end and is connected to a d-c source at the other end.

(a) Find the electric field and the magnetic field in the air space between the two conductors and within the inner conductor.
(b) Find the surface integral of Poynting's vector over a cross section of the cable.
(c) Find Poynting's vector inside the inner conductor.
(d) Find the flux of Poynting's vector into the inner conductor per unit length of cable.
(e) Find the power dissipated in the inner conductor per unit length.
(f) Compare the results of (d) and (e) in the light of Poynting's theorem.

**Problem 7.3.** Charge is uniformly distributed over the surface of a sphere of electrically inert material. The sphere spins about its axis with a constant angular velocity, thereby producing a magnetic-dipole field in the surrounding space. Find Poynting's vector outside the sphere.

**Problem 7.4.** An electrostatic field, produced by static charges, and a magnetic field, produced by permanently magnetized materials, can exist in the same region of space. Show that the divergence of Poynting's vector vanishes everywhere. Interpret this result in the light of Poynting's theorem.

**Problem 7.5.** Find the electrostatic energy associated with a charge distributed uniformly over the surface of a sphere. What is the energy if the same charge is distributed uniformly throughout the volume of the sphere?

**Problem 7.6.** Electric charge is distributed over a spherical surface in such a way as to produce, outside the sphere, an electric field identical to that of an electric dipole located at the center of the sphere.

(a) Calculate the electric energy stored within the sphere.
(b) Calculate the electric energy stored outside the sphere.
(c) Recalculate the total energy stored in the system from the electric potential and the charge distribution.

**Problem 7.7.** A dielectric sphere of uniform permittivity $\epsilon$ and radius $R$ is brought from infinity to a distance $d \gg R$ from a point charge. Compute the work done and, thus, the change in the stored field energy. You may assume that the field of the point charge is uniform within the dielectric sphere.

**Problem 7.8.** Two coils having the same self-inductance are connected in series. When a direct current $I$ flows through the coils, the magnetic energy stored in their field is $W$ joules. If the connections of one coil are interchanged and the current is reduced to $\frac{1}{2}I$, the energy stored is again $W$ joules. Calculate the ratio of the mutual inductance and the self-inductance.

**Problem 7.9.** The magnetic energy associated with the field of an air coil is found to be equal to $W$ when a current $I$ flows through the coil. The coil is then immersed in a suspension of iron particles in oil with a uniform and constant permeability $\mu$. The current in the coil is held constant during immersion, and the dimensions of the coil are very much smaller than those of the region filled by the suspension.

(a) What is the total magnetic energy when the coil is immersed in the suspension?
(b) What is the energy supplied by the electric source feeding the coil during the immersion process?
(c) What is the mechanical work done by external forces during the immersion?

**Problem 7.10.** A current source is connected between opposite edges of a square sheet of uniformly conducting material. A circular hole of diameter much smaller than the edges of the square is drilled through the sheet at the center of the square. Determine the change of power dissipation caused by the hole.

# CHAPTER EIGHT

# The Sinusoidal Steady State

The sinusoidal steady-state method of analysis plays a role of paramount importance in connection with electromagnetic fields, even more important, perhaps, than in connection with networks. There are two main reasons for this fact. The first one is that the simplifications resulting from this method of analysis are particularly helpful in connection with field problems in view of their inherent complexity. The second one is that the various characteristic behaviors of electromagnetic fields, which become predominant in different frequency ranges, are brought into sharper light by a frequency-domain analysis than by a time-domain analysis.

One of our main objectives will be, as in the preceding chapters, to establish a relation between circuit theory and field theory. We shall see that the circuit concept of impedance can be related to the storage and dissipation of energy and, therefore, to the electromagnetic field. This relation will be exploited in the study of circuit components.

## 8.1 The Complex Representation of Fields

The representation of field vectors in the sinusoidal steady state is an extension of the representation of voltages and currents used in circuit theory [1, Secs. 6.1 and 6.2]. This extension is based on the fact that a three-dimensional vector is completely specified by its components in any three noncoplanar directions. These components are scalar quantities and therefore their sinusoidal time variations can be represented by means of complex numbers just as voltages and currents in circuit theory. Thus, if we use a system of Cartesian coordinates,

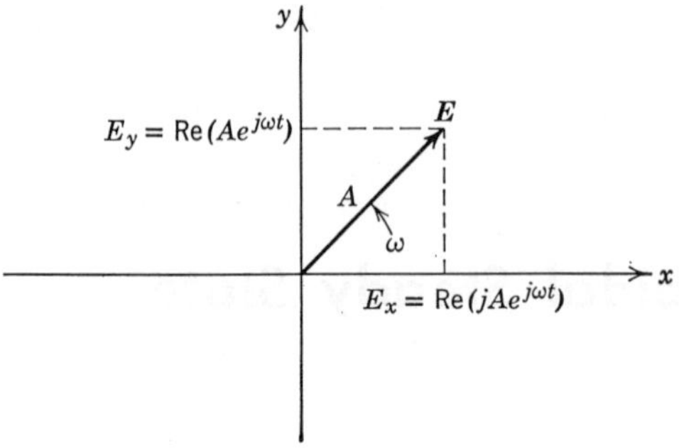


**Fig. 8.1.** Rotating vector.

the vector $\boldsymbol{E}$ can be expressed in the form

$$\begin{aligned}\boldsymbol{E} &= \boldsymbol{i}_x \,\mathrm{Re}\,(\mathrm{E}_x e^{j\omega t}) + \boldsymbol{i}_y \,\mathrm{Re}\,(\mathrm{E}_y e^{j\omega t}) + \boldsymbol{i}_z \,\mathrm{Re}\,(\mathrm{E}_z e^{j\omega t}) \\ &= \mathrm{Re}\,[(\boldsymbol{i}_x \mathrm{E}_x + \boldsymbol{i}_y \mathrm{E}_y + \boldsymbol{i}_z \mathrm{E}_z)e^{j\omega t}] \end{aligned} \tag{8.1}$$

where $\omega$ is the frequency variable, $\mathrm{E}_x$, $\mathrm{E}_y$, $\mathrm{E}_z$ are complex quantities and Re indicates the operation of taking the real part.[1]

The time dependence of $\boldsymbol{E}$ may also be expressed in the simpler abbreviated form

$$\boldsymbol{E} = \mathrm{Re}\,(\mathbf{E}e^{j\omega t}) = \tfrac{1}{2}(\mathbf{E}e^{j\omega t} + \mathbf{E}^* e^{-j\omega t}) \tag{8.2}$$

where

$$\mathbf{E} = \boldsymbol{i}_x \mathrm{E}_x + \boldsymbol{i}_y \mathrm{E}_y + \boldsymbol{i}_z \mathrm{E}_z \tag{8.3}$$

is a *complex vector* in the sense that its components are complex quantities. Its complex conjugate,[2] $\mathbf{E}^*$, is a vector whose components are the conjugate of the components of $\mathbf{E}$. It should be stressed in this regard that, in general, the magnitude of $\boldsymbol{E}$ does not vary sinusoidally with time; it varies sinusoidally only in the special case in which the direction of $\boldsymbol{E}$ is time-invariant, i.e., when $\mathrm{E}_x$, $\mathrm{E}_y$, and $\mathrm{E}_z$ have the same phase angle. As a matter of fact, the magnitude of $\boldsymbol{E}$ may well be time-invariant, as for instance when

$$\mathbf{E} = \boldsymbol{i}_x(jA) + \boldsymbol{i}_y(A) \tag{8.4}$$

In this case, the two nonvanishing components of $\boldsymbol{E}$ are 90° out of phase; the magnitude of $\boldsymbol{E}$ is equal at all times to $A$, and its direction rotates counterclockwise at the angular velocity $\omega$, as illustrated in Fig. 8.1.

[1] Symbols representing complex quantities are set roman lightface. Thus, symbols representing complex vectors are set roman boldface.

[2] The asterisk indicates in this chapter the conjugate of a complex number or of a complex vector.

All the other sinusoidal field vectors can be represented similarly in terms of corresponding complex vectors, and all sinusoidal scalar quantities in terms of corresponding complex scalars. We must note, however, that, in order for all the electromagnetic quantities to be sinusoidal functions of time, the entire electromagnetic system must be linear; in fact, if the constituent relations between $\boldsymbol{E}$ and $\boldsymbol{D}$, $\boldsymbol{H}$ and $\boldsymbol{B}$, $\boldsymbol{E}$ and $\boldsymbol{J}$ are nonlinear, only one of each pair of vectors can vary sinusoidally with time. Thus, a sinusoidal steady state can exist only if

$$\boldsymbol{D} = \epsilon \boldsymbol{E} \tag{8.5}$$

$$\boldsymbol{B} = \mu \boldsymbol{H} \tag{8.6}$$

$$\boldsymbol{J} = \sigma \boldsymbol{E} \tag{8.7}$$

where $\epsilon$, $\mu$, and $\sigma$ are constant at each point of space, although they may vary from point to point. In this case the differential field laws can be written as linear differential equations between the field vectors and the free-source densities:

$$\text{curl}\, \boldsymbol{E} = -\mu \frac{\partial \boldsymbol{H}}{\partial t} \tag{8.8}$$

$$\text{curl}\, \boldsymbol{H} = \boldsymbol{J}_f + \epsilon \frac{\partial \boldsymbol{E}}{\partial t} \tag{8.9}$$

$$\text{div}\, \mu \boldsymbol{H} = 0 \tag{8.10}$$

$$\text{div}\, \epsilon \boldsymbol{E} = \rho_f \tag{8.11}$$

$$\text{div}\, \boldsymbol{J}_f = -\frac{\partial \rho_f}{\partial t} \tag{8.12}$$

Substitution of the sinusoidal vectors defined above for $\boldsymbol{E}$ and $\boldsymbol{H}$ in Eq. 8.8 yields

$$\text{curl}\, \mathbf{E} e^{j\omega t} + \text{curl}\, \mathbf{E}^* e^{-j\omega t} = -j\omega\mu \mathbf{H} e^{j\omega t} + j\omega\mu \mathbf{H}^* e^{-j\omega t} \tag{8.13}$$

This equation must be satisfied regardless of the time origin selected; i.e., it must still be satisfied when an arbitrary constant $t_0$ is added to $t$. Suppose, for instance, that $t_0$ is such that

$$e^{j\omega t_0} = j \tag{8.14}$$

We obtain then

$$j\, \text{curl}\, \mathbf{E} e^{j\omega t} - j\, \text{curl}\, \mathbf{E}^* e^{-j\omega t} = -(j)^2 \omega\mu \mathbf{H} e^{j\omega t} - (j)^2 \omega\mu \mathbf{H}^* e^{-j\omega t} \tag{8.15}$$

Adding Eq. 8.15 divided by $j$ to Eq. 8.13 yields

$$2\, \text{curl}\, \mathbf{E} e^{j\omega t} = -2j\omega\mu \mathbf{H} e^{j\omega t} \tag{8.16}$$

from which we obtain finally

$$\text{curl}\,\mathbf{E} = -j\omega\mu\mathbf{H} \tag{8.17}$$

We can conclude then that Eq. 8.17 is equivalent to Eq. 8.8 in the sinusoidal steady state. Similarly, the equations

$$\text{curl}\,\mathbf{H} = \mathbf{J}_f + j\omega\epsilon\mathbf{E} \tag{8.18}$$

$$\text{div}\,\mathbf{J}_f = -j\omega\bar{\rho}_f \tag{8.19}$$

can be shown to be equivalent to Eqs. 8.8 and 8.12.[1] The equations corresponding to Eqs. 8.10 and 8.11, namely,

$$\text{div}\,\mu\mathbf{H} = 0 \tag{8.20}$$

$$\text{div}\,\epsilon\mathbf{E} = \bar{\rho}_f \tag{8.21}$$

can be obtained directly from Eqs. 8.17 and 8.18 by equating to zero the divergence of their right-hand sides.

Clearly, all linear relations between sinusoidal time functions can be transformed into equivalent complex relations by substituting for the time functions the corresponding complex quantities, and for the differential operator $\partial/\partial t$ the imaginary quantity $j\omega$.

## 8.2 The Complex Poynting's Theorem

All electromagnetic quantities representing energy or power are quadratic functions of the field vectors and the source densities. Thus, if the latter quantities are sinusoidal functions of time of frequency $\omega$, the former quantities must be expected to be sums of two components, one independent of time and the other a sinusoidal function of frequency $2\omega$. This situation is, of course, similar to that encountered in circuit theory for the analogous quantities [1, Secs. 7.1 through 7.3].

Let us begin by deriving an expression for Poynting's vector when $\boldsymbol{E}$ and $\boldsymbol{H}$ are sinusoidal functions of time. We have from Eq. 8.2 and the analogous expression for $\boldsymbol{H}$,

$$\begin{aligned} \boldsymbol{S} = \boldsymbol{E} \times \boldsymbol{H} &= \tfrac{1}{4}(\mathbf{E}e^{j\omega t} + \mathbf{E}^*e^{-j\omega t}) \times (\mathbf{H}e^{j\omega t} + \mathbf{H}^*e^{-j\omega t}) \\ &= \tfrac{1}{4}(\mathbf{E} \times \mathbf{H}^* + \mathbf{E}^* \times \mathbf{H}) + \tfrac{1}{4}(\mathbf{E} \times \mathbf{H}e^{j2\omega t} + \mathbf{E}^* \times \mathbf{H}^*e^{-j2\omega t}) \\ &= \tfrac{1}{2}\,\text{Re}\,(\mathbf{E} \times \mathbf{H}^*) + \tfrac{1}{2}\,\text{Re}\,(\mathbf{E} \times \mathbf{H}e^{j2\omega t}) \end{aligned} \tag{8.22}$$

[1] The complex character of a quantity represented by a Greek letter is indicated by a bar above the letter.

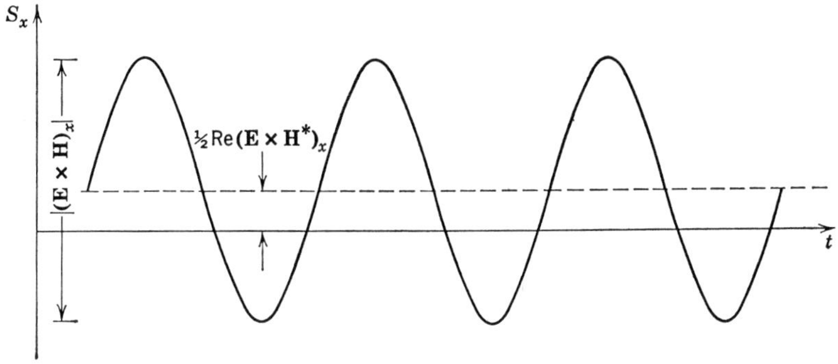


**Fig. 8.2.** Time dependence of $S_x$ in the sinusoidal steady state.

The first term of this expression is independent of time and represents the average value of Poynting's vector over a cycle. More precisely, the real parts of the three components of ½(**E** × **H***) represent the average values of the three components of **S**. The second term is a sinusoidal vector of frequency $2\omega$; its three components represent double-frequency sinusoidal variations of the three components of **S**. This situation is illustrated for the component $S_x$ in Fig. 8.2.

A similar computation yields for the energy densities

$$w_e = \tfrac{1}{2}\epsilon(\boldsymbol{E}\cdot\boldsymbol{E}) = \tfrac{1}{4}\epsilon(\mathbf{E}\cdot\mathbf{E}^*) + \tfrac{1}{4}\epsilon \operatorname{Re}(\mathbf{E}\cdot\mathbf{E}e^{j2\omega t}) \tag{8.23}$$

$$w_m = \tfrac{1}{2}\mu(\boldsymbol{H}\cdot\boldsymbol{H}) = \tfrac{1}{4}\mu(\mathbf{H}\cdot\mathbf{H}^*) + \tfrac{1}{4}\mu \operatorname{Re}(\mathbf{H}\cdot\mathbf{H}e^{j2\omega t}) \tag{8.24}$$

and for the power dissipation density

$$p_d = \sigma(\boldsymbol{E}\cdot\boldsymbol{E}) = \tfrac{1}{2}\sigma(\mathbf{E}\cdot\mathbf{E}^*) + \tfrac{1}{2}\sigma \operatorname{Re}(\mathbf{E}\cdot\mathbf{E}e^{j2\omega t}) \tag{8.25}$$

The first term of each of these expressions is real and independent of time. In fact,

$$\mathbf{E}\cdot\mathbf{E}^* = \mathrm{E}_x\mathrm{E}_x^* + \mathrm{E}_y\mathrm{E}_y^* + \mathrm{E}_z\mathrm{E}_z^* = |\mathrm{E}_x|^2 + |\mathrm{E}_y|^2 + |\mathrm{E}_z|^2 = |\mathbf{E}|^2 \tag{8.26}$$

$$\mathbf{H}\cdot\mathbf{H}^* = |\mathrm{H}_x|^2 + |\mathrm{H}_y|^2 + |\mathrm{H}_z|^2 = |\mathbf{H}|^2 \tag{8.27}$$

where the symbols $|\mathbf{E}|^2$ and $|\mathbf{H}|^2$ stand for the sum of the squared magnitudes of the components of the corresponding complex vectors; they are equal to twice the average values of the squared magnitudes (lengths) of $\boldsymbol{E}$ and $\boldsymbol{H}$. Thus the first term on the right-hand side of Eq. 8.23 is real and independent of time; it must represent the average value of the electric-energy density. Similarly, the corresponding terms in Eqs. 8.24 and 8.25 must represent the average values of the magnetic-energy density and of the power-dissipation density. The second term on the right-hand side of Eq. 8.23 represents the double-frequency variation of the energy density which, in turn, consists of the sum of three terms corresponding to the three components of $\boldsymbol{E}$. The three terms are in phase only if the three components of $\mathbf{E}$ are in phase or 180° out of phase. They cancel out when $\boldsymbol{E}$ is a vector of constant length rotating with a velocity $\omega$, as illustrated in Fig. 8.1. We have in this particular case from Eq. 8.4

$$\mathbf{E} \cdot \mathbf{E}^* = |\mathbf{E}|^2 = 2A^2 \tag{8.28}$$

$$\mathbf{E} \cdot \mathbf{E} e^{j2\omega t} = (-A^2 + A^2) e^{j2\omega t} = 0 \tag{8.29}$$

The second term on the right-hand side of Eq. 8.24 and that on the right-hand side of Eq. 8.25 can be interpreted in a similar manner.

The form of Eq. 8.22 suggests that it would be useful to define a complex Poynting's vector

$$\mathbf{S} = \tfrac{1}{2}(\mathbf{E} \times \mathbf{H}^*) \tag{8.30}$$

This definition is analogous to that of the vector (in the complex sense) power in circuit theory [1, Chapter 7]. We have seen that the real part of each component of $\mathbf{S}$ represents the average value of the corresponding component of $\boldsymbol{S}$, i.e., of the density of power flow in the corresponding direction. Using the nomenclature of circuit theory, the imaginary part of each component of $\mathbf{S}$ may be said to represent the density of the reactive power flowing in the corresponding direction.

The average energy and power densities defined above will appear very frequently in our discussion. For this reason, it is convenient to represent them together with other related densities by the special symbols listed in Table 8.1. Corresponding symbols are also defined for the energies stored and for the power dissipated in a volume $V$, and for the average power and the reactive power flowing into $V$ through the surface $S$ enclosing $V$. The symbol $\mathbf{J}_c$ indicates the density of the conduction current, and $\mathbf{J}_f$ indicates the density of the entire free current.

The physical significance of the reactive power is clearly brought out by the complex analog of Poynting's theorem. We have from Eq. A4.16, Appendix 4,

$$\operatorname{div} \mathbf{S} = \operatorname{div} \tfrac{1}{2}(\mathbf{E} \times \mathbf{H}^*) = \tfrac{1}{2}(\mathbf{H}^* \cdot \operatorname{curl} \mathbf{E} - \mathbf{E} \cdot \operatorname{curl} \mathbf{H}^*) \tag{8.31}$$

which becomes, with the help of Eqs. 8.17 and 8.18,

$$\operatorname{div} \mathbf{S} = -\tfrac{1}{2}(\mathbf{E} \cdot \mathbf{J}_f^*) - 2j\omega(\tfrac{1}{4}\mu|\mathbf{H}|^2 - \tfrac{1}{4}\epsilon|\mathbf{E}|^2) \tag{8.32}$$

**TABLE 8.1. Symbols**

| | | | |
|---|---|---|---|
| Average electric-energy density | = | $\langle w_e \rangle$ | $= \frac{1}{4}\epsilon\lvert\mathbf{E}\rvert^2$ |
| Average magnetic-energy density | = | $\langle w_m \rangle$ | $= \frac{1}{4}\mu\lvert\mathbf{H}\rvert^2$ |
| Average power-dissipation density | = | $\langle p_d \rangle$ | $= \frac{1}{2}\mathbf{E}\cdot\mathbf{J}_c^* = \frac{1}{2}\sigma\lvert\mathbf{E}\rvert^2$ |
| Average source-power density | = | $\langle p_s \rangle$ | $= -\frac{1}{2}\,\mathrm{Re}\,[\mathbf{E}\cdot(\mathbf{J}_f^* - \mathbf{J}_c^*)]$ |
| Reactive source-power density | = | $q_s$ | $= -\frac{1}{2}\,\mathrm{Im}\,[\mathbf{E}\cdot(\mathbf{J}_f^* - \mathbf{J}_c^*)]$ |
| Average electric energy in $V$ | = | $\langle W_e \rangle$ | $= \int_V \frac{1}{4}\epsilon\lvert\mathbf{E}\rvert^2\,dv$ |
| Average magnetic energy in $V$ | = | $\langle W_m \rangle$ | $= \int_V \frac{1}{4}\mu\lvert\mathbf{H}\rvert^2\,dv$ |
| Average power dissipated in $V$ | = | $\langle P_d \rangle$ | $= \int_V \frac{1}{2}\sigma\lvert\mathbf{E}\rvert^2\,dv$ |
| Average source power supplied in $V$ | = | $\langle P_s \rangle$ | $= -\,\mathrm{Re}\int_V \frac{1}{2}[\mathbf{E}\cdot(\mathbf{J}_f^* - \mathbf{J}_c^*)]\,dv$ |
| Reactive source power supplied in $V$ | = | $Q_s$ | $= -\,\mathrm{Im}\int_V \frac{1}{2}[\mathbf{E}\cdot(\mathbf{J}_f^* - \mathbf{J}_c^*)]\,dv$ |
| Average power flowing into $V$ | = | $\langle P \rangle$ | $= -\,\mathrm{Re}\oint_S \frac{1}{2}(\mathbf{E}\times\mathbf{H}^*)\cdot\boldsymbol{n}\,da$ |
| Reactive power flowing into $V$ | = | $Q$ | $= -\,\mathrm{Im}\oint_S \frac{1}{2}(\mathbf{E}\times\mathbf{H}^*)\cdot\boldsymbol{n}\,da$ |

This equation, being complex, breaks into two real equations, one for the real part and one for the imaginary part. We have, using the symbols defined in Table 8.1,

$$-\,\mathrm{Re}\,(\mathrm{div}\,\mathbf{S}) = \frac{1}{2}\,\mathrm{Re}\,(\mathbf{E}\cdot\mathbf{J}_f^*) \tag{8.33}$$

$$-\,\mathrm{Im}\,(\mathrm{div}\,\mathbf{S}) = \frac{1}{2}\,\mathrm{Im}\,(\mathbf{E}\cdot\mathbf{J}_f^*) + 2\omega(\langle w_m\rangle - \langle w_e\rangle) \tag{8.34}$$

The right-hand side of Eq. 8.33 represents the average value of $\boldsymbol{E}\cdot\boldsymbol{J}_f$, i.e., the average density of the electromagnetic power transformed into some other form of energy (if positive), or vice versa (if negative). This can be readily checked by expanding the scalar product of the sinusoidal vectors $\boldsymbol{E}$ and $\boldsymbol{J}_f$. On the other hand, the free-current density consists, in general, of a conduction component $\mathbf{J}_c$ and a source component

$$\mathbf{J}_s = \mathbf{J}_f - \mathbf{J}_c = \mathbf{J}_f - \sigma\mathbf{E} \tag{8.35}$$

so that

$$\frac{1}{2}\,\mathrm{Re}\,(\mathbf{E}\cdot\mathbf{J}_f^*) = \frac{1}{2}\sigma\lvert\mathbf{E}\rvert^2 + \frac{1}{2}\,\mathrm{Re}\,(\mathbf{E}\cdot\mathbf{J}_s^*) = \langle p_d\rangle - \langle p_s\rangle \tag{8.36}$$

The first term on the right-hand side of Eq. 8.34 is the reactive power density associated with the average power density of Eq. 8.33.

It results entirely from source currents because the conduction current is in phase with the electric field. Thus, Eqs. 8.33 and 8.34 can be rewritten in the form

$$-\operatorname{Re}(\operatorname{div}\mathbf{S}) = \langle p_d \rangle - \langle p_s \rangle \tag{8.37}$$

$$-\operatorname{Im}(\operatorname{div}\mathbf{S}) = 2\omega(\langle w_m \rangle - \langle w_e \rangle) - q_s \tag{8.38}$$

where $q_s$ is the reactive-power density defined in Table 8.1.

The significance of Eqs. 8.37 and 8.38 can be better appreciated when they are integrated over an arbitrary volume $V$ enclosed by a surface $S$. We have with the help of Gauss' theorem,

$$-\operatorname{Re}\oint_S \mathbf{S}\cdot\boldsymbol{n}\,da = \langle P \rangle = \langle P_d \rangle - \langle P_s \rangle \tag{8.39}$$

$$-\operatorname{Im}\oint_S \mathbf{S}\cdot\boldsymbol{n}\,da = Q = 2\omega(\langle W_m \rangle - \langle W_e \rangle) - Q_s \tag{8.40}$$

The first equation states that the sum of the average power flowing into $V$ through its surface and the average power supplied by sources located within $V$ is equal to the average power dissipated in $V$. The second equation states that the sum of the reactive power flowing into $V$ through its surface and the reactive power supplied by sources located within $V$ is equal to $2\omega$ times the difference between the average magnetic energy and the average electric energy stored in $V$. Thus, this second equation provides a physical interpretation for the reactive power, i.e., for the imaginary component associated with the average power.

It is sometimes stated that the reactive power input to a passive system is proportional to the amount of energy that enters and leaves the system during a cycle as a result of the fact that the instantaneous power flow reverses its direction during part of the cycle. Although this happens to be true in the special case of a passive, two-terminal network, it is not true in general for networks with more than two terminals or for electromagnetic fields.

## 8.3 Impedance, Power, and Energy

Let us apply the results of the preceding section to a two-terminal, passive electromagnetic system enclosed by a surface $S$, such as that illustrated in Fig. 8.3. Let us assume further that a terminal voltage and a terminal current can be defined for such a system on the surface

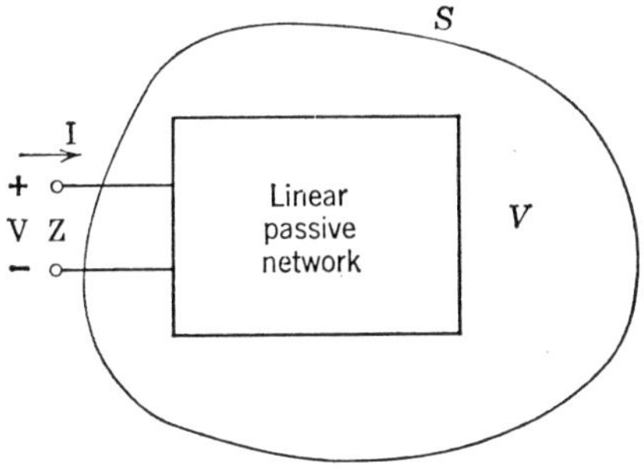


**Fig. 8.3.** Two-terminal linear passive network enclosed by a surface $S$.

$S$, as discussed in Sec. 7.6. Then, the inward flux through $S$ of the complex Poynting's vector can be identified with the complex power input to the system as defined in circuit theory,

$$-\oint_S \mathbf{S}\cdot\boldsymbol{n}\,da = \langle P\rangle + jQ = \tfrac{1}{2}\mathrm{VI}^*$$

where V is the complex terminal voltage and I* is the conjugate of the complex terminal current input to the system. It will be noted, in this regard, that the vector power is usually defined in circuit theory as $\frac{1}{2}\mathrm{IV}^*$. These two definitions lead to the same average power (the real part is the same) but to reactive powers with opposite signs. There are no serious grounds for preferring one definition to the other. It turns out, however, that the definition $\frac{1}{2}\mathbf{E} \times \mathbf{H}^*$ for Poynting's vector (corresponding to $\frac{1}{2}\mathrm{VI}^*$ in circuit theory) is the one most frequently used in electromagnetic theory, whereas the definition $\frac{1}{2}\mathrm{IV}^*$ (corresponding to $\frac{1}{2}\mathbf{E}^* \times \mathbf{H}$ in field theory) is the one most frequently used in circuit theory. The field theory convention will be followed here.

Using the reference directions indicated in Fig. 8.3, the complex power input to the system may be expressed with the help of Eqs. 8.39 and 8.40 in the form

$$\tfrac{1}{2}\mathrm{VI}^* = \langle P_d\rangle + j2\omega(\langle W_m\rangle - \langle W_e\rangle) \tag{8.41}$$

The term $\langle P_d\rangle$, defined in Table 8.1, represents the average power dissipated within V, i.e., the total average power dissipated in the resistances. The term $\langle W_m\rangle$ represents the average magnetic energy stored within $V$, i.e., the total average energy stored in the inductances. The term $\langle W_e\rangle$ represents the average electric energy stored within $V$, i.e., the total average energy stored in the capacitances.

The left-hand side of Eq. 8.41 can also be expressed in terms of the impedance Z of the network, by noting that, by definition,

$$\mathrm{V} = \mathrm{ZI} \tag{8.42}$$

We have then, dividing Eq. 8.41 by $\dfrac{|\mathrm{I}|^2}{2}$,

$$\frac{\mathrm{VI}^*}{|\mathrm{I}|^2} = \mathrm{Z} = \frac{2}{|\mathrm{I}|^2}[\langle P_d\rangle + j2\omega(\langle W_m\rangle - \langle W_e\rangle)] \tag{8.43}$$

from which we obtain for the resistive part of the impedance

$$R = \frac{2\langle P_d\rangle}{|\mathrm{I}|^2} \tag{8.44}$$

and for the reactive part

$$X = \frac{4\omega}{|\mathrm{I}|^2}(\langle W_m\rangle - \langle W_e\rangle) \tag{8.45}$$

These results are limited only by the requirement that it be possible to define the voltage V and the current I at the terminals of the network. It is not necessary for the electromagnetic system within $S$ to be analyzable as a circuit. It is interesting to note that the magnitude of the input current controls the scale factor of the impedance but not its frequency dependence. Thus, Eq. 8.43 can be used to define in a consistent manner the impedance of any electromagnetic structure as seen from a surface $S$ enclosing it, apart only from a constant multiplier.

The relation between input resistance and average power dissipated, provided by Eq. 8.44 does not come as a surprise. On the other hand, the relation between input reactance and average energy stored provided by Eq. 8.45 is indeed unexpected, particularly in view of its great generality. The validity of this relation for a simple series connection of an inductance and a capacitance can be readily checked. However, the circuit theory proof of its validity for all passive networks is rather involved compared to the simplicity of its derivation from Poynting's theorem [1, Sec. 10.6].

The expression for the input admittance, analogous to Eq. 8.43, can be obtained in a similar manner from the complex conjugate of Eq. 8.41. We have

$$\tfrac{1}{2}\mathrm{IV}^* = \langle P\rangle - jQ = \langle P_d\rangle + j2\omega(\langle W_e\rangle - \langle W_m\rangle) \tag{8.46}$$

which, when divided by $|\mathrm{V}|^2/2$ yields

$$\frac{\mathrm{IV}^*}{|\mathrm{V}|^2} = \mathrm{Y} = \frac{2}{|\mathrm{V}|^2}[\langle P_d\rangle + j2\omega(\langle W_e\rangle - \langle W_m\rangle)] \tag{8.47}$$

Finally, the conductance $G$ and the susceptance $B$ are obtained by separating the real and imaginary parts of this equation,

$$G = \frac{2\langle P_d\rangle}{|\mathrm{V}|^2} \tag{8.48}$$

$$B = \frac{4\omega}{|\mathrm{V}|^2}(\langle W_e\rangle - \langle W_m\rangle) \tag{8.49}$$

An important conclusion that can be drawn from Eqs. 8.45 and 8.49 is that the input impedance and the input admittance are purely real when the system stores, on the average, equal amounts of electric energy and magnetic energy. A system operating in this condition is said to be in *resonance.*

Let us consider as a simple example the series $R$-$L$-$C$ circuit illustrated in Fig. 8.4. The average magnetic energy and the average electric energy are given by

$$\langle W_m\rangle = \tfrac{1}{4}L|\mathrm{I}|^2 \tag{8.50}$$

$$\langle W_e\rangle = \frac{1}{4}\frac{|\mathrm{I}|^2}{\omega^2 C} \tag{8.51}$$

Thus resonance occurs, as expected, when the excitation frequency is equal to

$$\omega_0 = \frac{1}{\sqrt{LC}} \tag{8.52}$$

The behavior of the input reactance in the vicinity of this resonance frequency is illustrated in Fig. 8.4*c*. The slope of the reactance at resonance can be readily evaluated from Eqs. 8.45, 8.50 and 8.51. We obtain

$$\left(\frac{dX}{d\omega}\right)_0 = \frac{4}{|\mathrm{I}|^2}(\langle W_m\rangle + \langle W_e\rangle)_0 \tag{8.53}$$

where the subscript zero indicates that the quantity in parentheses is

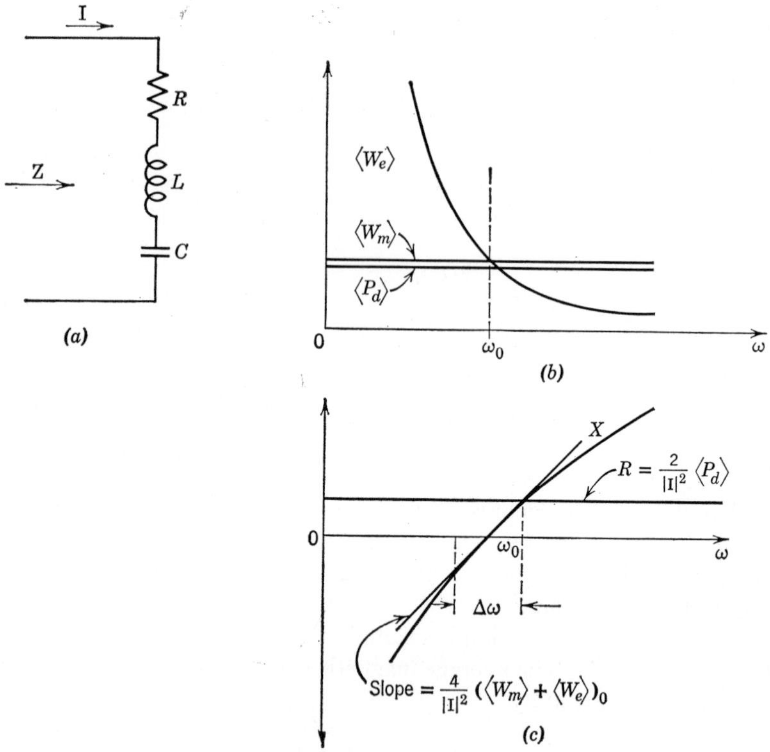


**Fig. 8.4.** Frequency behavior of series-resonant circuit.

evaluated for $\omega = \omega_0$. Thus, in the vicinity of the resonance frequency, the impedance is approximately given by

$$Z \simeq \frac{2}{|I|^2}[\langle P_d\rangle + j2(\omega - \omega_0)(\langle W_m\rangle + \langle W_e\rangle)_0] \tag{8.54}$$

It follows that, if the width $\Delta\omega$ of the resonance between half-power points is much smaller than $\omega_0$, it can be expressed in the form

$$\Delta\omega = \frac{\langle P_d\rangle}{(\langle W_m\rangle + \langle W_e\rangle)_0} \tag{8.55}$$

and the figure of merit of the resonant circuit becomes

$$Q = \frac{\omega_0}{\Delta\omega} = \omega_0\frac{(\langle W_m\rangle + \langle W_e\rangle)_0}{\langle P_d\rangle} \tag{8.56}$$

Thus, the figure of merit is proportional to the ratio of the total average energy stored to the average power dissipated.

A similar analysis can be carried out for a parallel $G$-$L$-$C$ circuit, with the help of Eq. 8.47. We obtain in the vicinity of the resonance frequency

$$\mathrm{Y} \simeq \frac{2}{|\mathrm{V}|^2} [\langle P_d \rangle + j2(\omega - \omega_0)(\langle W_m \rangle + \langle W_e \rangle)_0] \tag{8.57}$$

Again, if the width $\Delta\omega$ is much smaller than $\omega_0$, its value and the corresponding value of $Q$ are given by Eqs. 8.55 and 8.56. We shall show in Sec. 8.9 that Eqs. 8.54 and 8.57 are valid in the vicinity of any resonance frequency for which the figure of merit given by Eq. 8.56 is much larger than unity.

## 8.4 The Power Series in $\omega$

The practical use of circuit theory presupposes that the idealized behaviors of resistances, capacitances, and inductances can be realized physically to a sufficient degree of approximation. Clearly, physical devices can behave like ideal circuit elements only over limited frequency ranges. For instance, Eq. 8.43 indicates that a resistor stops behaving like an ideal resistance when the frequency $\omega$ becomes so high that the product of $\omega$ by the electric energy or the magnetic energy associated with it is comparable to the power dissipated. Similarly, an inductor stops behaving like an ideal inductance when the average energy associated with the electric field (produced by the time variation of the magnetic field) becomes comparable with the average energy associated with the magnetic field. As a matter of fact, an ideal inductance cannot be physically realized at low frequencies because, for sufficiently small values of $\omega$, the power dissipated in the wire forming the inductor becomes larger than the product of $\omega$ and the average magnetic energy.

The frequency behavior of electromagnetic systems may be conveniently investigated with the help of the power series method of analysis developed in Chapter 6. Since our present interest is limited to linear systems, the pertinent zero-order and first-order equations are those given in Sec. 6.5 as Eqs. 6.96 through 6.105. The complex form of these equations in the sinusoidal steady state can be obtained by substituting for all time functions the corresponding complex quantities, and for the differential operator $\partial/\partial t$ the imaginary frequency variable $j\omega$. We obtain for the successive sets of equations

$$\left.\begin{aligned} \text{curl } \mathbf{E}_0 &= 0 \\ \text{curl } \mathbf{H}_0 &= \mathbf{J}_{f0} \\ \text{div } \epsilon\mathbf{E}_0 &= \bar{\rho}_{f0} \\ \text{div } \mu\mathbf{H}_0 &= 0 \\ \text{div } \mathbf{J}_{f0} &= 0 \end{aligned}\right\}\text{zero-order equations} \tag{8.58}$$

$$\left.\begin{aligned} \text{curl } \mathbf{E}_1 &= -j\omega\mu\mathbf{H}_0 \\ \text{curl } \mathbf{H}_1 &= \mathbf{J}_{f1} + j\omega\epsilon\mathbf{E}_0 \\ \text{div } \epsilon\mathbf{E}_1 &= \bar{\rho}_{f1} \\ \text{div } \mu\mathbf{H}_1 &= 0 \\ \text{div } \mathbf{J}_{f1} &= -j\omega\bar{\rho}_{f0} \end{aligned}\right\}\text{first-order equations} \tag{8.59}$$

$$\left.\begin{aligned} \text{curl } \mathbf{E}_2 &= -j\omega\mu\mathbf{H}_1 \\ \text{curl } \mathbf{H}_2 &= \mathbf{J}_{f2} + j\omega\epsilon\mathbf{E}_1 \\ \text{div } \epsilon\mathbf{E}_2 &= \bar{\rho}_{f2} \\ \text{div } \mu\mathbf{H}_2 &= 0 \\ \text{div } \mathbf{J}_{f2} &= -j\omega\bar{\rho}_{f1} \end{aligned}\right\}\text{second-order equations} \tag{8.60}$$

$$\left.\begin{aligned} \text{curl } \mathbf{E}_k &= -j\omega\mu\mathbf{H}_{k-1} \\ \text{curl } \mathbf{H}_k &= \mathbf{J}_{fk} + j\omega\epsilon\mathbf{E}_{k-1} \\ \text{div } \epsilon\mathbf{E}_k &= \bar{\rho}_{fk} \\ \text{div } \mu\mathbf{H}_k &= 0 \\ \text{div } \mathbf{J}_{fk} &= -j\omega\bar{\rho}_{f(k-1)} \end{aligned}\right\}k\text{th-order equations} \tag{8.61}$$

The resulting fields are given by the series

$$\mathbf{E} = \mathbf{E}_0 + \mathbf{E}_1 + \mathbf{E}_2 + \cdots + \mathbf{E}_k + \cdots \tag{8.62}$$

$$\mathbf{H} = \mathbf{H}_0 + \mathbf{H}_1 + \mathbf{H}_2 + \cdots + \mathbf{H}_k + \cdots \tag{8.63}$$

and the other electromagnetic quantities by similar expressions.

We shall show now that Eqs. 8.62 and 8.63 and the corresponding expressions for the other electromagnetic quantities are power series in the frequency $\omega$. The zero-order equations do not involve $\omega$ so that all the zero-order terms may be regarded as independent of $\omega$. In the first-order equations, all the zero-order terms and none of the first-order terms are multiplied by $\omega$. On the other hand, the first-order equations must be valid for all values of $\omega$. It follows that all the first-order terms must be proportional to $\omega$. The same pattern is repeated in the second-order equations and in all the successive sets of equations. We can conclude from this that the second-order terms must be proportional to $\omega^2$, the third-order terms to $\omega^3$, and the $k$th-order terms to $\omega^k$. Thus, for instance, Eq. 8.62 and 8.63 can be rewritten in the form

$$\mathbf{E} = \mathbf{e}_0 + \omega\mathbf{e}_1 + \omega^2\mathbf{e}_2 + \cdots + \omega^k\mathbf{e}_k + \cdots \tag{8.64}$$

$$\mathbf{H} = \mathbf{h}_0 + \omega\mathbf{h}_1 + \omega^2\mathbf{h}_2 + \cdots + \omega^k\mathbf{h}_k + \cdots \tag{8.65}$$

where

$$\mathbf{E}_k = \omega^k\mathbf{e}_k \qquad \mathbf{H}_k = \omega^k\mathbf{h}_k \tag{8.66}$$

and the **e** and the **h** are field vectors independent of frequency.

The successive sets of equations listed above can also be obtained directly from the complex Maxwell's equations (Eqs. 8.17 through 8.21) by expressing all electromagnetic quantities as power series in $\omega$, similar to those given by Eqs. 8.64 and 8.65. For instance, we obtain from Eq. 8.17

$$\text{curl}\,(\mathbf{e}_0 + \omega\mathbf{e}_1 + \omega^2\mathbf{e}_2 + \cdots) = -j\omega\mu(\mathbf{h}_0 + \omega\mathbf{h}_1 + \omega^2\mathbf{h}_2 + \cdots) \tag{8.67}$$

which can be rewritten in the form

$$\text{curl}\,\mathbf{e}_0 + \omega(\text{curl}\,\mathbf{e}_1 + j\mu\mathbf{h}_0) + \omega^2(\text{curl}\,\mathbf{e}_2 + j\mu\mathbf{h}_1) + \cdots = 0 \tag{8.68}$$

Then, since this equation must hold for all values of $\omega$, the individual terms of the series must be separately equal to zero. The first equations of the sets Eqs. 8.58 through 8.61 follow immediately with the help of Eq. 8.66.

We can conclude from the above derivation that the terms of each series become significant in succession with increasing frequency. Thus, at extremely low frequencies, only the zero-order terms need to be taken into account, which are governed by static-field equations. At somewhat higher frequencies, the first-order terms become appreciable, at still higher frequencies the second-order terms, etc. This situation is not surprising because in the sinusoidal steady state the family of electromagnetic fields generated by varying the frequency $\omega$ is the same as the family generated by varying the time-rate parameter $\alpha$ for a fixed frequency. In fact, since all quantities have a time dependence of the form

$$E_x = \text{Re}\,(\mathrm{E}_x e^{j\omega t}) \tag{8.69}$$

the time-rate parameter and the frequency appear always together as in

$$E_x = \text{Re}\,(\mathrm{E}_x e^{j\omega\alpha\tau}) \tag{8.70}$$

when the family time $\tau$, defined by Eq. 6.15, is written in place of the real time $t$, in accordance with the procedure discussed in Sec. 6.2. Then, expressing each field quantity as a power series in $\omega$ for $\alpha = 1$ is equivalent to expressing the same quantity as a power series in $\alpha$ for a fixed $\omega$. This fact is illustrated by the example discussed in Sec. 6.4.

We should emphasize again that the zero-order terms are solutions of static-field equations. The first-order terms can be obtained from the zero-order terms by solving equations that are also of the static type. In general, the determination of the $k$th-order terms involves the solution of a static problem in which the $(k - 1)$th-order terms play the role of known sources. Thus, we have a method for determining fields in the sinusoidal steady state by successive approximations in which each successive step amounts to the solution of a new static-field problem. The number of steps that must be carried out in each specific instance depends on the upper limit of the frequency range to be considered. The higher the upper limit, the higher the order of the terms that must be evaluated. We shall see that the quasi-static terms (zero-order and first-order) are sufficient to account for the normal behavior of circuit components. The higher order terms represent the so-called stray or parasitic effects.

Let us turn our attention next to the power and energy quantities defined in Sec. 8.2. Each of these quantities, being a product of fields, can be expressed as a series in which the successive terms are proportional to the successive powers of $\omega$. We obtain for the complex Poynting's vector

$$\mathbf{S} = \tfrac{1}{2}(\mathbf{E} \times \mathbf{H}^*) = \mathbf{S}_0 + \mathbf{S}_1 + \mathbf{S}_2 + \cdots \tag{8.71}$$

where, according to Eqs. 8.64, 8.65, and 8.66,

$$\mathbf{S}_0 = \tfrac{1}{2}(\mathbf{e}_0 \times \mathbf{h}_0^*) = \tfrac{1}{2}(\mathbf{E}_0 \times \mathbf{H}_0^*) \tag{8.72}$$

$$\mathbf{S}_1 = \tfrac{1}{2}\omega(\mathbf{e}_0 \times \mathbf{h}_1^* + \mathbf{e}_1 \times \mathbf{h}_0^*) = \tfrac{1}{2}(\mathbf{E}_0 \times \mathbf{H}_1^* + \mathbf{E}_1 \times \mathbf{H}_0^*) \tag{8.73}$$

$$\begin{aligned}\mathbf{S}_2 &= \tfrac{1}{2}\omega^2(\mathbf{e}_0 \times \mathbf{h}_2^* + \mathbf{e}_2 \times \mathbf{h}_0^* + \mathbf{e}_1 \times \mathbf{h}_1^*) \\ &= \tfrac{1}{2}(\mathbf{E}_0 \times \mathbf{H}_2^* + \mathbf{E}_2 \times \mathbf{H}_0^* + \mathbf{E}_1 \times \mathbf{H}_1^*)\end{aligned} \tag{8.74}$$

Similarly, we obtain for the total electric-energy density

$$\langle w_e \rangle = \tfrac{1}{4}\epsilon|\mathbf{E}|^2 = \langle w_{e0} \rangle + \langle w_{e1} \rangle + \cdots \tag{8.75}$$

where

$$\langle w_{e0} \rangle = \tfrac{1}{4}\epsilon|\mathbf{e}_0|^2 = \tfrac{1}{4}\epsilon|\mathbf{E}_0|^2 \tag{8.76}$$

$$\begin{aligned}\langle w_{e1} \rangle &= \tfrac{1}{4}\omega\epsilon(\mathbf{e}_0 \cdot \mathbf{e}_1^* + \mathbf{e}_1 \cdot \mathbf{e}_0^*) = \tfrac{1}{4}\epsilon(\mathbf{E}_0 \cdot \mathbf{E}_1^* + \mathbf{E}_1 \cdot \mathbf{E}_0^*) \\ &= \tfrac{1}{2}\epsilon \operatorname{Re}(\mathbf{E}_0 \cdot \mathbf{E}_1^*)\end{aligned} \tag{8.77}$$

and analogous expressions for the power-dissipation density and for the total magnetic-energy density. Finally, we have for the source densities

$$\langle p_s \rangle + jq_s = -\tfrac{1}{2}(\mathbf{E} \times \mathbf{J}^*) = (\langle p_{s0} \rangle + jq_{s0}) + (\langle p_{s1} \rangle + jq_{s1}) + \cdots \tag{8.78}$$

where

$$(\langle p_{s0} \rangle + jq_{s0}) = -\tfrac{1}{2}(\mathbf{E}_0 \cdot \mathbf{J}_{s0}^*) \tag{8.79}$$

$$\langle p_{s1} \rangle + jq_{s1} = -\tfrac{1}{2}(\mathbf{E}_0 \cdot \mathbf{J}_{s1}^* + \mathbf{E}_1 \cdot \mathbf{J}_{s0}^*) \tag{8.80}$$

and each term is proportional to the power of $\omega$ equal to the sum of the subscripts involved in each product.

When the above series expressions are inserted in Eq. 8.32, the same line of reasoning used in deriving the successive sets of field equations yields the series of Poynting relations

$$\operatorname{div} \mathbf{S}_0 = (\langle p_{s0} \rangle - \langle p_{d0} \rangle) + jq_{s0} \tag{8.81}$$

$$\operatorname{div} \mathbf{S}_1 = (\langle p_{s1} \rangle - \langle p_{d1} \rangle) + j[q_{s1} - 2\omega(\langle w_{m0} \rangle - \langle w_{e0} \rangle)] \tag{8.82}$$

$$\operatorname{div} \mathbf{S}_2 = (\langle p_{s2} \rangle - \langle p_{d2} \rangle) + j[q_{s2} - 2\omega(\langle w_{m1} \rangle - \langle w_{e1} \rangle)] \tag{8.83}$$

etc. It is important to note that the zero-order energy densities do not appear in the zero-order relation. Rather, they are related to the divergence of the first-order Poynting vector. In general, the $k$th-order energy densities are associated with the $(k + 1)$th-order Poynting vector.

The expressions for the input impedance and the input admittance given by Eqs. 8.43 and 8.47 can also be expanded into series by substituting the appropriate series for the various terms. However, since ratios as well as products are involved, great care must be exercised in collecting terms proportional to the same power of $\omega$ and in breaking off the series. Because of the variety of situations that may arise, this question cannot be readily discussed in general terms. It will suffice to state here that the evaluation of an impedance can be greatly simplified by selecting as a reference the input current so that only the zero-order term is involved in the denominator of Eq. 8.43. Similarly, the evaluation of an admittance can be simplified by selecting as a reference the input voltage.

As already indicated above, one of our main objectives in this chapter is to develop a basic understanding of the frequency behavior of circuit components, and of the origin and nature of the stray or parasitic effects associated with them. We shall discuss in the next three sections illustrative examples of capacitors, inductors, and resistors with the help of the power-series method of analysis discussed in this section. It is worth stressing that these examples are idealizations of physical circuit components. They are selected with the objective of keeping the mathematical analysis as simple as possible. Their behavior is typical of actual circuit components, although their physical appearance may be unusual.

## 8.5 The Frequency Behavior of a Capacitor

Let us consider the simplest type of capacitor, one consisting of two parallel, perfectly conducting plates. Let $a$ be the length of the plates, $b$ their width, and $d$ their spacing, as indicated in Fig. 8.5. A sinusoidal voltage $\mathrm{V}_s$ is applied between the edges of the plates at $z = -a$. It is convenient to use this voltage as a reference by postulating that it consists entirely of a zero-order component equal to a real constant $V_0$. This convention is equivalent, from an experimental point of view, to holding the source voltage fixed when its frequency is changed. We shall assume furthermore that $a \gg b \gg d$, so that fringing at the edges of the plates can be disregarded. This is equivalent to assuming that the electromagnetic field is one-dimensional and uniform in the directions of the $x$- and $y$-axes, as in the example discussed in Sec. 6.4.

This example is representative of certain types of practical capacitors consisting of two thin conducting sheets, separated by a dielectric sheet, and wound to form a circular cylinder. The fact that the sheets are wound into a cylinder does not affect appreciably the field between them as long as their spacing is small compared to the radius of the cylinder.

The zero-order field equations are identical to the equations governing the behavior of static fields. Thus, we can state immediately that the zero-order magnetic field is equal to zero and that the zero-order

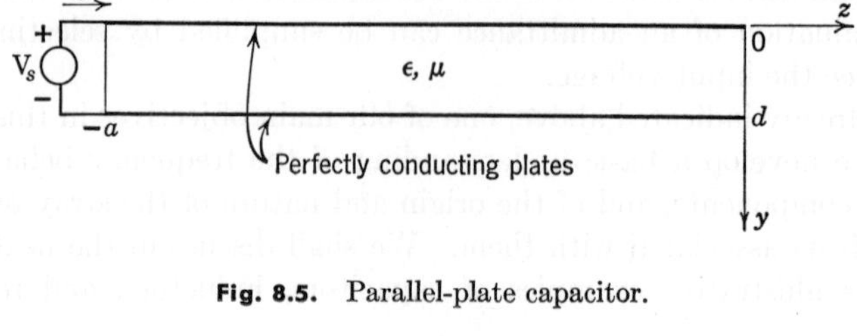


**Fig. 8.5.** Parallel-plate capacitor.

electric field is uniform and normal to the conducting plates. We have, in terms of the system of coordinates shown in Fig. 8.5,

$$\mathbf{E}_0 = \boldsymbol{i}_y \mathrm{E}_{y0} = \boldsymbol{i}_y \frac{V_0}{d} \tag{8.84}$$

A zero-order surface charge on the two plates is associated with this field. We have for its density on the plate at $y = 0$,

$$\bar{\sigma}_0 = \epsilon \mathrm{E}_{y0} = \epsilon \frac{V_0}{d} \tag{8.85}$$

where $\epsilon$ is the permittivity of the homogeneous dielectric between the plates. The density of the surface charge on the plate at $y = d$ has the same magnitude and opposite sign.

The zero-order charge on the plates gives rise to a first-order current which, on the assumption that the plates have infinite conductivity, can be regarded as flowing on their surfaces. The density of this surface current must satisfy the two-dimensional conservation law

$$\operatorname{div}_\Sigma \mathbf{K}_1 = -j\omega\bar{\sigma}_0 \tag{8.86}$$

where the two-dimensional divergence is defined by Eq. 3.21. We have on the plate at $y = 0$,

$$\frac{d\mathrm{K}_{z1}}{dz} = -j\omega\epsilon \frac{V_0}{d} \tag{8.87}$$

from which we obtain by integration

$$\mathrm{K}_{z1} = -j\omega\epsilon \frac{V_0}{d} z \tag{8.88}$$

The constant of integration has been set equal to zero because the surface current must vanish at the open-circuited edge of the plate at $z = 0$. The density of the surface current on the plate at $y = d$ has the same magnitude and opposite sign. The resulting source current at $z = -a$ is

$$\mathrm{I}_{s1} = j\omega \frac{\epsilon ab}{d} V_0 = j\omega C V_0 \tag{8.89}$$

where $C$ is the capacitance of the capacitor.

The first-order magnetic field is related to the zero-order electric field by the second equation of Eqs. 8.59. Since the field is independent of the $x$ and $y$ coordinates, we have in the space between the plates

$$\frac{d\mathrm{H}_{x1}}{dz} = j\omega\epsilon \frac{V_0}{d} \tag{8.90}$$

which yields by integration

$$\mathrm{H}_{x1} = j\omega\epsilon \frac{V_0}{d} z \tag{8.91}$$

The integration constant has been set equal to zero because, on the plate at $y = 0$, the magnetic field must satisfy the boundary condition

$$\mathrm{H}_{x1} = -\mathrm{K}_{z1} \tag{8.92}$$

The first-order electric field is equal to zero because the zero-order magnetic field as well as the first-order charge is equal to zero. Thus, the entire quasi-static field consists of the zero-order electric field given by Eq. 8.84 and of the first-order magnetic field given by Eq. 8.91. We shall turn our attention next to the energy and power terms associated with these fields.

The zero-order Poynting vector is equal to zero because of the absence of zero-order magnetic field. The first-order Poynting vector is given by

$$\mathbf{S}_1 = \frac{1}{2}(\mathbf{E}_0 \times \mathbf{H}_1^*) = \boldsymbol{i}_z \frac{1}{2} j\omega\epsilon \left(\frac{V_0}{d}\right)^2 z \tag{8.93}$$

The power flowing into the capacitor from the source is purely reactive, as expected. We obtain by integration over the plane $z = -a$,

$$jQ = -\frac{1}{2} j\omega\epsilon ab \left(\frac{V_0}{d}\right)^2 = \frac{1}{2}\mathrm{V}_{s0}\mathrm{I}_{s1}^* \tag{8.94}$$

On the other hand, the average zero-order electric energy stored between the plates is given by

$$\langle W_{e0}\rangle = abd\langle w_{e0}\rangle = \frac{1}{4}\epsilon\left(\frac{V_0}{d}\right)^2 abd = \frac{1}{4}CV_0^2 \tag{8.95}$$

It can be checked by inspection that the zero-order energy density and the first-order Poynting vector satisfy the first-order Poynting relation given by Eq. 8.82.

The quasi-static input admittance can be obtained by dividing the first-order source current by the zero-order source voltage. We have

$$\mathrm{Y}_1 = \frac{\mathrm{I}_{s1}}{\mathrm{V}_{s0}} = j\omega\frac{\epsilon ab}{d} = j\omega C \tag{8.96}$$

It can also be obtained from the quasi-static approximation to Eq. 8.47. We obtain with the help of Eq. 8.95,

$$\mathrm{Y}_1 = \frac{2}{{V_0}^2} j2\omega\langle W_{e0}\rangle = j\omega C \tag{8.97}$$

Thus, as expected, the quasi-static admittance is purely capacitive, and it is associated with the electric energy stored between the plates.

Let us turn our attention next to the stray effects that become apparent at frequencies somewhat higher than those for which the quasi-static approximation is valid. The second-order electric field can be obtained from the first-order magnetic field with the help of the first equation of Eqs. 8.60. We have, in view of the one-dimensional character of the field

$$-\frac{d\mathrm{E}_{y2}}{dz} = -j\omega\mu \mathrm{H}_x = \omega^2 \epsilon\mu \frac{V_0}{d} z \tag{8.98}$$

Integration with respect to $z$ yields

$$\mathrm{E}_{y2} = -\omega^2 \epsilon\mu \frac{z^2}{2} \frac{V_0}{d} + A \tag{8.99}$$

where $A$ is the constant of integration. The value of this constant must be such that the second-order voltage vanish at $z = -a$, in view of the fact that the input voltage has been selected as a reference and, therefore, by definition, it must consist entirely of a zero-order term. Thus, we obtain for the second-order electric field

$$\mathrm{E}_{y2} = \omega^2 \epsilon\mu \frac{a^2 - z^2}{2} \frac{V_0}{d} \tag{8.100}$$

The density of the second-order surface charge on the plate at $y = 0$ is given by

$$\bar{\sigma}_2 = \epsilon \mathrm{E}_{y2} = \omega^2 \epsilon^2 \mu \frac{a^2 - z^2}{2} \frac{V_0}{d} \tag{8.101}$$

On the other hand, the second-order magnetic field is equal to zero because of the absence of first-order electric field.

Because of the absence of first-order electric field and second-order magnetic field, the second-order Poynting vector and the first-order energy densities are equal to zero. The second-order average energy densities are given by

$$\langle w_{m2}\rangle = \frac{1}{4}\mu|\mathbf{H}_1|^2 = \frac{1}{4}\mu\omega^2\epsilon^2 z^2\left(\frac{V_0}{d}\right)^2 \tag{8.102}$$

$$\langle w_{e2}\rangle = \frac{1}{4}\epsilon(\mathbf{E}_0\cdot\mathbf{E}_2{}^* + \mathbf{E}_2\cdot\mathbf{E}_0{}^*) = \frac{1}{4}\mu\omega^2\epsilon^2(a^2 - z^2)\left(\frac{V_0}{d}\right)^2 \tag{8.103}$$

The corresponding total energies are obtained by integration over the space between the plates,

$$\langle W_{m2}\rangle = \frac{1}{4}\mu\omega^2\epsilon^2\left(\frac{V_0}{d}\right)^2 bd\int_{-a}^{0} z^2\,dz = \frac{1}{4}\omega^2\epsilon^2\mu\frac{ba^3}{3d}V_0{}^2 \tag{8.104}$$

$$\langle W_{e2}\rangle = \frac{1}{4}\omega^2\epsilon^2\mu\left(\frac{V_0}{d}\right)^2 bd\int_{-a}^{0}(a^2 - z^2)\,dz = \frac{1}{2}\omega^2\epsilon^2\mu\frac{ba^3}{3d}V_0{}^2 \tag{8.105}$$

Because of the absence of first-order energies and second-order power flow, the second-order admittance is equal to zero. The third-order admittance can be computed from the second-order energies with the help of Eq. 8.47. We obtain

$$Y_3 = \frac{2}{V_0{}^2}j2\omega(\langle W_{e2}\rangle - \langle W_{m2}\rangle) = j\omega^3\epsilon^2\mu\frac{ba^3}{3d} \tag{8.106}$$

This result can be readily checked by evaluating the third-order current from the second-order surface charge density given by Eq. 8.101. Thus, the input admittance, approximated to third-order terms, is

$$Y_1 + Y_3 = j\omega C(1 + \tfrac{1}{3}\omega^2\epsilon\mu a^2) \tag{8.107}$$

Since the third-order admittance has the same sign as the first-order capacitive admittance and is proportional to $\omega^3$, it can be attributed to the presence of a series stray inductance. Let us consider then the admittance of the series connection of a capacitance $C$ and an inductance $L$. We have

$$Y = \frac{1}{j\omega L + (1/j\omega C)} = \frac{j\omega C}{1 - \omega^2 LC} \tag{8.108}$$

which becomes, when approximated by a power series to third-order terms,

$$Y \simeq j\omega C(1 + \omega^2 LC) \tag{8.109}$$

Thus, by comparison with Eq. 8.107, the value of the stray inductance is

$$L = \mu\frac{ad}{3b} \tag{8.110}$$

It is clear from Eq. 8.107 that the inductive effect can be neglected at frequencies

$$\omega \ll \frac{1}{a\sqrt{\epsilon\mu}} \tag{8.111}$$

i.e., at frequencies for which the wave length in the medium between the plates,

$$\lambda = \frac{2\pi}{\omega\sqrt{\epsilon\mu}} \tag{8.112}$$

is much larger than the length $a$ of the plates. This conclusion is, of course, the same as that reached in Sec. 6.4.

It is interesting to note that the average value of the second-order electric energy exceeds by a factor of two the average value of the second-order magnetic energy. Yet, the two energies together give rise to an inductive effect. The fact of the matter is that the major effect of the series inductance is to increase the current through the capacitance for a fixed input voltage. This increase of current results in an increase of electric energy which outweighs the magnetic energy associated with the inductance. Thus, we must be very careful in interpreting the terminal effects of higher order energy terms. We must keep in mind, in particular, that Eqs. 8.43 and 8.47 relate the *input* impedance or admittance to the electric energy and to the magnetic energy stored in the system; any equivalent circuit that we might derive from these relations is equivalent only in so far as its *input* behavior is concerned, but not with respect to the *structure of the system.*

## ► 8.6 The Frequency Behavior of an Inductor

The simplest type of multiturn inductor, from the analytical point of view, is the spherical coil on which several previous illustrations have been based. We saw in Sec. 3.6 that, if the coil is wound on the surface of a sphere of radius $R$, with a uniform axial turn density, as illustrated in Fig. 3.6, and a direct current is forced through the coil, the magnetic field is uniform inside the sphere and coincides with the field of a dipole outside the sphere. Let us suppose now that the current through the coil is a sinusoidal function of time represented by a complex quantity I. We shall take this current as a reference by postulating that it consists entirely of a zero-order term $I_0$ which can then be taken to be a real number.

The zero-order field equations are identical in form to the static equations used in our discussion of the spherical coil in Sec. 3.6. Thus, we obtain directly from Eqs. 3.78, 3.79, and 3.81

$$\mathbf{H}_0 = I_0 \frac{N}{6R} \begin{cases} 2(\boldsymbol{i}_r \cos\theta - \boldsymbol{i}_\theta \sin\theta) & r < R \\ (R/r)^3(\boldsymbol{i}_r 2\cos\theta + \boldsymbol{i}_\theta \sin\theta) & r > R \end{cases} \tag{8.113}$$

where $N$ is the number of turns in the coil. The origin of the spherical system of coordinates coincides with the center of the sphere and the reference direction of the current is counterclockwise around the $z$-axis. The lines of force of this field are illustrated in Fig. 3.6. The magnetic-dipole moment associated with the field outside the sphere is related to the current in the coil by Eq. 3.81,

$$\boldsymbol{m} = \boldsymbol{i}_z \frac{2\pi R^2}{3} N I_0 \tag{8.114}$$

On the other hand, no zero-order electric field is present because the conductivity of the coil is assumed to be infinite.

The determination of the first-order electric field is somewhat involved. In the first place, according to Eqs. 8.59, the first-order electric field must satisfy the first-order field laws

$$\text{curl}\,\mathbf{E}_1 = -j\omega\mu_0\mathbf{H}_0 \tag{8.115}$$

$$\text{div}\,\mathbf{E}_1 = 0 \tag{8.116}$$

in the free space surrounding the coil. In addition, the tangential component of $\mathbf{E}_1$ must vanish on the surface of the conductor forming the coil because, otherwise, the first-order current in the conductor would be infinite.

It is convenient to deal with this problem in two successive steps as we did with a similar problem in Sec. 6.8. We shall disregard at first the boundary condition and determine the solenoidal electric field $\mathbf{E}_{1s}$ that would be produced by the zero-order magnetic field given by Eq. 8.113 if the conducting coil were not present. Next, we shall look for a conservative field $\mathbf{E}_{1c}$ which, when added to $\mathbf{E}_{1s}$ will cancel its tangential component on the surface of the conductor. This amounts, from a mathematical point of view, to writing the total first-order field in the form

$$\mathbf{E}_1 = \mathbf{E}_{1s} + \mathbf{E}_{1c} \tag{8.117}$$

where $\mathbf{E}_{1s}$ satisfies Eqs. 8.115 and 8.116 but not the boundary condition, and $\mathbf{E}_{1c}$ is derivable from a scalar potential $\Phi$,

$$\mathbf{E}_{1c} = -\,\text{grad}\,\Phi \tag{8.118}$$

which satisfies Laplace's equation in the space surrounding the coil. In addition, the tangential components of $\mathbf{E}_{1s}$ and $\mathbf{E}_{1c}$ must satisfy the requirement

$$(\mathbf{E}_{1s})_t = -(\mathbf{E}_{1c})_t \tag{8.119}$$

on the surface of the conductor.

The solenoidal field $\mathbf{E}_{1s}$ is determined most readily from the integral form of Eq. 8.115, namely

$$\oint_C \mathbf{E}_{1s}\cdot d\boldsymbol{s} = -j\omega\mu_0 \int_S \mathbf{H}_0\cdot\boldsymbol{n}\, da \tag{8.120}$$

where $S$ is any two-sided surface bounded by the closed path $C$ and $\boldsymbol{n}$ is the usual unit vector normal to $S$. Because of the circular symmetry of the zero-order magnetic field and the absence of any boundary condition, the lines of force of $\mathbf{E}_{1s}$ must be circles centered on the $z$-axis and lying on planes normal to it. Let us take one of these circles represented by particular values of $r$ and $\theta$ as the closed path $C$, and the spherical cap of radius $r$ bounded by the circle as the surface $S$. Since $\mathbf{E}_{1s}$ consists entirely of a $\varphi$ component, which must be constant over $C$, the left-hand side of Eq. 8.120 yields

$$\oint_C \mathbf{E}_{1s}\cdot d\boldsymbol{s} = 2\pi r \sin\theta\, (\mathrm{E}_{1s})_\varphi \tag{8.121}$$

On the other hand, we obtain for the flux of $\mathbf{H}_0$ through $S$,

$$\int \mathbf{H}_0\cdot\boldsymbol{n}\, da = \int_0^\theta 2\pi r^2 \sin\theta\, \mathrm{H}_{r0}\, d\theta = I_0 \frac{\pi N r}{3} \sin^2\theta \begin{cases} (r/R) & r < R \\ (R/r)^2 & r \geq R \end{cases} \tag{8.122}$$

Thus, Eq. 8.120 yields

$$\mathbf{E}_{1s} = -\boldsymbol{i}_\varphi \tfrac{1}{6} j\omega\mu_0 N I_0 \sin\theta \begin{cases} (r/R) & r < R \\ (R/r)^2 & r \geq R \end{cases} \tag{8.123}$$

It can be readily checked that this field satisfies Eq. 8.116.

Let us consider next the conservative field $\mathbf{E}_{1c}$ and the boundary condition that must be satisfied by the total first-order field. The field $\mathbf{E}_{1c}$ is extremely complex in the vicinity of the coil if the latter consists of a conventional type of wire wound on the spherical surface. On the other hand, its geometry becomes relatively simple, as we shall see, if the coil is constructed in a somewhat unconventional manner, as follows. Let us start with a perfectly conducting spherical shell of radius $R$ and negligibly small thickness, which may be approximated in practice by copper-plating a sphere of electrically inert material.

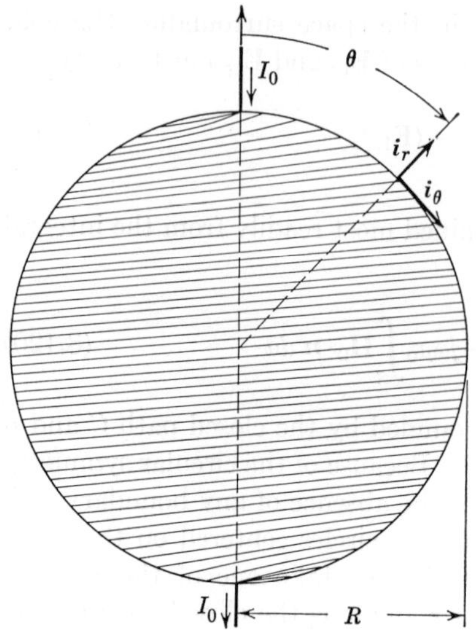


**Fig. 8.6.** Coil formed by uniformly spaced spiral cuts on a perfectly conducting spherical shell ($N = 6$, $M = 9$).

Next, let us cut the shell along spiral lines from one pole to the other by rotating the shell around its axis while a cutting tool is moved with uniform velocity in the direction of the axis. If $M$ uniformly spaced spirals are cut, each of them forming $N$ complete turns, as illustrated in Fig. 8.6, the shell becomes a parallel connection of $M$ identical coils, each of them consisting of $N$ turns. Each of the coils carries a fraction $1/M$ of the current $I_0$ and, together, form a current sheet of surface density

$$\mathbf{K}_0 = I_0 \left( \boldsymbol{i}_\theta \frac{1}{2\pi R \sin \theta} + \boldsymbol{i}_\varphi \frac{N}{2R} \sin \theta \right) \tag{8.124}$$

The $\varphi$ component of this current density produces the zero-order magnetic field given by Eq. 8.113, as discussed in Sec. 3.6. The $\theta$ component gives rise to an additional field of relatively small magnitude whose lines of force form circles centered on the $z$-axis; this second, additional field can be neglected for our purposes, as well as that produced by the current in the wires connecting the coil to the current source.

The purpose of the spiral cuts described above is to fix the direction of flow of the current at all points of the spherical shell. If the number of cuts is sufficiently large, we may regard the shell as a conductor whose conductivity is infinite in the direction parallel to the spiral cuts and equal to zero in the direction normal to the cuts. This implies that the component of the first-order electric field parallel to the spiral cuts must vanish on the surface of the sphere. On the other hand, the component normal to the cuts and tangent to the spherical surface may be different from zero in view of the fact that the conductivity in its direction is equal to zero. Thus, the boundary conditions to be satisfied on the surface of the conductor require

$$\mathbf{E}_1 \cdot \mathbf{K}_0 = 0 \qquad \text{for } r = R \tag{8.125}$$

while the component of $\mathbf{E}_1$ normal to the cuts and tangent to the spherical surface must be continuous through the surface.

Let us turn next to the determination of the conservative field $\mathbf{E}_{1c}$. The potential $\bar{\Phi}$ associated with this field must satisfy Laplace's equation, and must be continuous through the spherical surface of radius $R$. In addition, we have from Eq. 8.125, with the help of Eqs. 8.117, 8.123, and 8.124,

$$\frac{1}{I_0}\mathbf{K}_0 \cdot (\mathbf{E}_{1s} - \operatorname{grad} \bar{\Phi})_{r=R}$$
$$= -j\omega\mu_0 \frac{N^2}{12R} I_0 \sin^2\theta - \frac{\operatorname{grad}_\theta \bar{\Phi}_{r=R}}{2\pi R \sin\theta} - \frac{N}{2R}\sin\theta \operatorname{grad}_\varphi \bar{\Phi}_{r=R} = 0 \tag{8.126}$$

Because of the circular symmetry of the problem, we expect $\bar{\Phi}$ to be independent of $\varphi$, in which case Eq. 8.126 yields

$$\operatorname{grad}_\theta \bar{\Phi}_{r=R} = \frac{1}{R}\left(\frac{\partial \bar{\Phi}}{\partial \theta}\right)_{r=R} = -j\omega\mu_0 I_0 \frac{\pi N^2}{6}\sin^3\theta \tag{8.127}$$

Then, we obtain by integrating with respect to $\theta$,

$$\bar{\Phi}_{r=R} = j\omega\mu_0 \frac{\pi R N^2}{6} I_0 \left(\cos\theta - \frac{1}{3}\cos^3\theta\right) \tag{8.128}$$

A solution of Laplace's equation with the $\theta$ dependence indicated by Eq. 8.128 can be constructed as a linear combination of a dipole potential and an octupole potential (see Sec. 4.9). We obtain for $r > R$

$$\bar{\Phi}' = j\omega\mu_0 \frac{\pi R N^2}{6} I_0 \left[\frac{4}{5}\left(\frac{R}{r}\right)^2 \cos\theta - \left(\frac{R}{r}\right)^4 \left(\frac{1}{3}\cos^3\theta - \frac{1}{5}\cos\theta\right)\right] \tag{8.129}$$

Similarly, a second solution can be constructed as a linear combination of the corresponding potentials with singularities at infinity. We obtain for $r < R$,

$$\bar{\Phi}'' = j\omega\mu_0 \frac{\pi R N^2}{6} I_0 \left[\frac{4}{5}\left(\frac{r}{R}\right)\cos\theta - \left(\frac{r}{R}\right)^3\left(\frac{1}{3}\cos^3\theta - \frac{1}{5}\cos\theta\right)\right] \tag{8.130}$$

These two functions are both equal to the function given by Eq. 8.128 for $r = R$, and, therefore, satisfy the continuity requirement mentioned above. The corresponding electric field is, for $r > R$,

$$\mathbf{E}_{1c}' = -\operatorname{grad}\bar{\Phi}' = j\omega\mu_0 \frac{\pi N^2}{6} I_0 \left(\frac{R}{r}\right)^3 \times \left\{\boldsymbol{i}_r 4\cos\theta\left[\frac{2}{5} - \left(\frac{R}{r}\right)^2\left(\frac{1}{3}\cos^2\theta - \frac{1}{5}\right)\right] + \boldsymbol{i}_\theta \sin\theta\left[\frac{4}{5} - \left(\frac{R}{r}\right)^2\left(\cos^2\theta - \frac{1}{5}\right)\right]\right\} \tag{8.131}$$

and for $r < R$,

$$\mathbf{E}_{1c}'' = -\operatorname{grad}\bar{\Phi}'' = j\omega\mu_0 \frac{\pi N^2}{6} I_0 \times \left\{-\boldsymbol{i}_r \cos\theta\left[\frac{4}{5} - \left(\frac{r}{R}\right)^2\left(\cos^2\theta - \frac{3}{5}\right)\right] + \boldsymbol{i}_\theta \sin\theta\left[\frac{4}{5} - \left(\frac{r}{R}\right)^2\left(\cos^2\theta - \frac{1}{5}\right)\right]\right\} \tag{8.132}$$

Finally, the discontinuity of the radial component of $\mathbf{E}_{1c}$ at the surface of the sphere gives rise to a surface charge distribution of density

$$\bar{\sigma}_1 = \boldsymbol{i}_r \cdot \epsilon_0(\mathbf{E}_{1c}' - \mathbf{E}_{1c}'')_{r=R} = j\omega\mu_0\epsilon_0 \frac{\pi N^2}{6} I_0 \cos\theta\left(\frac{19}{5} - \frac{7}{3}\cos^2\theta\right) \tag{8.133}$$

This charge is induced on the surface of the sphere by the field $\mathbf{E}_{1s}$; in turn, it produces the conservative field $\mathbf{E}_{1c}$. This phenomenon is similar to that taking place when we introduce a conducting body in the static field produced by external, fixed charges: the total field is the sum of the field produced by the external charges and the field produced by the charges induced on the conducting body.

We saw in Sec. 6.8 that the voltage between the terminals of an inductor can be defined as the difference between the values assumed at the terminals by the potential associated with the conservative component of the first-order electric field, that is, the field produced by the charges on the coil. In our case, the terminals of the coil are the two poles of the sphere of radius $R$. Thus, we obtain for the terminal voltage, with the help of Eq. 8.128,

$$V_1 = (\bar{\Phi}_{\theta=0} - \bar{\Phi}_{\theta=\pi})_{r=R} = j\omega\mu_0 \frac{2\pi R N^2}{9} I_0 = j\omega L I_0 \qquad (8.134)$$

Thus, the inductance of the coil is

$$L = \mu_0 \frac{2\pi R N^2}{9} \qquad (8.135)$$

which is the same value obtained in Sec. 7.4 from the energy stored in the zero-order magnetic field, and from the flux linking the current $I_0$.

The analysis of the stray effects associated with the higher order terms is rather involved, and, for this reason, it will not be carried out here. On the other hand, we can make a rough estimate of the stray capacitance associated with the inductance on the basis of the second-order energy associated with the first-order electric field. The total energy associated with the conservative field $\mathbf{E}_{1c}$ is most readily evaluated by noting that, by analogy with Eq. 7.62,

$$\langle W_{e2} \rangle = \oint \frac{1}{4} \epsilon_0 |\mathbf{E}_{1c}|^2 \, dv = \oint_S \frac{1}{4} \bar{\sigma}_1 \bar{\Phi}^* \, da \qquad (8.136)$$

where $S$ is the spherical surface on which the first-order charge is located. Evaluation of the surface integral with the help of Eqs. 8.128 and 8.133 yields

$$\langle W_{e2} \rangle = \oint_S \left[ \frac{1}{4} \epsilon_0 R \left( \omega\mu_0 \frac{\pi N^2}{6} I_0 \right)^2 \cos^2\theta \times \left(1 - \frac{1}{3}\cos^2\theta\right)\left(\frac{19}{5} - \frac{7}{3}\cos^2\theta\right) \right] da$$

$$= \frac{1}{9}\frac{37}{225} \epsilon_0 (\omega\mu_0 N^2 I_0)^2 (\pi R)^3 \qquad (8.137)$$

The energy associated with the solenoidal field given by Eq. 8.123 can be safely neglected when the number of turns is large because it is proportional to $N^2$ while the energy given by Eq. 8.137 is proportional to $N^4$.

Let us now evaluate the input admittance from Eq. 8.47 on the basis of the information available from the zero-order and first-order fields. We obtain

$$Y \simeq \frac{j4\omega}{|V_1|^2}(-\langle W_{m0}\rangle + \langle W_{e2}\rangle) = \frac{1}{j\omega L} + j\omega\epsilon_0 \frac{37}{25}\pi R \qquad (8.138)$$

which indicates the presence of a stray capacitance

$$C = \epsilon_0 \tfrac{37}{25}\pi R \qquad (8.139)$$

in parallel with the inductance. Only the order of magnitude of this estimate is of significance because we have neglected the second-order magnetic energy resulting from the interaction of the second-order magnetic field with the zero-order magnetic field. It is interesting to note, nevertheless, that the estimate depends only on the radius of the sphere on which the coil is wound.

## 8.7 The Frequency Behavior of a Resistor

A common type of high-frequency resistor consists of a dielectric rod coated with a thin resistive film. The rod is usually inserted in a coaxial metallic shield, as illustrated in Fig. 8.7, to eliminate stray couplings with other parts of the circuit. The quasi-static behavior of such a coaxial resistor can be evaluated without too much difficulty. However, in order to keep the analysis as simple as possible, we shall discuss instead the parallel-plane resistor shown in Fig. 8.8. This resistor consists of a planar homogeneous resistive sheet shielded on both sides by parallel, perfectly conducting plates; the sheet is short-circuited to the two plates by a third end-plate, also perfectly conducting. We shall assume, as usual, that the entire system is two-dimensional in the sense that the fields associated with it as well as its geometry are uniform in the direction of the $x$-axis (normal to the plane of the figure).

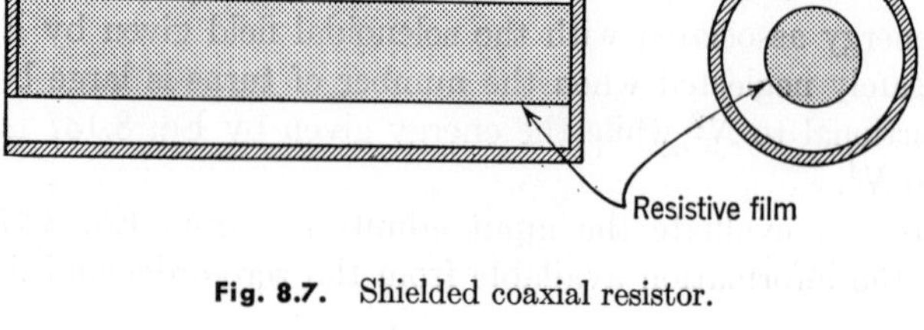


**Fig. 8.7.** Shielded coaxial resistor.

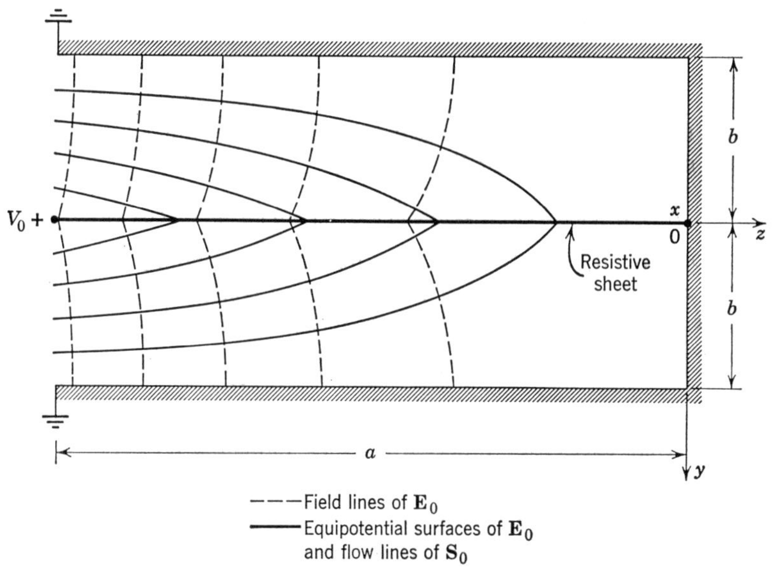


**Fig. 8.8.** Shielded resistive sheet.

Let us suppose that a sinusoidal voltage of amplitude $V_0$ is applied between the left-hand edge of the resistive sheet at $y = 0$ and the shield formed by the two parallel plates. The zero-order surface current in the sheet must be uniform because its divergence must vanish. Furthermore, the surface conductivity $\sigma_s$ of the sheet is also, by assumption, uniform. It follows that the zero-order surface current density is given by

$$\mathbf{K}_0 = \boldsymbol{i}_z \frac{\sigma_s}{a} V_0 \tag{8.140}$$

and the zero-order potential on the $x,z$-plane by

$$(\bar{\Phi}_0)_{y=0} = -\frac{z}{a} V_0 \tag{8.141}$$

It is important to note that this result depends only on the geometry and electrical characteristics of the resistive sheet and not on the geometry of the shield surrounding it.

The zero-order potential associated with the zero-order electric field must satisfy Laplace's equation in the space surrounding the resistive sheet. In addition, it must vanish on the perfectly conducting plates, i.e.,

$$(\bar{\phi}_0)_{y=b} = (\bar{\phi}_0)_{y=-b} = (\bar{\phi}_0)_{z=0} = 0 \tag{8.142}$$

and it must assume on the resistive sheet the values given by Eq. 8.141.

We saw in Sec. 4.7 that the function

$$\phi = (A_1 \sinh kz + A_2 \cosh kz)(B_1 \sin ky + B_2 \cos ky) \tag{8.143}$$

is a solution of Laplace's equation for arbitrary values of the coefficients $A_1$, $A_2$, $B_1$, $B_2$, and of the separation constant $k$. In the particular case of $k = 0$, this solution reduces to

$$\phi = (C_1 + C_2 z)(D_1 + D_2 y) \tag{8.144}$$

where $C_1$, $C_2$, $D_1$, $D_2$ are again arbitrary coefficients. It is immediately evident that this latter function satisfies Laplace's equation because its second partial derivatives with respect to $x$ and with respect to $y$ vanish for all values of the two variables.

By proper selection of the coefficients, the function given by Eq. 8.144 can be made to satisfy the required boundary conditions. We obtain, by inspection, for the zero-order potential

$$\bar{\phi}_0 = -V_0 \frac{z}{a} \begin{cases} (1 + y/b) & y \le 0 \\ (1 - y/b) & y \ge 0 \end{cases} \tag{8.145}$$

The corresponding zero-order electric field is

$$\mathbf{E}_0 = -\operatorname{grad} \bar{\phi}_0 = \frac{V_0}{b} \begin{cases} \mathbf{i}_y \dfrac{z}{a} + \mathbf{i}_z \dfrac{b}{a}\left(1 + \dfrac{y}{b}\right) & y < 0 \\ -\mathbf{i}_y \dfrac{z}{a} + \mathbf{i}_z \dfrac{b}{a}\left(1 - \dfrac{y}{b}\right) & y > 0 \end{cases} \tag{8.146}$$

The lines of force of this field and the traces of the equipotential surfaces are plotted in Fig. 8.8.

It is important to note that while the required boundary conditions are satisfied by the potential of Eq. 8.145, the same conditions would still be satisfied if we added to this potential any solution of Laplace's equation that vanished on the resistive sheet as well as on the perfectly conducting plates. The fact of the matter is that the boundary conditions stated above are not sufficient to identify uniquely the potential. We must also specify in detail the value assumed by the potential at each point of the plane $z = -a$ (the input surface), not just the difference of potential between the edge of the resistive sheet and the shield. On the other hand, the function that could be added to the potential of Eq. 8.145 on either side of the resistive sheet represents the potential that could exist in a slot of width $b$ cut in a conducting material, similar to that illustrated in Fig. 4.12. Furthermore, we saw in Sec. 4.7 that such a potential would have to decay exponentially from the mouth of the slot, and that, as a consequence, the electric field would be appreciable only in the immediate vicinity of the mouth. Thus, it seems reasonable to neglect for the purposes of our discussion such an additional potential term. This is equivalent to assuming that the voltage source connected to the resistor forces the potential to vary linearly on the plane $z = -a$, as specified by Eq. 8.145.

The $y$ component of the electric field given by Eq. 8.146 reverses its direction in passing through the resistive sheet. As a result, a charge distribution of surface density

$$\bar{\sigma}_0 = -2\epsilon_0 \frac{z}{a} \frac{V_0}{b} \tag{8.147}$$

must be present in the resistive sheet. Charge distributions having half this density and opposite polarity are present on the two conducting plates parallel to the sheet. Finally, a charge distribution of surface density

$$\bar{\sigma}_0{}' = -\frac{V_0}{a} \begin{cases} (1 + y/b) & y \leq 0 \\ (1 - y/b) & y \geq 0 \end{cases} \tag{8.148}$$

is present on the end plate at $z = 0$.

The zero-order magnetic field can be readily determined from the current flowing in the resistive sheet. We obtain by inspection

$$\mathbf{H}_0 = \boldsymbol{i}_x \frac{\sigma_s V_0}{2a} \begin{cases} 1 & y < 0 \\ (-1) & y > 0 \end{cases} \tag{8.149}$$

Let us turn our attention next to the zero-order power and energies. The expression for the zero-order Poynting's vector can be readily obtained from Eqs. 8.146 and 8.149,

$$\begin{aligned} \mathbf{S}_0 &= \frac{1}{2} (\mathbf{E}_0 \times \mathbf{H}_0{}^*) \\ &= \frac{\sigma_s V_0{}^2}{4ab} \left[ -\boldsymbol{i}_z \frac{z}{a} + \boldsymbol{i}_y \begin{cases} \dfrac{b}{a}\left(1 + \dfrac{y}{b}\right) & y < 0 \\ \left(-\dfrac{b}{a}\right)\left(1 - \dfrac{y}{b}\right) & y > 0 \end{cases} \right] \end{aligned} \tag{8.150}$$

Its flow lines coincide with the traces of the equipotential surfaces of $\bar{\Phi}_0$, and are shown in Fig. 8.8. The $y$ component changes direction in passing through the resistive sheet. The resulting discontinuity

$$\langle p_{d0}\rangle_s = \frac{1}{2}\sigma_s\left(\frac{V_0}{a}\right)^2 = \frac{1}{2}\sigma_s\left|\mathbf{E}_{z0}\right|^2_{y=0} \tag{8.151}$$

represents the average power dissipated per unit area of the resistive sheet.

The average zero-order electric-energy density is given by

$$\langle w_{e0}\rangle = \frac{1}{4}\epsilon_0|\mathbf{E}_0|^2 = \frac{1}{4}\epsilon_0\left[\left(\frac{z}{a}\right)^2 + \left(\frac{b}{a}\right)^2\left(1 - \left|\frac{y}{b}\right|\right)^2\right]\left(\frac{V_0}{b}\right)^2 \tag{8.152}$$

and the average zero-order magnetic-energy density by

$$\langle w_{m0}\rangle = \frac{1}{4}\mu_0|\mathbf{H}_0|^2 = \frac{1}{4}\mu_0\left(\frac{\sigma_s V_0}{2a}\right)^2 \tag{8.153}$$

Integration of these densities over the volume enclosed by the shield yields for the total zero-order electric energy per unit width in the $x$ direction

$$\langle W_{e0}\rangle = \int_{-b}^{b}\int_{-a}^{0}\langle w_{e0}\rangle\, dy\, dz = \frac{1}{6}\epsilon_0\left(\frac{a}{b} + \frac{b}{a}\right)V_0^2 \tag{8.154}$$

and for the total zero-order magnetic energy per unit width in the $x$ direction

$$\langle W_{m0}\rangle = \int_{-b}^{b}\int_{-a}^{0}\langle w_{m0}\rangle\, dy\, dz = \frac{1}{8}\mu_0\frac{b}{a}\sigma_s^2 V_0^2 \tag{8.155}$$

The total zero-order power dissipated in the resistive sheet per unit width in the $x$ direction can be readily obtained from Eq. 8.151,

$$\langle P_{d0}\rangle = \int_{-a}^{0}\langle p_{d0}\rangle\, dz = \frac{1}{2}\left(\frac{\sigma_s}{a}\right)V_0^2 \tag{8.156}$$

This completes the evaluation of zero-order quantities.

We are primarily interested here in studying the low-frequency behavior of the input impedance (or admittance) of the resistor, i.e., the behavior associated with its zero-order and first-order terms. For this purpose, we do not need to evaluate the first-order field or energy terms, except for showing that the first-order average power dissipated in the resistive sheet is equal to zero. In fact, the sum of the zero-order and first-order complex power flowing through the input surface (the plane $z = -a$) in the direction of the $z$-axis can be expressed in terms of the zero-order and first-order terms of the average power dissipated in the resistive sheet, and of the zero-order electric and magnetic energies stored in the volume enclosed by the shield. We obtain with the help of Eqs. 8.81 and 8.82,

$$(\langle P_0\rangle + \langle P_1\rangle) + j(Q_0 + Q_1) = \langle P_{d0}\rangle + \langle P_{d1}\rangle + j2\omega(\langle W_{m0}\rangle - \langle W_{e0}\rangle) \tag{8.157}$$

where all quantities are measured per unit width in the direction of the $x$-axis.

All the terms on the right-hand side of this equation have been evaluated, with the exception of $\langle P_{d1}\rangle$, the first-order component of the average power dissipated in the resistive sheet. The corresponding power density can be expressed in terms of the zero-order and first-order currents in the sheet as follows,

$$\langle p_{d1}\rangle = \frac{1}{2\sigma_s}(\mathbf{K}_0\cdot\mathbf{K}_1{}^* + \mathbf{K}_1\cdot\mathbf{K}_0{}^*) = \frac{1}{\sigma_s}\,\mathrm{Re}\,(\mathbf{K}_0\cdot\mathbf{K}_1{}^*) \tag{8.158}$$

We observe, on the other hand, that all the zero-order quantities appear in the first-order field equations (Eqs. 8.59) multiplied by the imaginary unit $j$, whereas none of the first-order quantities are multiplied by it. It follows that, in the absence of first-order driving forces, all the first-order quantities must be purely imaginary when, as in our case, the zero-order quantities are real. In particular, the first-order current must be imaginary and the zero-order current must be real. Then, it follows from Eq. 8.158 that the first-order average power dissipated is equal to zero. The input complex power can now be rewritten in the form

$$\langle P_0\rangle + jQ_1 = \langle P_{d0}\rangle + j2\omega(\langle W_{m0}\rangle - \langle W_{e0}\rangle) \tag{8.159}$$

where $\langle P_1\rangle$ and $Q_0$ have been eliminated from the left-hand side because they are evidently equal to zero. Finally, substitution of Eqs. 8.154, 8.155, and 8.156 into Eq. 8.159 yields

$$\langle P_0\rangle + jQ_1 = \frac{1}{2}V_0{}^2\left\{\left(\frac{\sigma_s}{a}\right) + j\omega\left[\frac{1}{2}\mu_0\frac{b}{a}\sigma_s{}^2 - \frac{2}{3}\epsilon_0\left(\frac{a}{b}+\frac{b}{a}\right)\right]\right\} \tag{8.160}$$

To proceed further, we must identify the input complex power given by Eq. 8.160 with the corresponding expression in terms of input voltage and input current. With reference to our discussion in Sec. 7.6, the input voltage can be appropriately defined as the line integral of the electric field from the resistive sheet to the shield over any path on the plane $z = -a$; this integral is independent of the particular path selected because the electric field is independent of the $x$ coordinate. The current per unit width flowing into the resistive sheet is equal to $K_z$, the $z$ component of the surface current density in the sheet. On the other hand, we saw in Sec. 7.6 that, in order for the flux of Poynting's vector through any closed surface to be correctly identified with the power input computed from the circuit point of view in terms of terminal currents and terminal voltages, the component of the "displacement current" $\partial \boldsymbol{D}/\partial t$ normal to the surface must be equal to zero. In our case, the zero-order electric field gives rise to a first-order displacement current normal to the plane $z = -a$, and of density

$$j\omega\epsilon_0 E_{z0} = j\omega\epsilon_0 \frac{V_0}{a}\left(1 - \left|\frac{y}{b}\right|\right) \tag{8.161}$$

According to the complex form of Eq. 7.112 this displacement current produces a first-order component of complex input power equal to

$$\begin{aligned} -\frac{1}{2}\int_{-b}^{b} j\omega\epsilon_0(\Phi_0 E_{z0}^*)_{z=-a}\,dy &= -j\omega\epsilon_0\frac{V_0^2}{2a}\int_{-b}^{b}\left(1 - \left|\frac{y}{b}\right|\right)^2 dy \\ &= -\frac{1}{3}j\omega\epsilon_0\frac{b}{a}V_0^2 \end{aligned} \tag{8.162}$$

This component can be readily identified with the last term on the right-hand side of Eq. 8.160. Thus, it can be neglected when $b/a \ll a/b$, i.e., when the length of the resistive sheet is much greater than the separation between the sheet and the two shielding plates. Under these conditions, the input impedance and admittance can be defined in a consistent manner with the help of Eqs. 8.43 and 8.47. The impedance per unit width in the $x$ direction is given to first-order terms by

$$\begin{aligned} Z_0 + Z_1 &= \frac{2}{|I_0|^2}(\langle P_0\rangle + jQ_1) \\ &= \frac{2}{|K_{z0}|^2}[\langle P_{d0}\rangle + j2\omega(\langle W_{m0}\rangle - \langle W_{e0}\rangle)] \\ &= \frac{a}{\sigma_s} + j\omega\left[\frac{1}{2}\mu_0 ab - \frac{2}{3}\epsilon_0\frac{a}{b}\left(\frac{a}{\sigma_s}\right)^2\right] \end{aligned} \tag{8.163}$$

and the admittance per unit width, also to first-order terms, by

$$\begin{aligned} Y_0 + Y_1 &= \frac{2}{|V_0|^2}(\langle P_0\rangle - jQ_1) = \frac{2}{V_0^2}[\langle P_{d0}\rangle + j2\omega(\langle W_{e0}\rangle - \langle W_{m0}\rangle)] \\ &= \frac{\sigma_s}{a} + j\omega\left(\frac{2}{3}\epsilon_0\frac{a}{b} - \frac{1}{2}\mu_0\frac{b}{a}\sigma_s^2\right) \end{aligned} \tag{8.164}$$

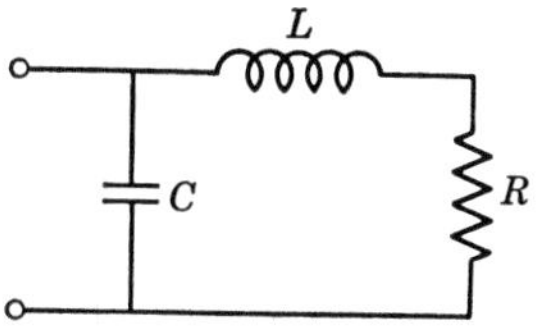


**Fig. 8.9.** Quasi-static equivalent circuit for shielded resistor of Fig. 8.8.

As expected, the zero-order impedance (or admittance) is equal to the d-c resistance (or conductance) of the resistive sheet. On the other hand, the first-order impedance (or admittance) cannot be identified with that of a single circuit element because it can be either positive or negative, depending on the value of $\sigma_s$, and it vanishes when $\sigma_s$ is equal to the critical value

$$(\sigma_s)_{\text{crit}} = \frac{2}{\sqrt{3}} \sqrt{\frac{\epsilon_0}{\mu_0} \frac{a}{b}} \tag{8.165}$$

When the conductivity is equal to this critical value, the resistor behaves like an ideal resistance within the frequency range in which our quasi-static approximation is valid. For smaller values of the conductivity, the first-order effect is capacitive, and for larger values inductive. In the limit of very large conductivity, the quasi-static equivalent circuit consists of an inductance

$$L = \tfrac{1}{2}\mu_0 ab \tag{8.166}$$

in series with the d-c resistance

$$R = \frac{a}{\sigma_s} \tag{8.167}$$

and in the limit of very small conductivity, it consists of a capacitance

$$C = \frac{2}{3} \epsilon_0 \frac{a}{b} \tag{8.168}$$

in parallel with the same resistance. The equivalent circuit shown in Fig. 8.9 involving both the series inductance and the parallel capacitance is a correct representation of the resistor for all values of the conductivity, with the provision that the impedance (or admittance) of the equivalent circuit must also be approximated to first-order terms. It must be stressed with regard to this equivalent circuit that the first-order impedance (or admittance) vanishes when the time constant $RC$ is equal to the time constant $L/R$ rather than when $L$ resonates with $C$.

We shall now show that the frequency behavior obtained for our model of resistor is characteristic of all resistors. As discussed in Sec. 6.5, the presence of zero-order current in a dissipative material implies the simultaneous existence of a zero-order electric field and of a zero-order magnetic field coupled by the zero-order conduction current. Thus, the storage of both zero-order electric energy and zero-order magnetic energy is inherently associated with zero-order power dissipation, with the result that the complex power input to the system must be expressible in the form given by Eq. 8.159. Furthermore, the zero-order magnetic energy $W_{m0}$ is proportional to the square of the intensity of the conduction current and, therefore, to the square of the input current, and the zero-order electric energy $W_{e0}$ is proportional to the square of the electric-field intensity and, therefore, to the square of the input voltage. It follows that, for any given geometry, there is always a critical value of the conductivity of the dissipative material for which the two zero-order energies are equal; in this critical condition, the first-order reactive power vanishes, and the input impedance is purely resistive within the range of validity of the quasi-static approximation. For larger values of the conductivity the impedance is inductive, and for smaller values capacitive, just as in the particular example discussed in this section.

## 8.8 The Skin Effect

The phenomenon known as *skin effect* is the salient characteristic of electromagnetic fields in conducting media. It amounts to the fact that the electromagnetic field in a good conductor is relegated, for all practical purposes, to a surface layer (skin) of thickness

$$\delta = \sqrt{\frac{2}{\omega\mu\sigma}} \tag{8.169}$$

Thus, for instance, in a wire of radius much larger than $\delta$, most of the current flows in the vicinity of the surface of the wire, and hardly any near its axis. The *skin depth* $\delta$ is quite small for all metals, even at relatively low frequencies; for copper it is equal to 2 mm at 1000 cps.

As we shall see below, the skin effect is inherently a wave propagation phenomenon. As such, it is outside the scope of our discussion, and it is treated in detail in a companion book by the same authors [2]. On the other hand, because of its importance in connection with circuit

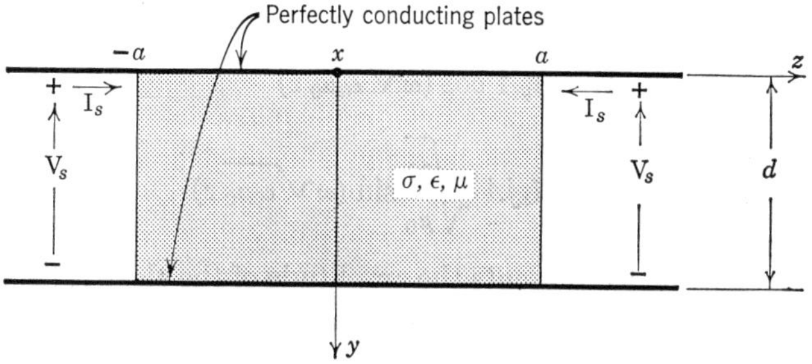


**Fig. 8.10.** Resistor consisting of a conducting slab inserted between perfectly conducting plates.

components, it deserves at least a preliminary discussion pointing out its main characteristics.

Let us consider, as an illustration, the system shown in Fig. 8.10, consisting of a slab of conducting material inserted between two perfectly conducting plates. Appropriate sources are connected symmetrically between the two plates on both sides of the slab in such a way as to force the electromagnetic field to be independent of the $x$ and $y$ coordinates. In other words, we assume that all fields are functions of $z$ only; furthermore, because of the symmetry of the sources, the electric field must be an even function of $z$. The conducting slab may be regarded as a simple form of resistor, and the perfectly conducting plates as an idealization of the leads connecting the resistor to a power source. Because of the uniformity of the system in the direction of the $x$-axis, all quantities characterizing the system will apply to a unit width in that direction.

The electromagnetic field in the conducting slab can be determined term by term following the power-series method. However, much tedious work can be avoided by making use of the results of the analysis carried out in Sec. 6.4. In fact, the system illustrated in Fig. 6.3 is identical to that considered here, except for the fact that the space between the perfectly conducting plates is now occupied by a linear, homogeneous, isotropic material represented by a permeability $\mu$, a permittivity $\epsilon$, and a conductivity $\sigma$. The fields associated with the system of Fig. 6.3 in the sinusoidal steady state are given by Eqs. 6.78 and 6.79. The complex form of these fields can be readily obtained by noting that

$$\cos \omega t = \text{Re}\, e^{j\omega t} \tag{8.170}$$

$$-\sin \omega t = \text{Re}\,(je^{j\omega t}) \tag{8.171}$$

We have then, by definition,

$$\mathbf{E} = \boldsymbol{i}_y A \cos\,(\omega\sqrt{\epsilon_0\mu_0}\, z) \tag{8.172}$$

$$\mathbf{H} = \boldsymbol{i}_x jA \sqrt{\frac{\epsilon_0}{\mu_0}} \sin\,(\omega\sqrt{\epsilon_0\mu_0}\, z) \tag{8.173}$$

The real constant $A$ represents the amplitude of the electric field on the $x,y$-plane, which is taken as a reference for all other electromagnetic quantities.

The electromagnetic field given by Eqs. 8.172 and 8.173 is a solution of Maxwell's equations in complex form (Eqs. 8.17 through 8.21) with

$$\epsilon = \epsilon_0 \qquad \mu = \mu_0 \qquad \mathbf{J}_f = \sigma\mathbf{E} = 0 \tag{8.174}$$

Clearly the substitution of constant values of $\epsilon$ and $\mu$ for $\epsilon_0$ and $\mu_0$ does not affect the form of the equations or of the solution. On the other hand, in the presence of finite conductivity, Eqs. 8.18, 8.19, and 8.21 yield

$$\text{curl}\,\mathbf{H} = (\sigma + j\omega\epsilon)\mathbf{E} \tag{8.175}$$

$$\text{div}\,\sigma\mathbf{E} = -j\omega\rho_f = -j\omega\,\text{div}\,\epsilon\mathbf{E} \tag{8.176}$$

Since $\sigma$ and $\epsilon$ are constants, this last equation can be satisfied only if

$$\text{div}\,\mathbf{E} = 0 \tag{8.177}$$

as in the free-space case. Then, it follows from Eq. 8.175 that the presence of uniform, finite conductivity can be taken into account by substituting $(\sigma + j\omega\epsilon)$ for $j\omega\epsilon$ wherever the latter appears. In conclusion, the electromagnetic field in the system under consideration can be obtained from Eqs. 8.172 and 8.173 by performing the following substitutions

$$\mu \rightarrow \mu_0 \qquad \left(\frac{\sigma}{j\omega} + \epsilon\right) \rightarrow \epsilon_0 \tag{8.178}$$

We have then for the desired electromagnetic field

$$\mathbf{E} = \boldsymbol{i}_y A \cos\,[-j\sqrt{j\omega\mu(\sigma + j\omega\epsilon)}\; z] = \boldsymbol{i}_y A \cosh \bar{\gamma} z \tag{8.179}$$

$$\mathbf{H} = \boldsymbol{i}_x jA \sqrt{\frac{\sigma + j\omega\epsilon}{j\omega\mu}} \sin\,[-j\sqrt{j\omega\mu(\sigma + j\omega\epsilon)}\; z] = \boldsymbol{i}_x \frac{A}{\bar{\eta}} \sinh \bar{\gamma} z \tag{8.180}$$

where

$$\bar{\gamma} = \sqrt{j\omega\mu(\sigma + j\omega\epsilon)} \qquad \text{and} \qquad \bar{\eta} = \sqrt{\frac{j\omega\mu}{\sigma + j\omega\epsilon}} \tag{8.181}$$

have positive real parts. The current density is given by

$$\mathbf{J}_c = \sigma \mathbf{E} = \boldsymbol{i}_y \sigma A \cosh \bar{\gamma} z \tag{8.182}$$

The behavior of this electromagnetic field can be more readily understood by expressing the hyperbolic functions in their exponential forms

$$\mathbf{E} = \boldsymbol{i}_y \tfrac{1}{2} A (e^{\bar{\gamma} z} + e^{-\bar{\gamma} z}) \tag{8.183}$$

$$\mathbf{H} = \boldsymbol{i}_x \frac{1}{2} \frac{A}{\bar{\eta}} (e^{\bar{\gamma} z} - e^{-\bar{\gamma} z}) \tag{8.184}$$

We observe then that the field may be regarded as the linear superposition of two fields whose magnitudes decay exponentially in opposite directions of the $z$-axis. It can be readily checked that these two fields satisfy individually Maxwell's equations.

For the sake of simplicity, we shall assume in what follows that at all frequencies of interest

$$\sigma \gg \omega \epsilon \tag{8.185}$$

This is certainly true for all metals; we shall see below that this must be true whenever the skin effect influences appreciably the behavior of circuit components. With this assumption, the exponential coefficient $\bar{\gamma}$ can be readily separated into its real and imaginary parts,

$$\bar{\gamma} = \alpha + j\beta = \sqrt{\omega \mu \sigma}\, \frac{1 + j}{\sqrt{2}} \qquad \alpha = \beta = \sqrt{\frac{\omega \mu \sigma}{2}} \tag{8.186}$$

Then, since

$$e^{\pm \bar{\gamma} z} = e^{\pm \alpha z} (\cos \beta z \pm j \sin \beta z) \tag{8.187}$$

one of the two exponential solutions becomes much smaller than the other whenever

$$|z| \sqrt{\frac{\omega \mu \sigma}{2}} \gg 1 \tag{8.188}$$

i.e., whenever $|z|$ is much greater than the thickness $\delta$ defined by Eq. 8.169. It follows that, if the width of the slab ($2a$) is much greater than $2\delta$, the magnitude of the field decays exponentially from the two faces of the slab toward the middle as illustrated for $|E_y|$ in Fig. 8.11. The skin depth $\delta$ represents the interval over which the magnitude of the field decays by a factor of $1/e$.

It is convenient, at this point, to concentrate our attention on one of the two exponential solutions; let us select the one whose magnitude decays in the positive direction of the $z$-axis. It is also convenient in

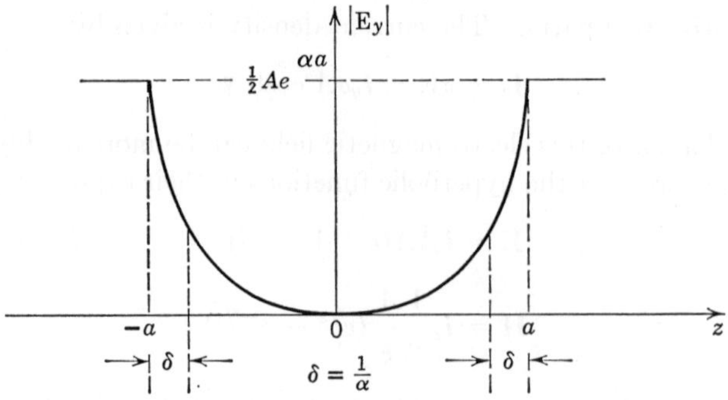


**Fig. 8.11.** Plot of the electric field in the slab of Fig. 8.10.

studying further this solution to measure the distance along the $z$-axis from the face of the slab on the plane $z = -a$, by introducing a new variable $\zeta$ related to $z$ by

$$z = \zeta - a \tag{8.189}$$

The solution on which we wish to focus our attention becomes then

$$\mathbf{E} = \boldsymbol{i}_y(\tfrac{1}{2}Ae^{\bar{\gamma}a})e^{-\bar{\gamma}\zeta} = -\boldsymbol{i}_y\bar{\eta}\mathrm{H}_{sx}e^{-\alpha\zeta}e^{-j\beta\zeta} \tag{8.190}$$

$$\mathbf{H} = -\boldsymbol{i}_x\left(\frac{1}{2}\frac{A}{\bar{\eta}}e^{\bar{\gamma}a}\right)e^{-\bar{\gamma}\zeta} = \boldsymbol{i}_x\mathrm{H}_{sx}e^{-\alpha\zeta}e^{-j\beta\zeta} \tag{8.191}$$

where

$$\mathrm{H}_{sx} = -\frac{1}{2}\frac{A}{\bar{\eta}}e^{\bar{\gamma}a} \tag{8.192}$$

represents the magnetic field tangent to the face of the slab at $z = -a$.

As stated above, the magnitude of these fields decreases exponentially in the positive direction of the $z$-axis. The reciprocal of the exponential coefficient $\alpha$ is the skin depth $\delta$ over which the magnitude of the fields decreases by a factor of $1/e$. Since $\alpha = \beta$, $\delta$ is also the distance over which the phase of the two fields changes by one radian; thus, the wave length, which is the distance over which the phase $\beta\zeta$ changes by $2\pi$ radians, is given by

$$\lambda_\sigma = 2\pi\delta = 2\pi\sqrt{\frac{2}{\omega\mu\sigma}} \tag{8.193}$$

It is important to compare this characteristic distance with the corresponding distance for a nonconducting material with the same values of $\epsilon$ and $\mu$. We obtain by setting $\sigma = 0$ in Eq. 8.181

$$\bar{\gamma} = j\beta = j\omega\sqrt{\epsilon\mu} \qquad \lambda = \frac{2\pi}{\beta} = \frac{2\pi}{\omega\sqrt{\epsilon\mu}} \tag{8.194}$$

so that

$$\frac{\lambda}{\lambda_\sigma} = \sqrt{\frac{\sigma}{2\omega\epsilon}} \tag{8.195}$$

This ratio is much greater than unity for all metals at all frequencies of radio-engineering interest. It is of the order of $10^7$ for copper at 1000 cps. Thus, devices whose dimensions are much smaller than the wave length in any practical, nonconducting medium may well include conductors whose dimensions are comparable to the wave length within them. This is the reason why in the analysis of circuit components the quasi-static approximation is usually valid in nonconductive media but not within ordinary conductors. It is also clear from Eq. 8.195 that the inequality Eq. 8.185 must be satisfied whenever the frequency behavior of a practical circuit is appreciably influenced by skin effect.

The conduction-current density can be readily obtained from Eq. 8.190,

$$\mathbf{J}_c = \sigma\mathbf{E} = -\boldsymbol{i}_y\sigma\bar{\eta}\mathrm{H}_{sx}e^{-\bar{\gamma}\zeta} = \boldsymbol{i}_y\bar{\gamma}\mathrm{H}_{sx}e^{-\bar{\gamma}\zeta} \tag{8.196}$$

where use has been made of the inequality Eq. 8.185; this inequality amounts to neglecting the displacement current in comparison with the conduction current. The total current flowing through the slab can be evaluated by integrating its density with respect to $\zeta$. On the assumption that $a \gg \delta$, the density given by Eq. 8.196 yields the current flowing in the left half of the slab,

$$\mathrm{I}_s = -\int_0^a \mathrm{H}_{sx}\bar{\gamma}e^{-\bar{\gamma}\zeta}d \simeq -\int_0^\infty \mathrm{H}_{sx}\bar{\gamma}e^{-\bar{\gamma}\zeta}\,d\zeta = -\mathrm{H}_{sx} \tag{8.197}$$

An equal amount of current resulting from the other exponential solution flows in the right half of the slab. The fact that $\mathrm{I}_s$ is equal to $-\mathrm{H}_{sx}$ should not come as a surprise. It could have been anticipated by noting that the net current flowing in the left half in the direction of the $y$-axis must be equal to the difference between the values assumed by the magnetic field at the center of the slab and on its left-hand face. On the assumption of $a \gg \delta$, the value at the center is negligibly small, and that on the left face is equal to $\mathrm{H}_{sx}$.

The current $\mathrm{I}_s$ is obviously the input current flowing toward the left face of the slab on the upper plate. An equal, symmetrically directed current flows toward the right face of the slab. The voltage between the plates on either face of the slab is, for $a \gg \delta$,

$$\mathrm{V}_s = d(\mathrm{E}_y)_{\zeta=0} = -d\bar{\eta}\mathrm{H}_{sx} \tag{8.198}$$

Thus the impedance of each half of the slab is

$$\mathrm{Z} = d\bar{\eta} \tag{8.199}$$

namely that of a sheet with a surface impedance equal to $\bar{\eta}$. For this reason, we refer to the quantity $\bar{\eta}$ defined by Eq. 8.181 as the surface impedance (or the intrinsic wave impedance) of the conducting medium. The resistive component of Z is

$$R = d\,\mathrm{Re}\,(\bar{\eta}) = d\sqrt{\frac{\omega\mu}{2\sigma}} = \frac{d}{\sigma\delta} \tag{8.200}$$

where use has been made of the inequality Eq. 8.185. Thus, we may regard the resistance of each half of the slab as the d-c resistance of a slab of thickness equal to $\delta$. For this reason $\delta$ is often called *the effective skin depth.*

Let us turn our attention next to the power and energy aspects of the skin effect. We shall assume again in what follows that $a \gg \delta$, so that the field can be considered as negligibly small at the center of the slab. This will allow us to disregard the interaction of the two exponential solutions in the evaluation of scalar products and vector products of fields.

The complex Poynting's vector associated with the fields given by Eqs. 8.190 and 8.191 is

$$\mathbf{S} = \frac{1}{2}\mathbf{E} \times \mathbf{H}^* = \boldsymbol{i}_z\frac{1}{2}\bar{\eta}|\mathrm{H}_{sx}|^2e^{-2\alpha\zeta} = \boldsymbol{i}_z\frac{1}{2}(1+j)\sqrt{\frac{\omega\mu}{2\sigma}}|H_{sx}|^2e^{-2\alpha\zeta} \tag{8.201}$$

Thus, the average (active) power and the reactive power have the same magnitude, and both flow in the positive direction of the $z$-axis. Their density decreases exponentially from the left-hand face of the slab toward the interior, and becomes vanishingly small (because $a \gg \delta$) by the time it reaches the center of the slab.

The average power-dissipation density is

$$\langle p_d \rangle = \tfrac{1}{2}\sigma|\mathbf{E}|^2 = \tfrac{1}{2}\sigma|\bar{\eta}|^2|\mathrm{H}_{sx}|^2e^{-2\alpha\zeta} = \tfrac{1}{2}\omega\mu|\mathrm{H}_{sx}|^2e^{-2\alpha\zeta} \tag{8.202}$$

and the average magnetic-energy density is

$$\langle w_m \rangle = \tfrac{1}{4}\mu|\mathbf{H}|^2 = \tfrac{1}{4}\mu|\mathrm{H}_{sx}|^2e^{-2\alpha\zeta} \tag{8.203}$$

The electric-energy density is negligibly small because of the inequality Eq. 8.185.

The power dissipation and the energy storage are related to the power flow by the complex Poynting's theorem. We have from Eq. 8.32,

$$\operatorname{div} \mathbf{S} = \frac{dS_z}{d\zeta} = -\alpha\bar{\eta}|H_{sx}|^2 e^{-2\alpha\zeta} = -\frac{1}{2}(1+j)\omega\mu|H_{sx}|^2 e^{-2\alpha\zeta}$$

$$= \langle p_d \rangle + j2\omega\langle w_m \rangle \qquad (8.204)$$

which checks with Eqs. 8.202 and 8.203. It is interesting to note that the exponential decay of $|E_y|$ and $|H_x|$ may be regarded as a consequence of their proportionality and of the law of conservation of energy as expressed by the real part of Poynting's theorem. In fact, since

$$E_y = -\bar{\eta}H_x \qquad (8.205)$$

the real part of Poynting's vector and the average power dissipation density can be expressed in the form

$$\operatorname{Re}(S_z) = \frac{1}{2}\sqrt{\frac{\omega\mu}{2\sigma}}|H_x|^2 \qquad \langle p_d \rangle = \tfrac{1}{2}\omega\mu|H_x|^2 \qquad (8.206)$$

On the other hand, the real part of Poynting's theorem requires

$$\operatorname{Re}\left(\frac{\partial S_z}{\partial \zeta}\right) = -\langle p_d \rangle \qquad (8.207)$$

from which we obtain by substitution

$$\frac{\partial |H_x|^2}{\partial \zeta} = -\sqrt{2\omega\mu\sigma}\,|H_x|^2 = -2\alpha|H_x|^2 \qquad (8.208)$$

The solution of this differential equation is

$$|H_x|^2 = |H_{sx}|^2 e^{-2\alpha\zeta} \qquad (8.209)$$

where $|H_{sx}|^2$ is an arbitrary positive constant. This solution exhibits the expected exponential decay.

The results obtained for the system of Fig. 8.10 can be generalized to apply to a variety of situations of practical interest; unfortunately, however, the key argument involved in the generalization is based on properties of waves that cannot be discussed in sufficient detail at this point. The argument itself, on the other hand, can be stated very simply as follows. Let us consider a homogeneous, linear conductor, whose conductivity satisfies the inequality Eq. 8.185 at the frequency of interest. Let us suppose further that the dimensions of the conductor and the radius of curvature at all points of its surface are much larger than the skin depth $\delta$ defined by Eq. 8.169. It can be shown that at all points of the surface separating the conducting material from the surrounding nonconducting material the electric field and the magnetic field on the conductor side of the surface are approximately tangent to the surface and are related to each other by

$$\mathbf{E}_s = \mathbf{H}_s \times \boldsymbol{n}\bar{\eta} \tag{8.210}$$

The unit vector $\boldsymbol{n}$ is normal to the surface and directed toward the conductor, and $\bar{\eta}$ is the intrinsic impedance of the conducting material defined by Eq. 8.181. This is just the relation between the fields exhibited by the exponential solutions of Eqs. 8.190 and 8.191. The complex power entering the conductor is then given by the complex Poynting's vector

$$\mathbf{S}_s = \boldsymbol{n}\tfrac{1}{2}\bar{\eta}|\mathbf{H}_s|^2 \tag{8.211}$$

where $\mathbf{H}_s$ represents the magnetic field tangent to the surface.

We can conclude that, as far as the fields surrounding the conductor are concerned, we can substitute for the conductor a conducting sheet coinciding with its surface, of surface impedance equal to $\bar{\eta}$, with the added provision that the surface current in the sheet must be related to the tangential magnetic field by

$$\mathbf{K} = \mathbf{H}_s \times \boldsymbol{n} \tag{8.212}$$

In the case of a perfect conductor ($\sigma = \infty$), the surface impedance is equal to zero and so is the skin depth. This implies that the tangential component of the electric field must vanish on the surface of a perfect conductor, regardless of its shape. This is the boundary condition used in the preceding illustrative examples.

The illustrative example of Fig. 8.10 has focused our attention on conductors whose circuit function is to provide a current path. The results of our analysis, however, are not restricted to conducting bodies intended to perform such a function. For instance, they apply as well to the iron core of a transformer, intended to provide a path for the magnetic flux, rather than for the current. Let us suppose that the conducting slab of Fig. 8.10 is made of a linear homogeneous material which is both conducting and magnetic such as iron, and that we wish to produce in it a magnetic flux in the direction of the $x$-axis. For this purpose, we connect antisymmetric current sources on opposite sides of the slab, as illustrated in Fig. 8.12.

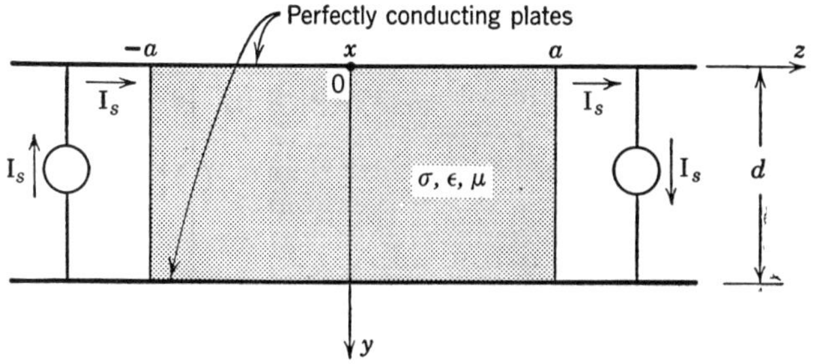


**Fig. 8.12.** Homogeneous magnetic core excited by current $I_s$.

Under static conditions (d-c sources), the sources together with the perfectly conducting plates would produce in the magnetic slab a uniform magnetic field of intensity equal to the surface current density on the plates. In the sinusoidal steady state, however, the magnetic field is appreciable only in the vicinity of the two surfaces of the slab. The exact expressions for the electromagnetic field are

$$\mathbf{H} = \boldsymbol{i}_x B \cosh \bar{\gamma} z = \boldsymbol{i}_x \tfrac{1}{2} B(e^{\bar{\gamma} z} + e^{-\bar{\gamma} z}) \tag{8.213}$$

$$\mathbf{E} = \boldsymbol{i}_y \bar{\eta} B \sinh \bar{\gamma} z = \boldsymbol{i}_y \tfrac{1}{2} \bar{\eta} B(e^{\bar{\gamma} z} - e^{-\bar{\gamma} z}) \tag{8.214}$$

where $B$ represents the magnetic-field intensity at the center of the slab. Again, the electromagnetic field may be regarded as the superposition of two exponential solutions. The only difference from the case of Fig. 8.10 is that one of the solutions has the opposite sign so that **E** is now an odd function of $z$ and **H** an even function.

The important point to remember is that regardless of the geometry of the system and of the location of the sources, all fields in a conducting material can have appreciable intensity only in the vicinity of the surface separating the conducting material from the surrounding, nonconducting medium. This phenomenon may be regarded as resulting from the fact that the power dissipated in a conducting body must flow into it through its surface. The power-flow density is proportional to the square of the field intensity, and so is the power dissipation density. The net result is that the field intensity must decay from the surface of the conducting body toward its interior, and becomes negligibly small at distances from the surface appreciably greater than the skin depth $\delta$.

Various techniques are used in practice to eliminate or reduce the undesirable aspects of the skin effect. They all involve dividing the conducting body in question into pieces insulated from one another, of

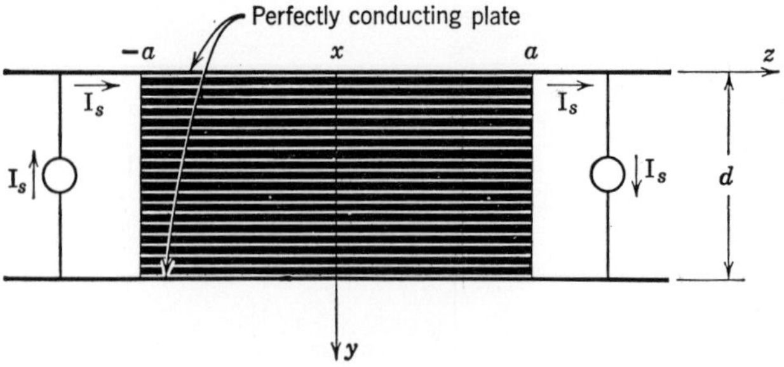


**Fig. 8.13.** Laminated magnetic core excited by current $I_s$.

which at least one dimension is smaller than the skin depth. The best known example of such techniques is the use of thin sheets of magnetic material in the fabrication of transformer cores. The sheets are made parallel to the magnetic field and normal to the electric field in such a way as to reduce as much as possible the flow of current without obstructing the magnetic flux. This technique is illustrated in Fig. 8.13, where a stack of thin sheets has been substituted for the slab of Fig. 8.12. This technique reduces power dissipation very substantially, but does not eliminate it completely. It is interesting to note that the insulation between sheets provides canals through which power can flow to all parts of the surface of each sheet. This makes it possible for the power dissipation to have an almost uniform density throughout the stack.

Another example is provided by the use of stranded conductors, in the place of solid conductors, when the cross-section dimensions of the latter are larger than the skin depth. A stranded conductor consists of a large number of small wires insulated from each other (except at the terminals). The wires are interwoven in such a way that each wire occupies each position in a bundle for approximately the same length of conductor. In this manner the current is forced to divide equally between the wires, and to be uniformly distributed throughout the cross section of the stranded conductor. The insulation surrounding each wire provides a canal through which power can reach the surface of the wire throughout its length. The radius of each wire must, of course, be smaller than the skin depth.

The use of insulated sheets in magnetic cores and the stranding in conductors may be regarded as ways of fabricating materials with anisotropic conductivity. A stack of insulated sheets has appreciable conductivity only in the direction of the laminations, and a stranded conductor conducts only in the direction of the wires. If the construction forces the magnetic field or the current to be uniformly distributed, it must automatically provide paths through which power can reach all parts of the material.

## ► 8.9 Multiterminal Networks

The preceding sections dealt primarily with two-terminal circuit components. We wish to discuss now some of the properties of multiterminal components and networks.

Let us consider an electromagnetic system enclosed by a surface $S$, and connected to energy sources and other systems by current-carrying wires, as illustrated in Fig. 8.14. We assume further that the system under consideration is linear and passive (no energy sources are present within $S$). We saw in Section 7.6 that terminal voltages can be defined in a consistent manner at the points at which the wires pierce the surface $S$ whenever the electric field tangent to $S$ can be represented to a reasonable degree of approximation by the negative gradient of a scalar potential $\phi$. In other words, terminal voltages can be defined if the line integral of the electric field between any two terminals is closely independent of the path of integration for any reasonably direct path on $S$. Furthermore, if the displacement current flowing through $S$ is small compared with the conduction current in the wires piercing $S$, the power flowing through $S$ can be expressed as the sum of the prod-

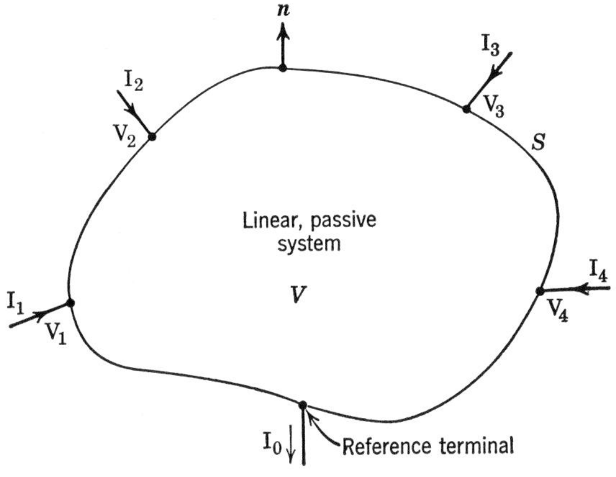


**Fig. 8.14.** Multiterminal linear passive system.

ucts of terminal voltages and terminal currents, i.e., in the form of Eq. 7.107.

Because of the linearity of the laws governing the behavior of the electromagnetic field within $S$, the terminal voltages must be linearly related to the terminal currents, i.e., they must be expressible, in the sinusoidal steady state, in the form of

$$\mathrm{V}_j = \mathrm{Z}_{j1}\mathrm{I}_1 + \mathrm{Z}_{j2}\mathrm{I}_2 + \cdots + \mathrm{Z}_{jk}\mathrm{I}_k + \cdots + \mathrm{Z}_{jn}\mathrm{I}_n \qquad (8.215)$$

where $\mathrm{V}_j$ is the voltage of the $j$th terminal measured with respect to a reference terminal, $\mathrm{I}_k$ is the current flowing *into* $S$ through the $k$th terminal, and the $\mathrm{Z}_{jk}$ are impedances characterizing the system within $S$.

It is clear that $\mathrm{Z}_{kk}$ is the input impedance measured between the $k$th terminal and the reference terminal when the currents at all other terminals are equal to zero, i.e., when all other terminals are open-circuited. The transfer impedance $\mathrm{Z}_{jk}$, on the other hand, is given by

$$\mathrm{Z}_{jk} = \left(\frac{\mathrm{V}_j}{\mathrm{I}_k}\right) \quad \text{for } \mathrm{I}_1 = \mathrm{I}_2 = \cdots = \mathrm{I}_{k-1} = \mathrm{I}_{k+1} = \cdots = \mathrm{I}_n = 0 \quad (8.216)$$

i.e., by the ratio of the voltage at the $j$th terminal and the current at the $k$th terminal when all the terminals except for the $k$th are open-circuited.

If we wish to express the terminal currents as functions of the terminal voltages, we obtain equations of the form

$$\mathrm{I}_j = \mathrm{Y}_{j1}\mathrm{V}_1 + \mathrm{Y}_{j2}\mathrm{V}_2 + \cdots + \mathrm{Y}_{jk}\mathrm{V}_k + \cdots + \mathrm{Y}_{jn}\mathrm{V}_n \qquad (8.217)$$

where the $\mathrm{Y}_{jk}$ are admittances related to the $\mathrm{Z}_{jk}$. It is clear, again, that $\mathrm{Y}_{kk}$ is the input admittance measured between the $k$th terminal and the reference terminal when all other terminals are short-circuited, i.e., when their voltages are equal to zero. Similarly, the transfer admittance $\mathrm{Y}_{jk}$ is given by the ratio of $\mathrm{I}_j$ and $\mathrm{V}_k$ when all the other voltages are equal to zero, i.e., when the corresponding terminals are short-circuited.

A very important property of the transfer impedances and of the transfer admittances is that their values are independent of the order of their subscripts, i.e.,

$$\mathrm{Z}_{jk} = \mathrm{Z}_{kj} \qquad \mathrm{Y}_{jk} = \mathrm{Y}_{kj} \qquad (8.218)$$

This property follows from the *reciprocity theorem*, which, in turn, is a consequence of the linearity and of the symmetry of Maxwell's equations in linear, passive media

$$\text{curl } \mathbf{E} = -j\omega\mu\mathbf{H} \tag{8.219}$$

$$\text{curl } \mathbf{H} = (\sigma + j\omega\epsilon)\mathbf{E} \tag{8.220}$$

This theorem is a generalization of the theorem discussed in Sec. 7.7 for systems of charged conductors, and of the related theorems discussed in Secs. 7.8 and 7.9 for multiterminal conductors and multiwinding systems.

Let $\mathbf{E}^1$, $\mathbf{H}^1$ and $\mathbf{E}^2$, $\mathbf{H}^2$ represent two different electromagnetic fields that satisfy Maxwell's equations within a volume $V$ enclosed by a surface $S$. Let us suppose further that $V$ contains only linear materials, and that it is free of energy sources, i.e., no free currents other than conduction currents are present. In other words, the electromagnetic system enclosed by $S$ is linear and passive, and the two different electromagnetic fields are produced by different sets of sources outside $S$. We have within $V$,

$$\begin{aligned} \text{div } (\mathbf{E}^1 \times \mathbf{H}^2) &= \mathbf{H}^2 \cdot \text{curl } \mathbf{E}^1 - \mathbf{E}^1 \cdot \text{curl } \mathbf{H}^2 \\ &= -\sigma\mathbf{E}^1 \cdot \mathbf{E}^2 - j\omega(\mu\mathbf{H}^1 \cdot \mathbf{H}^2 + \epsilon\mathbf{E}^1 \cdot \mathbf{E}^2) \end{aligned} \tag{8.221}$$

where use has been made of Eqs. 8.219 and 8.220 and of Eq. A4.16 of Appendix 4. We note next that the right-hand side of Eq. 8.221 is symmetrical with respect to the superscripts 1 and 2. It follows that

$$\text{div } (\mathbf{E}^1 \times \mathbf{H}^2) = \text{div } (\mathbf{E}^2 \times \mathbf{H}^1) \tag{8.222}$$

and, with the help of Gauss' theorem,

$$\oint_S (\mathbf{E}^1 \times \mathbf{H}^2) \cdot \boldsymbol{n}\, da = \oint_S (\mathbf{E}^2 \times \mathbf{H}^1) \cdot \boldsymbol{n}\, da \tag{8.223}$$

This equation constitutes the field formulation of the reciprocity theorem.

To obtain the circuit formulation of the reciprocity theorem, we apply Eq. 8.223 to the network illustrated in Fig. 8.15. In this connection, let the electromagnetic field with the superscript 1 represent the situation in which a source is connected between terminal 1 of the network and the reference terminal while terminal 2 is open-circuited, so that

$$\mathrm{I}_1 = \mathrm{I}_1^1 \qquad \mathrm{I}_2 = 0 \qquad \mathrm{V}_1 = \mathrm{V}_1^1 \qquad \mathrm{V}_2 = \mathrm{V}_2^1 \tag{8.224}$$

Similarly, let the field with the superscript 2 represent the situation in which a source is connected between terminal 2 and the reference ter-

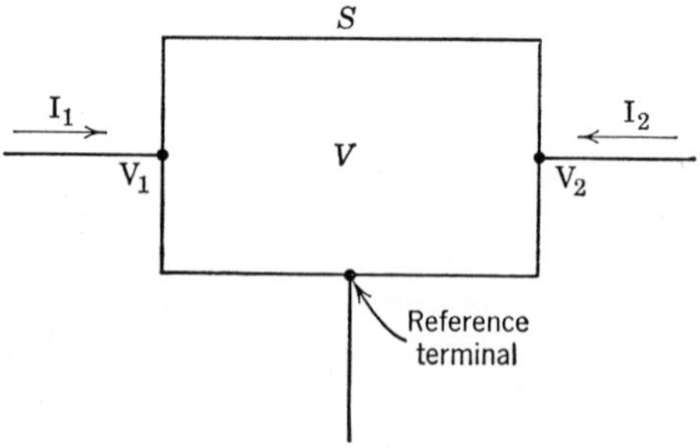


**Fig. 8.15.** Network employed in the derivation of reciprocity theorem.

minal while terminal 1 is open-circuited, so that

$$I_1 = 0 \qquad I_2 = I_2^2 \qquad V_1 = V_1^2 \qquad V_2 = V_2^2 \tag{8.225}$$

Then, following the same procedure used in deriving Eq. 7.112 from Eq. 7.108, we obtain from Eq. 8.223

$$\oint_S \bar{\phi}^1(\mathbf{J}^2 + j\omega\epsilon\mathbf{E}^2)\cdot\boldsymbol{n}\,da = \oint_S \bar{\phi}^2(\mathbf{J}^1 + j\omega\epsilon\mathbf{E}^1)\cdot\boldsymbol{n}\,da \tag{8.226}$$

where $\bar{\phi}^1$ and $\bar{\phi}^2$ are the scalar potentials from which we assume that the tangential components of $\mathbf{E}^1$ and $\mathbf{E}^2$ on $S$ can be obtained. For the sake of convenience, these potentials are made to vanish at the reference terminal so that their values at each terminal represent the corresponding terminal voltages. Finally, if we assume that the displacement current through $S$ is negligible compared with the conduction current, Eq. 8.226 yields

$$V_2^1 I_2^2 = V_1^2 I_1^1 \tag{8.227}$$

and

$$Z_{12} = \frac{V_1^2}{I_2^2} = \frac{V_2^1}{I_1^1} = Z_{21} \tag{8.228}$$

If, on the other hand, the two electromagnetic fields are made to correspond to the short-circuit conditions

$$I_1 = I_1^1 \qquad I_2 = I_2^1 \qquad V_1 = V_1^1 \qquad V_2 = 0 \tag{8.229}$$

$$I_1 = I_1^2 \qquad I_2 = I_2^2 \qquad V_1 = 0 \qquad V_2 = V_2^2 \tag{8.330}$$

Equation 8.226 yields

$$Y_{12} = \frac{I_1^2}{V_2^2} = \frac{I_2^1}{V_1^1} = Y_{21} \tag{8.231}$$

This completes the proof of the reciprocity theorem for a network with two terminals in addition to a reference terminal. It is clear, on the other hand, that the same results apply to any two terminals of a multiterminal network; in fact, in determining the transfer impedance and the transfer admittance, all other terminals are either open-circuited or short-circuited to the reference terminal and, therefore, do not contribute to the surface integrals in Eq. 8.226.

Let us turn our attention next to the power input to the multiterminal network. We know from Sec. 7.6, that the complex power input can be expressed either in terms of the flux of Poynting's vector through the surface $S$ enclosing the network or in terms of the terminal voltages and currents: i.e.,

$$\mathrm{P} = -\frac{1}{2}\oint_S (\mathbf{E} \times \mathbf{H}^*)\cdot \boldsymbol{n}\, da = \frac{1}{2}\sum_{j=1}^{n} \mathrm{V}_j \mathrm{I}_j^* \qquad (8.232)$$

Furthermore, substituting for each $\mathrm{V}_j$ the corresponding expression given by Eq. 8.215 yields

$$\mathrm{P} = \frac{1}{2}\sum_{k=1}^{n}\sum_{j=1}^{n} \mathrm{Z}_{jk}\mathrm{I}_k\mathrm{I}_j^* \qquad (8.233)$$

On the other hand, the terminal voltages can be considered as the sums of the values obtained when the currents are fed to the network one at a time, with all the other terminals open-circuited. Thus, for instance,

$$\mathrm{V}_j = \sum_{k=1}^{n} \mathrm{V}_j^k = \sum_{k=1}^{n} \mathrm{Z}_{jk}\mathrm{I}_k \qquad (8.234)$$

where

$$\mathrm{V}_j^k = \mathrm{Z}_{jk}\mathrm{I}_k \qquad (8.235)$$

is the voltage produced at the $j$th terminal by the current $\mathrm{I}_k$ when all other terminal currents are equal to zero. The superscript indicates the one terminal at which the current differs from zero. Similarly, let $\mathbf{E}^k$ and $\mathbf{H}^k$ represent the fields produced by $\mathrm{I}_k$ when all the other currents are equal to zero. The total fields can then be expressed in the form

$$\mathbf{E} = \sum_{j=1}^{n} \mathbf{E}^j \qquad \mathbf{H} = \sum_{k=1}^{n} \mathbf{H}^k \qquad (8.236)$$

and the complex power input in the form

$$\mathrm{P} = -\frac{1}{2}\sum_{k=1}^{n}\sum_{j=1}^{n}\oint_S (\mathbf{E}^j \times \mathbf{H}^{k*})\cdot \boldsymbol{n}\, da \qquad (8.237)$$

Comparison of Eqs. 8.233 and 8.237 suggests equating the terms corresponding to the same values of $k$ and $j$. Actually we obtain by direct evaluation of the surface integrals in Eq. 8.237,

$$-\frac{1}{2}\oint_S (\mathbf{E}^j \times \mathbf{H}^{k*})\cdot \boldsymbol{n}\, da$$
$$= \frac{1}{2}\mathrm{V}_k{}^j\mathrm{I}_k{}^* = \frac{1}{2}\mathrm{Z}_{kj}\mathrm{I}_j\mathrm{I}_k{}^*$$
$$= \frac{1}{2}\int_V [\sigma\mathbf{E}^j\cdot\mathbf{E}^{k*} + j\omega(\mu\mathbf{H}^j\cdot\mathbf{H}^{k*} - \epsilon\mathbf{E}^j\cdot\mathbf{E}^{k*})]\, dv \quad (8.238)$$

and similarly,

$$-\frac{1}{2}\oint_S (\mathbf{E}^{k*} \times \mathbf{H}^j)\cdot \boldsymbol{n}\, da$$
$$= \frac{1}{2}\mathrm{V}_j^{k*}\mathrm{I}_j = \frac{1}{2}\mathrm{Z}_{jk}{}^*\mathrm{I}_k{}^*\mathrm{I}_j$$
$$= \frac{1}{2}\int_V [\sigma\mathbf{E}^{k*}\cdot\mathbf{E}^j + j\omega(\mu\mathbf{H}^{k*}\cdot\mathbf{H}^j - \epsilon\mathbf{E}^{k*}\cdot\mathbf{E}^j)]\, dv \quad (8.239)$$

Adding and subtracting these two equations yields, for the real and imaginary parts of $\mathrm{Z}_{jk} = \mathrm{Z}_{kj}$,

$$R_{jk} = \frac{1}{\mathrm{I}_j\mathrm{I}_k{}^*}\int_V \sigma\mathbf{E}^j\cdot\mathbf{E}^{k*}\, dv \quad (8.240)$$

$$X_{jk} = \frac{\omega}{\mathrm{I}_j\mathrm{I}_k{}^*}\int_V (\mu\mathbf{H}^j\cdot\mathbf{H}^{k*} - \epsilon\mathbf{E}^j\cdot\mathbf{E}^{k*})\, dv \quad (8.241)$$

These two expressions reduce to Eqs. 8.44 and 8.45 for $j = k$. In general, if $\mathrm{I}_j$ and $\mathrm{I}_k$ have the same phase, the integral in Eq. 8.240 is equal to twice the power dissipated as a result of the interaction of the electric field produced by $\mathrm{I}_j$ with the electric field produced by $\mathrm{I}_k$. Similarly, the integral in Eq. 8.241 is equal to four times the difference between the average magnetic energy stored and the average electric energy stored as a result of the interaction of the fields produced by $\mathrm{I}_j$ with the fields produced by $\mathrm{I}_k$. Thus all the impedances characterizing the terminal behavior of a linear, passive system can be related to energies stored and dissipated in the system.

Another important result can be obtained by evaluating in a similar manner, for constant $I_j$ and $I_k$, the surface integrals,

$$-\frac{1}{2}\oint_S \left(\mathbf{E}^j \times \frac{\partial \mathbf{H}^{k*}}{\partial\omega} + \frac{\partial \mathbf{E}^{k*}}{\partial\omega} \times \mathbf{H}^j\right) \cdot \boldsymbol{n}\, da = \frac{1}{2}\frac{dZ_{jk}{}^*}{d\omega} I_j I_k{}^*$$

$$= \int_V \left[\sigma \mathbf{E}^j \cdot \frac{\partial \mathbf{E}^{k*}}{\partial\omega} - j\frac{1}{2}(\epsilon \mathbf{E}^j\cdot\mathbf{E}^{k*} + \mu \mathbf{H}^j\cdot\mathbf{H}^{k*})\right] dv \quad (8.242)$$

$$-\frac{1}{2}\oint_S \left(\mathbf{E}^{k*} \times \frac{\partial \mathbf{H}^{j}}{\partial\omega} + \frac{\partial \mathbf{E}^{j}}{\partial\omega} \times \mathbf{H}^{k*}\right) \cdot \boldsymbol{n}\, da = \frac{1}{2}\frac{dZ_{jk}}{d\omega} I_j I_k{}^*$$

$$= \int_V \left[\sigma \mathbf{E}^{k*} \cdot \frac{\partial \mathbf{E}^{j}}{\partial\omega} + j\frac{1}{2}(\epsilon \mathbf{E}^j\cdot\mathbf{E}^{k*} + \mu \mathbf{H}^j\cdot\mathbf{H}^{k*})\right] dv \quad (8.243)$$

Adding and subtracting these two equations yields for the real and imaginary parts of $dZ_{jk}/d\omega$,

$$\frac{dR_{jk}}{d\omega} = \frac{1}{I_j I_k{}^*}\int_V \sigma \frac{d(\mathbf{E}^j\cdot\mathbf{E}^{k*})}{d\omega}\, dv \quad (8.244)$$

$$\frac{dX_{jk}}{d\omega} = \frac{1}{I_j I_k{}^*}\int_V \left[\sigma\left(\mathbf{E}^{k*}\cdot\frac{\partial \mathbf{E}^j}{\partial\omega} - \mathbf{E}^j\cdot\frac{\partial \mathbf{E}^{k*}}{\partial\omega}\right) + j(\epsilon \mathbf{E}^j\cdot\mathbf{E}^{k*} + \mu \mathbf{H}^j\cdot\mathbf{H}^{k*})\right] dv \quad (8.245)$$

This second equation is particularly useful in expressing the behavior of $Z_{jk}$ in the vicinity of a resonance, i.e., in the neighborhood of the frequency $\omega_0$ for which $X_{jk} = 0$. In fact, in the case of a sharp resonance, the first term of Eq. 8.245 turns out to be negligible compared with the second term. Thus, in the neighborhood of resonance,

$$Z_{jk} \simeq \frac{1}{I_j I_k{}^*}\int_V [\sigma \mathbf{E}^j\cdot\mathbf{E}^{k*} + j(\omega-\omega_0)(\epsilon \mathbf{E}^j\cdot\mathbf{E}^{k*} + \mu \mathbf{H}^j\cdot\mathbf{H}^{k*})]\, dv \quad (8.246)$$

In the particular case of $j = k$, this equation reduces to Eq. 8.54. In general, if $I_j$ and $I_k$ have the same phase, the real and imaginary parts of $Z_{jk}$ are seen to depend on the power dissipated, and on the total energy stored as a result of the interaction of the electromagnetic field produced by $I_j$ with that produced by $I_k$. Thus the expression for the $Q$ of a resonant system given by Eq. 8.56 can be generalized to apply to transfer impedances as well as to input impedances.

Results similar to those obtained above can be readily derived for the short-circuit admittances defined by Eq. 8.231. As a matter of fact, the pertinent equations can be obtained by simply substituting $G_{jk}$, $B_{jk}$, $\mathrm{Y}_{jk}$, $\mathrm{V}_k$, and $\mathrm{V}_j$ for $R_{jk}$, $X_{jk}$, $Z_{jk}$, $\mathrm{I}_k$, and $\mathrm{I}_j$ in Eqs. 8.240, 8.241, 8.244, 8.245, and 8.246.

## 8.10 Summary and Conclusions

The subject matter presented in this chapter can be grouped into three main topics: the complex form of Maxwell's equations and of Poynting's theorem; the relationship between impedances (or admittances) on the one hand, and power dissipation and energy storage on the other; the frequency behavior of representative circuit components.

The first topic is basic to the study of all electromagnetic fields in the sinusoidal steady state, whether they are associated with circuit components, transmission lines, or antennas. The second topic provides a bridge between circuit theory and field theory, which is of great importance in the study of the mutual interactions of electromagnetic devices over the entire frequency spectrum. The third topic, which was discussed primarily through illustrative examples, is a continuation of the study of quasi-static fields in Chapters 6 and 7.

Except for a brief discussion of the skin effect, we did not consider wave-propagation phenomena; they are treated in a companion book by the same authors [2]. However, the general properties of electromagnetic fields presented in this chapter are basic to the study of wave-propagation phenomena and of the related resonance phenomena. As a matter of fact, the importance and physical significance of some of them (e.g., the relation between the $Q$ of a resonance system and the power dissipated and the total energy stored) could not be properly illustrated by means of quasi-static fields.

In concluding this chapter, it is important to stress again that the character of the electromagnetic field associated with a particular device varies considerably with the frequency of excitation. The quasi-static components of the fields predominate at low frequencies, and their properties are responsible for the normal behavior of circuit components. Radically different properties may be exhibited by a device at higher frequencies as soon as the wave character of the electromagnetic field becomes apparent. We saw in connection with various illustrative examples that, roughly speaking, this occurs when the wave length corresponding to the frequency of excitation becomes comparable with the dimensions of the device in question. In particular, we saw that the wave length in a good conductor is much, much shorter than in an insulator with the same permeability and permittivity; thus the wave character of the field may become apparent in a good conductor at frequencies at which the quasi-static components still predominate in the surrounding insulating media. This is the reason why the skin effect may play a significant role in determining the low-frequency behavior of circuit components.

This chapter concludes our discussion of electromagnetic fields in stationary systems. The following two chapters are devoted to the study of electromagnetic fields in moving media and to the associated phenomenon of electromechanical energy conversion.

## 8.11 Selected References

1. E. A. Guillemin, *Introductory Circuit Theory*, John Wiley and Sons, New York, 1953. Secs. 6.1 to 6.4, 6.7 and the whole of Chapter 7 should be carefully reviewed. A general discussion of the relation between energy and impedance in a network is presented in Secs. 10.6 and 10.7.
2 R. B. Adler, L. J. Chu, R. M. Fano, *Electromagnetic Energy Transmission and Radiation*, John Wiley and Sons, New York, 1960.

## PROBLEMS

**Problem 8.1.** The two parallel perfectly conducting rectangular plates of Fig. 8.5 are short-circuited by a third perfectly conducting plate on the plane $z = 0$. A sinusoidal source is connected between the two plates at the opposite end from the short circuit as shown in the same figure. The field can be assumed to be one-dimensional. Using the surface current density in the short-circuiting plate as a reference, find:

(a) The zero-order and first-order electric and magnetic fields between the plates.
(b) The first-order complex power per unit width of the plates at the input terminals.
(c) The zero-order and first-order voltage and current density at the input terminals.
(d) The zero-order average energy stored and the equivalent inductance.
(e) The second-order electric field.
(f) The second-order electric and magnetic energy.
(g) Can you define a capacitance per unit length?
(h) Find the equivalent circuit for the system. Compare the elements in the equivalent circuit with the results of (d) and (g).

**Problem 8.2.** The short-circuiting plate of Prob. 8.1 is replaced by a thin resistive sheet of uniform surface conductivity $\sigma_s$. Using the surface-current density in the resistive sheet as a reference and neglecting fringing, find:

(a) The zero-order and first-order electric and magnetic fields.
(b) The zero-order average power dissipated in the resistive sheet per unit width.

(c) The zero-order average electric and magnetic energies stored, and the value of $\sigma_s$ for which they are equal.

(d) The zero-order and first-order complex power input per unit width. Relate this answer to the answers to (b) and (c).

(e) The equivalent circuit at the input terminals for the critical value of $\sigma_s$ found in (c).

(f) The equivalent circuit for values of $\sigma_s$ much smaller than the critical one.

(g) The equivalent circuit for values of $\sigma_s$ much greater than the critical one.

**Problem 8.3.** A perfectly conducting (lossless) coaxial cable is terminated at one end by a resistive sheet of uniform surface conductivity $\sigma_s$. A sinusoidal source is connected to the cable at the other end. Using the voltage across the resistive sheet as a reference and neglecting fringing, determine:

(a) The zero-order and the first-order electric and magnetic fields between the two concentric conductors.

(b) The zero-order average power dissipated in the resistive sheet.

(c) The zero-order average electric and magnetic energies stored in the cable and the value of $\sigma_s$ for which they are equal.

(d) The zero-order and the first-order complex power input to the cable. Relate this complex power to the answers to (b) and (c).

(e) The equivalent circuit at the input terminals for the critical value of $\sigma_s$ found in (c).

(f) The equivalent circuit for values of $\sigma_s$ much smaller than the critical one.

(g) The equivalent circuit for values of $\sigma_s$ much greater than the critical one.

(h) Can you find a single equivalent circuit for arbitrary values of $\sigma_s$?

**Problem 8.4.** A thin, circular disk of uniform surface conductivity is placed in a sinusoidal magnetic field whose zero-order component is perpendicular to the disk and uniform.

(a) Find the first-order current density in the disk.

(b) Find the power dissipated in the disk to second-order terms.

**Problem 8.5.** A uniform, linear, spherical conductor is located in a sinusoidal magnetic field whose zero-order component is uniform.

(a) Find the first-order electric field.

(b) Find the first-order current density.

(c) Find the average power dissipation in the sphere to second-order terms.

**Problem 8.6.** A thin, spherical shell of uniform resistive material is located in a sinusoidal magnetic field whose zero-order component is uniform.

(a) Find the first-order electric field.

(b) Find the power dissipated in the spherical shell to second-order terms.

**Problem 8.7.** Determine the quasi-static behavior of the shielded coaxial resistor illustrated in Fig. 8.7, by analogy with the analysis of the shielded resistive sheet carried out in Sec. 8.7. Use for the zero-order potential the solution of Laplace's equation

$$\phi = (B_1 + B_2 z) \ln \frac{a}{r}$$

where $B_1$, $B_2$ and $a$ are arbitrary constants.

**Problem 8.8.** Determine the a-c resistance per unit length of a copper wire at a frequency for which the skin depth is much smaller than the diameter of the wire.

**Problem 8.9.** A sinusoidal current is distributed with circular symmetry over the cross section of a circular cylindrical conductor. The frequency is such that the skin depth is much smaller than the diameter of the conductor. Determine:

(a) The electric field and the magnetic field in the conductor.

(b) Poynting's vector on the surface of the conductor and the power per unit length dissipated in the conductor.

**Problem 8.10.** A sinusoidal current is distributed with circular symmetry over the cross section of a circular cylindrical conductor. Determine:

(a) The zero-order and first-order fields and current density in the conductor.

(b) The zero-order and first-order components of Poynting's vector in the conductor.

(c) The zero-order and first-order power dissipation in the conductor.

# CHAPTER NINE

# Electromagnetic Fields in the Presence of Moving Matter

Chapters 9 and 10 are devoted to the electromagnetism of bodies in relative motion, and are intended to provide the theoretical foundations for the study of electromechanical energy conversion. In this chapter the generalization of Maxwell's equations to moving bodies is discussed, and in the following chapter a generalized form of Poynting's theorem will be developed which relates the electromagnetic power flow to the power dissipated, the time rate of change of the energy stored, and the power converted into mechanical form.

The theoretical foundations of the electrodynamics of moving bodies lie in the special theory of relativity, formulated by Einstein in 1905. Minkowski, in 1908, applied Einstein's theory to the problem of moving macroscopic bodies; his work, however, was terminated shortly thereafter by his untimely death, and thus failed to provide a completely satisfactory theory. In spite of later work by various authors, much confusion still exists in the literature, and a number of important questions have not yet been resolved in a generally accepted manner.

We shall present here a formulation of the electrodynamics of moving macroscopic bodies, developed very recently by one of the authors (L. J. Chu), which has the merit of being free from inconsistencies present in previous formulations.[1] This formulation is an extension of the macroscopic theory of electromagnetism in material bodies presented in Chapter 5. In that theory a clear separation was made between the role played by polarized and magnetized bodies as sources

[1] For a discussion of other formulations, see [1, 2]. Various, four-dimensional formulations are compared in detail in Appendix 1.

of electromagnetic fields, and the action exerted by the fields in the polarization and magnetization of material bodies. The importance of this separation will become even more evident below in connection with moving material bodies.

The theory will be developed along the following lines. We shall discuss first moving matter, either polarized or magnetized, in its role as a field source. We shall deal with electrically polarized bodies as in Sec. 5.2, by substituting for them appropriate charge and current distributions. The polarization-charge distribution will be found to depend only on the state of polarization of the bodies, whereas the polarization-current distribution will be found to depend on the motion of the bodies as well as on the time rate of change of the state of polarization. Magnetized bodies will be treated in an analogous manner by substituting for them appropriate distributions of magnetic charge and of magnetic current.

After discussing the role played by moving matter as a field source, we shall turn our attention to the problem of determining the state of conduction, polarization, and magnetization of moving matter, on the assumption that its rest properties, namely, its constituent relations, are known. To solve this problem, we will need to determine the *effective fields* acting on moving matter. These fields will be obtained from the Lorentz forces discussed in Sec. 7.1.

The next topic in this chapter will be a method of successive approximations for solving Maxwell's equations and the associated constituent relations in the presence of moving bodies. This method is a generalization of the power-series method developed in Chapter 6. It reduces the solution of any field problem involving matter moving at low velocities to the determination of a series of static fields in the presence of stationary matter. This technique will be used to develop illustrative examples of interaction of fields with moving matter. The same examples will be used in the next chapter to illustrate the process of electromechanical energy conversion. An outline of this second part of the theory will be given in the introduction to the next chapter.

A few final remarks are in order, in view of the significant departures made in the theory presented here from the postulates on which previous theories are based. We must stress again that these departures, some of which will appear only in the next chapter, permit us to preserve both internal consistency and agreement with well-established experimental evidence. In other theories, agreement with experimental evidence is preserved at the cost of internal consistency. Actually, the area of agreement with previous theories is surprisingly large. It is mainly in the case of deformable bodies and when large velocities are involved that significant disagreements appear. Unfortunately, the available experimental evidence is inconclusive in this area, and critical experiments will have to be performed to resolve these disagreements.

It is important to reiterate that the theory presented here is macroscopic, in the sense that it disregards the fine structure of matter and the corresponding fine structure of the fields within matter. For this reason, it yields, at best, approximate results, and it cannot be expected to account for all macroscopically observable phenomena. It would be very desirable, of course, to justify the models used in the theory for polarized and magnetized materials on the basis of their atomic structures, but this does not seem to be possible at present; the gap between microscopic and macroscopic theory is still too wide.

Only the three-dimensional formulation of the theory developed by L. J. Chu is presented in the text. The four-dimensional, relativistic formulation is beyond the scope of our discussion because of the additional mathematical tools it requires. However, for the sake of completeness, it is presented in Appendix 1.

## 9.1 Interaction of Fields and Moving Matter

The interaction of electromagnetic fields with moving matter can be divided in two parts: the action of the electromagnetic field in changing the state of matter, and the reaction of the induced state on the electromagnetic field. For instance, a dielectric material becomes polarized when subjected to the action of an electric field; the resulting polarization generates, in turn, an additional electric field. In the case of a conducting material, free charges are set in motion by the electric field, and the resulting current generates a magnetic field. The separation of these two aspects of the interaction of fields and matter has already proved useful in our study of the electromagnetism of bodies at rest. It becomes of critical importance, however, in connection with moving bodies, because the field generated, for instance, by the polarization of a dielectric body, depends on the motion of the body as well as on its polarization state. Conversely, the state of a moving body, such as its polarization, will be seen to depend on its velocity as well as on the electromagnetic field observed in the frame of reference with respect to which the body's velocity is measured.

We shall turn our attention first to the second part of the problem, namely, to the determination of the fields produced by a moving body in a given state, i.e., for instance, to the fields produced by a dielectric body with a given polarization. For the purposes of our macroscopic theory, the electromagnetic state of a body can be assumed to be completely described by the following four quantities:

1. The distribution of free charges, represented by the volume density $\rho_f$ and the surface density $\sigma_f$.
2. The free-current distribution, represented by the volume density $\boldsymbol{J}_f$ and by the surface density $\boldsymbol{K}_f$.
3. The electric polarization, represented by the dipole-moment density $\boldsymbol{P}$.
4. The magnetization, represented by the magnetic-dipole-moment density $\boldsymbol{M}$.

To these quantities, specifying the electromagnetic state of a body, we must add the velocity $\boldsymbol{v}$, a function of position, specifying its state of motion. Our objective is to study how these five quantities contribute to the generation of electromagnetic fields; i.e., our goal is to determine the roles played by these quantities in Maxwell's equations. We shall approach this problem, in the case of moving bodies, from the same point of view that proved helpful in the simpler case of bodies at rest; namely, we shall substitute for all material bodies appropriate distributions of charges and currents which we shall then insert in the free-space Maxwell's equations. Thus the electromagnetic field in material bodies will again be treated macroscopically as a free-space electromagnetic field in the presence of distributed sources.

Maxwell's equations in free space can be written, for our purposes, in the form

$$\operatorname{curl} \boldsymbol{H} - \epsilon_0 \frac{\partial \boldsymbol{E}}{\partial t} = \boldsymbol{J} \tag{9.1}$$

$$\operatorname{curl} \boldsymbol{E} + \mu_0 \frac{\partial \boldsymbol{H}}{\partial t} = -\boldsymbol{J}^* \tag{9.2}$$

$$\epsilon_0 \operatorname{div} \boldsymbol{E} = \rho \tag{9.3}$$

$$\mu_0 \operatorname{div} \boldsymbol{H} = \rho^* \tag{9.4}$$

The current density $\boldsymbol{J}$ and the charge density $\rho$ ($\boldsymbol{K}$ and $\sigma$ in the limiting case of surface distributions) represent the sum total of all electric-current distributions and of all electric-charge distributions, resulting from bound charges as well as from free charges. The magnetic-current density $\boldsymbol{J}^*$ and the magnetic-charge density $\rho^*$ are included in order to take into account the presence of magnetized matter. The electric-current and charge densities and their magnetic counterparts must satisfy the usual conservation equations, which are repeated below for convenience of reference,

$$\operatorname{div} \boldsymbol{J} = -\frac{\partial \rho}{\partial t} \tag{9.5}$$

$$\operatorname{div} \boldsymbol{J}^* = -\frac{\partial \rho^*}{\partial t} \tag{9.6}$$

We are now in a position to state our first objective more precisely. We wish to express the current and charge densities, $\boldsymbol{J}$, $\boldsymbol{J}^*$, $\rho$, $\rho^*$ in terms of the four quantities describing the electromagnetic state of matter and of the velocity field describing its state of motion. It is clear, first of all, that the free current $\boldsymbol{J}_f$ is directly a part of the total electric current $\boldsymbol{J}$, and that the free charge $\rho_f$ is directly a part of $\rho$. Furthermore, the motion of the net free charge represented by $\rho_f$ constitutes a convection current $\rho_f \boldsymbol{v}$ which must be considered as a component of $\boldsymbol{J}_f$. All other currents and charges, both electric and magnetic, arise from polarization and magnetization of matter. They are evaluated in the next two sections.

## 9.2 Polarization Currents and Charges

The contributions resulting from electric polarization are best evaluated with the help of the same model used in Sec. 5.2. More precisely, we regard a dielectric material, in the neutral state, as consisting of two uniform charge distributions with the same density $\rho_0$ and opposite polarities, superimposed on each other. The common density $\rho_0$ is proportional to the mass density of the material, so that $\rho_0$ may vary from point to point when the material is stretched or compressed. In the unpolarized state, the two charge distributions of opposite polarities neutralize each other. The state of polarization, on the other hand, may be visualized as resulting from a displacement $\boldsymbol{d}$ of the positive charge contained in each volume element with respect to the negative charge contained in the same volume element.[1] Thus, each volume element $dv$ forms a dipole of moment $\rho_0 \boldsymbol{d}\, dv$, and the resulting dipole-moment density is given by

$$\boldsymbol{P} = \rho_0 \boldsymbol{d} \tag{9.7}$$

It should be understood that the displacement represented by the vector $\boldsymbol{d}$ is extremely small and that, strictly speaking, $\boldsymbol{P}$ is defined in

[1] Of course, a model in which the negative charge is assumed to move with respect to the positive charge would be equivalent for our purposes.

the limit when $\rho_0$ approaches infinity and $\boldsymbol{d}$ approaches zero while their product remains constant.

The procedure for determining the polarization-charge density is the same as that used in Sec. 5.2, and yields also the same result, namely

$$\rho_p = -\operatorname{div} \boldsymbol{P} \tag{9.8}$$

In fact, regardless of the motion of the polarized material, the net charge in any volume $V$ must be equal in magnitude and opposite in sign to the net amount of charge that moved out of $V$ as a result of the displacement $\boldsymbol{d}$, i.e., to the net amount of charge that has crossed the surface $S$ enclosing $V$ in the outward direction. Thus, we have for the net charge in a volume $V$

$$Q_p = -\oint_S \rho_0 \boldsymbol{d} \cdot \boldsymbol{n}\, da = -\oint_S \boldsymbol{P} \cdot \boldsymbol{n}\, da \tag{9.9}$$

where $\boldsymbol{n}$ is a unit vector normal to $S$ and outwardly directed. Dividing $Q_p$ by the volume $V$ yields, in the limit when $V$ approaches zero,

$$\rho_p = \lim_{V \to 0} \frac{Q_p}{V} = -\operatorname{div} \boldsymbol{P} \tag{9.10}$$

The evaluation of the polarization current is considerably more involved than in the case of stationary bodies because of the presence of two superimposed velocities, namely, $\boldsymbol{v}$ and the time rate of change of $\boldsymbol{d}$. We shall evaluate it as the sum of the currents resulting from the motions of the two superimposed charge distributions. We observe first that the density of the negative charge distribution is equal to $-\rho_0$, because, by assumption, only the positive charge is displaced when the material is polarized. The velocity of this charge distribution is, according to the assumed model, equal to the velocity $\boldsymbol{v}$ of the material. It follows that at any point $A$, the negative charge gives rise to a current density

$$\boldsymbol{J}_{p-} = -\rho_0 \boldsymbol{v} \tag{9.11}$$

where $\rho_0$ and $\boldsymbol{v}$ are, of course, evaluated at the point $A$.

The density of the positive charge distribution at the same point $A$ is not, in general, equal to $\rho_0$ because of the displacement $\boldsymbol{d}$. As a matter of fact, since we have already found that the net charge density is given by Eq. 9.10, the density of the positive charge alone must be

$$\rho_{0+} = \rho_0 - \operatorname{div} \boldsymbol{P} \tag{9.12}$$

The velocity of the positive charge consists of two components; a component resulting from the motion of the material which, by assumption, is the motion of the negative charge, and a component resulting from the time rate of change of the displacement $\boldsymbol{d}$ of the positive charge with respect to the negative charge. The first component is not simply equal to $\boldsymbol{v}$ because the positive charge located at the point $A$ does not move with the velocity of the material at the point $A$, but rather with the velocity of the material at the point $B$ from which it has been displaced, whose position relative to $A$ is given by the vector $-\boldsymbol{d}$. On the other hand, the velocity of the material at the point $B$ can be determined by adding to $\boldsymbol{v}$ (at the point $A$) an appropriate increment $\delta\boldsymbol{v}$ proportional to $-\boldsymbol{d}$. We have for the $x$ component of this increment

$$\delta v_x = -(\boldsymbol{d}\cdot\text{grad } v_x) \tag{9.13}$$

where terms of second and higher order in $\boldsymbol{d}$ have been disregarded because, in the model assumed, $\boldsymbol{d}$ is intended to vanish while $\rho_0$ approaches infinity. In fact, the component of grad $v_x$ in the direction of $\boldsymbol{d}$ is, by definition, the derivative of $v_x$ in the direction of $\boldsymbol{d}$. The other components of $\delta\boldsymbol{v}$ are computed in a similar manner, with the result that

$$\delta\boldsymbol{v} = -(\boldsymbol{d}\cdot\nabla)\boldsymbol{v} \tag{9.14}$$

where use is made of the differential operator

$$\boldsymbol{d}\cdot\nabla = d_x\frac{\partial}{\partial x} + d_y\frac{\partial}{\partial y} + d_z\frac{\partial}{\partial z}$$

This operator when applied to the $x$ component of $\boldsymbol{v}$ yields the term in parentheses in Eq. 9.13.

The second component of the velocity of the positive charge is the time rate of change of the displacement vector $\boldsymbol{d}$, evaluated at the point $A$ which moves with the material. In other words, this second component is $d\boldsymbol{d}/dt$, the *total* (rather than the partial) time derivative of $\boldsymbol{d}$. Thus, the velocity of the positive charge at the point $A$ is given by

$$\boldsymbol{v}_+ = \boldsymbol{v} + \delta\boldsymbol{v} + \frac{d\boldsymbol{d}}{dt} = \boldsymbol{v} + \frac{d\boldsymbol{d}}{dt} - (\boldsymbol{d}\cdot\nabla)\boldsymbol{v} \tag{9.15}$$

and the corresponding current density by

$$\begin{aligned}\boldsymbol{J}_{p+} &= (\rho_0 - \text{div } \boldsymbol{P})\left[\boldsymbol{v} + \frac{d\boldsymbol{d}}{dt} - (\boldsymbol{d}\cdot\nabla)\boldsymbol{v}\right]\\ &= \rho_0\boldsymbol{v} + \rho_0\left[\frac{d\boldsymbol{d}}{dt} - (\boldsymbol{d}\cdot\nabla)\boldsymbol{v}\right] - \boldsymbol{v}\text{ div } \boldsymbol{P} - \left[\frac{d\boldsymbol{d}}{dt} - (\boldsymbol{d}\cdot\nabla)\boldsymbol{v}\right]\text{div } \boldsymbol{P}\end{aligned} \tag{9.16}$$

The last term on the right-hand side of Eq. 9.16 can be disregarded because it is proportional to $\rho_0|\boldsymbol{d}|^2$ while the second and third terms are proportional to $\rho_0|\boldsymbol{d}|$. It must be remembered, in this regard, that $\boldsymbol{d}$ is assumed to be vanishingly small and $\rho_0$ infinitely large, whereas their product, which is equal to $\boldsymbol{P}$, has a finite magnitude. Finally, adding the current densities associated with positive and negative charges yields

$$\boldsymbol{J}_p = \boldsymbol{J}_{p+} + \boldsymbol{J}_{p-} = \rho_0\left[\frac{d\boldsymbol{d}}{dt} - (\boldsymbol{d}\cdot\nabla)\boldsymbol{v}\right] - \boldsymbol{v}\operatorname{div}\boldsymbol{P} \tag{9.17}$$

We shall see below that the form of the right-hand side of Eq. 9.17 is the one that lends itself most readily to physical interpretation. However, it is desirable for other purposes to derive an expression for the polarization-current density involving $\boldsymbol{P}$ and $\boldsymbol{v}$ only. Such an expression can be readily obtained by transforming the first term on the right-hand side of Eq. 9.17 as follows:

$$\rho_0\frac{d\boldsymbol{d}}{dt} - \rho_0(\boldsymbol{d}\cdot\nabla)\boldsymbol{v} = \frac{d\boldsymbol{P}}{dt} - \boldsymbol{d}\frac{d\rho_0}{dt} - (\boldsymbol{P}\cdot\nabla)\boldsymbol{v} \tag{9.18}$$

On the other hand

$$\frac{d\rho_0}{dt} = \frac{\partial\rho_0}{\partial t} + \boldsymbol{v}\cdot\operatorname{grad}\rho_0 \tag{9.19}$$

and, because of the law of conservation of charge,

$$\operatorname{div}(\rho_0\boldsymbol{v}) = \rho_0\operatorname{div}\boldsymbol{v} + \boldsymbol{v}\cdot\operatorname{grad}\rho_0 = -\frac{\partial\rho_0}{\partial t} \tag{9.20}$$

It follows that

$$\boldsymbol{d}\frac{d\rho_0}{dt} = -\rho_0\boldsymbol{d}\operatorname{div}\boldsymbol{v} = -\boldsymbol{P}\operatorname{div}\boldsymbol{v} \tag{9.21}$$

Substitution of this result in Eq. 9.18, and of Eq. 9.18 in Eq. 9.17, yields

$$\boldsymbol{J}_p = \frac{d\boldsymbol{P}}{dt} + \boldsymbol{P}\operatorname{div}\boldsymbol{v} - (\boldsymbol{P}\cdot\nabla)\boldsymbol{v} - \boldsymbol{v}\operatorname{div}\boldsymbol{P} \tag{9.22}$$

The right-hand side of Eq. 9.22 meets the requirement of being a function of only $\boldsymbol{P}$, $\boldsymbol{v}$, and their time and space derivatives. However, it can be further simplified as follows. The total time derivative of $\boldsymbol{P}$ can be expressed in terms of the partial derivative,

$$\frac{d\boldsymbol{P}}{dt} = \frac{\partial\boldsymbol{P}}{\partial t} + \frac{\partial\boldsymbol{P}}{\partial x}\frac{dx}{dt} + \frac{\partial\boldsymbol{P}}{\partial y}\frac{dy}{dt} + \frac{\partial\boldsymbol{P}}{\partial z}\frac{dz}{dt} = \frac{\partial\boldsymbol{P}}{\partial t} + (\boldsymbol{v}\cdot\nabla)\boldsymbol{P} \tag{9.23}$$

so that Eq. 9.22 becomes

$$\boldsymbol{J}_p = \frac{\partial \boldsymbol{P}}{\partial t} + \boldsymbol{P} \operatorname{div} \boldsymbol{v} - (\boldsymbol{P}\cdot\nabla)\boldsymbol{v} - \boldsymbol{v} \operatorname{div} \boldsymbol{P} + (\boldsymbol{v}\cdot\nabla)\boldsymbol{P} \qquad (9.24)$$

Finally, we obtain with the help of Eq. A4.18 of App. 4,

$$\boldsymbol{J}_p = \frac{\partial \boldsymbol{P}}{\partial t} + \operatorname{curl} (\boldsymbol{P} \times \boldsymbol{v}) \qquad (9.25)$$

This is the most concise expression for the polarization-current density.

Let us turn our attention next to the physical interpretation of the polarization-current density on the basis of the right-hand side of Eq. 9.17. There appear to be two different components of polarization current. The component corresponding to the last term in Eq. 9.17 is the one most readily identified: it is the convection current resulting from the motion of the polarization charge whose density is given by Eq. 9.10. The other component is proportional to $\rho_0$ and to the vector quantity

$$\left(\frac{d\boldsymbol{d}}{dt}\right)_m = \frac{d\boldsymbol{d}}{dt} - (\boldsymbol{d}\cdot\nabla)\boldsymbol{v} \qquad (9.26)$$

to which we shall refer as the *material time derivative* of the displacement vector $\boldsymbol{d}$.

To understand the physical significance of this material derivative, we must discuss further the relative motion of the charges located initially at the points $A$ and $B$, shown in Fig. 9.1. The positive charge located at $A$ is associated with the negative charge located at $B$; their distance is given at all times by the displacement vector $\boldsymbol{d}$. According to our model of polarization, these two charges move with the same velocity (that corresponding to the point $B$) when $\boldsymbol{d}$ is held constant. The negative charge located at $A$ moves with the velocity correspond-

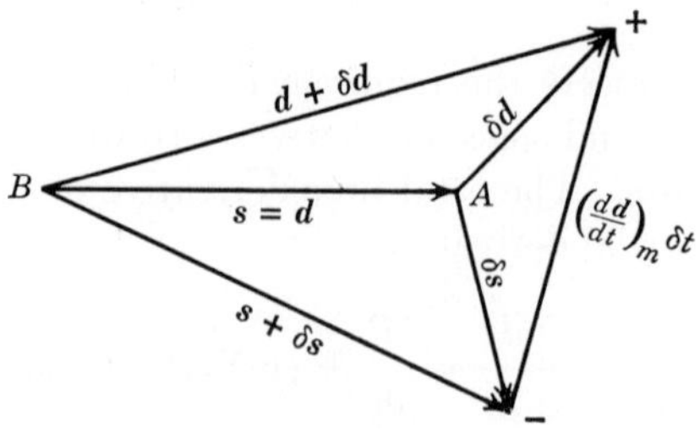


**Fig. 9.1.** Displacement diagram for the charges located initially at the point $A$.

ing to $A$. Let us indicate with $\boldsymbol{s}$ the distance of the negative charge initially located at $A$ from the negative charge initially located at $B$; thus, initially, $\boldsymbol{s} = \boldsymbol{d}$.

We saw that the velocity of the negative charge located at $B$ with respect to the negative charge located at $A$ is the velocity increment $\delta\boldsymbol{v}$ given by Eq. 9.14. Thus, the increment $\delta\boldsymbol{s}$ of the distance $\boldsymbol{s}$ in a time interval $\delta t$ is given by

$$\delta\boldsymbol{s} = \frac{d\boldsymbol{s}}{dt}\,\delta t = -\delta\boldsymbol{v}\,\delta t = (\boldsymbol{d}\cdot\nabla)\boldsymbol{v}\,\delta t \tag{9.27}$$

This increment is shown in Fig. 9.1 as the relative displacement of the negative charge located at $A$; the position of the negative charge initially located at $B$ is held fixed in the figure as the reference point for the displacement diagram.

The increment $\delta\boldsymbol{d}$ of the displacement $\boldsymbol{d}$ of the positive charge located initially at $A$ and associated with the negative charge at $B$ is given by

$$\delta\boldsymbol{d} = \frac{d\boldsymbol{d}}{dt}\,\delta t \tag{9.28}$$

This increment is shown in Fig. 9.1 as the relative displacement of the positive charge located initially at $A$. Thus, the displacement between the positive and negative charges located initially at $A$ is given by

$$\delta\boldsymbol{d} - \delta\boldsymbol{s} = \left[\frac{d(\boldsymbol{d} - \boldsymbol{s})}{dt}\right]_{\boldsymbol{s}=\boldsymbol{d}} \delta t = \left[\frac{d\boldsymbol{d}}{dt} - (\boldsymbol{d}\cdot\nabla)\boldsymbol{v}\right]\delta t = \left(\frac{d\boldsymbol{d}}{dt}\right)_m \delta t \tag{9.29}$$

The distance $\boldsymbol{s}$ is the distance between two negative charge elements, and, therefore, according to our model of polarization, is the distance between two points moving with the material. It follows that the increment $\delta\boldsymbol{d} - \delta\boldsymbol{s}$ for $\boldsymbol{s}$ initially equal to $\boldsymbol{d}$ represents the increment of the displacement $\boldsymbol{d}$ relative to the material, that is measured with respect to the distance $\boldsymbol{s}$ between two points moving with the material. In other words, the increment that appears in the material derivative is the excess of the increment of $\boldsymbol{d}$ over the part of the increment that can be attributed to the motion (including deformation) of the material.

Let us illustrate this interpretation of the material derivative in two special cases. Let us consider first a rigid body with an arbitrary polarization $\boldsymbol{P}$. Since the body is rigid, the magnitude of the vector $\boldsymbol{s}$

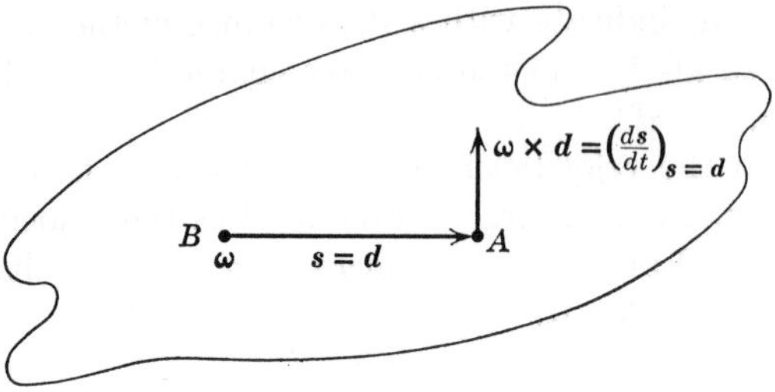


**Fig. 9.2.** The relative velocity of the negative charge at $A$ with respect to that at $B$. The vector $\boldsymbol{\omega}$ is normal to the figure.

is independent of time while its direction rotates with the body. Thus

$$\left(\frac{d\boldsymbol{s}}{dt}\right)_{\boldsymbol{s}=\boldsymbol{d}} = \boldsymbol{\omega} \times \boldsymbol{d} \tag{9.30}$$

and

$$\left(\frac{d\boldsymbol{d}}{dt}\right)_m = \frac{d\boldsymbol{d}}{dt} - \boldsymbol{\omega} \times \boldsymbol{d} \tag{9.31}$$

where $\boldsymbol{\omega}$ is a vector whose magnitude is equal to the angular velocity and whose direction is parallel to the axis of rotation, as illustrated in Fig. 9.2.

The total derivative $d\boldsymbol{d}/dt$ as well as $d\boldsymbol{s}/dt$ are evaluated at a point moving with the body, but with respect to a stationary system of coordinates. If the magnitude of $\boldsymbol{d}$ were independent of time and its direction were rotating with the body, $\boldsymbol{d}$ would coincide with $\boldsymbol{s}$ at all times and the material derivative of $\boldsymbol{d}$ would be equal to zero. It follows that, in the case of a rigid body, the material derivative given by Eq. 9.31 represents the time rate of change of the displacement $\boldsymbol{d}$ evaluated with respect to a system of coordinates rotating with the body. Finally, since $\rho_0$ is independent of time in a rigid body, the total polarization-current density arising from the motion of a rigid body is given by

$$\boldsymbol{J}_p = \left(\frac{d\boldsymbol{P}}{dt}\right)_m - \boldsymbol{v} \operatorname{div} \boldsymbol{P} \tag{9.32}$$

where the material time derivative of $\boldsymbol{P}$ represents the time rate of change of $\boldsymbol{P}$ evaluated by a stationary observer with respect to a system of coordinates moving rigidly with the body.

Let us consider next the case of an elastic body which is being uniformly stretched in the direction of polarization. Let the direction of polarization coincide with that of the $z$-axis, so that

$$\boldsymbol{P} = \boldsymbol{i}_z P_z \tag{9.33}$$

Uniform stretching in the $z$ direction implies that, for any vector $\boldsymbol{s}$ representing the distance between two points,

$$\frac{d\boldsymbol{s}}{dt} = \boldsymbol{i}_z \alpha s_z \tag{9.34}$$

where $\alpha$ is a function of time only. Because of the stretching, the density of the material and, therefore, $\rho_0$ vary with time. We have for the time rate of change of $\rho_0$

$$\frac{d\rho_0}{dt} = -\alpha\rho_0 \tag{9.35}$$

so that

$$\rho_0 \frac{d\boldsymbol{d}}{dt} = \frac{d\boldsymbol{P}}{dt} - \boldsymbol{d}\frac{d\rho_0}{dt} = \frac{d\boldsymbol{P}}{dt} + \alpha\boldsymbol{P} \tag{9.36}$$

It follows that the component of the polarization-current density proportional to the material derivative of $\boldsymbol{d}$ is given by

$$\begin{aligned} \boldsymbol{J}_p + \boldsymbol{v} \operatorname{div} \boldsymbol{P} &= \rho_0 \left(\frac{d\boldsymbol{d}}{dt} - \frac{d\boldsymbol{s}}{dt}\right)_{\boldsymbol{s}=\boldsymbol{d}} \\ &= \frac{d\boldsymbol{P}}{dt} + \alpha\boldsymbol{P} - \boldsymbol{i}_z\rho_0\alpha d_z = \frac{d\boldsymbol{P}}{dt} \end{aligned} \tag{9.37}$$

In words, this component of the polarization-current density is just equal to the total time derivative of $\boldsymbol{P}$. If $\boldsymbol{P}$ were independent of time, the decrease of $\rho_0$ would be exactly compensated by an increase of $\boldsymbol{d}$ equal to the amount by which the distance $\boldsymbol{s} = \boldsymbol{d}$ is stretched in the material, with the result that the material derivative of $\boldsymbol{d}$ would be equal to zero.

## 9.3 Magnetization Currents and Charges

We saw in Secs. 5.3 and 5.4 that the magnetization associated with ferromagnetism, ferrimagnetism, and paramagnetism results from the preferential orientation of microscopic magnetic dipoles, and that it can be represented macroscopically by means of distributions of magnetic charges and magnetic currents. A perfect analogy was established between magnetic charges and magnetic currents resulting from magnetization, on the one hand, and electric charges and electric currents resulting from polarization, on the other hand. Similarly, in the study of moving magnetized bodies, the resulting magnetic-charge density and magnetic-current density can be obtained by a procedure exactly analogous to that followed in Sec. 9.2. As a matter of fact, the results obtained for moving polarized bodies can be translated into the corresponding results for moving magnetized bodies by substituting $\rho_m{}^*$, $\boldsymbol{J}_m{}^*$ and $\mu_0 \boldsymbol{M}$ for $\rho_p$, $\boldsymbol{J}_p$, and $\boldsymbol{P}$ (note the comments in Sec. 5.3 concerning the factor $\mu_0$ which appears because of established, although arbitrary, conventions on the unit of magnetization). Thus, if $\boldsymbol{v}$ is the velocity field describing the motion of magnetized matter, we have from Eqs. 9.10, 9.24 and 9.25 for the magnetic-charge density

$$\rho_m{}^* = -\operatorname{div} \mu_0 \boldsymbol{M} \tag{9.38}$$

and for the magnetic-current density

$$\begin{aligned} \boldsymbol{J}_m{}^* &= \frac{\partial}{\partial t}(\mu_0 \boldsymbol{M}) + \operatorname{curl}(\mu_0 \boldsymbol{M} \times \boldsymbol{v}) \\ &= \mu_0 \left[ \frac{\partial \boldsymbol{M}}{\partial t} + (\boldsymbol{v} \cdot \nabla)\boldsymbol{M} + \boldsymbol{M} \operatorname{div} \boldsymbol{v} - (\boldsymbol{M} \cdot \nabla)\boldsymbol{v} - \boldsymbol{v} \operatorname{div} \boldsymbol{M} \right] \end{aligned} \tag{9.39}$$

The interpretation of the various terms on the right-hand side of this equation is entirely analogous to the interpretation given in Sec. 9.2 for the corresponding terms in Eq. 9.17. Similarly, by analogy with Eq. 9.32, the magnetic-current density becomes, in the case of a rigid body

$$\boldsymbol{J}_m{}^* = \mu_0 \left[ \left( \frac{d\boldsymbol{M}}{dt} \right)_m - \boldsymbol{v} \operatorname{div} \boldsymbol{M} \right] \tag{9.40}$$

where the time derivative of $\boldsymbol{M}$ is a material derivative evaluated by a stationary observer with respect to a system of coordinates moving rigidly with the body, as discussed in Sec. 9.2.

## 9.4 Macroscopic Maxwell Equations in Moving Matter

The results of Secs. 9.2 and 9.3 allow us to represent the presence of moving polarized and magnetized matter in terms of the source distributions that appear on the right-hand side of Maxwell's equations.

Substitution of Eqs. 9.10, 9.25, 9.38, and 9.39 in Eqs. 9.1 to 9.4 yields

$$\operatorname{curl} \boldsymbol{H} - \epsilon_0 \frac{\partial \boldsymbol{E}}{\partial t} = \boldsymbol{J}_f + \frac{\partial \boldsymbol{P}}{\partial t} + \operatorname{curl} (\boldsymbol{P} \times \boldsymbol{v}) \tag{9.41}$$

$$\operatorname{curl} \boldsymbol{E} + \mu_0 \frac{\partial \boldsymbol{H}}{\partial t} = - \frac{\partial}{\partial t} (\mu_0 \boldsymbol{M}) - \operatorname{curl} (\mu_0 \boldsymbol{M} \times \boldsymbol{v}) \tag{9.42}$$

$$\operatorname{div} \epsilon_0 \boldsymbol{E} = \rho_f - \operatorname{div} \boldsymbol{P} \tag{9.43}$$

$$\operatorname{div} \mu_0 \boldsymbol{H} = - \operatorname{div} \mu_0 \boldsymbol{M} \tag{9.44}$$

where $\rho_f$ and $\boldsymbol{J}_f$ are the free-charge density and the free-current density. The free-convection-current density $\rho_f \boldsymbol{v}$ resulting from the motion of free charges is included in $\boldsymbol{J}_f$.

These equations relate the electromagnetic field to the quantities representing the state of matter and to the velocity field representing its motion. We shall discuss in the next section the action of the electromagnetic field in changing the state of moving matter.

## 9.5 The Constituent Relations for Moving Matter

We turn now our attention to the problem of determining the conduction current, the polarization, and the magnetization in a moving body. We assume in this connection that we know, for each material involved, how these three quantities depend on the electromagnetic field in which the material is immersed, when the material is at rest. That is, we assume that we know the constituent relations in the absence of motion. These depend, of course, on the particular material in question and on its physical state, including temperature, pressure, strain, etc. Our implicit assumption that the physical state of the material is known does not imply that it is independent of the electromagnetic field, but only that we regard its determination as a separate problem which lies outside the scope of our discussion. The same is true for the motion of the material, which depends, among other factors, on the forces exerted on it by the electromagnetic field.

We saw in Chapter 5 that, when a stationary material body is immersed in an electromagnetic field, the resulting conduction-current density, polarization, and magnetization are functions of the forces exerted by the electromagnetic field on the atomic particles constituting matter. These forces do not appear directly in the macroscopic constituent relations but only indirectly through the macroscopic electric field and the macroscopic magnetic field. This amounts, in effect, to expressing the conduction-current density $\boldsymbol{J}_c$, $\boldsymbol{P}$, and $\boldsymbol{M}$ in terms of the forces that would be exerted by the macroscopic fields on unit electric charges and unit magnetic charges at rest in each grain of matter. In fact, if we indicate with $\boldsymbol{F}$ the force exerted on a point charge $q$, we have for a stationary charge

$$\boldsymbol{F} = q\boldsymbol{E} \tag{9.45}$$

Similarly, if we indicate with $\boldsymbol{F}^*$ the force exerted on a magnetic point charge $q^*$, we have for a stationary magnetic charge

$$\boldsymbol{F}^* = q^*\boldsymbol{H} \tag{9.46}$$

The reader is reminded that $\boldsymbol{F}^*$ enters our discussion because in our macroscopic representation of magnetized materials we chose to treat magnetic dipoles as neutral aggregates of magnetic charges.

Now, if the body in question is moving, the force that would be exerted by the macroscopic fields on a point charge $q$ moving with a grain of matter is no longer given by Eq. 9.45, but it is equal to the Lorentz force

$$\boldsymbol{F} = q(\boldsymbol{E} + \boldsymbol{v} \times \mu_0\boldsymbol{H}) \tag{9.47}$$

where $\boldsymbol{v}$ is the velocity of the grain. Clearly, Eq. 9.47 reduces to Eq. 9.45 when the velocity of the grain is equal to zero. Thus, the vector quantity that plays with respect to a moving body the same role played by $\boldsymbol{E}$ with respect to a stationary body is the force per unit charge.

$$\boldsymbol{E}_{\text{eff}} = \boldsymbol{E} + \boldsymbol{v} \times \mu_0\boldsymbol{H} \tag{9.48}$$

We shall refer to $\boldsymbol{E}_{\text{eff}}$ as the *effective electric field* acting on a grain of matter moving with velocity $\boldsymbol{v}$.

The *effective magnetic field* acting on a grain of matter moving with velocity $\boldsymbol{v}$ can be obtained in a similar manner. We saw in Sec. 7.1 that, if we treat magnetic dipoles as neutral aggregates of magnetic charges, the Lorentz force given by Eq. 9.47 implies the existence of an analogous force on a magnetic charge moving with velocity $\boldsymbol{v}$, given by

$$\boldsymbol{F}^* = q^*(\boldsymbol{H} - \boldsymbol{v} \times \epsilon_0\boldsymbol{E}) \tag{9.49}$$

which reduces to Eq. 9.46 when the velocity is equal to zero. Thus, the effective magnetic field is given by

$$\boldsymbol{H}_{\text{eff}} = \boldsymbol{H} - \boldsymbol{v} \times \epsilon_0\boldsymbol{E} \tag{9.50}$$

After evaluating the effective fields responsible for the conduction, polarization, and magnetization of moving matter, we must consider the effect of motion on the response of matter to these fields. We observe, in this regard that, if the motion involves acceleration, additional forces of inertia will act on the individual particles. The forces of inertia acting on the nuclei (which account for practically the entire mass of the material) give rise to stress and strain in the moving body, which, in turn, may influence appreciably its electromagnetic state. The forces of inertia acting on the electron are negligibly small in situations of practical interest because of the very small mass of the electrons. Finally, relativistic effects are present even in the absence of acceleration, which, however, can be safely disregarded when the velocity is small compared to that of light.

In many cases of practical interest, the effects of acceleration resulting from strain can be disregarded, or, at least, can be taken into account by determining the stationary constituent relations of the material in question under stress. In all such cases, the constituent relations may be taken to be independent of the motion of the body, with the only provision that the effective fields given by Eqs. 9.48 and 9.50 be used in place of $\boldsymbol{E}$ and $\boldsymbol{H}$. In the case of linear, isotropic materials, for instance, the constituent relations become

$$\boldsymbol{J}_c = \sigma(\boldsymbol{E} + \boldsymbol{v} \times \mu_0 \boldsymbol{H}) \tag{9.51}$$

$$\boldsymbol{P} = (\epsilon - \epsilon_0)(\boldsymbol{E} + \boldsymbol{v} \times \mu_0 \boldsymbol{H}) \tag{9.52}$$

$$\boldsymbol{M} = (\mu - \mu_0)(\boldsymbol{H} - \boldsymbol{v} \times \epsilon_0 \boldsymbol{E}) \tag{9.53}$$

where $\sigma$, $\epsilon$, and $\mu$ are constant for each grain of matter, and $\boldsymbol{v}$ is the velocity of the grain.

## 9.6 The Power Series in the Time-Rate Parameter

The presence of a velocity field in Maxwell's equations complicates matters considerably, particularly if the velocity field is unspecified and has to be obtained from a self-consistent solution of Maxwell's equations and of Newton's equations of motion. On the other hand, it is often possible to deal effectively with moving systems by prescribing from the beginning the velocity field, on the assumption that such a motion can be impressed upon the system by suitable external forces. The problem of determining such external forces can then be solved separately, once the electromagnetic field and the associated electromagnetic forces have been evaluated.

We shall assume in what follows that the velocity field is specified in advance, and represents a motion impressed upon the system by external forces. We shall also assume, for the sake of simplicity, that all material media are linear, and are therefore represented by constituent relations of the form of Eqs. 9.51, 9.52, and 9.53. (On the other hand, we shall see that the complications introduced by nonlinear constituent relations are essentially the same as in stationary systems.) Under these conditions, all the basic equations are still linear, as for stationary systems. The coefficients of these equations, however, may vary with time, not only because $\boldsymbol{v}$ may be a function of time but also because the properties of matter at any given point in a stationary system of coordinates may change as a result of the motion of the matter itself.

The fact that the coefficients of the basic equations may vary with time complicates considerably their solution. We shall develop here a procedure for determining the fields by successive approximations, by extending the procedure discussed in Chapter 6. That procedure, through the use of power series in the time-rate parameter $\alpha$, reduced the determination of time-varying fields to the evaluation of a series of static fields. The extension presented below will reduce the determination of fields in the presence of moving matter and time-varying excitations to the evaluation of a series of static fields in the presence of only stationary matter. Just as the procedure of Chapter 6 was found to be of particular value in studying the low-frequency, quasi-static behavior of electromagnetic systems, the new, more general procedure will be of particular value in studying their low-velocity, quasi-stationary behavior.

The central concept in the procedure of Chapter 6 was the family of electromagnetic fields generated by stretching and compressing the time scale. Formally, we defined a time-rate parameter $\alpha$, and substituted the family time

$$\tau = \alpha t \tag{9.54}$$

for the real time $t$ in the expressions for the quantities controlled independently by external forces (e.g., sources or quantities used as references in their places). The family of electromagnetic fields $\boldsymbol{E}(x, y, z, \tau, \alpha)$, $\boldsymbol{H}(x, y, z, \tau, \alpha)$ was then generated by varying the value of the parameter $\alpha$.

The new aspect with which we are confronted here is the presence of the velocity field $\boldsymbol{v}$, or, more precisely, the fact that the position of each grain of matter is a function of time. Since the position of each grain of matter is, by assumption, controlled by external forces independently of the electromagnetic field, it must be treated as an independent quantity. Thus, if $\boldsymbol{r}(t)$ is the vector representing the position of a particular grain of matter as a function of time, the corresponding family of positions is represented by the vector function $\boldsymbol{r}(\tau) = \boldsymbol{r}(\alpha t)$ obtained by substituting the family time $\tau$ for the real time $t$. It is important to note that the position of each particular grain is uniquely specified by the value of the family time $\tau$. Conversely each grain is uniquely identified by its position for a given value of $\tau$.

The family of the velocities of a particular grain can be obtained by differentiating the family of its positions with respect to the real time. We obtain for each particular grain,

$$\boldsymbol{v}(\tau, \alpha) = \frac{d\boldsymbol{r}(\tau)}{dt} = \alpha \frac{d\boldsymbol{r}(\tau)}{d\tau} = \alpha \boldsymbol{u}(\tau) \tag{9.55}$$

where $\boldsymbol{u}(\tau)$ is the velocity of the grain for $\alpha = 1$ (which implies $\tau = t$). Thus, if $\boldsymbol{u}(x, y, z, t)$ is the specified velocity field, the family of velocity fields obtained by varying $\alpha$ is represented by

$$\boldsymbol{v}(x, y, z, \tau, \alpha) = \alpha \boldsymbol{u}(x, y, z, \tau) \tag{9.56}$$

In fact, the coordinates $x$, $y$, $z$ identify a particular grain for any given value of $\tau$. In other words, the family of velocity fields is obtained by multiplying the prescribed velocity field (with $\tau$ substituted for $t$) by the time-rate parameter $\alpha$; i.e., $\alpha$ plays the role of a velocity scale factor.

The next step in Chapter 6 was to rewrite Maxwell's equations in such a way as to place in evidence the time-rate parameter $\alpha$. We shall repeat this procedure for Maxwell's equations in moving media. With all quantities expressed as functions of $\tau$, we have for the operation of differentiation with respect to $t$,

$$\frac{\partial}{\partial t} = \frac{d\tau}{dt}\frac{\partial}{\partial \tau} = \alpha \frac{\partial}{\partial \tau} \tag{9.57}$$

Then, substitution of Eqs. 9.56 and 9.57 into Eqs. 9.41 and 9.42 yields

$$\operatorname{curl} \boldsymbol{H} - \alpha\epsilon_0 \frac{\partial \boldsymbol{E}}{\partial \tau} = \boldsymbol{J}_f + \alpha \frac{\partial \boldsymbol{P}}{\partial \tau} + \alpha \operatorname{curl} (\boldsymbol{P} \times \boldsymbol{u}) \tag{9.58}$$

$$\operatorname{curl} \boldsymbol{E} + \alpha\mu_0 \frac{\partial \boldsymbol{H}}{\partial \tau} = -\alpha \frac{\partial}{\partial \tau} (\mu_0 \boldsymbol{M}) - \alpha \operatorname{curl} (\mu_0 \boldsymbol{M} \times \boldsymbol{u}) \tag{9.59}$$

The parameter $\alpha$ can be similarly placed in evidence in the constituent relations. For linear materials, for instance, we have from Eqs. 9.51, 9.52, and 9.53,

$$\boldsymbol{J}_c = \sigma(\boldsymbol{E} + \alpha\boldsymbol{u} \times \mu_0\boldsymbol{H}) \tag{9.60}$$

$$\boldsymbol{P} = (\epsilon - \epsilon_0)(\boldsymbol{E} + \alpha\boldsymbol{u} \times \mu_0\boldsymbol{H}) \tag{9.61}$$

$$\mu_0\boldsymbol{M} = (\mu - \mu_0)(\boldsymbol{H} - \alpha\boldsymbol{u} \times \epsilon_0\boldsymbol{E}) \tag{9.62}$$

Next, we place in evidence the dependence on $\alpha$ of all electromagnetic quantities, by writing each of them as a power series in $\alpha$. We have, for instance,

$$\boldsymbol{E} = \boldsymbol{E}_0 + \alpha\boldsymbol{E}_1 + \alpha^2\boldsymbol{E}_2 + \cdots \tag{9.63}$$

$$\boldsymbol{H} = \boldsymbol{H}_0 + \alpha\boldsymbol{H}_1 + \alpha^2\boldsymbol{H}_2 + \cdots \tag{9.64}$$

Substituting these power series in Eqs. 9.58 and 9.59 and equating the terms involving the same power of $\alpha$ yields the zero-order set of equations

$$\text{curl}\,\boldsymbol{H}_0 = \boldsymbol{J}_{f0} \tag{9.65}$$

$$\text{curl}\,\boldsymbol{E}_0 = 0 \tag{9.66}$$

the first-order set of equations

$$\text{curl}\,\boldsymbol{H}_1 = \boldsymbol{J}_{f1} + \frac{\partial}{\partial\tau}(\epsilon_0\boldsymbol{E}_0 + \boldsymbol{P}_0) + \text{curl}\,(\boldsymbol{P}_0 \times \boldsymbol{u}) \tag{9.67}$$

$$\text{curl}\,\boldsymbol{E}_1 = -\frac{\partial}{\partial\tau}(\mu_0\boldsymbol{H}_0 + \mu_0\boldsymbol{M}_0) - \text{curl}\,(\mu_0\boldsymbol{M}_0 \times \boldsymbol{u}) \tag{9.68}$$

and all similar sets of equations obtained by substituting for the subscripts 1 and 0 in Eqs. 9.67 and 9.68 the integers $k$ and $k - 1$.

Operating in a similar manner on Eqs. 9.60 to 9.62 yields

$$\boldsymbol{J}_{c0} = \sigma\boldsymbol{E}_0 \tag{9.69}$$

$$\boldsymbol{P}_0 = (\epsilon - \epsilon_0)\boldsymbol{E}_0 \tag{9.70}$$

$$\mu_0\boldsymbol{M}_0 = (\mu - \mu_0)\boldsymbol{H}_0 \tag{9.71}$$

and

$$\boldsymbol{J}_{c1} = \sigma(\boldsymbol{E}_1 + \boldsymbol{u} \times \mu_0\boldsymbol{H}_0) \tag{9.72}$$

$$\boldsymbol{P}_1 = (\epsilon - \epsilon_0)(\boldsymbol{E}_1 + \boldsymbol{u} \times \mu_0\boldsymbol{H}_0) \tag{9.73}$$

$$\mu_0\boldsymbol{M}_1 = (\mu - \mu_0)(\boldsymbol{H}_1 - \boldsymbol{u} \times \epsilon_0\boldsymbol{E}_0) \tag{9.74}$$

Finally, we have for the total free-current density

$$\boldsymbol{J}_{f0} = \boldsymbol{J}_{c0} \tag{9.75}$$

$$\operatorname{div} \boldsymbol{J}_{f0} = 0 \tag{9.76}$$

and

$$\boldsymbol{J}_{f1} = \boldsymbol{J}_{c1} + \boldsymbol{u}\rho_{f0} \tag{9.77}$$

$$\operatorname{div} \boldsymbol{J}_{f1} = -\frac{\partial}{\partial \tau}\rho_{f0} \tag{9.78}$$

The sets of equations resulting from Eqs. 9.43 and 9.44 are the same as for stationary systems. All zero-order equations are identical to the corresponding equations for static fields in the presence of only stationary matter. All zero-order electromagnetic quantities are functions of the parameter $\tau$, but this parameter does not appear explicitly in any of the equations and, therefore, does not play any role at all in their solution. As expected, the zero-order terms represent a "slowly varying static field" in a "slowly varying stationary system." The first-order equations are also of the static and stationary type on the assumption that all zero-order quantities are known. In fact only zero-order quantities appear in derivatives with respect to $\tau$ and in terms involving $\boldsymbol{u}$. The terms involving such zero-order quantities play the role of sources of the first-order fields. The same is true for all higher order sets of equations, on the assumption that all quantities of the next lower order are known. We can conclude, therefore, that the problem has been reduced to the successive determination of fields of the static type in the presence of only stationary matter.

It is well to stress, in closing this section, that the role played in our discussion by the power series method of analysis is not that of a goal but rather that of a tool. The real value of the method will be in facilitating our understanding of electromagnetic phenomena associated with moving matter. The field aspects of some of these phenomena are discussed in the remaining sections of this chapter, and their energy aspects will be discussed in the next chapter.

## 9.7 Uniform Motion of a Conductor in a Magnetic Field (Power Series Method)

The example discussed in this section illustrates how an electromotive force is generated by the motion of a conductor in a magnetic field. This is the phenomenon exploited by all rotating electric generators and motors to convert mechanical energy into electric energy, or vice

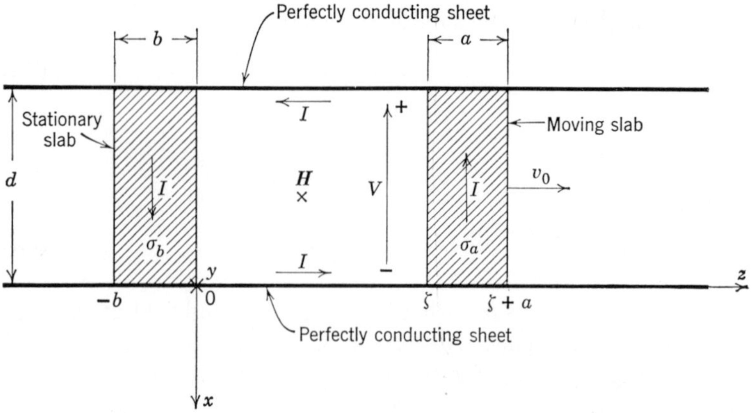


**Fig. 9.3.** System illustrating the motion of a conductor in a magnetic field.

versa. We shall consider here the simplest possible configuration of conductors, consistent with our objective, so as to minimize the complexity of the resulting field. Yet the conclusions drawn from our analysis will hold for a very broad class of systems involving moving conductors.

The system illustrated in Fig. 9.3 consists of two infinite, perfectly conducting sheets normal to the $x$-axis; the two sheets are separated by a distance $d$. Two conducting slabs of infinite length in the direction of the $y$-axis are inserted between the two sheets and make perfect contacts with them. The slab on the left side of the $x$-axis is fixed, whereas the slab on the right side moves with uniform velocity $v_0$ in the positive direction of the $z$-axis. Both slabs are made of linear homogeneous material; we shall represent with $\sigma_a$ the conductivity of the moving slab, and with $\sigma_b$ the conductivity of the fixed slab. The right side of the fixed slab coincides with the plane $z = 0$; the left side of the moving slab coincides with the same plane $z = 0$ at time $t = 0$; the entire system is immersed in a uniform magnetic field parallel to the $y$-axis and of intensity

$$H_{y0} = A \tag{9.79}$$

Since the impressed magnetic field is independent of time, the only independent quantity (controlled by external forces) that varies with time is the position of the left side of the moving slab. If we indicate with $\zeta$ its position along the $z$-axis, we have for the real-time process

$$\zeta = v_0 t \tag{9.80}$$

The family of processes and of corresponding electromagnetic fields introduced in the preceding section is then generated by substituting the family time $\tau$ for the real time $t$ in Eq. 9.80,

$$\zeta = v_0\tau = \alpha v_0 t \tag{9.81}$$

The corresponding family of velocity fields is

$$\boldsymbol{v} = \alpha \boldsymbol{u} \tag{9.82}$$

where

$$\boldsymbol{u} = \begin{cases} \boldsymbol{i}_z v_0 & \text{within the moving slab} \\ 0 & \text{everywhere else} \end{cases} \tag{9.83}$$

Thus, the family of processes generated by the time-rate parameter $\alpha$ is obtained, in effect, by varying the velocity of the moving slab. We shall now determine the electromagnetic field by successive approximations, as discussed in the preceding section. We observe, first of all, as we did in Sec. 6.5, that the purpose for which the parameter $\alpha$ was introduced was that of providing a general variable for the power-series expansion of each electromagnetic quantity, and for the resulting separation of the field equations into a corresponding series of equations to be solved in succession. Once the successive sets of equations have been obtained, the parameter $\alpha$ is no longer needed and can be eliminated without any loss of generality by setting

$$\alpha = 1 \qquad \tau = \alpha t = t \tag{9.84}$$

Thus, for instance, $t$ is substituted for $\tau$ in the successive sets of field equations (such as Eqs. 9.67 and 9.68), and the series for the fields, given by Eqs. 9.63 and 9.64, become simply the sums of the resulting solutions. We can now proceed to evaluate these successive solutions.

The zero-order electromagnetic field must satisfy the static equations (Eqs. 9.65 and 9.66). The zero-order magnetic field is the impressed field given by Eq. 9.79, which we assume to be produced by an appropriate current distribution $\boldsymbol{J}_{f0}$. The zero-order electric field is equal to zero because there are no zero-order sources. Since the slabs are neither polarizable nor magnetizable, $\boldsymbol{P}$ and $\boldsymbol{M}$ are equal to zero for all orders.

The first-order equations (Eqs. 9.67 and 9.68) reduce, in our special case, to

$$\text{curl}\, \boldsymbol{H}_1 = \boldsymbol{J}_{f1} \tag{9.85}$$

$$\text{curl}\, \boldsymbol{E}_1 = 0 \tag{9.86}$$

in view of the fact that the impressed magnetic field is independent of the position of the moving slab and, therefore, of time. On the other hand, because of the conductivity of the slabs, we have from Eq. 9.72

$$\boldsymbol{J}_{c1} = \sigma_a(\boldsymbol{E}_1 + \boldsymbol{i}_z \times \boldsymbol{i}_y v_0 \mu_0 A) = \sigma_a(\boldsymbol{E}_1 - \boldsymbol{i}_x v_0 \mu_0 A) \qquad (9.87)$$

within the moving slab, and

$$\boldsymbol{J}_{c1} = \sigma_b \boldsymbol{E}_1 \qquad (9.88)$$

within the fixed slab. Current may be present (and will be present) also in the perfectly conducting sheets. However, because of their infinite conductivity, the tangential component of $\boldsymbol{E}_1$ must vanish on their surfaces.

Because of Eq. 9.86, the electric field $\boldsymbol{E}_1$ can be expressed as the negative gradient of a potential $\phi_1$

$$\boldsymbol{E}_1 = -\operatorname{grad} \phi_1 \qquad (9.89)$$

Furthermore, since there is no zero-order charge, we obtain from Eqs. 9.77 and 9.78,

$$\operatorname{div} \boldsymbol{J}_{f1} = \operatorname{div} \boldsymbol{J}_{c1} = 0 \qquad (9.90)$$

and, when Eqs. 9.87 and 9.88 are substituted for $\boldsymbol{J}_{c1}$,

$$\operatorname{div} \boldsymbol{E}_1 = 0 \qquad (9.91)$$

Thus $\boldsymbol{E}_1$ is solenoidal as well as conservative, and the potential $\phi_1$ must be a solution of Laplace's equation in the entire space between the two conducting sheets.

The boundary condition imposed on $\boldsymbol{E}_1$ is that it be normal to the two perfectly conducting sheets. The only field satisfying Laplace's equation which meets this requirement is a uniform field parallel to the $x$-axis, so that

$$\boldsymbol{E}_1 = \boldsymbol{i}_x C_1 \qquad (9.92)$$

where $C_1$ is a constant to be determined. Thus, within the moving slab

$$\boldsymbol{J}_{c1} = \boldsymbol{i}_x \sigma_a (C_1 - v_0 \mu_0 A) \qquad (9.93)$$

and within the fixed slab

$$\boldsymbol{J}_{c1} = \boldsymbol{i}_x \sigma_b C_1 \qquad (9.94)$$

To determine the constant $C_1$, we observe that, because of the law of conservation of charge, all the current flowing through the moving slab from one conducting sheet to the other must return through the fixed slab. Thus, we obtain from Eqs. 9.93 and 9.94,

$$a\sigma_a(C_1 - v_0 \mu_0 A) = -b\sigma_b C_1 \qquad (9.95)$$

where $a$ and $b$ are the widths of the two slabs; solving this equation yields

$$C_1 = v_0\mu_0 A \frac{a\sigma_a}{a\sigma_a + b\sigma_b} = v_0\mu_0 K A \tag{9.96}$$

where $K$ is a constant.

The constant $K$ can also be expressed in terms of the resistances $R_a$ and $R_b$ of the slabs (computed per unit length in the $y$ direction) as

$$K = \frac{R_b}{R_a + R_b} \tag{9.97}$$

It follows that the electric field in the entire space between the two perfectly conducting sheets is given by

$$\boldsymbol{E}_1 = \boldsymbol{i}_x v_0 \mu_0 A K \tag{9.98}$$

and the current density by

$$\boldsymbol{J}_{c1} = \begin{cases} \boldsymbol{i}_x v_0 \sigma_b \mu_0 A K & \text{in the fixed slab} \\ -\boldsymbol{i}_x v_0 \sigma_b (b/a) \mu_0 A K & \text{in the moving slab} \end{cases} \tag{9.99}$$

In terms of circuit quantities, the first-order voltage between the upper plate and the lower plate is

$$V_1 = v_0\mu_0 A d K = v_0 \mu_0 A d \frac{R_b}{R_a + R_b} \tag{9.100}$$

and the magnitude of the corresponding current flowing through the slabs is

$$I_1 = v_0 b \sigma_b \mu_0 A K = v_0 \frac{\mu_0 A d}{R_a + R_b} \tag{9.101}$$

The current flows in the moving slab from the negative sheet to the positive sheet and in the opposite direction in the fixed slab.

It is clear that the moving slab acts as a voltage source with an internal resistance $R_a$, and the fixed slab as a load of resistance $R_b$, both resistances being computed per unit length in the $y$ direction. The source voltage is given by

$$V_{s1} = v_0 \mu_0 A d \tag{9.102}$$

as indicated in the equivalent circuit of Fig. 9.4. The conducting sheets play the role of leads connecting the generator to the load. The voltage between the sheets is the terminal voltage of the generator.

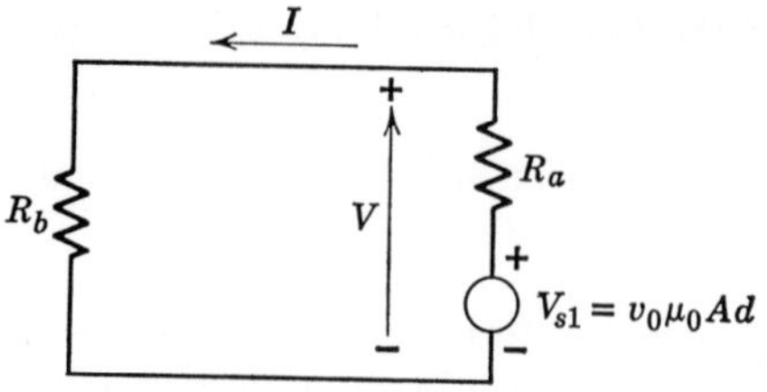


**Fig. 9.4.** Equivalent circuit for the system of Fig. 9.3.

Let us turn our attention next to the first-order magnetic field. With reference to Eq. 4.82, we observe that the conduction current constitutes the entire free current, and that $\boldsymbol{E}_1$ is independent of the position of the moving slab and, therefore, of $t$. Thus the first-order magnetic field is produced entirely by the conduction current in the two slabs and in the portions of the conducting sheets between the slabs. Clearly $\boldsymbol{H}_1$ consists entirely of a $y$ component, and Eq. 9.85 reduces with the help of Eq. 9.99 to

$$-\boldsymbol{i}_x \frac{\partial H_{y1}}{\partial z} = \begin{cases} -\boldsymbol{i}_x v_0 \sigma_b (b/a) \mu_0 A K & \zeta \leq z \leq \zeta + a \\ 0 & 0 < z < \zeta \\ \boldsymbol{i}_x v_0 \sigma_b \mu_0 A K & -b \leq z \leq 0 \end{cases} \tag{9.103}$$

The right-hand side of this equation, i.e. the component $J_{cx1}$, is plotted in Fig. 9.5$a$. Integration with respect to $z$ yields

$$H_{y1} = -v_0 \mu_0 A K \sigma_b \begin{cases} (b/a)(\zeta + a - z) & \zeta \leq z \leq \zeta + a \\ b & 0 < z < \zeta \\ (z + b) & -b \leq z \leq 0 \end{cases} \tag{9.104}$$

and $H_{y1} = 0$ on the left of the fixed slab, on the right of the moving slab, above the upper sheet, and below the lower sheet. The behavior of $H_{y1}$ is illustrated in Fig. 9.5$b$. Note that the direction of the first-order magnetic field is opposite to that of the zero-order, applied, magnetic field.

Let us consider, finally, the second-order electric field. We have for it, with the help of Eqs. 9.80 and 9.104

$$\operatorname{curl} \boldsymbol{E}_2 = \boldsymbol{i}_y \frac{\partial E_{x2}}{\partial z} = -\mu_0 \frac{\partial \boldsymbol{H}_1}{\partial t} = -v_0 \mu_0 \frac{\partial \boldsymbol{H}_1}{\partial \zeta} \frac{d\zeta}{dt}$$

$$= \begin{cases} \boldsymbol{i}_y v_0^2 \mu_0^2 A K \sigma_b (b/a) & \text{in moving slab} \\ 0 & \text{everywhere else} \end{cases} \tag{9.105}$$

from which we obtain by integration

$$E_2 = \begin{cases} i_x v_0^2 \mu_0^2 AK\sigma_b b - \text{grad } \phi_2 & \zeta + a < z \\ i_x v_0^2 \mu_0^2 AK\sigma_b (b/a)(z - \zeta) - \text{grad } \phi_2 & \zeta \leq z \leq \zeta + a \\ - \text{grad } \phi_2 & z < \zeta \end{cases} \quad (9.106)$$

where $\phi_2$ is a potential function be to determined. On the other hand, we have for the current density in the slabs, with the help of Eqs. 9.83, 9.104, and 9.106

$$J_{c2} = \sigma(E_2 + u \times \mu_0 H_1)$$

$$= \begin{cases} i_x v_0^2 \sigma_a \sigma_b b \mu_0^2 AK - \sigma_a \text{ grad } \phi_2 & \text{in moving slab} \\ -\sigma_b \text{ grad } \phi_2 & \text{in stationary slab} \end{cases} \quad (9.107)$$

Furthermore, since $\rho_{f1} = 0$ within both slabs,

$$\text{div } J_{f2} = \text{div } J_{c2} = 0 \quad (9.108)$$

Then, it follows from Eqs. 6.107 and 6.108 that

$$\text{div grad } \phi_2 = 0 \quad (9.109)$$

In other words, $\phi_2$ must be a solution of Laplace's equation. As in the case of the first-order electric field, the only function $\phi_2$ which satisfies the necessary boundary conditions on the two perfectly con-

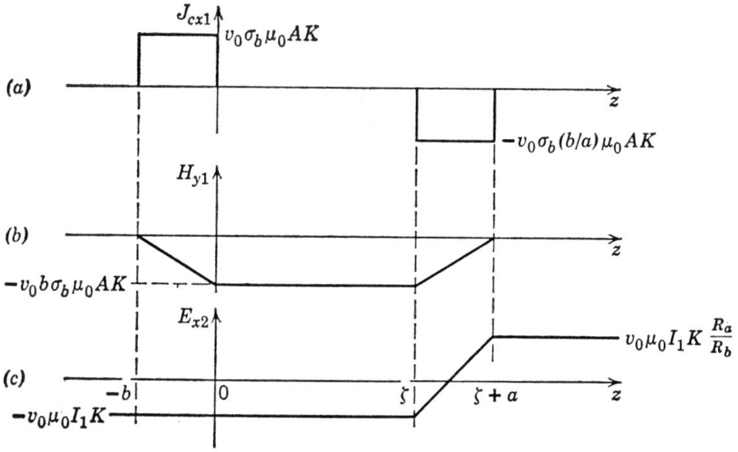


Fig. 9.5. Behavior of field components with $z$.

ducting sheets is the potential of a uniform field parallel to the $x$-axis, i.e.,

$$- \operatorname{grad} \phi_2 = \boldsymbol{i}_x C_2 \tag{9.110}$$

where $C_2$ is a constant to be determined.

To determine the constant $C_2$, we require the total second-order current flowing in the moving slab to be equal to the total second-order current flowing in the stationary slab in the opposite direction. We obtain from Eqs. 9.107 and 9.110,

$$v_0{}^2 a\sigma_a b\sigma_b \mu_0{}^2 AK + a\sigma_a C_2 = -b\sigma_b C_2 \tag{9.111}$$

so that

$$C_2 = -v_0{}^2 b\sigma_b \mu_0{}^2 AK^2 = -v_0\mu_0 I_1 K \tag{9.112}$$

Substituting this expression in Eqs. 9.110 and 9.106 yields

$$\boldsymbol{E}_2 = \boldsymbol{i}_x v_0 \mu_0 I_1 \begin{cases} K\dfrac{R_a}{R_b} & \zeta + a < z \\ \left(\dfrac{z - \zeta}{a} - K\right) & \zeta \le z \le \zeta + a \\ (-K) & z < \zeta \end{cases} \tag{9.113}$$

where $I_1$ is the first-order current given by Eq. 9.101. The behavior of the $x$ component $E_{x2}$ of the second-order electric field is illustrated in Fig. 9.5*c*.

Operating in a similar manner on Eq. 9.107 yields

$$\boldsymbol{J}_{c2} = \boldsymbol{i}_x v_0 \mu_0 I_1 \sigma_b K \begin{cases} b/a & \text{in moving slab} \\ (-1) & \text{in stationary slab} \end{cases} \tag{9.114}$$

The terminal voltage of the generator is given, to second approximation, by

$$V_1 + V_2 = \mu_0 v_0 dK(A - I_1) \tag{9.115}$$

where $I_1$ is the first approximation to the current flowing through the slabs. The term in parentheses is the actual magnetic-field intensity in the space between the slabs, evaluated to first approximation. Comparison of Eq. 9.115 with Eq. 9.100 indicates that the second-order term simply takes into account the fact that the first-order current decreases the applied magnetic field in the space between the two slabs. Further corrections of the magnetic field intensity in Eq. 9.115 are introduced by higher order currents; these corrections have alternate signs because a positive current causes a decrease of magnetic field, which results in a decrease of terminal voltage, which in turn causes a negative current. In fact, the second-order current in the stationary slab,

$$I_2 = -v_0 b \sigma_b \mu_0 K I_1 \tag{9.116}$$

has direction opposite to that of the first-order current $I_1$, and results, therefore, in a positive correction of the magnetic field intensity in the space between the two slabs. The current fed by the generator to the load per unit length in the $y$ direction is, to second approximation,

$$I_1 + I_2 = A[(v_0 \mu_0 g) - (v_0 \mu_0 g)^2] \tag{9.117}$$

where

$$g = b\sigma_b K = \frac{a\sigma_a b\sigma_b}{a\sigma_a + b\sigma_b} = \frac{d}{R_a + R_b} \tag{9.118}$$

represents the conductance of the two slabs connected in series, per unit spacing between the sheets and per unit length in the direction of the $y$-axis.

It is clear from Eq. 9.117 that the number of terms that must be computed in order to obtain a satisfactory approximation to the load current depends on the magnitude of the product $v_0 \mu_0 g$. This product should be a small fraction of unity in order for the first approximation to be satisfactory; this amounts to saying that the magnetic field produced by the load current should be small compared to the impressed field $A$. This condition, however, is not met in the normal operation of practical electric generators. It is important, therefore, to push our analysis further, and to develop, if possible, a complete solution to the problem under consideration.

We note, for this purpose, that the general character of the higher order terms is clearly suggested by the terms already evaluated. For instance, both the second-order current and the first-order current are uniformly distributed over the cross section of each slab. For this reason, the magnetic field produced by the second-order current must be proportional to the first-order magnetic field whose behavior with $z$ is illustrated in Fig. 9.5$b$. It seems reasonable to expect then that the higher order currents will also be uniformly distributed and that the corresponding magnetic fields will also be proportional to the first-order field. If this were actually the case, the higher-order electric fields should have the same general character as the second-order field illustrated in Fig. 9.5$c$. We shall see in the next section that the field equations and the constituent relation for conducting materials are satisfied by an electromagnetic field of this type.

## 9.8 Uniform Motion of a Conductor in a Magnetic Field (Direct Solution)

The power series analysis of the preceding section strongly suggests that the electric field and the magnetic field in the system of Fig. 9.3 should be independent of $x$ and $y$, and should behave with $z$ in the manner illustrated in Fig. 9.6. More precisely, let us inquire whether fields of the form

$$\boldsymbol{H} = \boldsymbol{i}_y \begin{cases} A & \zeta + a < z \\ A + \dfrac{z - \zeta - a}{a} I & \zeta \leq z \leq \zeta + a \\ A - I & 0 < z < \zeta \\ A - \dfrac{z + b}{b} I & -b \leq z \leq 0 \\ A & z < -b \end{cases} \tag{9.119}$$

$$\boldsymbol{E} = \boldsymbol{i}_x \begin{cases} C + B & \zeta + a < z \\ C + \dfrac{z - \zeta}{a} B & \zeta \leq z \leq \zeta + a \\ C & z < \zeta \end{cases} \tag{9.120}$$

can be made to satisfy the field equations and the constituent relations by appropriately selecting the constants $B$, $C$, and $I$; the constant $A$ is the intensity of the applied magnetic field. Because of the absence of polarizable and magnetizable materials, the equations to be satisfied reduce to

$$\text{curl}\, \boldsymbol{E} + \mu_0 \frac{\partial \boldsymbol{H}}{\partial t} = 0 \tag{9.121}$$

$$\text{curl}\, \boldsymbol{H} - \epsilon_0 \frac{\partial \boldsymbol{E}}{\partial t} = \boldsymbol{J}_c + \boldsymbol{v}\rho_f \tag{9.122}$$

$$\boldsymbol{J}_c = \sigma(\boldsymbol{E} + \boldsymbol{v} \times \mu_0 \boldsymbol{H}) \tag{9.123}$$

$$\rho_f = \epsilon_0 \,\text{div}\, \boldsymbol{E} \tag{9.124}$$

We observe, first of all, that the divergence of $\boldsymbol{E}$ vanishes in the entire space between the two perfectly conducting sheets. Thus, $\rho_f = 0$, and no free charges are present except on the surfaces of the two perfectly conducting sheets. We observe next that the assumed fields are both static and uniform in the space not occupied by the

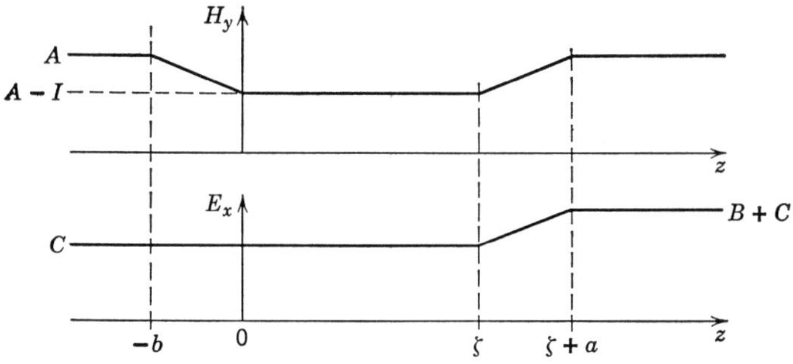


**Fig. 9.6.** Assumed behavior of field components.

conducting slabs and, therefore, they satisfy there Eqs. 9.121 and 9.122. Within the stationary slab, we have from Eqs. 9.122 and 9.123

$$-\frac{\partial H_y}{\partial z} = \sigma_b E_x \qquad \frac{I}{b} = \sigma_b C \tag{9.125}$$

Within the moving slab, on the other hand, we have from Eq. 9.121,

$$\frac{\partial E_x}{\partial z} + \mu_0 \frac{\partial H_y}{\partial \zeta}\frac{\partial \zeta}{\partial t} = \frac{B}{a} - v_0\mu_0 \frac{I}{a} = 0 \tag{9.126}$$

Thus,

$$C = \frac{I}{b\sigma_b} \qquad B = v_0\mu_0 I \tag{9.127}$$

Furthermore, we have from Eqs. 9.122 and 9.123, also within the moving slab,

$$-\frac{\partial H_y}{\partial z} - \epsilon_0 \frac{\partial E_x}{\partial \zeta}\frac{\partial \zeta}{\partial t} = \sigma_a(E_x - v_0\mu_0 H_y) \tag{9.128}$$

and with the help of Eq. 9.127,

$$-\frac{I}{a}(1 - \epsilon_0\mu_0{v_0}^2) = \sigma_a\left[\frac{I}{b\sigma_b} + v_0\mu_0\frac{z - \zeta}{a}I - v_0\mu_0\left(A + \frac{z - \zeta - a}{a}I\right)\right] \tag{9.129}$$

Solving this last equation for $I$ yields

$$I = \mu_0 v_0 g A\left[1 + \mu_0 v_0 g\left(1 - \frac{\epsilon_0 v_0}{a\sigma_a}\right)\right]^{-1} \tag{9.130}$$

where $g$ is the normalized conductance defined by Eq. 9.118. This completes the determination of the constants appearing in the expressions for $\boldsymbol{H}$ and $\boldsymbol{E}$. It is clear also, that the fields satisfy the necessary boundary conditions.

The current density can now be expressed in terms of the constant $I$. We have

$$\boldsymbol{J}_c = \boldsymbol{i}_x \begin{cases} -\dfrac{I}{a}(1 - \epsilon_0\mu_0 v_0{}^2) & \text{in moving slab} \\ \dfrac{I}{b} & \text{in stationary slab} \end{cases} \tag{9.131}$$

Clearly, $I$ represents the total current in the stationary slab. In the moving slab, however, the total current is $I$ multiplied by the factor $1 - (v_0/c)^2$ where $c$ is the velocity of light in vacuum. The difference between the current in the moving slab and in the stationary slab supplies the charge taken away by the moving slab from the upper conducting sheet as the slab moves in the positive $z$ direction. In fact, the surface charge density is equal to $\epsilon_0(I/b\sigma_b)$ on the left of the moving slab, and is equal to $\epsilon_0(I/b\sigma_b) + \epsilon_0\mu_0 v_0 I$ on the right of the moving slab. It follows that the amount of charge taken away from the upper sheet per unit time is equal to $I(v/c)^2$, which is just the difference between the currents in the two slabs. In any case, this difference between the two currents is very small at velocities of practical interest, and must be neglected in order to be consistent with the approximations made in Sec. 9.5.

If the factor $(v/c)^2$ is neglected in comparison to one, as discussed above, Eq. 9.130 reduces to

$$I = \frac{\mu_0 v_0 g A}{1 + \mu_0 v_0 g} \tag{9.132}$$

and using the binomial expansion of $(1 + \mu_0 v_0 g)^{-1}$,

$$I = \mu_0 v_0 g A[1 - \mu_0 v_0 g + \tfrac{1}{2}(\mu_0 v_0 g)^2 - \cdots] \tag{9.133}$$

which agrees with the terms evaluated in the preceding section. The terminal voltage of the generator is

$$V = dC = \frac{dI}{b\sigma_b} = \mu_0 v_0 dKA[1 - \mu_0 v_0 g + \tfrac{1}{2}(\mu_0 v_0 g)^2 - \cdots] \tag{9.134}$$

which agrees again with the first- and second-order terms evaluated in the preceding section.

The terminal voltage can also be written in the form

$$V = \mu_0 v_0 d \frac{A}{1 + \mu_0 v_0 g}\left(1 - \frac{R_a}{R_a + R_b}\right) = V_s - IR_a \qquad (9.135)$$

where

$$V_s = \mu_0 v_0 d \frac{A}{1 + \mu_0 v_0 g} \qquad (9.136)$$

is the source voltage, and $R_a$ is the internal resistance of the generator. It should be noted that this source voltage is a function of the load resistance and of the source resistance through the conductance $g$. This dependence on $g$ results from the fact that the magnetic field acting on the moving slab is a function of the load current.

It is interesting to inquire, finally, whether the results of our analysis would be different if the moving slab were made of a material, such as iron, which is both magnetizable and conducting. The answer is that the results would be exactly the same. In fact, the only change in the equations to be satisfied by the electromagnetic field would be the introduction on the right-hand side of Eq. 9.121 of a magnetic-current term $-\boldsymbol{J}^*$, which we shall show to be equal to zero. The moving slab is, by assumption, a rigid body; therefore, as discussed in Sec. 9.3, the magnetic current is equal to the sum of the time rate of change of the magnetization with respect to a system of coordinates moving with the slab, and the convection current resulting from the motion of magnetization charge. On the other hand, the effective magnetic field acting on any particular grain of the moving slab is independent of time and, therefore, the magnetization of the grain must be also independent. Furthermore, the magnetization would be parallel to the surfaces of the slab and uniform in that direction, so that no magnetic charge could be present anywhere. We can conclude, therefore, that $\boldsymbol{J}^*$ is equal to zero at all points of the moving slab and on its surfaces.

## ► 9.9 A Model of Homopolar Generator

Let us consider as a second example, the system illustrated in Fig. 9.7. A conducting sphere of radius $a$ rotates about its axis with an angular velocity $\omega$. The sphere is surrounded by a homogeneous, stationary conducting material of infinite extent, with which it makes perfect contact. The entire system is immersed in a uniform magnetic field parallel to the axis of rotation of the sphere, and is generated by currents which may be assumed to be located at infinity. The sphere

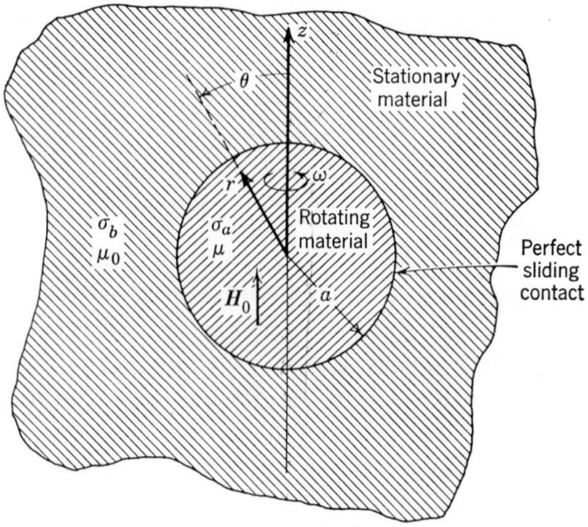


**Fig. 9.7.** Spherical model of homopolar generator.

is made of linear, homogeneous material, characterized by a conductivity $\sigma_a$ and a permeability $\mu$; its permittivity is that of vacuum. The material surrounding the sphere is also homogeneous and linear, and is characterized by a conductivity $\sigma_b$; its permeability and permittivity are those of vacuum.

The system described above will serve the purpose of illustrating the operation of the simplest type of d-c generator, known as the homopolar generator, and shown schematically in Fig. 9.8. This generator consists of a conducting disk rotating between the poles of a permanent magnet (or electromagnet). Two stationary brushes making contact with the outer edge of the disk and with the metal shaft driving the

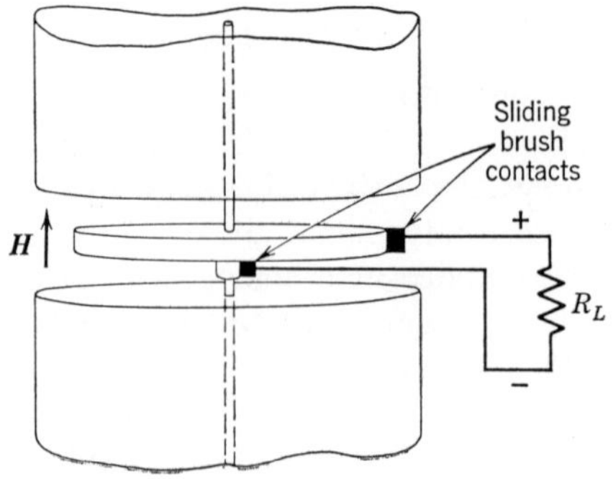


**Fig. 9.8.** Schematic diagram of a homopolar generator.

disk constitute the output terminals of the generator; the load, represented in Fig. 9.8 by the resistance $R_L$, is connected to these two brushes.

In the system of Fig. 9.7, the conducting material surrounding the sphere plays the role of the load, and the rotating sphere plays the role of the disk. The two brushes are extended to provide a continuous contact between the load and the generator over the entire surface of the sphere. The resulting current flow is illustrated by the solid lines in Fig. 9.9, and the equipotential surfaces in the stationary medium by the dotted lines in the same figure. Thus, our model of homopolar

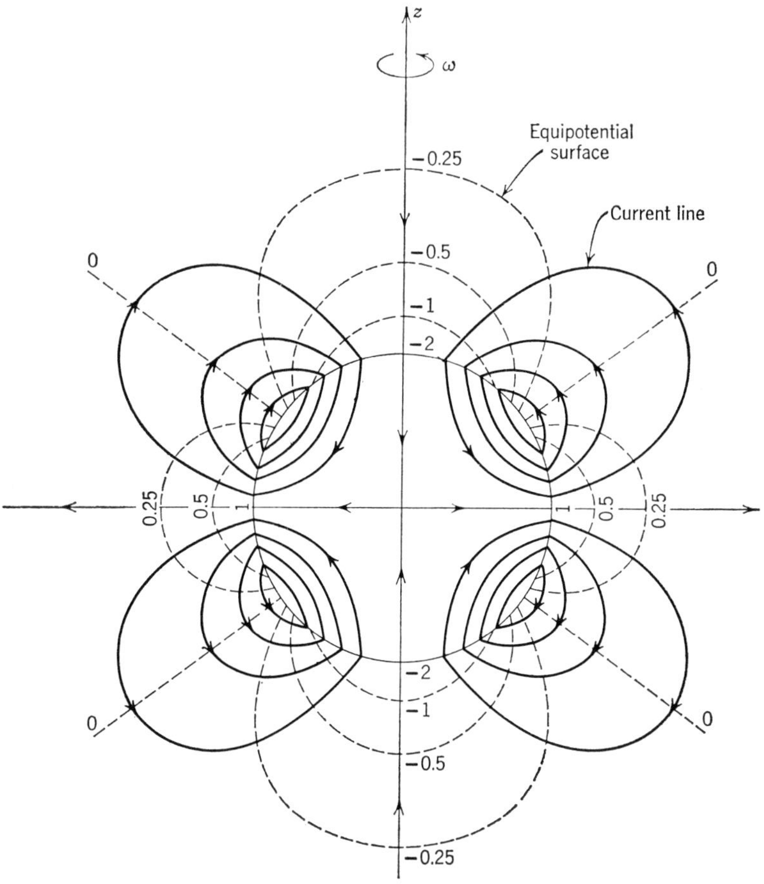


**Fig. 9.9.** Current lines and equipotential surfaces for system of Fig. 9.7.

generator cannot be represented by a single-loop equivalent circuit in which the load is connected to the generator at two well-identified terminals. On the other hand, we can regard the two points at which each current filament intersects the surface of the sphere as the terminals for that particular current filament. From this point of view, the generator could be considered as having an infinite number of terminal pairs, with a separate load connected to each terminal pair. Of course, this difficulty could be circumvented by restricting the contact between rotating and stationary matter to two small areas, but then it would become very difficult to determine the resulting current distribution in the two conducting media.

Let us proceed now with the analysis of our model of homopolar generator, using the power series method. Again, as in the example of Sec. 9.7, we shall set $\alpha = 1$, so that $\tau = t$. Then, using a spherical system of coordinates, with the $z$-axis coinciding with the axis of rotation, we have for the velocity field

$$\boldsymbol{v} = \boldsymbol{u} = \boldsymbol{i}_\varphi \omega r \sin\theta \qquad r \leq a \tag{9.137}$$

The zero-order electric field is evidently equal to zero because, by assumption, there are no zero-order electric charges. The zero-order magnetic field, on the other hand, is the field of a sphere of permeability $\mu$, immersed in a uniform magnetic field. The solution to this problem is well known and, therefore, will not be derived in detail here. The field inside the sphere is uniform and parallel to the $z$-axis. The field outside the sphere consists of a dipole field, with the dipole moment parallel to the $z$-axis, superimposed on the uniform, applied field. More precisely, using as a reference the intensity $A$ of the field inside the sphere,

$$\boldsymbol{H}_0 = \begin{cases} A(\boldsymbol{i}_r \cos\theta - \boldsymbol{i}_\theta \sin\theta) & r \leq a \\ \dfrac{A}{3\mu_0}\Big[(\mu + 2\mu_0)(\boldsymbol{i}_r \cos\theta - \boldsymbol{i}_\theta \sin\theta) & \\ \qquad + (\mu - \mu_0)\left(\dfrac{a}{r}\right)^3 (\boldsymbol{i}_r 2\cos\theta + \boldsymbol{i}_\theta \sin\theta)\Big] & r > a \end{cases} \tag{9.138}$$

Clearly the tangential component of the field (the $\theta$ component) is continuous through the surface of the sphere of radius $a$. The magnetization is given by

$$\mu_0 \boldsymbol{M}_0 = (\mu - \mu_0)A(\boldsymbol{i}_r \cos\theta - \boldsymbol{i}_\theta \sin\theta) \qquad r \leq a \tag{9.139}$$

which produces on the surface of the rotating sphere a magnetic charge of surface density

$$\sigma_0{}^* = (\mu - \mu_0)A \cos\theta \tag{9.140}$$

This surface magnetic-charge density is, of course, equal to the discontinuity of the normal (radial) component of $\mu_0\boldsymbol{H}_0$.

The first-order equations reduce in our case to

$$\operatorname{curl} \boldsymbol{E}_1 = -\operatorname{curl}(\mu_0\boldsymbol{M}_0 \times \boldsymbol{u}) \tag{9.141}$$

$$\operatorname{curl} \boldsymbol{H}_1 = \boldsymbol{J}_{c1} \tag{9.142}$$

$$\boldsymbol{J}_{c1} = \sigma(\boldsymbol{E}_1 + \boldsymbol{u} \times \mu_0\boldsymbol{H}_0) \tag{9.143}$$

All the derivatives with respect to $t$ are absent because neither the applied field nor the geometry of the system depends on time. Let us consider first the electric field and the current field. Since the right-hand side of Eq. 9.141 vanishes in the stationary material, $\boldsymbol{E}_1$ must be expressible there as the negative gradient of a potential function,

$$\boldsymbol{E}_1 = -\operatorname{grad}\phi_b \qquad r > a \tag{9.144}$$

The conduction current in the stationary material is then given by

$$\boldsymbol{J}_{c1} = -\sigma_b \operatorname{grad}\phi_b \qquad r > a \tag{9.145}$$

On the other hand, we have in the rotating sphere

$$\operatorname{curl}(\boldsymbol{E}_1 - \boldsymbol{u} \times \mu_0\boldsymbol{M}_0) = 0 \qquad r \leq a \tag{9.146}$$

Thus, the term in parentheses can be expressed as the negative gradient of a scalar potential $\phi_1$, and the electric field can be written with the help of Eqs. 9.137 and 9.139 in the form

$$\begin{aligned}\boldsymbol{E}_1 &= \boldsymbol{u} \times \mu_0\boldsymbol{M}_0 - \operatorname{grad}\phi_1 \\ &= \omega A(\mu - \mu_0)r \sin\theta(\boldsymbol{i}_r \sin\theta + \boldsymbol{i}_\theta \cos\theta) - \operatorname{grad}\phi_1 \qquad r \leq a\end{aligned} \tag{9.147}$$

The current density within the rotating sphere is obtained by substituting the expressions given by Eqs. 9.137, 9.138, and 9.147 respectively for $\boldsymbol{u}$, $\boldsymbol{H}_0$, and $\boldsymbol{E}_1$ in Eq. 9.143. We obtain

$$\boldsymbol{J}_{c1} = \omega\sigma_a\mu A r \sin\theta(\boldsymbol{i}_r \sin\theta + \boldsymbol{i}_\theta \cos\theta) - \sigma_a \operatorname{grad}\phi_1 \qquad r \leq a \tag{9.148}$$

We observe next that the current density must satisfy the requirement imposed by the law of conservation of charge, namely, in our case,

$$\operatorname{div}\boldsymbol{J}_{f1} = \operatorname{div}\boldsymbol{J}_{c1} = 0 \tag{9.149}$$

Evaluation of the divergence of the current density yields, with the help of Eqs. 9.145 and 9.148

$$\text{div grad } \phi_b = 0 \qquad r > a \tag{9.150}$$

$$\text{div grad } \phi_1 = 2\omega\mu A \qquad r \leq a \tag{9.151}$$

Thus, the potential $\phi_b$ must be a solution of Laplace's equation. The potential $\phi_1$, on the other hand, must satisfy Poisson's equation, and is associated with a uniform free-charge distribution of density equal to

$$-2\omega\epsilon_0\mu A \qquad r \leq a \tag{9.152}$$

The general solution of Eq. 9.151 consists of the sum of the potential produced in free space by the spherically symmetrical, uniform charge distribution and any potential satisfying Laplace's equation. Thus,

$$\phi_1 = \frac{\omega\mu r^2 A}{3} + \phi_a \qquad r \leq a \tag{9.153}$$

where $\phi_a$ is a solution of Laplace's equation. It follows that

$$-\text{ grad } \phi_1 = -\boldsymbol{i}_r\omega\tfrac{2}{3}\mu r A - \text{grad } \phi_a \qquad r \leq a \tag{9.154}$$

The two solutions of Laplace's equations $\phi_a$ and $\phi_b$ must be selected in such a way that $\boldsymbol{E}_1$ and $\boldsymbol{J}_{c1}$ satisfy the necessary boundary conditions on the spherical surface separating the rotating sphere from the stationary material surrounding it. The boundary condition associated with Eq. 9.146 requires the tangential component of $\boldsymbol{E}_1 - \boldsymbol{u} \times \mu_0\boldsymbol{M}_0$ to be continuous. We have, from Eqs. 9.144, 9.147, and 9.154,

$$\text{grad}_\theta\, \phi_a = \text{grad}_\theta\, \phi_b \qquad r = a \tag{9.155}$$

Because of the circular symmetry of the problem, $\phi_a$ and $\phi_b$ will be independent of $\varphi$, and therefore their gradients will have no $\varphi$ component. The boundary condition associated with the law of conservation of charge, Eq. 9.149, requires the normal component of $\boldsymbol{J}_{c1}$ to be continuous through the spherical surface. We have from Eqs. 9.145, 9.148, and 9.154,

$$\sigma_a[\omega\mu a(\tfrac{2}{3} - \sin^2\theta) + \text{grad}_r\, \phi_a] = \sigma_b \text{ grad}_r\, \phi_b \qquad r = a \tag{9.156}$$

i.e.,

$$\frac{\partial}{\partial r}\left(\phi_a - \frac{\sigma_b}{\sigma_a}\phi_b\right) = -\frac{\omega\mu a}{3}(3\cos^2\theta - 1) \qquad r = a \tag{9.157}$$

The requirement, expressed by Eq. 9.155, that the tangential component of the gradient be continuous, together with the requirement that the potential gradient be finite, although discontinuous, implies that

$$\phi_a = \phi_b \qquad r = a \tag{9.158}$$

Furthermore, because of Eq. 9.157, $\phi_a$ and $\phi_b$ must both be proportional to $(3\cos^2\theta - 1)$. We know from Sec. 4.10 that there are two solutions of Laplace's equation that depend on $\theta$ in this manner; one of them is proportional to $r^{-3}$, the other one to $r^2$. The potential $\phi_b$ must be identified with the first solution because the second solution becomes singular at infinity. Conversely, the potential $\phi_a$ must be identified with the second solution because the first solution becomes singular at the origin. Thus,

$$\phi_b = C\left(\frac{a}{r}\right)^3 (3\cos^2\theta - 1) \qquad r > a \tag{9.159}$$

$$\phi_a = C\left(\frac{r}{a}\right)^2 (3\cos^2\theta - 1) \qquad r \leq a \tag{9.160}$$

where $C$ is a constant to be determined. The potential $\phi_b$ corresponds to the field of an axial quadrupole located at the origin and parallel to the $z$-axis. The potential $\phi_a$ represents the corresponding field with the same type of singularity located at infinity.

Substitution of these expressions for $\phi_a$ and $\phi_b$ in Eq. 9.157, and solving for $C$, yields

$$C = -\frac{\omega\mu}{6} a^2 \frac{2\sigma_a}{2\sigma_a + 3\sigma_b} \tag{9.161}$$

Finally, entering in Eqs. 9.144 and 9.147 the expressions obtained above yields for the first-order electric field

$$\boldsymbol{E}_1 = -a\omega A \begin{cases} \mu \dfrac{g}{3\sigma_b}\left(\dfrac{a}{r}\right)^4 \left[\boldsymbol{i}_r \dfrac{1}{2}(3\cos^2\theta - 1) + \boldsymbol{i}_\theta \sin\theta\cos\theta\right] & r > a \\ \left(\dfrac{r}{a}\right)\left\{\boldsymbol{i}_r\left[\dfrac{\mu}{3}\dfrac{g}{2\sigma_a}(3\cos^2\theta - 1) + \mu_0\sin^2\theta\right]\right. & \\ \qquad \left. - \boldsymbol{i}_\theta\left(\mu\dfrac{g}{2\sigma_a} - \mu_0\right)\sin\theta\cos\theta\right\} & r \leq a \end{cases} \tag{9.162}$$

and entering the same expressions in Eqs. 9.145 and 9.148 yields for the first-order current density

$$\boldsymbol{J}_{c1} = -\omega\mu a g A \begin{cases} \dfrac{1}{3}\left(\dfrac{a}{r}\right)^4 \left[\boldsymbol{i}_r \dfrac{1}{2}(3\cos^2\theta - 1) + \boldsymbol{i}_\theta \sin\theta\cos\theta\right] & r > a \\ \dfrac{1}{2}\left(\dfrac{r}{a}\right)\left[\boldsymbol{i}_r \dfrac{1}{3}(3\cos^2\theta - 1) - \boldsymbol{i}_\theta \sin\theta\cos\theta\right] & r \leq a \end{cases} \tag{9.163}$$

where

$$g = \frac{6\sigma_a\sigma_b}{2\sigma_a + 3\sigma_b} \tag{9.164}$$

The corresponding first-order potential in the space occupied by the stationary material, i.e., in the external load connected to the generator, is the potential $\phi_b$ given by Eq. 9.159;

$$\phi_1 = \frac{\omega\mu}{6}\frac{g}{3\sigma_b}a^2 A\left(\frac{a}{r}\right)^3 (1 - 3\cos^2\theta) \qquad r > a \tag{9.165}$$

The current lines in the entire space and the traces of the equipotential surfaces in the stationary material are illustrated in Fig. 9.9. The geometry of the entire field is that of a figure of revolution about the $z$-axis.

Free charge is present within the rotating sphere and on its surface. We have for its volume density

$$\rho_{f1} = \operatorname{div} \epsilon_0 \boldsymbol{E}_1 = -2\omega\epsilon_0\mu_0 A = -\frac{2\omega A}{c^2} \qquad r \leq a \tag{9.166}$$

where $c$ is the velocity of light in vacuum.

The surface charge density is obtained from the discontinuity of the normal component of $\epsilon_0 \boldsymbol{E}_1$ with the help of Eq. 9.162; we have

$$\sigma_{f1} = \omega\epsilon_0\mu_0 a A \sin^2\theta + \omega\epsilon_0\mu \frac{\sigma_a - \sigma_b}{2\sigma_a + 3\sigma_b} aA(1 - 3\cos^2\theta) \tag{9.167}$$

The first term on the right-hand side of this equation represents a positive surface charge; its integrated value on the entire surface is just equal in magnitude (and opposite in sign) to the total charge distributed within the sphere (with density $\rho_{f1}$). The second term on the right-hand side of Eq. 9.167 represents a surface charge partly positive and partly negative; this term contributes no net integrated charge.

The potential distribution on the surface of the spherical cavity plays the role of terminal voltage. We have, to first-order approximation from Eq. 9.165

$$V_1 = \phi_1(r = a) = \omega \frac{\mu}{6} a^2 A(1 - 3\cos^2\theta) \frac{g}{3\sigma_b} \tag{9.168}$$

We observe, on the other hand, that the factor

$$K = \frac{g}{3\sigma_b} = \frac{2\sigma_a}{2\sigma_a + 3\sigma_b} \tag{9.169}$$

becomes equal to one for either $\sigma_b = 0$ (open-circuit operation) or $\sigma_a = \infty$ (zero generator resistance). Thus, the equivalent source voltage is given, to first approximation, by

$$V_{s1} = \omega \frac{\mu}{6} a^2 A(1 - 3\cos^2\theta) \tag{9.170}$$

For the quantity that plays the role of terminal current it is convenient to take the current per unit axial length flowing across the surface of the rotating sphere. Now, the area of the ring of spherical surface between two planes normal to the $z$-axis and spaced a distance $dz$ is equal to $2\pi a\, dz$. Thus, we have for the axial density of this current

$$I_1 = 2\pi a J_{cr1}(r = a) = 2\pi g V_{s1} \tag{9.171}$$

It is clear from this equation that the quantity $2\pi g$ plays the role of total circuit conductance per unit axial length; the corresponding load conductance per unit axial length is $6\pi\sigma_b$, and the corresponding internal conductance of the generator is $4\pi\sigma_a$.

The first-order current produces a first-order magnetic field in accordance with Eq. 9.142. It is clear, from the symmetry of the current distribution that the magnetic field consists entirely of a component $H_{\varphi 1}$, which must be independent of the $\varphi$ coordinate. This component can be readily computed by considering its line integral over the circle formed by the intersection of a sphere of radius $r$ with a cone of aperture $\theta$. Since $H_{\varphi 1}$ is independent of $\varphi$, we have, with the help of Stokes' theorem,

$$2\pi r \sin\theta\, H_{\varphi 1} = \int_S \boldsymbol{J}_{c1} \cdot \boldsymbol{n}\, da \tag{9.172}$$

The surface $S$ can be taken to be the spherical cap cut out by the cone from the spherical surface of radius $r$, in which case $\boldsymbol{n}$ becomes the unit vector $\boldsymbol{i}_r$. We have then,

$$2\pi r \sin\theta\, H_{\varphi 1} = 2\pi r^2 \int_0^\theta J_{rc1} \sin\theta\, d\theta \tag{9.173}$$

and finally, with the help of Eq. 9.163,

$$H_{\varphi 1} = -\omega \frac{\mu}{6} g a^2 A \sin\theta \cos\theta \begin{cases} (a/r)^3 & r > a \\ (r/a)^2 & r \le a \end{cases} \tag{9.174}$$

This magnetic field is tangent to the surface of the rotating sphere and is continuous through it. Thus the necessary boundary conditions are automatically satisfied.

It is interesting to note that the first-order magnetic field is parallel to the velocity field $\boldsymbol{u}$. Thus no second-order electric field and no second-order conduction current will be present. There will be, on the other hand, a second-order convection current resulting from the motion of the first-order free charges within the sphere and on its surface. This convection current, however, can be safely neglected at practical velocities, its density being proportional to the ratio $(v/c)^2$. If this convection current is neglected, no second-order magnetic field will be present and, therefore, no third- or higher order terms of any sort will be present. Thus the first-order quantities determined above constitute the entire electromagnetic field, at least at velocities of practical interest.

## 9.10 Summary and Conclusions

This chapter has been devoted to a discussion of the laws governing the behavior of electromagnetic fields in the presence of moving matter. We saw that three new terms appear in Maxwell's equations because of the presence of moving matter, namely:

1. A convection-current density, $\rho_f \boldsymbol{v}$, resulting from the motion of free electric charges that are at rest with respect to the moving matter. This current is treated as part of the free-current density $\boldsymbol{J}_f$.
2. A polarization-current density, curl $(\boldsymbol{P} \times \boldsymbol{v})$, resulting from the motion of electrically polarized matter.
3. A magnetic-current density, curl $(\mu_0 \boldsymbol{M} \times \boldsymbol{v})$, resulting from the motion of magnetized matter.

The motion of matter, in addition to introducing these three new terms into Maxwell's equations, affects its polarization, its magnetization and its conduction of electric current. We saw, in this connection, that the effective fields acting on a grain of moving matter are given by

$$\boldsymbol{E}_{\text{eff}} = \boldsymbol{E} + \boldsymbol{v} \times \mu_0 \boldsymbol{H} \tag{9.175}$$

$$\boldsymbol{H}_{\text{eff}} = \boldsymbol{H} - \boldsymbol{v} \times \epsilon_0 \boldsymbol{E} \tag{9.176}$$

In many cases, the polarization and the magnetization of moving matter can then be obtained by simply substituting these effective fields for the fields appearing in the constituent relations valid for the same matter at rest. Similarly, the conduction current density in a moving conductor can be taken to be the current density that would be present in the same conductor at rest if the electric field were equal to the effective field given by Eq. 9.175. In other words, the state of each grain of moving matter is a function of the effective fields acting on it.

The two examples discussed in this chapter illustrate the phenomena associated with the motion of conductors in a magnetic field. These phenomena are evidenced primarily by the presence of an electric field generated by the motion and of an associated current field (whenever the geometry of the conductors allows current to flow). The main phenomenon involved arises from the fact that the conduction-current density in a moving, linear conductor is proportional to the effective electric field given by Eq. 9.175. To appreciate how this fact can be responsible for the presence of an electric field, it is convenient to consider first the case in which the geometry of the system does not permit any current flow. For instance, no current field would be present in the two examples discussed in the preceding sections if the conductivity of the stationary material, $\sigma_b$, were equal to zero; i.e., in circuit terminology, if the electric generators represented by the two systems were open-circuited. Then, if the conduction-current density $\boldsymbol{J}_c$ is forced to vanish everywhere within the moving conductors, the effective electric field must also vanish because $\boldsymbol{J}_c$ is proportional to $\boldsymbol{E}_{\text{eff}}$. It follows that the electric field observed in the stationary frame within a moving conductor must be given by

$$\boldsymbol{E} = -\boldsymbol{v} \times \mu_0 \boldsymbol{H} \tag{9.177}$$

If this electric field is conservative, i.e., if curl $\boldsymbol{E} = 0$, its line integral between the terminals of the moving conductor constitutes the source voltage of the generator. This is the case for instance in the homopolar generator when the rotor is made of nonmagnetic material. On the other hand, when the electric field given by Eq. 9.177 is not conservative, the source voltage under open-circuit conditions must be determined by integrating the electric field along a path external to the moving conductor, in a region where the field is conservative or where it can be taken as approximately conservative in the sense of Sec. 7.6. In the example discussed in Secs. 9.7 and 9.8, the electric field is conservative everywhere except within the moving slab, where its finite curl results from the time variation of the magnetic field. In the case of the homopolar generator, the open-circuit electric field is conservative within the sphere, but a magnetic current is present on its surface because of the discontinuity of the tangential component of $\mu_0 \boldsymbol{M} \times \boldsymbol{v}$. This surface magnetic current, in turn, causes the tangential component of the electric field to be discontinuous, and with it the potential associated with the electric field. This potential discontinuity is responsible for the fact that the equivalent source voltage determined from the potential outside the sphere (Eq. 9.170) differs from the line integral of the electric field computed from the field within the sphere, namely $\omega(\mu_0/6)a^2A(1 - 3\cos^2\theta)$.

It is important to note that, in one of the examples discussed, the induced source voltage is independent of the magnetic characteristics of the moving conductor, whereas in the other example the equivalent source voltage is proportional to its permeability. This difference in behavior illustrates how careful one must be in applying the elementary induction laws to moving conductors. It is only when the moving conductors are nonmagnetic and the time variation of the magnetic field is negligible that the open-circuit source voltage can be safely determined by integrating the electric field given by Eq. 9.177.

When current is allowed to flow in the system, the electric field in the moving conductor differs from the right-hand side of Eq. 9.177 by an amount proportional to the current density. The resulting component of electric field proportional to the current density causes a decrease of terminal voltage which, in circuit terminology, is attributed to the internal resistance of the generator. However, if the conductivity of the moving conductor is infinite, Eq. 9.177 remains valid and the terminal voltage remains equal to the induced source voltage; in circuit terminology, the terminal voltage is independent of the load current because the internal resistance of the generator is equal to zero.

Finally, it is important to stress that a free-charge distribution equal to the divergence of $\epsilon \boldsymbol{E}$ must be associated to the conservative part of the electric field in a moving conductor. In the example discussed in Secs. 9.7 and 9.8, free charge is present only on the surfaces of the perfectly conducting plates because the electric field is solenoidal within the moving conductor. In the case of the homopolar generator, on the other hand, a free-charge distribution is present, both within the rotating sphere and on its surface.

## 9.11 Selected References

1. A. Sommerfeld, *Electrodynamics* (translated by E. G. Ramberg), Academic Press, New York, 1952. Part III is devoted to the theory of special relativity in vacuum; Secs. 34 and 35 of Part IV are devoted to Minkowski's formulation of the electrodynamics of moving media.
2. W. K. H. Panofsky and M. Phillips, *Classical Electricity and Magnetism*, Addison-Wesley, Cambridge, Mass., 1955. Chapter 9 presents a formulation of Maxwell's equations for moving media which parallels in many respects the formulation discussed in this chapter. Chapters 14 and 15 discuss the experimental basis for the theory of special relativity and the Lorentz transformation. Chapter 17 presents the four-dimensional formulation of vacuum electrodynamics, and Chapter 22 extends this formulation to material media.
3. A. Einstein et al., *The Principle of Relativity* (with notes by A. Sommerfeld), Dover Publications, New York. A collection of original memoirs on the special and general theory of relativity.
4. J. A. Stratton, *Electromagnetic Theory*, McGraw-Hill, New York, 1941. Sections 1.19 to 1.23 discuss the Lorentz transformation and the four-dimensional formulation of the field law.

## PROBLEMS

**Problem 9.1.** A dielectric rod is permanently and uniformly polarized in a direction normal to its axis. Determine the polarization-current distribution when the rod is rotated about its axis with a uniform angular velocity. The direction of polarization rotates with the rod. What is the value of the material time derivative of the polarization?

**Problem 9.2.** A dielectric rod rotates about its axis with a uniform angular velocity, and it is uniformly polarized in a direction normal to its axis by an external electric field. The direction of polarization remains fixed with respect to a stationary observer when the rod rotates. Determine the polarization-current distribution and the material time derivative of the polarization. Compare these quantities with the corresponding quantities in Prob. 9.1.

**Problem 9.3.** A permanently and uniformly magnetized sphere is rotated with uniform velocity about its axis parallel to the direction of magnetization. Determine the distribution of magnetization charges and currents.

**Problem 9.4.** Electric charge is uniformly distributed over the surface of an electromagnetically inert sphere. The sphere moves with a uniform velocity with respect to an observer. Determine the electromagnetic field produced by the moving sphere.

**Problem 9.5.** A sphere of homogeneous, linear, dielectric material moves with uniform velocity in a uniform magnetic field normal to the direction of motion, as determined by a stationary observer. Determine:

(a) The effective electric field acting on the sphere.

(b) The electric field resulting from the motion of the sphere, as measured by the stationary observer outside the sphere.

**Problem 9.6.** An infinite rod of homogeneous, linear conducting (but nonmagnetic) material rotates with uniform velocity about its axis in the presence of a uniform magnetic field normal to its axis. Determine:

(a) The first-order effective electric field acting on the rod.
(b) The first-order current distribution in the rod.
(c) The first-order magnetic field both inside and outside the rod.

**Problem 9.7.** Repeat Prob. 9.6 for a homogeneous rod of a material which is both linearly conducting and linearly magnetizable. Determine, in addition, the zero-order magnetic charge and the first-order magnetic current.

**Problem 9.8.** An infinite rod of linear, homogeneous conducting material rotates about its axis in the presence of a homogeneous magnetic field parallel to its axis. Determine the first-order electric field and magnetic field resulting from the rotation both inside and outside the rod.

**Problem 9.9.** An infinite rod of homogeneous, linear conducting (but nonmagnetic) material is divided in sections of equal length. Alternate sections rotate with uniform angular velocity about their axis, while the remaining sections are stationary. The entire rod is immersed in a uniform magnetic field normal to the axis of rotation, and perfect sliding contacts may be assumed between stationary and rotating sections. Determine:

(a) The first-order effective electric field acting on the stationary and rotating sections of the rod.
(b) The first-order electric field in the stationary and rotating sections of the rod.
(c) The first-order current distribution and the first-order magnetic field both inside and outside the rod.
(d) Sketch the first-order electric field outside the rod.

C H A P T E R   T E N

# Forces and Energy in Moving Systems

This chapter is devoted to the study of energy relations in moving systems, and, in particular, of the process of electromechanical energy conversion associated with macroscopic electromagnetic forces. We shall first derive a general expression for the macroscopic electromagnetic forces acting on moving matter by combining the results of Sec. 7.1, 9.2, 9.3, and 9.4. We shall develop next a generalization of Poynting's theorem, which relates the divergence of Poynting's vector to the time rates of change of the electromagnetic-energy density associated with the field, of the density of the work done by macroscopic electromagnetic forces, and of the density of the energy delivered to matter because of polarization, magnetization, and free-current conduction.

A virtual displacement method for determining macroscopic forces will be derived from the generalized Poynting's theorem. Illustrative examples will be used to point out the usefulness of this method when, because of mathematical difficulties, the electromagnetic field can be determined only approximately. Finally, the generalized Poynting's theorem will be used to study the process of electromechanical energy conversion in the two illustrative examples discussed in the preceding chapter.

## 10.1 Electromagnetic Forces, Stress, and Momentum

We saw in Sec. 7.1 that the macroscopic density of the forces exerted by an electromagnetic field on moving electric charges is given by

$$\boldsymbol{f} = \rho \boldsymbol{E} + \boldsymbol{J} \times \mu_0 \boldsymbol{H} \tag{10.1}$$

where $\rho$ is the net macroscopic charge density, and $\boldsymbol{J}$ is the net macroscopic current density resulting from the motion of the charges. Similarly, we saw that, if magnetic dipoles are treated as neutral aggregates of magnetic charges, the macroscopic density of the forces exerted by the electromagnetic field on a distribution of magnetic dipoles is given by

$$\boldsymbol{f}^* = \rho^* \boldsymbol{H} - \boldsymbol{J}^* \times \epsilon_0 \boldsymbol{E} \tag{10.2}$$

where $\rho^*$ and $\boldsymbol{J}^*$ are the macroscopic magnetic-charge density and magnetic-current density representing the dipole distribution. These expressions for the force densities are independent of the physical origin of the charges and the currents involved. In particular, they apply to charges and currents associated with moving matter as well as to charges and currents associated with stationary matter.

In addition, we saw in the preceding chapter that the total electric-charge density, and the total electric-current density in the presence of moving matter are given by

$$\rho = \rho_f + \rho_p = \rho_f - \operatorname{div} \boldsymbol{P} \tag{10.3}$$

$$\boldsymbol{J} = \boldsymbol{J}_f + \boldsymbol{J}_p = \boldsymbol{J}_f + \frac{\partial \boldsymbol{P}}{\partial t} + \operatorname{curl} (\boldsymbol{P} \times \boldsymbol{v}) \tag{10.4}$$

where $\rho_f$ is the free-charge density, $\boldsymbol{J}_f$ the free-current density, $\rho_p$ the polarization-charge density, $\boldsymbol{J}_p$ the polarization-current density, $\boldsymbol{P}$ the polarization vector, and $\boldsymbol{v}$ the velocity of the grain of matter in question. Similar expressions were obtained for the magnetic-charge density and the magnetic-current density;

$$\rho^* = \rho_m{}^* = - \operatorname{div} \mu_0 \boldsymbol{M} \tag{10.5}$$

$$\boldsymbol{J}^* = \boldsymbol{J}_m{}^* = \frac{\partial}{\partial t} (\mu_0 \boldsymbol{M}) + \operatorname{curl} (\mu_0 \boldsymbol{M} \times \boldsymbol{v}) \tag{10.6}$$

where $\rho_m{}^*$ is the magnetization-charge density, $\boldsymbol{J}_m{}^*$ is the magnetization-current density, and $\boldsymbol{M}$ is the magnetization vector. The terms analogous to $\rho_f$ and $\boldsymbol{J}_f$ are missing from Eqs. 10.5 and 10.6 because free magnetic charges and free magnetic currents have never been observed. Then, combining Eqs. 10.1 through 10.6 yields for the total force density

$$
\begin{aligned}
\boldsymbol{f} + \boldsymbol{f}^* &= \rho \boldsymbol{E} + \boldsymbol{J} \times \mu_0 \boldsymbol{H} + \rho^* \boldsymbol{H} - \boldsymbol{J}^* \times \epsilon_0 \boldsymbol{E} \\
&= (\rho_f - \operatorname{div} \boldsymbol{P})\boldsymbol{E} + \left[ \boldsymbol{J}_f + \frac{\partial \boldsymbol{P}}{\partial t} + \operatorname{curl} (\boldsymbol{P} \times \boldsymbol{v}) \right] \times \mu_0 \boldsymbol{H} \\
&\quad + (- \operatorname{div} \mu_0 \boldsymbol{M})\boldsymbol{H} \\
&\quad - \left[ \frac{\partial}{\partial t} (\mu_0 \boldsymbol{M}) + \operatorname{curl} (\mu_0 \boldsymbol{M} \times \boldsymbol{v}) \right] \times \epsilon_0 \boldsymbol{E}
\end{aligned} \tag{10.7}
$$

We shall now show that the total force density given by Eq. 10.7 can be expressed entirely in terms of the electromagnetic field. We observe, for this purpose, that the source densities that appear in Eq. 10.7 also appear on the right-hand sides of Maxwell's equations (Eqs. 9.1 to 9.4). Then, substituting for them the left-hand sides of Maxwell's equations yields

$$
\begin{aligned}
\boldsymbol{f} + \boldsymbol{f}^* &= \epsilon_0 (\boldsymbol{E} \operatorname{div} \boldsymbol{E} - \boldsymbol{E} \times \operatorname{curl} \boldsymbol{E}) \\
&\quad + \mu_0 (\boldsymbol{H} \operatorname{div} \boldsymbol{H} - \boldsymbol{H} \times \operatorname{curl} \boldsymbol{H}) - \epsilon_0 \mu_0 \frac{\partial}{\partial t} (\boldsymbol{E} \times \boldsymbol{H})
\end{aligned} \tag{10.8}
$$

i.e.,

$$
\begin{aligned}
\boldsymbol{f} + \boldsymbol{f}^* + \epsilon_0 \mu_0 \frac{\partial \boldsymbol{S}}{\partial t} &= \epsilon_0 (\boldsymbol{E} \operatorname{div} \boldsymbol{E} - \boldsymbol{E} \times \operatorname{curl} \boldsymbol{E}) \\
&\quad + \mu_0 (\boldsymbol{H} \operatorname{div} \boldsymbol{H} - \boldsymbol{H} \times \operatorname{curl} \boldsymbol{H})
\end{aligned} \tag{10.9}
$$

where $\boldsymbol{S}$ represents, as usual, the Poynting's vector.

The right-hand side of Eq. 10.9 has the important property that its integral over any volume $V$ can be transformed into an integral over the surface $S$ enclosing the volume. More precisely, as shown below,

$$
\int_V \left( \boldsymbol{f} + \boldsymbol{f}^* + \epsilon_0 \mu_0 \frac{\partial \boldsymbol{S}}{\partial t} \right) dv = \oint_S [\epsilon_0 (\boldsymbol{n} \cdot \boldsymbol{E}) \boldsymbol{E} + \mu_0 (\boldsymbol{n} \cdot \boldsymbol{H}) \boldsymbol{H} - \boldsymbol{n} w] \, da \tag{10.10}
$$

where $\boldsymbol{n}$ is a unit vector normal to the surface $S$, and

$$
w = \tfrac{1}{2} [\epsilon_0 (\boldsymbol{E} \cdot \boldsymbol{E}) + \mu_0 (\boldsymbol{H} \cdot \boldsymbol{H})] = \tfrac{1}{2} (\epsilon_0 |\boldsymbol{E}|^2 + \mu_0 |\boldsymbol{H}|^2) \tag{10.11}
$$

is the energy density associated with the electromagnetic field.

Equation 10.10 can be interpreted in a very interesting manner. Let us consider first the case of static fields. Since the time derivative of $\boldsymbol{S}$ vanishes, the left-hand side represents the total force exerted on the volume $V$. This suggests that the integrand on the right-hand side might be interpreted as a stress on the surface $S$ resulting from the forces exerted within $V$. In order for this interpretation to be acceptable, however, it is also necessary that the total torque exerted by the forces within $V$ be equal to the total torque exerted by the integrand on the right-hand side of Eq. 10.10, i.e.,

$$\int_V \boldsymbol{r} \times \left(\boldsymbol{f} + \boldsymbol{f}^* + \epsilon_0\mu_0 \frac{\partial \boldsymbol{S}}{\partial t}\right) dv$$

$$= \oint_S \boldsymbol{r} \times [\epsilon_0(\boldsymbol{n}\cdot\boldsymbol{E})\boldsymbol{E} + \mu_0(\boldsymbol{n}\cdot\boldsymbol{H})\boldsymbol{H} - \boldsymbol{n}w]\, da \quad (10.12)$$

where $\boldsymbol{r}$ is the vector distance from an arbitrary origin. This equation is in fact correct, as shown below.

The interpretation of the integrand on the right-hand side of Eq. 10.10 as an electromagnetic stress has an important historical significance. Since the existence of a surface stress corresponding to a volume distribution of forces is characteristic of elastic media, the theorems expressed by Eqs. 10.10 and 10.12 were considered in the past as supporting evidence for the "ether" theory of electromagnetism. This theory postulated that electromagnetic forces are transmitted as stresses in a fictitious elastic medium—the ether—pervading the entire space. Although this point of view is now regarded as having no physical basis, the theorems that suggested it are still of great value because they relate the forces exerted on a material body to the electromagnetic field surrounding it.

Let us consider now the general case of time-varying fields. If the volume $V$ does not contain any free charge or matter, $\boldsymbol{f}$ and $\boldsymbol{f}^*$ are equal to zero. On the other hand, the total stress on the surface $S$ may be different from zero. This forces us to interpret the term involving the time derivative of Poynting's vector as a volume force associated with the electromagnetic field, even in the absence of matter. More precisely, we interpret this term as the time rate of change of a momentum density

$$\boldsymbol{g}_e = \epsilon_0\mu_0(\boldsymbol{E} \times \boldsymbol{H}) = \frac{\boldsymbol{S}}{c^2} \quad (10.13)$$

where $c$ represents, as usual, the velocity of light in vacuum. Then, if we represent by $\boldsymbol{g}_m$ the momentum density of the matter inside $V$,

$$\boldsymbol{f} + \boldsymbol{f}^* = \frac{\partial \boldsymbol{g}_m}{\partial t} \quad (10.14)$$

and Eq. 10.10 becomes

$$\frac{d}{dt}\int_V (\boldsymbol{g}_m + \boldsymbol{g}_e)\, dv = \oint_S [\epsilon_0(\boldsymbol{n}\cdot\boldsymbol{E})\boldsymbol{E} + \mu_0(\boldsymbol{n}\cdot\boldsymbol{H})\boldsymbol{H} - \boldsymbol{n}w]\, da \quad (10.15)$$

The left-hand side of this equation is the time rate of change of the total momentum, mechanical plus electromagnetic, associated with the volume $V$. The right-hand side is the total electromagnetic stress on the surface $S$ enclosing $V$. Although associating a momentum to an electromagnetic field may seem at first rather strange, the presence of such a momentum is in agreement with a variety of experimental evidence, including measurements of the pressure exerted by light.

Equations 10.10 and 10.12 throw some additional light on the role played in our theory by the selection of a particular macroscopic model for matter. These two equations follow from Maxwell's equations (Eqs. 9.1 to 9.4) and the equations for the force densities on charges and currents, both electric and magnetic (Eqs. 10.1 and 10.2). Thus, as long as the presence of matter is taken into account by means of such source distributions, the validity of Eqs. 10.10 and 10.12 is not affected by the particular choice of macroscopic model. Let us suppose now that the volume $V$ includes polarized and magnetized matter, but the surface $S$ is entirely in vacuum. Then, since the electromagnetic field in vacuum is independent of the particular model of matter selected, the right-hand sides of Eqs. 10.10 and 10.12 must also be independent of the model. It follows that the total force and torque on the volume $V$, including the time rate of change of the electromagnetic momentum, must be independent of the model selected. In particular, the total force and torque on an isolated magnetized body in a static magnetic field are independent of whether the body is represented by means of amperian currents or magnetic charges. On the other hand, it should be kept in mind that the definition of the electromagnetic field in matter, as well as the distribution of electromagnetic forces, depends on the model selected. Thus, if the surface $S$ cuts through matter, the resulting total force and torque on $V$ may be different for different models.

Let us now prove the validity of Eqs. 10.10 and 10.12. Using the vector identity

$$\tfrac{1}{2} \operatorname{grad} (\boldsymbol{A} \cdot \boldsymbol{A}) = (\boldsymbol{A} \cdot \nabla)\boldsymbol{A} + \boldsymbol{A} \times \operatorname{curl} \boldsymbol{A} \tag{10.16}$$

Equation 10.9 can be rewritten in the form

$$\boldsymbol{f} + \boldsymbol{f}^* + \frac{\partial}{\partial t}\frac{\boldsymbol{S}}{c^2} = \epsilon_0[\boldsymbol{E} \operatorname{div} \boldsymbol{E} + (\boldsymbol{E} \cdot \nabla)\boldsymbol{E}] + \mu_0[\boldsymbol{H} \operatorname{div} \boldsymbol{H} + (\boldsymbol{H} \cdot \nabla)\boldsymbol{H}] - \operatorname{grad} w \tag{10.17}$$

where $w$ is the energy density given by Eq. 10.11. The volume integral of grad $w$ can be expressed as a surface integral with the help of Eq. 2.122

$$\int_V \text{grad } w \, dv = \oint_S \boldsymbol{n} w \, da \tag{10.18}$$

where $\boldsymbol{n}$ is a unit vector normal to $S$ and outwardly directed. Furthermore, the volume integral of each Cartesian component of the terms in square brackets can be transformed into a surface integral with the help of Eq. A4.14 and of Gauss' theorem,

$$\int_V (E_x \text{ div } \boldsymbol{E} + \boldsymbol{E} \cdot \text{grad } E_x) \, dv = \int_V \text{div } (E_x \boldsymbol{E}) \, dv = \oint_S E_x (\boldsymbol{E} \cdot \boldsymbol{n}) \, da \tag{10.19}$$

Similar expressions are obtained for the other two Cartesian components of the first term in square brackets and for all Cartesian components of the second term in square brackets. It is clear that Eq. 10.10 follows immediately from Eqs. 10.17, 10.18, and 10.19.

The proof of Eq. 10.12 involves showing that the volume integrals of the cross products of $\boldsymbol{r}$ and each of the terms on the right-hand side of Eq. 10.17 can be transformed into surface integrals. We have for the cross product involving the last term, with the help of Eqs. A4.15, 2.126, and 2.159,

$$\int_V \boldsymbol{r} \times \text{grad } w \, dv = \int_V (w \text{ curl } \boldsymbol{r} - \text{curl } w\boldsymbol{r}) \, dv = \oint_S w\boldsymbol{r} \times \boldsymbol{n} \, da \tag{10.20}$$

Furthermore each Cartesian component of the cross product of $\boldsymbol{r}$ and each of the terms in square brackets can be transformed as follows:

$$\begin{aligned} \{\boldsymbol{r} \times [\boldsymbol{E} \text{ div } \boldsymbol{E} + (\boldsymbol{E} \cdot \nabla)\boldsymbol{E}]\}_x & \\ &= (yE_z - zE_y) \text{ div } \boldsymbol{E} + \boldsymbol{E} \cdot (y \text{ grad } E_z - z \text{ grad } E_y) \\ &= (\boldsymbol{r} \times \boldsymbol{E})_x \text{ div } \boldsymbol{E} + \boldsymbol{E} \cdot \text{grad } (\boldsymbol{r} \times \boldsymbol{E})_x = \text{div } (\boldsymbol{r} \times \boldsymbol{E})_x \boldsymbol{E} \end{aligned} \tag{10.21}$$

Then, with the help of Gauss' theorem,

$$\int_V \{\boldsymbol{r} \times [\boldsymbol{E} \text{ div } \boldsymbol{E} + (\boldsymbol{E} \cdot \nabla)\boldsymbol{E}]\}_x \, dv = \oint_S (\boldsymbol{r} \times \boldsymbol{E})_x (\boldsymbol{E} \cdot \boldsymbol{n}) \, da \tag{10.22}$$

Similar expressions are obtained for the other components of the same cross product, and for all Cartesian components of the corresponding cross product involving $\boldsymbol{H}$. Clearly, Eq. 10.12 follows from Eqs. 10.20 and 10.22.

## 10.2 A Generalization of Poynting's Theorem

We shall now derive a generalized form of Poynting's theorem which places in evidence the electromechanical energy conversion resulting from the action of electromagnetic forces on matter. We begin, as in the derivation of the usual form of Poynting's theorem, by forming the sum of the scalar products of the electric field with the electric-current density, and of the magnetic field with the magnetic-current density. This sum of products can be written, with the help of Eqs. 9.1 and 9.2 in the form

$$\boldsymbol{E}\cdot\boldsymbol{J} + \boldsymbol{H}\cdot\boldsymbol{J}^* = \boldsymbol{E}\cdot\operatorname{curl}\boldsymbol{H} - \boldsymbol{H}\cdot\operatorname{curl}\boldsymbol{E} - \epsilon_0\boldsymbol{E}\cdot\frac{\partial\boldsymbol{E}}{\partial t} - \mu_0\boldsymbol{H}\cdot\frac{\partial\boldsymbol{H}}{\partial t} \tag{10.23}$$

Then, noting that

$$\operatorname{div}\boldsymbol{S} = \operatorname{div}(\boldsymbol{E}\times\boldsymbol{H}) = \boldsymbol{H}\cdot\operatorname{curl}\boldsymbol{E} - \boldsymbol{E}\cdot\operatorname{curl}\boldsymbol{H} \tag{10.24}$$

and

$$\frac{\partial w}{\partial t} = \frac{\partial}{\partial t}\left[\frac{1}{2}\,\epsilon_0(\boldsymbol{E}\cdot\boldsymbol{E}) + \frac{1}{2}\,\mu_0(\boldsymbol{H}\cdot\boldsymbol{H})\right] = \epsilon_0\boldsymbol{E}\cdot\frac{\partial\boldsymbol{E}}{\partial t} + \mu_0\boldsymbol{H}\cdot\frac{\partial\boldsymbol{H}}{\partial t} \tag{10.25}$$

Equation 10.23 can be rewritten in the form

$$-\left(\operatorname{div}\boldsymbol{S} + \frac{\partial w}{\partial t}\right) = \boldsymbol{E}\cdot\boldsymbol{J} + \boldsymbol{H}\cdot\boldsymbol{J}^* \tag{10.26}$$

and, with the help of Gauss' theorem, in the equivalent integral form

$$-\oint_S \boldsymbol{S}\cdot\boldsymbol{n}\,da - \int_V \frac{\partial w}{\partial t}\,dv = \int_V (\boldsymbol{E}\cdot\boldsymbol{J} + \boldsymbol{H}\cdot\boldsymbol{J}^*)\,dv \tag{10.27}$$

We saw in Sec. 7.2 that the first term on the left-hand side of this equation can be interpreted as the electromagnetic power entering the volume $V$ through its surface $S$, and the second term on the same side can be interpreted as the negative time rate of change of the energy associated with the electromagnetic field within $V$ (exclusive of the energy absorbed by polarized and magnetized matter). The right-hand side of Eq. 10.27 represents the total electromagnetic power transformed within $V$ to some other form of energy through the motion of electric and magnetic charges in the presence of an electromagnetic field.

Part of the electromagnetic power converted must be identifiable as work per unit time done by the macroscopic electromagnetic forces acting on each grain of matter. The rest must represent energy stored or dissipated in matter. To identify these two components of the power converted, we consider separately the density of the work per unit time done by the electromagnetic forces, namely, $\boldsymbol{v}\cdot(\boldsymbol{f}+\boldsymbol{f}^*)$, where $\boldsymbol{v}$ is a function of time and position representing the velocity of each grain of matter. We have from Eq. 10.7

$$\boldsymbol{v}\cdot(\boldsymbol{f}+\boldsymbol{f}^*) = \boldsymbol{v}\cdot\rho\boldsymbol{E} + \boldsymbol{v}\cdot(\boldsymbol{J}\times\mu_0\boldsymbol{H}) + \boldsymbol{v}\cdot\rho^*\boldsymbol{H} - \boldsymbol{v}\cdot(\boldsymbol{J}^*\times\epsilon_0\boldsymbol{E}) \tag{10.28}$$

and, with the help of Eq. A4.3

$$0 = \boldsymbol{v}\cdot(\boldsymbol{f}+\boldsymbol{f}^*) + (\boldsymbol{v}\times\mu_0\boldsymbol{H})\cdot\boldsymbol{J} - \boldsymbol{E}\cdot\rho\boldsymbol{v} - (\boldsymbol{v}\times\epsilon_0\boldsymbol{E})\cdot\boldsymbol{J}^* - \boldsymbol{H}\cdot\rho^*\boldsymbol{v} \tag{10.29}$$

Then, adding to the right-hand side of the last equation the term $-\rho\boldsymbol{v}\cdot(\boldsymbol{v}\times\mu_0\boldsymbol{H}) + \rho^*\boldsymbol{v}\cdot(\boldsymbol{v}\times\epsilon_0\boldsymbol{E})$ which is identically equal to zero, and to both sides of the same equation the term $(\boldsymbol{E}\cdot\boldsymbol{J}+\boldsymbol{H}\cdot\boldsymbol{J}^*)$, yields

$$\begin{aligned}(\boldsymbol{E}\cdot\boldsymbol{J}+\boldsymbol{H}\cdot\boldsymbol{J}^*) &= \boldsymbol{v}\cdot(\boldsymbol{f}+\boldsymbol{f}^*) + (\boldsymbol{E}+\boldsymbol{v}\times\mu_0\boldsymbol{H})\cdot(\boldsymbol{J}-\rho\boldsymbol{v}) \\ &\quad + (\boldsymbol{H}-\boldsymbol{v}\times\epsilon_0\boldsymbol{E})\cdot(\boldsymbol{J}^*-\rho^*\boldsymbol{v})\end{aligned} \tag{10.30}$$

Finally, substituting the right-hand side of this equation for the right-hand side of Eq. 10.26 yields

$$\begin{aligned}-\left(\operatorname{div}\boldsymbol{S}+\frac{\partial w}{\partial t}\right) &= \boldsymbol{v}\cdot(\boldsymbol{f}+\boldsymbol{f}^*) + (\boldsymbol{E}+\boldsymbol{v}\times\mu_0\boldsymbol{H})\cdot(\boldsymbol{J}-\rho\boldsymbol{v}) \\ &\quad + (\boldsymbol{H}-\boldsymbol{v}\times\epsilon_0\boldsymbol{E})\cdot(\boldsymbol{J}^*-\rho^*\boldsymbol{v})\end{aligned} \tag{10.31}$$

This is the desired differential form of Poynting's theorem.

The right-hand side of Eq. 10.31 represents, as before, the total density of electromagnetic power converted to some other form of energy. The first term of it is the density of the work per unit time done by the electromagnetic forces, which is transformed, presumably, into mechanical energy. The second term is the scalar product of the *effective electric field*

$$\boldsymbol{E}_{\text{eff}} = \boldsymbol{E} + \boldsymbol{v}\times\mu_0\boldsymbol{H} \tag{10.32}$$

and the *effective current density*

$$\boldsymbol{J}_{\text{eff}} = \boldsymbol{J} - \rho\boldsymbol{v} \tag{10.33}$$

We saw in Sec. 9.5 that $\boldsymbol{E}_{\text{eff}}$ is the force per unit charge acting on a grain of matter moving with velocity $\boldsymbol{v}$. The effective current density

$\boldsymbol{J}_{\text{eff}}$ is the total current density less the convection component resulting from the motion of the net charge present in a grain of matter. Thus, $\boldsymbol{J}_{\text{eff}}$ is the density of the current within a grain of matter, i.e., of the current resulting from the motion of charges with respect to the grain. In other words, $\boldsymbol{E}_{\text{eff}}$ and $\boldsymbol{J}_{\text{eff}}$ are the electric-field and the current density measured by a stationary observer at a point moving with respect to him. It must be stressed that these quantities are not in general equal to the electric field and to the current density measured by an observer moving with the point. These quantities coincide with them only for velocities much smaller than that of light (see Appendix 1). It follows that the second term on the right-hand side of Eq. 10.31 represents power delivered by the field to the moving matter.

The last term on the right-hand side of Eq. 10.31 is the scalar product of the *effective magnetic field*

$$\boldsymbol{H}_{\text{eff}} = \boldsymbol{H} - \boldsymbol{v} \times \epsilon_0 \boldsymbol{E} \tag{10.34}$$

and the *effective magnetic-current density*

$$\boldsymbol{J}_{\text{eff}}^* = \boldsymbol{J}^* - \rho^* \boldsymbol{v} \tag{10.35}$$

The effective magnetic field was defined in Sec. 9.6 as the force per unit magnetic charge acting on a grain of matter moving with velocity $\boldsymbol{v}$. The effective magnetic-current density is the density of the magnetic current within a grain of matter, i.e., of the current resulting from the motion of magnetic charges with respect to the grain. In other words, $\boldsymbol{H}_{\text{eff}}$ and $\boldsymbol{J}_{\text{eff}}^*$ are the magnetic field and the magnetic-current density measured by a stationary observer at a point moving with respect to him. Again, these quantities should not be confused with the magnetic field and the magnetic-current density measured by an observer moving with the point; these quantities coincide with them only for velocities much smaller than that of light (see Appendix 1). It follows that the last term on the right-hand side of Eq. 10.31 represents additional power delivered by the field to the moving matter.

The power density resulting from the scalar product of $\boldsymbol{E}_{\text{eff}}$ and $\boldsymbol{J}_{\text{eff}}$ can be further divided into two parts corresponding to the free and polarization components of $\boldsymbol{J}_{\text{eff}}$. We obtain

$$\boldsymbol{E}_{\text{eff}} \cdot \boldsymbol{J}_{\text{eff}} = \boldsymbol{E}_{\text{eff}} \cdot (\boldsymbol{J}_f - \rho_f \boldsymbol{v}) + \boldsymbol{E}_{\text{eff}} \cdot (\boldsymbol{J}_p + \boldsymbol{v} \operatorname{div} \boldsymbol{P}) \tag{10.36}$$

The free component of $\boldsymbol{J}_{\text{eff}}$ represents conduction current, so that its scalar product with $\boldsymbol{E}_{\text{eff}}$ represents power dissipated into heat. The polarization component of $\boldsymbol{J}_{\text{eff}}$ can be expressed in the form

$$\boldsymbol{J}_p + \boldsymbol{v} \operatorname{div} \boldsymbol{P} = \rho_0 \left( \frac{d\boldsymbol{d}}{dt} \right)_m \tag{10.37}$$

where the time derivative of $\boldsymbol{d}$ is the material derivative defined by Eq. 9.26. We saw in Sec. 9.2 that this material derivative is the time rate of change of the displacement $\boldsymbol{d}$ evaluated with respect to the moving material. Thus, the last term on the right-hand side of Eq. 10.36 represents power absorbed by the material because of its changing state of polarization.

In the particular case of a rigid body, we have from Eq. 9.32

$$\boldsymbol{E}_{\text{eff}} \cdot (\boldsymbol{J}_p + \boldsymbol{v} \operatorname{div} \boldsymbol{P}) = \boldsymbol{E}_{\text{eff}} \cdot \left(\frac{d\boldsymbol{P}}{dt}\right)_m \tag{10.38}$$

where the time derivative of $\boldsymbol{P}$ is evaluated with respect to a system of coordinates moving rigidly with the body. Thus, the polarization power absorbed by each grain of a rigid body is the same whether the body is in motion or at rest, provided $\boldsymbol{E}_{\text{eff}}$ and $(d\boldsymbol{P}/dt)_m$ are the same. This is certainly in agreement with our intuition because the energy absorbed by matter should depend only on its change of state and on the force per unit charge exerted by the field.

Because of Eq. 10.38, the density of the energy absorbed by a polarized rigid body in motion can be expressed in the same form as for a stationary body (see Eq. 7.57)

$$w_P = \int_0^P \boldsymbol{E}_{\text{eff}} \cdot (d\boldsymbol{P})_m \tag{10.39}$$

where $(d\boldsymbol{P})_m$ is the increment of $\boldsymbol{P}$ measured by a stationary observer with respect to a system of coordinates moving rigidly with the body. Furthermore, if the polarization characteristics of the material involved are conservative, i.e., if $\boldsymbol{P}$ is a single-valued function of $\boldsymbol{E}_{\text{eff}}$, $w_P$ can be regarded as the density of the energy stored in the polarized material. Finally, in the special case of a linear dielectric material characterized by a permittivity $\epsilon$, we obtain for the polarization energy density

$$w_P = \tfrac{1}{2}\boldsymbol{E}_{\text{eff}} \cdot \boldsymbol{P} = \tfrac{1}{2}(\epsilon - \epsilon_0)\,|\boldsymbol{E}_{\text{eff}}|^2 \tag{10.40}$$

The physical significance of the second term on the right-hand side of Eq. 10.31 can be discussed in a completely analogous manner. Since there is no free magnetic current, the entire term represents power absorbed by matter as a result of its changing state of magnetization. In the particular case of a rigid body, we obtain from Eq. 9.40

$$\boldsymbol{H}_{\text{eff}} \cdot \boldsymbol{J}_{\text{eff}}{}^* = \boldsymbol{H}_{\text{eff}} \cdot \mu_0 \left(\frac{d\boldsymbol{M}}{dt}\right)_m \tag{10.41}$$

where the time derivative of $\boldsymbol{M}$ is again evaluated by a stationary observer with respect to a system of coordinates moving rigidly with the body. Correspondingly, the density of the magnetization energy absorbed by the rigid body can be written in the form

$$w_M = \int_0^{\boldsymbol{M}} \boldsymbol{H}_{\text{eff}} \cdot \mu_0 \, (d\boldsymbol{M})_m \tag{10.42}$$

where the increment of $\boldsymbol{M}$ is again measured with respect to a system of coordinates moving rigidly with the body. Finally, if the rigid body is made of linear material characterized by a permeability $\mu$,

$$w_M = \mu_0 \boldsymbol{H}_{\text{eff}} \cdot \boldsymbol{M} = \tfrac{1}{2}(\mu - \mu_0) \, |\boldsymbol{H}_{\text{eff}}|^2 \tag{10.43}$$

We can conclude then, that in the special case of a rigid body the generalized Poynting's theorem can be written in the form

$$-\left(\operatorname{div} \boldsymbol{S} + \frac{\partial w}{\partial t}\right) = p_d + \frac{d}{dt}(w_P + w_M) + \boldsymbol{v} \cdot (\boldsymbol{f} + \boldsymbol{f}^*) \tag{10.44}$$

where $w_P$ and $w_M$ are defined by Eqs. 10.39 and 10.42, and

$$p_d = \boldsymbol{E}_{\text{eff}} \cdot (\boldsymbol{J}_f - \rho_f \boldsymbol{v}) \tag{10.45}$$

is the power-dissipation density resulting from conduction current.

## 10.3 Static Forces and Virtual Work

The total force and the total torque exerted by an electromagnetic field on a rigid body can be computed, in principle, as volume integrals of the force density $\boldsymbol{f} + \boldsymbol{f}^*$ and of its moment; if desired, such volume integrals can, in turn, be reduced to surface integrals with the help of Eqs. 10.10 and 10.12, whenever the electromagnetic momentum can be neglected, as in the case of a stationary body in a static field. This possibility of substituting a surface integral involving the field outside the body in question for a volume integral involving the force density inside the body may be of critical importance in actual computations; for instance, the field might be known with sufficient accuracy over a particular surface enclosing the body while not within the body itself. On the other hand, there are cases in which neither computational technique can yield a sufficiently accurate answer, in spite of the fact that our knowledge of the field may be adequate for other purposes. A typical case is that of a dielectric slab partially inserted between the parallel plates of a capacitor, as illustrated in Fig. 10.1. If the dimensions of the plates are large compared to their spacing, the electric field in the region between the plates is very closely normal to the plates and equal in magnitude to the applied voltage divided by the spacing. On the other hand, the force acting on the slab is parallel to the plates, as indicated in Fig. 10.1, and, therefore, cannot result from the component of the electric field normal to the plates. It follows, that the force must result from the action of the field near the left edge of the plates which possesses a component parallel to the plates. This is just the part of the field that is difficult to evaluate precisely. Similar difficulties are met when we attempt to compute the force by surface integration.

Problems such as the one illustrated in Fig. 10.1 can often be handled by exploiting the relationship between forces and energy provided by the generalized Poynting's theorem which expresses the law of conservation of energy for electromagnetic systems. In a nutshell, the force or the torque on a rigid body can be computed by requiring the work done by it for a small displacement plus the corresponding increase of energy stored in the system to be equal to the energy supplied (if any) by external electric sources. This procedure is often referred to as the virtual-work or virtual-displacement method. While the validity of this procedure may seem obvious because of our intuitive acceptance of the law of conservation of energy, it is instructive to see how it can be derived from the generalized Poynting's theorem. For the sake of simplicity, we shall restrict our discussion to fields which, in the absence of motion, are static.

The appropriate tools for our study are provided again by the power series method of analysis discussed in Sec. 9.6. Therefore, for any given system we consider the family of processes generated by varying the time-rate parameter $\alpha$, and express all quantities involved as power series in $\alpha$. Our first objective is to determine the zero-order and first-order equations corresponding to the generalized Poynting's theorem.

For this purpose, we first write the generalized Poynting's theorem for the family of processes with the help of Eqs. 9.54, 9.56, and 9.57. We obtain from Eq. 10.31, in the special case of rigid bodies,

$$-\left(\operatorname{div}\boldsymbol{S} + \alpha\frac{\partial w}{\partial\tau}\right) = \alpha\boldsymbol{u}\cdot(\boldsymbol{f}+\boldsymbol{f}^*) + (\boldsymbol{E} + \alpha\boldsymbol{u}\times\mu_0\boldsymbol{H})\cdot(\boldsymbol{J}_f - \alpha\rho_f\boldsymbol{u})$$
$$+ (\boldsymbol{E} + \alpha\boldsymbol{u}\times\mu_0\boldsymbol{H})\cdot\alpha\left(\frac{d\boldsymbol{P}}{d\tau}\right)_m + (\boldsymbol{H} - \alpha\boldsymbol{u}\times\epsilon_0\boldsymbol{E})\cdot\alpha\mu_0\left(\frac{d\boldsymbol{M}}{d\tau}\right)_m \tag{10.46}$$

The reader is reminded in this connection that $\boldsymbol{u}$ is the member of the velocity-field family that corresponds to $\alpha = 1$, and is obtained by substituting $\tau$ for $t$ in the specified, real-time velocity field. Then, we express all quantities as power series in $\alpha$, and equate the terms in Eq. 10.46 that are proportional to each individual power of $\alpha$. We obtain from the zero-order terms

$$- \operatorname{div} \boldsymbol{S}_0 = \boldsymbol{E}_0 \cdot \boldsymbol{J}_{f0} \tag{10.47}$$

and from the first-order terms

$$- \left( \operatorname{div} \boldsymbol{S}_1 + \frac{\partial w_0}{\partial \tau} \right) = \boldsymbol{u} \cdot (\boldsymbol{f}_0 + \boldsymbol{f}_0^*) + \boldsymbol{E}_0 \cdot (\boldsymbol{J}_{f1} - \rho_{f0} \boldsymbol{u}) + (\boldsymbol{u} \times \mu_0 \boldsymbol{H}_0) \cdot \boldsymbol{J}_{f0} + \boldsymbol{E}_0 \cdot \left( \frac{d\boldsymbol{P}_0}{d\tau} \right)_m + \boldsymbol{H}_0 \cdot \mu_0 \left( \frac{d\boldsymbol{M}_0}{d\tau} \right)_m \tag{10.48}$$

where

$$\boldsymbol{S}_0 = \boldsymbol{E}_0 \times \boldsymbol{H}_0 \tag{10.49}$$

$$\boldsymbol{S}_1 = \boldsymbol{E}_0 \times \boldsymbol{H}_1 + \boldsymbol{E}_1 \times \boldsymbol{H}_0 \tag{10.50}$$

$$w_0 = \tfrac{1}{2}(\epsilon_0 |\boldsymbol{E}_0|^2 + \mu_0 |\boldsymbol{H}_0|^2) \tag{10.51}$$

The zero-order equation is of no interest to us because it does not contain any electromagnetic forces. The first-order equation, on the other hand, provides a relation between the zero-order forces (static forces) and other zero-order and first-order electromagnetic quantities. This is the fundamental relation on which our discussion of virtual work is based. Our next step is to integrate this first-order equation over the entire space. Integration over any volume $V$ of the first term on the left-hand side of Eq. 10.48 yields, with the help of Gauss' theorem,

$$- \int_V \operatorname{div} \boldsymbol{S}_1 \, dv = - \oint_S (\boldsymbol{E}_0 \times \boldsymbol{H}_1 + \boldsymbol{E}_1 \times \boldsymbol{H}_0) \cdot \boldsymbol{n} \, da \tag{10.52}$$

where $S$ is the surface enclosing the volume $V$, and $\boldsymbol{n}$ a unit vector normal to $S$ and outwardly directed. Let us suppose now that the volume $V$ is a sphere, and that all charges and matter in the system are located within a finite distance from the center of the sphere. It can be shown by the argument used in Sec. 7.3 in connection with Eq. 7.51 that the right-hand side of Eq. 10.52 vanishes when the radius of the sphere approaches infinity. We observe, on the other hand, that extending the volume integration over the entire space implies considering any electric source connected to the system as part of the system itself, in the sense that we would have to deal in detail with the energy conversion process within the source. It is more convenient instead to consider all electric sources as external to the system, and to take into account the power supplied (or absorbed) by them in terms of their terminal voltages and terminal currents. This can be accomplished by excluding such sources from the volume $V$, in which case the surface of integration on the right-hand side of Eq. 10.52 will consist of closed surfaces surrounding the individual sources, in addition to the surface at infinity. The contribution to the surface integral of each of these surfaces represents the first-order power flowing into the volume $V$ from the source in question, with the result that the left-hand side of Eq. 10.52 represents the total first-order power $P_{s1}$ supplied to the system by external electric sources.

The volume integration of the other terms in Eq. 10.48 does not present any special problem. Let us indicate with

$$P_{f1} = \int_V \boldsymbol{u} \cdot (\boldsymbol{f}_0 + \boldsymbol{f}_0{}^*)\, dv \tag{10.53}$$

the total first-order power supplied by the field through the action of electromagnetic forces, with

$$P_{d1} = \int_V [\boldsymbol{E}_0 \cdot (\boldsymbol{J}_{f1} - \rho_{f0}\boldsymbol{u}) + (\boldsymbol{u} \times \mu_0 \boldsymbol{H}_0) \cdot \boldsymbol{J}_{f0}]\, dv \tag{10.54}$$

the total first-order power dissipated by conduction currents, with

$$W_{P0} = \int_V \left[ \int_0^{\boldsymbol{P}_0} \boldsymbol{E}_0 \cdot (d\boldsymbol{P}_0)_m \right] dv \tag{10.55}$$

the total zero-order energy supplied by the field to polarized matter, with

$$W_{M0} = \int_V \left[ \mu_0 \int_0^{\boldsymbol{M}_0} \boldsymbol{H}_0 \cdot (d\boldsymbol{M}_0)_m \right] dv \tag{10.56}$$

the total zero-order energy supplied by the field to magnetized matter, and with

$$W_0 = \int_V \tfrac{1}{2}(\epsilon_0 |\boldsymbol{E}_0|^2 + \mu_0 |\boldsymbol{H}_0|^2)\, dv \tag{10.57}$$

the total zero-order energy associated with the electromagnetic field, where the volume $V$ is the entire space exclusive of the regions occupied by electric sources. Then, the volume integral over $V$ of Eq. 10.48 can be expressed in the form

$$P_{s1} = P_{f1} + P_{d1} + \frac{d}{d\tau}(W_0 + W_{P0} + W_{M0}) \tag{10.58}$$

Finally, multiplication of this equation by the differential time increment $d\tau$ yields, for $\alpha = 1$, $d\tau = dt$,

$$P_{s1}\,dt = P_{f1}\,dt + P_{d1}\,dt + dW_0 + dW_{P0} + dW_{M0} \qquad (10.59)$$

This last equation expresses the law of conservation of energy for differential displacements of rigid bodies. It equates the energy supplied by external electric source, because of the displacements, to the sum of the work done by electromagnetic forces, the energy dissipated by conduction currents, the energy stored in the field, and the polarization and magnetization energy supplied to matter. It is assumed, of course, that the motion of the rigid bodies represented by the velocity field $\boldsymbol{u}$ is so slow that all the terms in Eq. 10.46 of order higher than the first can be neglected. The application of the method of virtual displacement based on Eq. 10.59 is illustrated in the following section.

## 10.4 Examples of Evaluation of Static Forces

We shall now illustrate the use of Eq. 10.59 by evaluating the force acting on the dielectric slab of Fig. 10.1. The dielectric slab is made of linear, homogeneous material, with a dielectric constant $\epsilon$. The slab and the plates have the same width $b$; the length of the plates is equal to $a$, and the thickness of the slab, which fills the space between the plates, is equal to $d$. We wish to determine the force on the slab in the direction of the $z$-axis when the voltage source is disconnected after placing charges $q_0$ and $-q_0$ on the two plates. The plates can be assumed to be perfectly conducting, in view of the fact that their conductivity does not affect the state of the system for any given position of the slab.

Since no source is connected to the system, and since the plates are perfectly conducting, $P_{s1}$ and $P_{d1}$ in Eq. 10.59 are both equal to zero. Furthermore, because of the absence of any zero-order magnetic field, and because of the linearity of the dielectric slab, the total zero-order

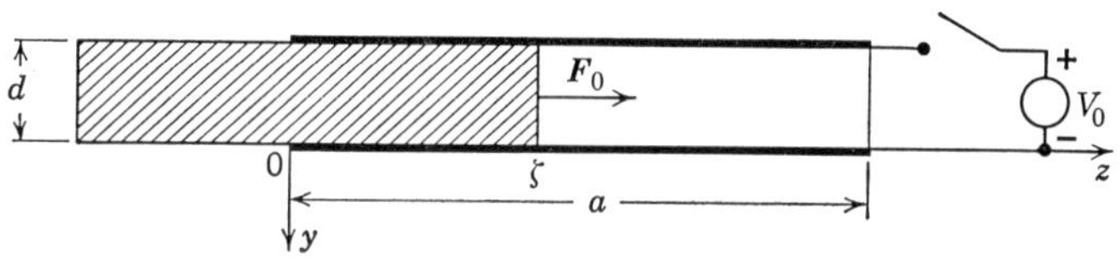


**Fig. 10.1.** Dielectric slab partially inserted between the plates of a capacitor.

energy in the system can be written in the form

$$W_{t0} = W_0 + W_{P0} + W_{M0} = \int_V \tfrac{1}{2}\epsilon |\boldsymbol{E}_0|^2 \, dv \qquad (10.60)$$

Now, if we indicate with $\zeta$ the position of the front edge of the slab, we obtain from Eq. 10.59,

$$\boldsymbol{i}_z \cdot \boldsymbol{F}_0 \frac{d\zeta}{dt} + \frac{dW_{t0}}{d\zeta}\frac{d\zeta}{dt} = 0 \qquad q_0 = \text{const} \qquad (10.61)$$

The zero-order electric field between the plates is uniform, and parallel to the $y$-axis, apart from the edge effect which may be neglected for our purposes. The magnitude of the corresponding surface charge density on the upper plates is equal to $\epsilon E_{y0}$ where the plates are covered by the slab, and to $\epsilon_0 E_{y0}$ on the rest of the plates. Thus, the total zero-order charge on the upper plate, $q_0$, is related to $E_{y0}$ by

$$b[\epsilon\zeta + \epsilon_0(a - \zeta)]E_{y0} = q_0 \qquad (10.62)$$

Most of the electric energy is stored in the space between the plates where the field is most intense. If we neglect the energy stored outside this region, we obtain for $W_{t0}$

$$W_{t0} = \frac{1}{2} bdE_{y0}{}^2[\epsilon\zeta + \epsilon_0(a - \zeta)] = \frac{dq_0{}^2}{2b[\epsilon\zeta + \epsilon_0(a - \zeta)]} \qquad (10.63)$$

Substitution of this expression for $W_{t0}$ in Eq. 10.61 yields for the $z$ component of the zero-order force

$$\begin{aligned} F_{z0} &= \frac{dq_0{}^2}{2b[\epsilon\zeta + \epsilon_0(a - \zeta)]^2}(\epsilon - \epsilon_0) = \frac{1}{2} bd(\epsilon - \epsilon_0)E_{y0}{}^2 \\ &= \frac{b}{2d}(\epsilon - \epsilon_0)V_0{}^2 \end{aligned} \qquad (10.64)$$

where $V_0$ is the zero-order voltage between the plates. It will be noted that the force depends on $\zeta$ for a given charge on the plates, but it is independent of $\zeta$ for a given electric field, i.e., for a given voltage.

The above computation leads to an accurate result in spite of the fact that the fringing of the field near the edges of the plates has been neglected. This may seem strange at first in view of the fact that the force results just from the fringing of the field. It is clear, on the other hand, that the field near the edges does not depend on the position of the slab as long as neither end of the slab is too close to the edges of the plates. Thus it should not be surprising that the rate of change of the energy with $\zeta$, which determines the force, can be evaluated with good accuracy by neglecting the fringing of the field.

Let us suppose next that the voltage source shown in Fig. 10.1 is left connected to the plates. It should be clear that the same force must act on the slab when the same voltage exists between the plates, regardless of whether the source is connected to the plates or not. It is instructive, nevertheless, to carry out the computation of the force under this different system condition.

Since the voltage source remains connected to the plates, $P_{s1}$ in Eq. 10.59 is no longer equal to zero, so that we obtain instead of Eq. 10.61

$$V_0 I_1 = \boldsymbol{i}_z \cdot \boldsymbol{F}_0 \frac{d\zeta}{dt} + \frac{dW_{t0}}{d\zeta}\frac{d\zeta}{dt} \tag{10.65}$$

where $I_1$ is the first-order component of the source current; the source voltage is held constant and, therefore, its first-order component is equal to zero.

The current $I_1$ is most readily computed with the help of the law of conservation of charge which requires the source current to be equal to the time rate of change of the total charge $q$ on the upper plate,

$$I = \frac{dq}{dt} \tag{10.66}$$

The first-order term in this equation yields

$$I_1 = \frac{dq_0}{dt} = \frac{d\zeta}{dt}\frac{dq_0}{d\zeta} \qquad V_0 = \text{const} \tag{10.67}$$

where $q_0$ is the zero-order charge on the upper plate, and with the help of Eq. 10.62,

$$I_1 = \frac{b}{d}(\epsilon - \epsilon_0)V_0 \tag{10.68}$$

where $V_0$ has been substituted for $E_{y0}d$. Thus, we have for the first-order power supplied by the voltage source

$$P_{s1} = V_0 I_1 = \frac{b}{d}(\epsilon - \epsilon_0)V_0^2 \tag{10.69}$$

The derivative of $W_{t0}$ with respect to $\zeta$ must now be computed with the voltage held constant rather than the charge. We obtain from the first part of Eq. 10.63

$$\frac{dW_{t0}}{d\zeta} = \frac{b}{2d}(\epsilon - \epsilon_0)V_0^2 \qquad V_0 = \text{const} \tag{10.70}$$

Substitution of these expressions in Eq. 10.65 yields finally

$$F_{z0} = \frac{b}{2d}(\epsilon - \epsilon_0)V_0^2 \tag{10.71}$$

which checks with Eq. 10.64, as expected. It is interesting to note that the work done by the force is just equal to the increase of energy stored in the system. Thus half of the energy delivered by the source is transformed into mechanical work while the other half is stored in the system.

Problems involving the determination of a torque are handled in a similar manner. Let us consider, for instance, the case of a variable capacitor consisting of two semicircular, parallel plates, one of which is free to rotate about an axis normal to both plates and passing by their centers, as illustrated in Fig. 10.2. Let this axis coincide with the $z$-axis, $R$ be the radius of the plates, $d$ their spacing, and $\varphi$ the angle between corresponding radial edges of the plates, as shown in the same figure. We wish to compute the torque on the movable plate when a voltage $V_0$ is applied between the plates, for a particular value of the angle $\varphi$.

We shall assume that the voltage source has been disconnected from the capacitor after charging it to the desired voltage. If fringing is neglected, the zero-order electric field between the plates is uniform, normal to the plates, and equal in magnitude to $V_0/d$. The zero-order charge density on the plates is equal to $\epsilon_0 V_0/d$, so that the total zero-order charge on the plates is given by

$$q_0 = \frac{1}{2}(\pi - \varphi)\frac{R^2}{d}V_0 \tag{10.72}$$

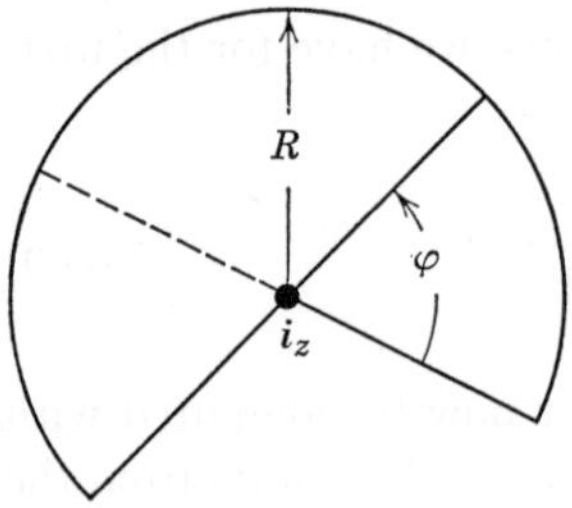


**Fig. 10.2.** Variable semicircular capacitor.

Again, $P_{s1}$ and $P_{d1}$ in Eq. 10.59 are equal to zero, and the total energy $W_{t0}$ is given by Eq. 10.60. If the energy associated with the field near the edges of the plates is neglected, we obtain for $W_{t0}$

$$W_{t0} = \frac{1}{4}(\pi - \varphi)\left(\frac{R}{d}\right)^2 \epsilon_0 V_0^2 = \frac{\epsilon_0 q_0^2}{(\pi - \varphi)R^2} \tag{10.73}$$

Then, Eq. 10.59 yields

$$P_{f1} = T_{z0}\frac{d\varphi}{dt} = -\frac{dW_{t0}}{d\varphi} = -\epsilon_0\left[\frac{q_0}{(\pi - \varphi)R}\right]^2$$

$$= -\frac{1}{4}\epsilon_0\left(\frac{R}{d}\right)^2 V_0^2 \qquad q_0 = \text{const} \tag{10.74}$$

where $T_{z0}$ is the component of the torque along the axis of rotation. Thus the torque is independent of the angle $\varphi$, for a given voltage (as long as $\varphi$ is not close to either 0 or $\pi$), and tends to decrease the angle $\varphi$ between the plates.

The fringing of the field near the radial edges of the plates plays the same secondary role as in the preceding illustration. On the other hand, the energy associated with the fringing field near the circular edges of the plates is approximately a linear function of the angle $\varphi$, and, therefore, yields a component of torque which may or may not be negligible, depending on the ratio $d/R$.

It is important to stress, in closing this section, that the forces exerted by a static field on a stationary body depend only on the field itself and on the distributions of electric and magnetic charges and of free currents. In particular, the forces do not depend directly on how these quantities change when the body is displaced. It follows that, whenever we wish to determine the force or torque on a rigid body by the method discussed in this section, we can use for the body any constituent relation that yields the correct polarization, magnetization, and free-current density in the absence of motion. Thus, for instance, we can assume that a magnetic material is linear, provided the value of the permeability at each point is chosen in such a way as to give the correct magnetization. This assumption facilitates considerably the evaluation of the rate of change of the magnetization energy with the displacement of the body.

## 10.5 Energy Conversion Resulting from the Uniform Motion of a Conductor in a Magnetic Field

This section is devoted to the study of the energy conversion aspects of the illustrative example discussed in Secs. 9.7 and 9.8. In view of the fact that we were able, in Sec. 9.8, to obtain the total electromagnetic field, we shall disregard, in what follows, the power-series terms obtained in Sec. 9.7.

Let us begin by studying the power flow in the system. We observe, with reference to Fig. 9.6 and Eqs. 9.119 and 9.120, that Poynting's vector is everywhere parallel to the $z$-axis, and can be viewed as consisting of four components (not to be confused with terms of a power series),

$$\boldsymbol{S} = (\boldsymbol{E} \times \boldsymbol{H}) = \boldsymbol{S}_1 + \boldsymbol{S}_2 + \boldsymbol{S}_3 + \boldsymbol{S}_4$$

where

$$\boldsymbol{S}_1 = -\boldsymbol{i}_z \frac{I^2}{b\sigma_b} \begin{cases} (a + \zeta - z)/a & \zeta \le z \le \zeta + a \\ 1 & 0 < z < \zeta \\ (z + b)/b & -b \le z \le 0 \\ 0 & z < -b \quad \text{and} \quad \zeta + a < z \end{cases} \tag{10.75}$$

results from the products involving the constants $C$ and $I$, with $C$ expressed in terms of $I$ by means of Eq. 9.127,

$$\boldsymbol{S}_2 = \boldsymbol{i}_z \frac{AI}{b\sigma_b} \qquad \text{for all values of } z \tag{10.76}$$

results from the products involving the constants $A$ and $C$, with $C$ expressed in terms of $I$,

$$\boldsymbol{S}_3 = \boldsymbol{i}_z \mu_0 v_0 A I \begin{cases} 1 & \zeta + a < z \\ (z - \zeta)/a & \zeta \le z \le \zeta + a \\ 0 & z < \zeta \end{cases} \tag{10.77}$$

results from the products involving the constants $A$ and $B$, with $B$ expressed in terms of $I$ by means of Eq. 9.127, and

$$\boldsymbol{S}_4 = \boldsymbol{i}_z \mu_0 v_0 I^2 \begin{cases} [(z - \zeta)(z - \zeta - a)]/a^2 & \zeta \le z \le \zeta + a \\ 0 & z < \zeta \quad \text{and} \quad \zeta + a < z \end{cases} \tag{10.78}$$

results from products involving the constants $I$ and $B$, with $B$ expressed in terms of $I$. The $z$ behavior of these four components is illustrated

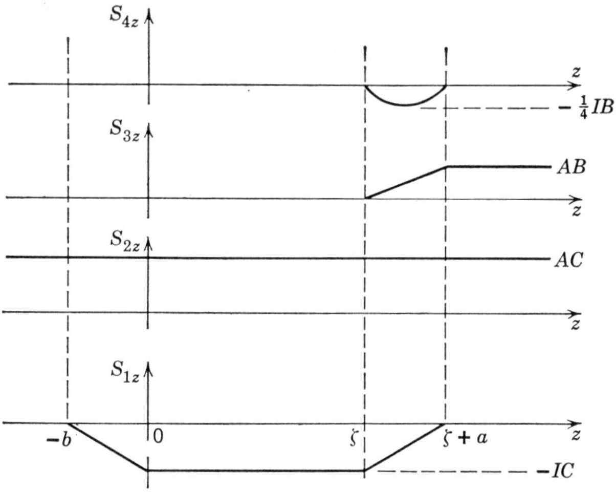


**Fig. 10.3.** The four components of Poynting's vector for the system of Figs. 9.3 and 10.4.

in Fig. 10.3. The constant $I$ can be expressed in terms of $A$, if desired, with the help of Eq. 9.130.

The first component represents power flowing from the moving slab to the stationary slab. The corresponding total power flowing in the negative $z$ direction across any plane normal to the $z$-axis and located between the two slabs is given by

$$P_1 = I^2 \frac{d}{b\sigma_b} = I^2 R_b = VI \tag{10.79}$$

where $R_b$ is the resistance of the stationary slab per unit length in the $y$ direction, and $V$ is the terminal voltage (voltage between the two perfectly conducting sheets) given by Eq. 9.134. It is clear that $P_1$ is the load power, dissipated in the stationary slab, and generated in the moving slab.

The second component $\mathbf{S}_2$ represents power flowing in the positive $z$ direction from $-\infty$ to $+\infty$. The corresponding total power flowing across any plane normal to the $z$-axis is

$$P_2 = AI \frac{d}{b\sigma_b} = AV \tag{10.80}$$

This component of power flow does not involve the process of energy

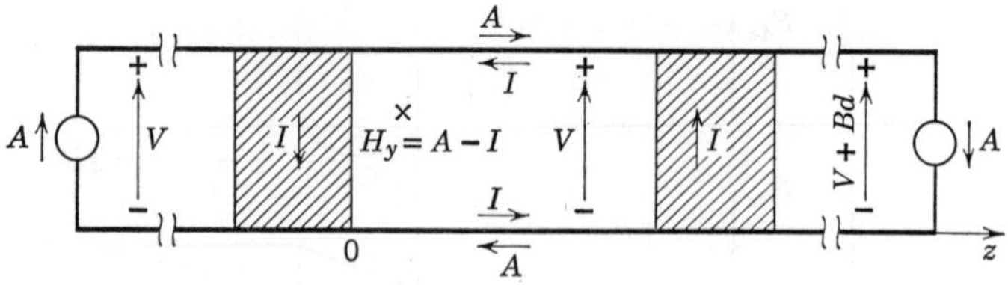


**Fig. 10.4.** Generation of the impressed magnetic field in the system of Fig. 9.3.

conversion. We shall now show that it represents an interchange of energy between the sources producing the uniform magnetic field of intensity equal to $A$. This magnetic field could, in fact, be produced by a current in the upper conducting sheet of surface density $\mathbf{i}_z A$, and a current in the lower sheet of surface density $-\mathbf{i}_z A$, as illustrated in Fig. 10.4. These currents could be forced into the sheets by the antisymmetric current sources in the same figure. Then the magnetic field of intensity $A$ would exist only in the space between the two current sources, and the power flow corresponding to the second component of Poynting's vector would originate from the current source on the left and terminate at the current source on the right. The source on the left forces current in the direction opposite to that of the electric field generated by the motion of the right-hand slab and, therefore, it must deliver a power (per unit length in the $y$ direction) equal to the product of the surface current density $A$ and the terminal voltage $V$, which is just the value given by Eq. 10.80. This power is absorbed by the source on the right which forces current in the direction of the electric field.

The third component of Poynting's vector represents additional power flowing toward the current source on the right-hand side. This power is given by

$$P_3 = \mu_0 v_0 A I d = A(Bd) \tag{10.81}$$

where $Bd$ represents the difference between the voltage on the right of the moving slab, and the voltage on the left of the moving slab. Thus

$$P_2 + P_3 = A(V + Bd) \tag{10.82}$$

is the total power absorbed by the current source on the right, being the product of the surface current density $A$ and the voltage $V + Bd$ between the two sheets on the right of the moving slab.

The fourth component of Poynting's vector differs from zero only within the moving slab, and gives rise to a transfer of energy from the right half of the slab to the left half of the slab. This energy transfer has no important physical significance.

Let us turn our attention next to the power converted from mechanical form to electromagnetic form. There is only one component of the electromagnetic-force density, namely that arising from the conduction current, because there are no electric charges, magnetic charges, or magnetic currents in the moving slab. Thus $\boldsymbol{f}^*$ is equal to zero and

$$\boldsymbol{f} = \boldsymbol{J}_c \times \mu_0 \boldsymbol{H} = -\boldsymbol{i}_z \left[ \mu_0 A \frac{I}{a} + \mu_0 \frac{I^2}{a^2} (z - \zeta - a) \right] \tag{10.83}$$

within the moving slab, where $\boldsymbol{J}_c$ is the conduction-current density given by Eq. 9.131, apart from the factor $1 - (v_0/c)^2$ which is neglected because it is extremely close to one in practical cases. The total electromagnetic force on the moving slab is, therefore,

$$\boldsymbol{F} = d \int_{\zeta}^{\zeta+a} \boldsymbol{f}\, dz = -\boldsymbol{i}_z(\mu_0 A I d - \tfrac{1}{2}\mu_0 I^2 d) \tag{10.84}$$

This force exerted by the field on the moving slab must be balanced by an external force, equal in magnitude and opposite in direction, in order for the slab to be in dynamic equilibrium. The mechanical power supplied by this external force, namely,

$$P_m = -\boldsymbol{v} \cdot \boldsymbol{F} = \mu_0 v_0 A I d - \tfrac{1}{2}\mu_0 v_0 I^2 d \tag{10.85}$$

is converted into electromagnetic power. We shall see that part of this electromagnetic power is dissipated within the moving slab, part is dissipated in the stationary slab, with a small fraction being absorbed by the current source on the right.

The electromagnetic energy stored in the system changes with time because of the motion of the right-hand slab, and of the difference between the field intensities on the right side and on the left side of that slab. We obtain for the time rate of change of the energy stored in the electromagnetic field within the moving slab

$$\frac{\partial w}{\partial t} = \epsilon_0 \boldsymbol{E} \cdot \frac{\partial \boldsymbol{E}}{\partial t} + \mu_0 \boldsymbol{H} \cdot \frac{\partial \boldsymbol{H}}{\partial t} = -\mu_0 v_0 A \frac{I}{a} - \mu_0 v_0 \frac{I^2}{a^2} (z - \zeta - a) \tag{10.86}$$

where the term associated with the electric field has been neglected because it turns out to be proportional to $(v_0/c)^2$. Thus, the total time rate of change of the energy in the moving slab is given by

$$\frac{\partial W}{\partial t} = d\int_{\zeta}^{\zeta+a} \frac{\partial w}{\partial t}\, dz = -(\mu_0 v_0 A I d - \tfrac{1}{2}\mu_0 v_0 I^2 d) \tag{10.87}$$

It is interesting to note that

$$P_m = -\frac{\partial W}{\partial t} \tag{10.88}$$

In other words, the power made available by the decrease of energy stored is exactly equal to the mechanical power converted into electromagnetic form.

Let us consider next the power dissipation. We have in the stationary slab

$$\boldsymbol{E}\cdot\boldsymbol{J}_c = \frac{1}{\sigma_b}(\boldsymbol{J}_c\cdot\boldsymbol{J}_c) = \frac{I^2}{b^2\sigma_b} \tag{10.89}$$

and in the moving slab

$$(\boldsymbol{E} + \boldsymbol{v}_0 \times \mu_0\boldsymbol{H})\cdot\boldsymbol{J}_c = \frac{1}{\sigma_a}(\boldsymbol{J}_c\cdot\boldsymbol{J}_c) = \frac{I^2}{a^2\sigma_a} \tag{10.90}$$

where the factor $1 - (v_0/c)^2$ in the current density has been neglected as before. Thus the total power dissipated in the stationary slab is

$$P_b = I^2\frac{d}{b\sigma_b} = I^2R_b \tag{10.91}$$

where $R_b$ is the resistance of the stationary slab per unit length in the $y$ direction. The total power dissipated in the moving slab is, similarly,

$$P_a = I^2\frac{d}{a\sigma_a} = I^2R_a \tag{10.92}$$

where $R_a$ is the resistance of the moving slab per unit length in the $y$ direction.

We are now ready to check the energy balance. The net power leaving the moving slab is equal to

$$P_1 + P_3 = I^2R_b + \mu_0 v_0 A I d \tag{10.93}$$

This power must be equal to

$$P_m - \frac{\partial W}{\partial t} - P_a = 2\mu_0 v_0 A I d - \mu_0 v_0 I^2 d - I^2 R_a \tag{10.94}$$

Equating the right-hand sides of these two equations yields after some manipulations

$$\mu_0 v_0 A I d - \mu_0 v_0 I^2 d = I^2(R_a + R_b) \tag{10.95}$$

The constant $A$ on the left-hand side of this equation can now be expressed in terms of $I$ with the help of Eq. 9.132. We obtain then

$$\mu_0 v_0 I(A - I)d = \mu_0 v_0 I^2 d\left(1 + \frac{1}{\mu_0 v_0 g} - 1\right) = I^2 \frac{d}{g} \tag{10.96}$$

Finally, substituting for $g$ by means of Eq. 9.118 yields

$$I^2 \frac{d}{g} = I^2(R_a + R_b) \tag{10.97}$$

which is the right-hand side of Eq. 10.95. It is important to note that the total power dissipated is not equal to $P_m$, the mechanical power converted. Part of the mechanical power converted, namely, $\frac{1}{2}\mu_0 v_0 I^2 d$, is absorbed by the current source on the right side of Fig. 10.4.

The energy balance for the stationary slab is immediately evident. The net power entering the slab, $P_1$, must be equal to the total power dissipated in the slab, $P_b$. Equations 10.79 and 10.91 show that this equality is, in fact, satisfied.

## ► 10.6 Energy Conversion in a Model of Homopolar Generator

This section is devoted to the study of the energy conversion aspects of the illustrative example discussed in Sec. 9.9. We shall begin by evaluating Poynting's vector, both inside and outside the rotating sphere. Since the fields have been determined in terms of successive coefficients of power series in $\alpha$, Poynting's vector must be written, correspondingly, as a power series,

$$\mathbf{S} = \mathbf{S}_0 + \alpha \mathbf{S}_1 + \alpha^2 \mathbf{S}_2 + \cdots = (\mathbf{E} \times \mathbf{H}) \tag{10.98}$$

where

$$\mathbf{S}_0 = \mathbf{E}_0 \times \mathbf{H}_0 \tag{10.99}$$

$$\mathbf{S}_1 = \mathbf{E}_1 \times \mathbf{H}_0 + \mathbf{E}_0 \times \mathbf{H}_1 \tag{10.100}$$

$$\mathbf{S}_2 = \mathbf{E}_1 \times \mathbf{H}_1 + \mathbf{E}_2 \times \mathbf{H}_0 + \mathbf{E}_0 \times \mathbf{H}_2 \tag{10.101}$$

The zero-order term is equal to zero because the zero-order electric field is equal to zero. The first-order term is readily evaluated from Eqs.

9.138 and 9.162. We obtain, after some manipulations,

$$
\boldsymbol{S}_1 = \boldsymbol{i}_\varphi \omega \frac{a}{3} \sin\theta A^2 \begin{cases} \dfrac{r}{a}\left(3\mu_0 - \mu\dfrac{g}{2\sigma_a}\right) & r \leq a \\ \left(\dfrac{a}{r}\right)^4 \dfrac{g}{3\sigma_b}\mu\left[\left(1+\dfrac{\mu}{2\mu_0}\right)(5\cos^2\theta - 1) \right. \\ \qquad \left. + \dfrac{1}{2}\left(\dfrac{\mu}{\mu_0} - 1\right)\left(\dfrac{a}{r}\right)^3 (1+\cos^2\theta)\right] & r > a \end{cases} \tag{10.102}
$$

This first-order component of Poynting's vector represents power circulating in the $\varphi$ direction, with neither sources nor sinks. In other words, its flow lines close upon themselves with no transfer of energy taking place in any physical sense.

The second-order component of Poynting's vector can be evaluated with the help of Eqs. 9.162 and 9.174, while noting that both $\boldsymbol{E}_0$ and $\boldsymbol{E}_2$ are equal to zero. We obtain after some manipulations

$$
\boldsymbol{S}_2 = -\omega^2 a^3 \mu_0 \mu \frac{g}{6}\left(\frac{r}{a}\right)^3 A^2 \left\{\boldsymbol{i}_r\left(\frac{\mu}{\mu_0}\frac{g}{2\sigma_a} - 1\right)\sin\theta\cos\theta \right.
$$

$$
\left. + \boldsymbol{i}_\theta\left[\frac{\mu}{\mu_0}\frac{g}{6\sigma_a}(3\cos^2\theta - 1) + \sin^2\theta\right]\right\}\sin\theta\cos\theta \tag{10.103}
$$

for $r \leq a$, i.e., inside the rotating sphere, and

$$
\boldsymbol{S}_2 = \omega^2 a^3 \mu^2 \frac{g}{6}\frac{g}{3\sigma_b}\left(\frac{a}{r}\right)^7 A^2 \left[\boldsymbol{i}_r \sin\theta\cos\theta - \boldsymbol{i}_\theta \frac{1}{2}(3\cos^2\theta - 1)\right]\sin\theta\cos\theta \tag{10.104}
$$

for $r > a$, i.e., in the stationary material surrounding the sphere. It is important to note that the radial component of this second-order Poynting's vector is discontinuous at the surface of the rotating sphere. This discontinuity is equal to

$$
\omega^2 a^3 \mu_0 \mu \frac{g}{6} A^2 \left(\frac{\mu}{\mu_0} - 1\right)\sin^2\theta\cos^2\theta \tag{10.105}
$$

We shall see that it accounts for the mechanical power converted into electromagnetic power at the surface of the rotating sphere as a result of the force exerted by the magnetic field on the surface magnetic charge whose density is given by Eq. 9.140.

The second-order Poynting's vector has no $\varphi$ component. Furthermore, being a vector product of the first-order field vectors, it must be normal to $\boldsymbol{E}_1$. Thus, in the stationary medium outside the rotating sphere, where $\boldsymbol{J}_1$ is proportional to $\boldsymbol{E}_1$, the flow lines of $\boldsymbol{S}_2$ must be normal to the current lines illustrated in Fig. 9.9; they must coincide, therefore, with the traces of the equipotential surfaces shown as dotted lines in the same figure. On the other hand, the factor $\sin\theta\cos\theta$ included in $\boldsymbol{S}_2$ results in the vanishing of $\boldsymbol{S}_2$ on the axis of the spherical system of coordinates and on its equatorial plane. Therefore, most of the power enters the stationary medium from the rotating sphere in the neighborhood of the zero-potential cones shown in Fig. 9.9, and spreads toward the $z$-axis and the equatorial plane; however, the density of power flow is attenuated to zero because of dissipation by the time it reaches the $z$-axis and the equatorial plane. The direction of power flow inside the rotating sphere is not normal to that of the current flow because, in the moving medium, $\boldsymbol{J}_1$ is proportional to $\boldsymbol{E}_1 + \boldsymbol{u} \times \mu_0\boldsymbol{H}_0$ rather than to $\boldsymbol{E}_1$. Furthermore, inspection of the expression for $\boldsymbol{S}_2$ (Eq. 10.103) indicates that its direction, inside the rotating sphere, is a function of the parameters representing the electromagnetic characteristics of the medium, so that its flow lines cannot be pictured precisely unless the characteristics of the medium are known. We can say, however, that the power-flow lines tend to become normal to the current lines shown in Fig. 9.9 when the permeability of the rotating sphere becomes much larger than that of free space.

Let us turn our attention next to the conversion of mechanical energy into electromagnetic energy. In this connection, we are interested only in the electromagnetic forces on each grain of matter that are parallel to the velocity of the grain. Therefore, since the velocity field has only a $\varphi$ component, only the $\varphi$ components of the forces need to be evaluated. There are only two types of forces possessing $\varphi$ components, and both of them are first-order terms from a power-series point of view. The first one is the volume force exerted by the zero-order magnetic field on the first-order current in the rotating sphere. The second one is the surface force exerted by the first-order magnetic field on the zero-order magnetic charge on the surface of the rotating sphere.

The $\varphi$ component of the force density $\boldsymbol{f}$ can be evaluated with the help of Eqs. 9.138 and 9.163 for $r < a$. We obtain

$$f_{1\varphi} = (\boldsymbol{J}_{c1} \times \mu_0\boldsymbol{H}_0)_\varphi = -\omega\mu_0\mu a \frac{g}{6}\frac{r}{a} A^2 \sin\theta \qquad (10.106)$$

This force density is proportional to the distance $r \sin\theta$ from the axis of rotation. The $\varphi$ component of the surface force $\boldsymbol{f}_{S1}^*$ can be evaluated with the help of Eqs. 9.140 and 9.174 for $r = a$. We obtain

$$f_{S1\varphi}^* = \sigma^* H_{1\varphi} = -\omega\mu(\mu - \mu_0)a^2 \frac{g}{6} A^2 \sin\theta \cos^2\theta \qquad (10.107)$$

Since the dynamic equilibrium of the sphere requires these electromagnetic-force distributions to be balanced by external forces, the power supplied by these external forces must be given by

$$P_{m2} = -\int_V (\boldsymbol{v}\cdot\boldsymbol{f}_1)\, dv - \oint_S (\boldsymbol{v}\cdot\boldsymbol{f}_{S1}^*)\, da \qquad (10.108)$$

Evaluation of the power associated to the electric volume force yields

$$-\int_V (\boldsymbol{v}\cdot\boldsymbol{f}_1)\, dv = -\omega \int_V f_{1\varphi} r \sin\theta (r^2 \sin\theta\, dr\, d\theta\, d\varphi)$$

$$= \frac{8\pi}{15}\omega^2 \mu_0 \mu \frac{g}{6} a^5 A^2 \qquad (10.109)$$

and evaluation of the power associated with the surface magnetic force yields

$$-\oint_S (\boldsymbol{v}\cdot\boldsymbol{f}_{S1}^*)\, da = -\omega \oint_S f_{S1\varphi}^* a \sin\theta (a^2 \sin\theta\, d\theta\, d\varphi)$$

$$= \frac{8\pi}{15}\omega^2 \mu(\mu - \mu_0) \frac{g}{6} a^5 A^2 \qquad (10.110)$$

Thus the total mechanical power converted into electromagnetic power is

$$P_{m2} = \omega T_m = \frac{8\pi}{15}\omega^2 \mu^2 \frac{g}{6} a^5 A^2 \qquad (10.111)$$

where $T_m$ is the magnitude of the mechanical torque that must be applied to the rotating sphere by external forces. It is important to note that the power converted is proportional to the square of the angular velocity, the square of the permeability of the rotating sphere, the square of the magnetic-field intensity, and the fifth power of the radius of the sphere. It is important to note also that the integrand in Eq. 10.110, apart from the differential surface element in parentheses, is just equal to the discontinuity of the radial component of $\mathbf{S}_2$ at the surface of the rotating sphere, given by Eq. 10.105. In other words, electromagnetic power becomes available right at the surface of the rotating sphere because of the presence of a surface electromagnetic force.

Part of the mechanical energy transformed into electromagnetic energy within the rotating sphere is dissipated right within the sphere; the rest flows into the surrounding stationary medium where it is similarly dissipated. Since the electromagnetic field is independent of time, the energy stored in the field remains constant, and, therefore, plays no part in the energy balance. The same is true for the energy associated with the magnetization of the rotating sphere, as long as the velocity of rotation remains constant.

The total power dissipated within the rotating sphere and within the surrounding stationary medium can be readily evaluated with the help of Eq. 9.163. We obtain for the rotating sphere

$$P_{a2} = \int_{V_a} \frac{1}{\sigma_a} (\boldsymbol{J}_{c1} \cdot \boldsymbol{J}_{c1})\, dv = \frac{8\pi}{15} \omega^2 \mu^2 a^5 \frac{g}{6} \frac{g}{2\sigma_a} A^2 \tag{10.112}$$

where $V_a$ is the volume of the rotating sphere, and for the rest of the space

$$P_{b2} = \int_{V_b} \frac{1}{\sigma_b} (\boldsymbol{J}_{c1} \cdot \boldsymbol{J}_{c1})\, dv = \frac{8\pi}{15} \omega^2 \mu^2 a^5 \frac{g}{6} \frac{g}{3\sigma_b} A^2 \tag{10.113}$$

here $V_b$ is the volume of the space outside the rotating sphere. It is easy to see, with the help of Eq. 9.164 which defines $g$, that $P_{a2} + P_{b2}$ is just equal to $P_{m2}$, the total power converted into electromagnetic form. Similarly, evaluation of the flux of $\boldsymbol{S}_2$ through the inner surface of the stationary medium shows that the total power entering the space occupied by the stationary medium is just equal to $P_{b2}$.

Finally, the reader is reminded that all field quantities of order higher than the first vanish when the velocities involved are much smaller than that of light, as discussed at the end of Sec. 9.9. Thus the second-order power flow discussed above constitutes in practice the entire power flow.

## 10.7 Summary and Conclusions

This chapter has presented a theory of forces and energy exchanges in electromagnetic system, based on assumed macroscopic models of matter. The theory by itself is self-consistent, and it agrees with previous theories in all respects about which conclusive experimental evidence is available. Some disagreements exist, however, as, for instance, with respect to the distribution of forces in magnetized bodies, about which presently available experimental evidence is still inconclusive.

The key topic in this chapter is the generalized Poynting's theorem discussed in Sec. 10.2. This theorem is a mathematical consequence of the field equations, and, strictly speaking, does not add any new information about the behavior of electromagnetic systems. On the other hand, the fact that it relates mechanical power to electromagnetic quantities having the same physical dimensions permits us to interpret it as a statement of the law of conservation of energy for electromagnetic systems. This interpretation adds a new dimension to our study of electromagnetic phenomena by providing a firm basis for the concept of electromagnetic energy, and for its relation to other forms of energy.

It is important to note in this regard that the concepts of electric energy and of magnetic energy, as introduced in Chapter 7, suffered from serious limitations. In particular, there was no assurance that the energy associated with a particular field was independent of the manner in which the field was created since the positions of all material bodies were supposed to be fixed. The general validity of these concepts could be argued only by making use of the law of conservation of energy as an additional physical law not implied by Maxwell's equations, or by the Lorentz force law. The generalized Poynting's theorem, on the other hand, shows, without making use of any additional physical law, that the previous definition of electromagnetic energy was actually quite general.

The theory presented in the last two chapters deals only with the macroscopic electromagnetic aspects of the interaction between fields and matter, on the assumption that the motion and the electromagnetic state of all material bodies are either known *a priori*, or otherwise determinable with the help of separate physical laws. More specifically, the theory does not deal either with the constituent relations of matter or with the dynamics of material bodies. Thus, the solution of actual physical problems will require, in general, the use of other physical theories, such as theoretical mechanics, in conjunction with the theory presented here. As a matter of fact, one of the merits of the point of view that has guided our discussion is that it leads to a clear-cut separation between macroscopic electromagnetic phenomena and other physical phenomena which are best discussed in a different context.

## 10.8 Selected References

1. A. Sommerfeld, *Electrodynamics* (translated by E. G. Ramberg), Academic Press, New York, 1952. Sections 31, 32, and 35 present a relativistic discussion of electromagnetic forces and energy.
2. W. K. H. Panofsky and M. Phillips, *Classical Electricity and Magnetism*, Addison-Wesley Publishing Co., Inc., Cambridge, Mass., 1955. Chapter 6 discusses forces and energy in electrostatic fields, Chapter 10 discusses the same topic for time varying electromagnetic fields. A corresponding four-dimensional formulation of the conservation laws of electromagnetism is presented in Chapter 22.
3. J. A. Stratton, *Electromagnetic Theory*, McGraw-Hill Book Co., New York, 1941. Chapter 2 is entirely devoted to the study of forces, stresses in elastic media, and energy. Most of the discussion, however, is limited to static fields.

## PROBLEMS

**Problem 10.1.** Electric charge is uniformly distributed over the surface of a sphere made of electromagnetically inert material. Determine the torque exerted by a uniform magnetic field on the sphere when the latter is rotated with uniform angular velocity about an axis normal to the magnetic field.

**Problem 10.2.** Determine Poynting's vector for the situation of Prob. 10.1, and show that its divergence vanishes everywhere.

**Problem 10.3.** For the system described in Prob. 9.6, determine:

(a) The first-order force distribution on the rod and the corresponding total torque per unit length.
(b) The second-order power-dissipation density in the rod and the corresponding total power dissipated per unit length.
(c) The second-order mechanical power per unit length that must be supplied to the rod.
(d) Check the energy balance for each element of the rod to second-order terms.

**Problem 10.4.** For the system described in Prob. 9.9, determine:

(a) The first-order force distribution on the rotating sections of the rod and the corresponding total torque per unit length.
(b) The second-order power-dissipation density in the rod and the corresponding total power dissipated per unit length, for both the stationary sections and the rotating sections.
(c) The second-order Poynting's vector and its divergence in the stationary and in the rotating sections of the rod.
(d) The second-order power per unit length crossing the surface of the rod for both the rotating sections and the stationary sections.
(e) Check the energy balance at all points of the rod, and sketch the flow lines of Poynting's vector outside the rod.

**Problem 10.5.** A parallel-plate capacitor is connected to a direct-voltage source. Using the virtual work method:

(a) Determine the force per unit area on the two plates when the voltage source is kept connected to the plates, and when the source is disconnected after charging the capacitor.

(b) Discuss the effect of the fringing field on the accuracy of the computation.

**Problem 10.6.** A parallel-plate capacitor is immersed part way into a liquid with the plates normal to the surface of the liquid. The spacing between the plates is 1 cm, the mass density of the liquid is equal to 4 times that of water, and its permittivity is $\epsilon = 4\epsilon_0$. How high will the liquid rise between the plates when 100 v is applied to the capacitor?

**Problem 10.7.** A long solenoid sets up a substantially constant magnetic field in the interior of the coil. A rod of linear magnetic material of length and diameter equal to those of the solenoid is partially inserted in the solenoid. Neglecting fringe effects, determine the energy changes resulting from an axial motion of the rod and the axial force on the rod.

**Problem 10.8.** A simple magnetic clutch consists of two crowns with teeth and an exciting coil, as illustrated in Fig. 10.5. For a given magnetic flux through the magnetic circuit formed by the clutch, determine the maximum torque that can be transmitted. Assume that the magnetic circuit consists of linear material.

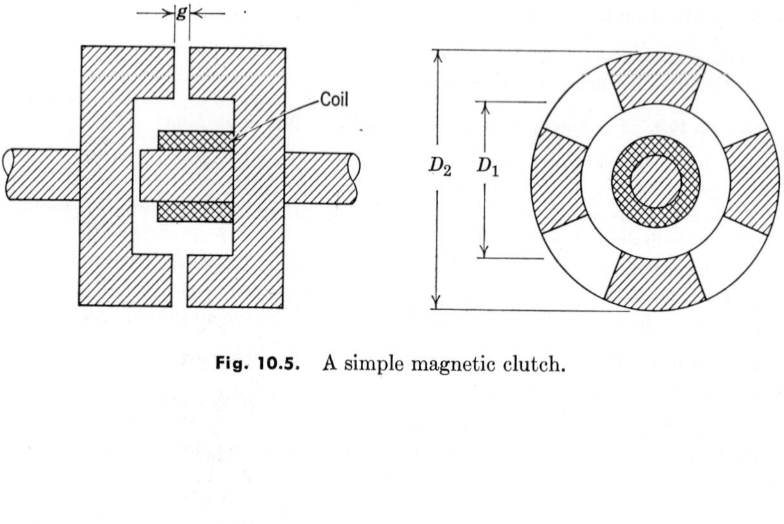


**Fig. 10.5.** A simple magnetic clutch.

# APPENDIX ONE

# Four-Dimensional Formulation of Electrodynamics

## A1.1 Introduction

A four-dimensional formulation of macroscopic electrodynamics will be presented in this appendix. Einstein's special theory of relativity has made a tremendous impact on physics in the past half century. One of its direct consequences is the requirement that the laws of physics deduced from experimental observations and formulated in terms of three space coordinates and time be expressible in four-dimensional form.

The formulation of macroscopic electromagnetic theory presented here differs in many respects from the conventional formulation. These differences result from requiring the four-space formulation to be internally consistent as well as consistent with experimental evidence. The material presented here is not to be considered as an introduction to the special theory of relativity. Einstein's original papers and many excellent works are available on this subject.

After an introductory discussion of the special theory of relativity, we shall discuss the four-space kinematics of electromagnetic material quantities. We shall formulate it in terms of four-space vectors representing the electric-current density, the magnetic-current density, the polarization density, and the magnetization density. The relationships between the four-space vectors and the corresponding three-space vectors will be derived. Since, from a macroscopic point of view, material media can be regarded as aggregates of electric charges, electric dipoles, and magnetic dipoles, the material four-space vectors will give a complete macroscopic description of matter in motion.

Next, the three-space Maxwell equations will be rewritten in four-space form by introducing two four-space field tensors whose components are proportional to the components of $\boldsymbol{E}$ and $\boldsymbol{H}$. In the three-space formulation, Maxwell's equations relate the field vectors $\boldsymbol{E}$ and $\boldsymbol{H}$ to the charge and current densities, both electric and magnetic. Correspondingly, in the four-space formulation the two field tensors are related to the material four-space vectors. Three different versions of four-space relations will be given in succession.

The first version will be designated as the $\boldsymbol{E}$-$\boldsymbol{H}$ formulation; it is the four-dimensional counterpart of the formulation used in the main body of the text. The second version will be introduced through the conventional form of the three-space Maxwell equations in terms of $\boldsymbol{E}$, $\boldsymbol{D}$, $\boldsymbol{H}$, and $\boldsymbol{B}$. The third version, to which we shall refer as the amperian or $\boldsymbol{E}$-$\boldsymbol{B}$ formulation is similar to the $\boldsymbol{E}$-$\boldsymbol{H}$ formulation except for the fact that magnetized matter is represented in terms of electric currents rather than magnetic charges. We shall show that the three four-space versions of the field laws are equivalent except for the definitions of the three-space field vectors.

The four-space-vector forces and the stress tensor will be introduced next in terms of the field tensors and the material four-space vectors. In dealing with electromagnetic forces and stress tensors we shall be dealing with product quantities. In the three-space formulation the product quantities are the electromagnetic-force densities, the energy densities, and the power-conversion densities. Three versions of electrodynamics will be presented concurrently. In the $\boldsymbol{E}$-$\boldsymbol{H}$ formulation, two four-space-vector force densities will be defined (electric and magnetic) as the dot products of the two field tensors and the two four-space-vector current densities (electric and magnetic). It will be shown that the sum of these two four-space vectors is the divergence of a four-space electromagnetic stress tensor. We shall also relate the components of the two four-space-vector force densities to the three-space-vector force densities and to the electromagnetic power converted.

We shall consider next the Minkowski formulation and show that the resulting four-space-vector force density cannot be regarded, in general, as the divergence of a stress tensor. Furthermore, it does not take into account all the forces that are known to be exerted on polarized and magnetized matter. On the other hand the four-space force density in the amperian formulation can be expressed as the divergence of a stress tensor. However, the resulting space distribution of the power converted in the presence of magnetized matter will be found to disagree with experimental evidence.

The constituent relations are not, strictly speaking, part of any macroscopic theory of electromagnetism because they involve other branches of physics such as mechanics and thermodynamics. For completeness, however, we shall discuss at the very end of this appendix the special case of linear constituent relations. The constants involved in such linear relations do not transform as four-space vectors or as four-space tensors. Nevertheless, we shall be able to deduce their transformation properties from those of the fields and of the material quantities.

## A1.2 Concepts of Special Relativity

In describing physical laws such as those of electromagnetism, we express physical quantities in terms of four independent variables, $x$, $y$, $z$, and $t$. The first three describe the location of the point of interest in a system of Cartesian coordinates (frame of reference) with respect to which the observer is at rest. The last variable is the time indicated by a clock stationary with respect to the same frame of reference. Physical laws are expressed in the form of mathematical relations among the physical quantities measured by such an observer at the point of interest and in its neighborhood in the course of time. Of course, a second observer moving with respect to the first one would express his measurements and deduce from them physical laws in terms of a different set of variables, $x'$, $y'$, $z'$, $t'$. The first three variables are Cartesian coordinates of the point of interest in the frame of reference in which the second observer is at rest together with the clock indicating the time $t'$.

Thus each observer measures time by means of a clock stationary with respect to him. For measuring his distance to a point, he can use a light source generating an impulse that propagates with the velocity of light $c$. The light impulse is reflected by the point and received back at the location of the light source. He observes the time elapsed between the transmission and the reception of the impulse. The distance to the point is then equal to one half the elapsed time multiplied by the velocity of light. The time at which the distance is measured is the time at which the impulse is reflected by the point. Of course, three such measurements of distance are required to determine the three coordinates of a point; these measurements must be performed simultaneously in the sense that the three impulses must be reflected at the same time as indicated by a clock at rest in the frame of reference of the observer. The three coordinates can be computed from any three appropriate measurements of distance. All of these measurements are considered as being performed under ideal conditions.

If the point of interest is stationary with respect to the observer, he is free to measure the position of the point at any time. Under these conditions, the time of the measurement is truly an independent variable. However, if the point is in motion relative to the observer, the variable $t$ associated with the space coordinates of the point represents the time at which the light impulses used in measuring the coordinates are reflected by the point.

The components of the velocity of a point moving with respect to the observer can be measured by the same means. Let us suppose, for the sake of simplicity, that the point moves along the $x$-axis of the reference system and that the observer is located at the origin. A light impulse is sent out from the origin at time $t = t_1 - \frac{1}{2}\,\Delta t_1$, and the reflected impulse is received back at the origin $\Delta t_1$ later. A second impulse is sent out, also from the origin, at $t = t_2 - \frac{1}{2}\,\Delta t_2$, and the reflected impulse is received back $\Delta t_2$ later. Thus the $x$ coordinate of the point is $x_1 = \frac{1}{2}\,c\Delta t_1$ at time $t_1$, and $x_2 = \frac{1}{2}\,c\Delta t_2$ at time $t_2$. The limit of the ratio of the incremental distance $x_2 - x_1$ and the time interval $t_2 - t_1$ when $t_2$ and $t_1$ approach a common value $t$ is the velocity assigned by the observer to the point at the time $t$.

An observer encounters greater difficulties in measuring the distance between two points in motion, even when the points travel with the same velocity. Let us suppose again, for the sake of simplicity, that the two points are located on the $x$-axis and move in the positive direction of the $x$-axis. If the observer sends out an impulse from the origin at time $t_0$ and receives back two impulses $\Delta t_1$ and $\Delta t_2$ later, the distance between the two points is not equal to $\frac{1}{2}c(\Delta t_2 - \Delta t_1)$ because the positions of the two points are measured at two different times, namely, $t_0 + \frac{1}{2}\,\Delta t_1$ and $t_0 + \frac{1}{2}\,\Delta t_2$. In order to get the correct distance between the two points, he must transmit two impulses and adjust the interval between the two transmissions in such a way that it is equal to the interval between the receptions of the two reflected impulses. (The reflections of the second impulse from the farther point and that of the first impulse from the nearer point must somehow be discarded.) In this manner, the first impulse is reflected by the farther point at the same time that the second impulse is reflected by the nearer point. *Then the distance between the points is measured at one time.* If the two points are stationary with respect to the observer, such an elaborate procedure is not required because the position of each point can be determined at any time, and the distance between them can be computed at the observer's leisure.

More generally, when we speak of a length, an area, or a volume, we imply that the positions of the points included in them are measured at the same time, as indicated by a clock at rest with respect to the observer. When we speak of a time interval in connection with an event, we imply that the interval is deduced from indications of a clock at rest with respect to the observer. In this sense, the four variables $x$, $y$, $z$, and $t$ are independent. When we speak of the velocity of a particle, however, the space coordinates of the particles are functions of time and, therefore, not independent of it.

Physical laws are deduced from observations of physical phenomena, with the space and time coordinates determined as indicated above. Their formulation must be consistent with the two special-relativity postulates of Einstein. The first postulate states that the velocity of light in vacuum is a universal constant in the sense that it has the same magnitude for all observers moving at a constant velocity relative to one another; in particular, the velocity of a light impulse is independent of the velocity of its source. This universal constant, in conjunction with a clock, is the only yardstick available to an observer for determining the space coordinates of a point. The second postulate states that two observers in uniform relative motion must deduce the same laws from observations on the same physical phenomena. This second postulate implies that all physical quantities involved in the laws must be defined in the same manner for each observer in terms of measurements performed with respect to his frame of reference.

To be sure that the laws of physics under consideration satisfy the relativity postulates, we must be able to relate mathematically the sets of measurements obtained by two observers in uniform relative motion. What are the common bases for the two observers? They are both observing the same physical events following identical experimental procedures and using identical sets of measuring instruments. Each of them refers the results of his measurements to the space and time coordinates associated with his own frame of reference.

Let us suppose that the phenomenon under consideration is the reflection of a light impulse by a material particle of negligibly small dimensions. We wish to relate the time interval between the generation of the impulse and its reflection to the distance of the particle from the light source. We assume, for the sake of simplicity, that the origins of the two systems of coordinates with respect to which the two observers are at rest coincide with the light source when the impulse is generated; let us suppose also that the two clocks associated with the two systems of coordinates are set to indicate zero time when the origins coincide. Each observer can determine with respect to his own frame of reference the time at which the light impulse is reflected by the particle and the coordinates of the particle at that time; this can be readily accomplished by means of appropriately located mirrors at rest with respect to the observer. The first observer finds that the coordinates of the particle are related to the time by

$$x^2 + y^2 + z^2 - (ct)^2 = 0 \tag{A1.1}$$

where $c$ is the velocity of the light impulse and $t$ is the time elapsed from its generation at the origin. In other words, he finds that light travels with velocity $c$. On the other hand, according to the first relativity postulate, the velocity of light must be the same for the two observers. It follows that the second observer must find that the space coordinates of the particle and the time elapsed in his own frame of reference are related by a similar equation,

$$(x')^2 + (y')^2 + (z')^2 - (ct')^2 = 0 \tag{A1.2}$$

Let us see now how the two sets of space and time coordinates can be related to each other. Suppose for the moment that the two observers are not in relative motion. In this special case, they can use the same clock and, therefore, $t'$ must be equal to $t$. On the other hand, the space coordinates measured by one observer are still different from those measured by the other observer unless the axes of the two systems of coordinates as well as the two origins coincide. Then Eqs. A1.1 and A1.2 reduce to

$$x^2 + y^2 + z^2 = (x')^2 + (y')^2 + (z')^2 \qquad t = t' \tag{A1.3}$$

This equation states the well-known fact that the sum of the squares of the Cartesian coordinates of a point (the square of the distance from the origin) is *invariant* to a rotation of the system of coordinates.

The invariance of the sum of the squares of the Cartesian coordinates of a point is a property of all spaces, regardless of their dimensionality. In particular, if $x_1$, $x_2$, $x_3$, and $x_4$ are the Cartesian coordinates of a point in a four-dimensional space, and $x_1'$, $x_2'$, $x_3'$, and $x_4'$ are the coordinates of the same point after a rotation of the axes, we have

$$x_1{}^2 + x_2{}^2 + x_3{}^2 + x_4{}^2 = (x_1')^2 + (x_2')^2 + (x_3')^2 + (x_4')^2 \tag{A1.4}$$

In general, the primed coordinates are related to the unprimed coordinates by linear equations of the form

$$x_i' = \sum_j a_{ij}x_j \tag{A1.5}$$

where the subscripts $i$ and $j$ assume the values 1, 2, 3, and 4 for a four-dimensional space. Necessary and sufficient conditions for the linear transformation given by Eq. A1.5 to represent a rotation of a Cartesian system of axes are

$$\sum_i a_{ij}a_{ik} = \begin{cases} 1 & \text{for } j = k \\ 0 & \text{for } j \neq k \end{cases} \tag{A1.6}$$

$$|a_{ij}| = 1 \tag{A1.7}$$

where $|a_{ij}|$ represents the determinant of the coefficients of the linear transformation. Actually, it can be shown that Eq. A1.6 by itself implies that the absolute value of the determinant is equal to unity, so that Eq. A1.7 adds only the condition that it be positive.

Let us return now to the problem of relating the two sets of space and time variables that satisfy Eqs. A1.1 and A1.2 respectively. Let

$$\begin{array}{llll} x = x_1 & y = x_2 & z = x_3 & ict = x_4 \\ x' = x_1' & y' = x_2' & z' = x_3' & ict' = x_4' \end{array} \tag{A1.8}$$

where $i = \sqrt{-1}$. Then, the left-hand side of Eq. A1.1 becomes identical to the left-hand side of Eq. A1.4, and the left-hand side of Eq. A1.2 becomes identical to the right-hand side of Eq. A1.4. It follows that any transformation of the form of Eq. A1.5, with coefficients satisfying Eqs. A1.6 and A1.7, will insure that Eq. A1.2 will be satisfied whenever Eq. A1.1 is satisfied. In other words, if the space and time coordinates measured by each observer are regarded as the Cartesian coordinates of a point in four-dimensional space with the help of Eq. A1.8, the transformation from one set of coordinates to the other corresponds to a rotation of the four Cartesian axes.

Let us consider the special case of a rotation that leaves invariant the $x_2$- and $x_3$-axes. In this case, the matrix of the coefficients $a_{ij}$ reduces to

| $i \backslash j$ | 1 | 2 | 3 | 4 |
|---|---|---|---|---|
| 1 | $a_{11}$ | 0 | 0 | $a_{14}$ |
| 2 | 0 | 1 | 0 | 0 |
| 3 | 0 | 0 | 1 | 0 |
| 4 | $a_{41}$ | 0 | 0 | $a_{44}$ |

In addition, Eqs. A1.6 and A1.7 require

$$a_{11}^2 + a_{41}^2 = a_{14}^2 + a_{44}^2 = 1 \tag{A1.9}$$

$$a_{11}a_{14} + a_{41}a_{44} = 0 \tag{A1.10}$$

$$a_{11}a_{44} - a_{41}a_{14} = 1 \tag{A1.11}$$

This set of equations yields

$$a_{11} = a_{44} = \gamma_0 \qquad a_{14} = -a_{41} = i\beta_0\gamma_0 \tag{A1.12}$$

where

$$\gamma_0 = \frac{1}{\sqrt{1 - \beta_0{}^2}} \tag{A1.13}$$

and $\beta_0$ is a constant to be determined. Thus,

$$\begin{aligned} x_1' &= \gamma_0(x_1 + i\beta_0 x_4) \qquad & x_2' &= x_2 \\ x_3' &= x_3 & x_4' &= \gamma_0(x_4 - i\beta_0 x_1) \end{aligned} \tag{A1.14}$$

The constant $\beta_0$ must, of course, depend on the velocity of the primed frame of reference relative to the unprimed frame. Since Eqs. A1.1 and A1.2 are valid for all relative velocities (they simply state that the velocity of light has the same value $c$ in the two frames of reference), they cannot possibly yield the relation between $\beta_0$ and the relative velocity. Let us consider then a point fixed in the primed frame of reference; this implies that the coordinates $x'$, $y'$, $z'$ of the point must be independent of the time $t$ measured in the unprimed frame as well as of the time $t'$. Then, equating to zero the derivative with respect to $t$ of $x_1'$, $x_2'$, $x_3'$ yields, with the help of Eq. A1.8,

$$\frac{dx}{dt} - \beta_0 c = 0 \qquad \frac{dy}{dt} = 0 \qquad \frac{dz}{dt} = 0 \tag{A1.15}$$

where $x$, $y$, and $z$ are the coordinates of the point in the unprimed frame. It follows that the motion of the primed frame relative to the unprimed frame is a translation in the positive direction of the $x$-axis with a constant velocity

$$v_0 = \beta_0 c \tag{A1.16}$$

Thus, for such a relative motion of the two frames, we obtain from Eq. A1.14

$$\begin{aligned} x' &= \gamma_0(x - v_0 t) \qquad & y' &= y \qquad z' = z \\ t' &= \gamma_0\left(t - \frac{v_0}{c^2}x\right) & \gamma_0 &= \frac{1}{\sqrt{1 - (v_0/c)^2}} \end{aligned} \tag{A1.17}$$

This is the transformation that relates the space and time coordinates in the primed frame to the space and time coordinates in the unprimed frame when the former moves with a uniform velocity $\boldsymbol{v} = \boldsymbol{i}_x v_0$ relative to the latter. We shall refer to it as a *Lorentz transformation.* The transformation equations are more involved when the relative velocity is not parallel to one of the axes. However, no loss of generality results from focusing our attention on the particular case discussed above because we are always free to choose the $x$-axis parallel to the relative velocity.

In conclusion, the coordinates of a point and the time at which the coordinates are measured in a given frame of reference can be conveniently represented by means of a point in a four-dimensional space whose coordinates are related to the space and time coordinates by Eq. A1.8. Measuring the space and time coordinates of the same point in a different frame of reference amounts to rotating the coordinate axes in the four-dimensional space. If the two frames of reference are at rest with respect to each other, the rotation in four-dimensional space leaves the $x_4$-axis invariant and corresponds to a simple rotation in three-dimensional space. Conversely, if the rotation in four-dimensional space displaces the $x_4$-axis, the two frames of reference are in relative motion.

The coordinates $x_1$, $x_2$, $x_3$, and $x_4$ of a point in a four-dimensional space (four-space for short) can be regarded as the Cartesian components of a four-dimensional vector (four-vector for short) representing the position of the point with respect to the origin. The general definition of four-vector is analogous to that of three-vector. It is a set of four components associated with the four Cartesian axes, which transform together like the coordinates of a point when the axes are rotated. Thus, for instance, if $\mathsf{A}$ is a four-vector[1] with componenst $A_1$, $A_2$, $A_3$, $A_4$, with respect to a given set of Cartesian axes, its components with respect to a different set of Cartesian axes with the same origin are given by

$$A_i' = \sum_j a_{ij} A_j \tag{A1.18}$$

where the coefficients $a_{ij}$ are associated with the rotation that makes the first set of axes coincide with the second one. We shall use in connection with four-vectors the notation $\mathsf{A} = (A_1, A_2, A_3, A_4)$. In the special case in which the first three components happen to be the components of a three-vector, $\boldsymbol{A} = \boldsymbol{i}_x A_1 + \boldsymbol{i}_y A_2 + \boldsymbol{i}_z A_3$, we shall write the four-vector in the simpler form $\mathsf{A} = (\boldsymbol{A}, A_4)$.

Tensors of second rank in a four-dimensional space are defined similarly as sets of 16 components $T_{ij}$ that transform according to the law

$$T_{ij}' = \sum_l \sum_k a_{il} a_{jk} T_{lk} \tag{A1.19}$$

Vector and tensor analysis in four-space will be used extensively in the

[1] Four-space vectors are indicated by symbols set bold face sans serif italic.

rest of this appendix. The reader is assumed to be familiar with this branch of mathematics.

We are now in a position to state Einstein's second postulate in mathematical form. We saw that the space and time coordinates of the same physical event measured by observers in uniform relative motion are represented by the same point in the four-space defined by Eq. A1.8. In other words, the point in four-space representing the space and time coordinates of the event is independent of the frame of reference in which the coordinates are measured. In mathematical terminology, the four-vector representing the position of the point is *invariant* to a rotation of the Cartesian axes, i.e., to a change of the observer's frame of reference. Einstein's second postulate requires all laws of physics to be expressible as relations between four-space quantities that are invariant to a rotation of the axes. These invariant quantities must, of course, be definable in terms of conceptual measurements performed by a single observer with respect to his own frame of reference, and their definitions must be the same for all observers moving with uniform velocities with respect to one another. Thus, for instance, the components of a four-vector appearing in a physical law must be determinable by all such observers through identical measurement procedures. The values of the individual components will, in general, be different for different observers, being representations of the same four-vector with respect to different systems of Cartesian axes.

We shall discuss in the next section the invariant quantities in four-space associated with the differential elements of length, area, and volume in the three-dimensional physical space.

## A1.3 Kinematics

Let us examine the physical meaning of the components of a four-vector $\mathbf{s}$ representing the space and time coordinates of a point in three-space. We shall consider the point of interest to be at rest in a particular frame of reference which we shall indicate with $\Sigma'$, and indicate with $x'$, $y'$, $z'$ the three-space coordinates of the point and with $t'$ the time measured by a clock at rest in $\Sigma'$. Thus, the expression for $\mathbf{s}$ in terms of its components with respect to the four-space Cartesian axes corresponding to $\Sigma'$ is

$$\mathbf{s} = (x', y', z', ict') \tag{A1.20}$$

Since the point of interest is at rest in $\Sigma'$, the coordinates $z'$, $y'$, and $z'$ are independent of $t'$.

Let us consider next a different frame of reference $\Sigma$ with axes $x$, $y$, and $z$ parallel to the $x'$-, $y'$-, and $z'$-axes of $\Sigma'$, and with respect to which $\Sigma'$ moves with a uniform velocity $\boldsymbol{i}_x v_0$.

The time $t$ in this new frame is measured by a different clock at rest in $t$; without loss of generality, we can assume that the two clocks indicate $t = t' = 0$ at the instant at which the origins of the two frames coincide. Then, the four-space Cartesian axes corresponding to $\Sigma'$ can be obtained from those corresponding to $\Sigma$ by the rotation in four-space represented by the Lorentz transformation of Eq. A1.17. The expression for $\mathbf{s}$ with respect to the four-space axes corresponding to $\Sigma$ is

$$\mathbf{s} = (x, y, z, ict) \tag{A1.21}$$

In the $\Sigma$ frame the point of interest moves with a uniform velocity $v_0$ in the direction of the $x$-axis. Its coordinates $x$, $y$, and $z$ give the position of the point in three-space at the time $t$ indicated by the clock at rest in $\Sigma$.

For any given value of $t'$, the four-vector $\mathbf{s}$ represents a fixed point in four-space. As $t'$ varies, the vector $\mathbf{s}$ generates a four-space straight line parallel to the $(ict')$-axis. When referred to the four-space Cartesian axes corresponding to the $\Sigma$ frame, the straight line is interpreted as the locus of the space-time coordinates of the point of interest as measured by an observer in $\Sigma$. The four components of $\mathbf{s}$ with respect to $\Sigma'$ are related to the components with respect to $\Sigma$ by the Lorentz transformation of Eqs. A1.14 and A1.17.

The increment $d\mathbf{s}$ of $\mathbf{s}$ resulting from an increment $dt'$ of $t'$ is given by

$$d\mathbf{s} = (0, 0, 0, ic\, dt') \tag{A1.22}$$

when referred to the $\Sigma'$ frame. The first three components are the increments of $x'$, $y'$, and $z'$ in the time interval $dt'$; they are equal to zero because the point is at rest in the $\Sigma'$ frame. Thus $d\mathbf{s}$ represents an increment of time in the frame in which the point of interest is at rest. The same increment $d\mathbf{s}$ is given by

$$d\mathbf{s} = (dx, dy, dz, ic\, dt) \tag{A1.23}$$

when referred to the $\Sigma$ frame. The increment $dt$ is the time interval measured by the clock in the $\Sigma$ frame that corresponds to $dt'$ in the $\Sigma'$ frame. The first three components, on the other hand, are the increments of the three-space coordinates of the point in the $\Sigma$ frame, that take place during the time $dt$.

The increment $d\mathbf{s}$ is a four-vector, being the increment of a four-vector. It follows that its components transform like the components of $\mathfrak{s}$, and we obtain from Eqs. A1.13, A1.14, and A1.16

$$\begin{aligned} dx &= \gamma_0 v_0 \, dt' \\ dy &= dy' = dz = dz' = 0 \\ dt &= \gamma_0 \, dt' \end{aligned} \tag{A1.24}$$

Since $\gamma_0$ is larger than one, the time interval $dt$ measured in the $\Sigma$ frame is larger than the corresponding interval $dt'$ measured in the $\Sigma'$ frame. This result is known as the *relativistic dilatation of time.* It must be stressed that this time dilatation is associated with the time interval between successive measurements of the position of a moving point. It is not associated directly with the relative motion of two observers without a common point of interest in their three-dimensional space.

In dealing with a point in three-space which is at rest in the $\Sigma'$ frame, both $dt'$ and $dt$ are correctly measured time intervals between observations of the position of the point in the two different frames. The corresponding time interval between observations measured by an observer in a third frame traveling at a different uniform velocity with respect to $\Sigma'$ will differ from $dt$ as well as from $dt'$. On the other hand, to formulate physical laws in four-space, we need a common measure of the time interval between observations of the location of a point of interest in three-space. This common, or proper, measure of time interval must be defined in the same manner for each observer in terms of measurements in his own frame, without requiring the presence of other observers. Thus, although this measure can depend on the velocity of the point of interest with respect to the observer in question, it cannot depend on the relative velocity between two observers. We note in this regard that the relation between $dt'$ and $dt$ given by Eq. A1.24 involves only $\gamma_0$, which, in turn, depends only on the velocity of the point of interest with respect to the observer in the $\Sigma$ frame, namely, $v_0$. The same is true, of course, for the relation between the time interval measured by any other observer and $dt'$, provided $\gamma_0$ is evaluated from the velocity of the point with respect to the observer in question. This includes an observer in the frame of reference in which the point is at rest, in which case $\gamma_0$ would be equal to one. Thus, we can define the *proper time interval* between successive measurements of the position of a point as

$$d\tau = dt/\gamma \tag{A1.25}$$

where $dt$ is the time interval indicated by the clock in the frame of the observer,

$$\gamma = \frac{1}{\sqrt{1 - \left(\frac{v}{c}\right)^2}} \tag{A1.26}$$

and $v$ is the magnitude of the velocity of the point with respect to the observer. Thus $d\tau$ coincides with the time interval $dt'$ indicated by the clock in the frame of reference in which the point is at rest. In conclusion, any two observers traveling at a uniform velocity with respect to each other would obtain the same value of $d\tau$ by performing the same measurements in their respective frames of reference. For this reason $d\tau$ is invariant to a Lorentz transformation in four-space.

The definition of $d\tau$ and the proof of its invariance can also be approached from a different angle. We saw that the magnitude of a four-vector is invariant to a Lorentz transformation, and so is the velocity of light in vacuum. Thus if $d\mathbf{s}$ is the four-vector representing the incremental changes of the space-time coordinates of a point, the scalar

$$\frac{ds}{ic} = \sqrt{\frac{d\mathbf{s}}{ic} \cdot \frac{d\mathbf{s}}{ic}} = \sqrt{dt^2 - (dx^2 + dy^2 + dz^2)/c^2}$$

$$= dt\sqrt{1 - \left(\frac{v}{c}\right)^2} = d\tau \tag{A1.27}$$

is invariant to a Lorentz transformation. This alternate definition of $d\tau$ provides a new insight into its physical significance. It can be readily seen that $d\tau^2$ is equal to the difference between $dt^2$ and the square of the time that it would take a light pulse to travel the same distance as the point in question.

The symbol $\gamma$ rather than $\gamma_0$ has been used in Eq. A1.25 to emphasize the fact that $d\tau$ is defined in terms of the time interval $dt$ and the magnitude of the velocity $v$ of the point of interest, both measured in the frame of the observer. It has not been defined as the time interval measured in the frame in which the point is at rest. There is a subtle difference between these two definitions, although they may appear to be entirely equivalent. The $\Sigma'$ frame in which the point is at rest has been introduced in our discussion only for the purpose of proving that $d\tau$, as defined by Eqs. A1.25 and A1.26, is invariant to a Lorentz transformation. The fact that the velocity of the point with respect to the observer coincides with the relative velocity between two frames of reference is accidental. On the other hand, defining $d\tau$ as the time interval measured by an observer in the frame of reference in which the point is at rest would imply that there is a preferred frame of reference in which the laws of physics are to be formulated. This would be incorrect; in general, the points of interest in a physical system cannot be all at rest in the same frame of reference. If we were to use the other definition, we would be restricted to dealing with physical systems in which all material points are at rest with respect to one another.

The proof that $d\tau$, as defined by Eqs. A1.25 and A1.26, is invariant to a Lorentz transformation involves, strictly speaking, the assumption that the point of interest has a uniform velocity with respect to the observer. However, this assumption can be eliminated if and only if the increment $d\tau$ is understood to be of vanishingly small magnitude. Then, the increments of the space coordinates of the point have also vanishingly small magnitudes, and the velocity of the point with respect to the observer is constant during the interval $d\tau$. Under these conditions, the proof that $d\tau$ is invariant remains valid, provided the rest frame of the point is taken to be the frame in which the point is momentarily at rest during the differential time interval.

We are now in a position to define a four-vector $\mathsf{v}$ representing the velocity of a point in three-space. We shall define $\mathsf{v}$ as the ratio of the differential four-vector $d\mathsf{s}$, representing the incremental changes of the space-time coordinates of the point of interest, and the corresponding proper time differential $d\tau$, which has been shown to be invariant to a Lorentz transformation. We obtain, with the help of Eq. A1.25,

$$\mathsf{v} = \frac{d\mathsf{s}}{d\tau} = \frac{(dx, dy, dz, ic\, dt)}{d\tau} = \gamma\left(\frac{dx}{dt}, \frac{dy}{dt}, \frac{dz}{dt}, ic\right) = \gamma(\boldsymbol{v}, ic) \qquad \text{(A1.28)}$$

where the three-vector $\boldsymbol{v}$ denotes the velocity of the point with respect to the observer. It is important to note that the expression for $\mathsf{v}$ in the rest frame of the particle is

$$\mathsf{v} = (0, 0, 0, ic) \qquad \text{(A1.29)}$$

This follows immediately from the fact that the three-vector $\boldsymbol{v}$ vanishes in the rest frame; it can be readily checked also by transforming the components given by Eq. A1.28. We note also that $\mathsf{v}/ic$ is a unit vector in four-space parallel to the $ict'$-axis, and that we have from Eq. A1.29

$$\mathsf{v}\cdot\mathsf{v} = (ic)^2 \qquad \text{(A1.30)}$$

In words, the length of the four-vector velocity is a constant equal to $ic$; this result can also be obtained directly from Eqs. A1.27 and A1.28.

Let us consider next the problem of representing in four-space the distance between two points at rest in the same frame of reference $\Sigma'$. Let $\mathbf{s}_1$ and $\mathbf{s}_2$ be the four-vectors representing the space-time coordinates of the two points. The space components of these two vectors relative to $\Sigma'$ are independent of the respective time components because the two points are at rest in $\Sigma'$. It follows that the space components relative to $\Sigma'$ of the four-vector $\mathbf{s}_2 - \mathbf{s}_1$ are independent of the times at which the positions of the two points are determined by an observer in the $\Sigma'$ frame. This fact can be placed in evidence by writing

$$\mathbf{s}_2 - \mathbf{s}_1 = (L_x', L_y', L_z', 0) + (0, 0, 0, icT') \qquad \text{(A1.31)}$$

where

$$\mathbf{L} = (L_x', L_y', L_z', 0) \qquad \text{(A1.32)}$$

is the four-vector representing the distance between the two points when the positions of the two points are measured simultaneously in the $\Sigma'$ frame, and $T'$ is an arbitrary time interval in $\Sigma'$.

The situation is quite different in any frame of reference $\Sigma$ in which the two points travel with a uniform velocity of magnitude $v_0$ (assumed to be parallel to the $x$-axis). In any such frame, the space coordinates of the two points are functions of the corresponding time coordinates, so that an observer in $\Sigma$ wishing to determine the distance between the two points is forced to measure their space coordinates simultaneously. Let

$$\mathbf{l} = (l_x, l_y, l_z, 0) \qquad \text{(A1.33)}$$

be the four-vector representing the distance between the two points when their positions are measured simultaneously in the $\Sigma$ frame.

Unfortunately, the four-vector $\mathbf{L}$ resulting from simultaneous measurements in the $\Sigma'$ frame does not coincide with the four-vector $\mathbf{l}$ resulting from simultaneous measurements in the $\Sigma$ frame. In fact the components of $\mathbf{L}$ in the $\Sigma$ frame and of $\mathbf{l}$ in the $\Sigma'$ frame are related to the components in Eqs. A1.32 and A1.33 by

$$L_x = \gamma_0 L_x' \qquad L_y = L_y' \qquad L_z = L_z' \qquad T = \gamma_0 \frac{v_0}{c^2} L_x' \qquad \text{(A1.34)}$$

$$l_x' = \gamma_0 l_x \qquad l_y' = l_y \qquad l_z' = l_z \qquad \Delta t' = -\gamma_0 \frac{v_0}{c^2} l_x \qquad \text{(A1.35)}$$

where $l_x'$, $l_y'$, $l_z'$, $ic\Delta t'$ are the components of $\mathbf{l}$ in the $\Sigma'$ frame and $L_x$, $L_y$, $L_z$, $icT$ are the components of $\mathbf{L}$ in the $\Sigma$ frame. Clearly, the components $L_x$, $L_y$, and $L_z$ do not result from simultaneous measurements in the $\Sigma$ frame. On the other hand, $l_x'$, $l_y'$, $l_z'$ must be equal to the corresponding components $L_x'$, $L_y'$, $L_z'$ because the space components in the $\Sigma'$ frame of any four-vector $\mathbf{s}_2 - \mathbf{s}_1$ are the same for all values of the time component, as indicated by Eq. A1.31. Thus, $\mathbf{s}_2 - \mathbf{s}_1$ coincides with $\mathbf{l}$ if $T'$ is chosen equal to $\Delta t'$.

Our objective is to represent the distance between the two points by means of a four-vector whose components can be defined in the same manner in any inertial frame of reference in terms of measurements performed by an observer in that frame. Clearly $\mathbf{l}$ cannot be an appropriate vector because its components relative to $\Sigma'$ depend on the relative velocity of $\Sigma$ and $\Sigma'$ which is not determinable by an observer in $\Sigma'$. On the other hand, the appearance of the same relative velocity $v_0$ in Eq. A1.34 does not present any problem because for the observer in $\Sigma$ it coincides with the velocity of the two points which is certainly determinable by him. Furthermore, since the space components of $\mathbf{L}$ and $\mathbf{l}$ coincide in the $\Sigma'$ frame, we obtain from Eqs. A1.34 and A1.35 for the components of $\mathbf{L}$ relative to $\Sigma$

$$L_x = \gamma_0{}^2 l_x \qquad L_y = l_y \qquad L_z = l_z \qquad icT = i\gamma_0{}^2 \frac{v_0}{c} l_x \tag{A1.36}$$

Since all four components depend only on measurements that can be performed by an observer in the $\Sigma$ frame, the four-vector $\mathbf{L}$ can be defined in any frame of reference by the expression

$$\mathbf{L} = \left(\gamma^2 l_x, l_y, l_z, i\gamma^2 \frac{v}{c} l_x\right) \tag{A1.37}$$

where $\gamma$ and $v$ have been substituted for $\gamma_0$ and $v_0$ to stress the fact that $v$ represents the velocity of the two points in question relative to the observer rather than the velocity of another frame of reference. Clearly, Eq. A1.37 reduces to Eq. A1.32 for an observer in the rest frame of the two points. We must remember that $\mathbf{l}$ represents the distance between the two points, evaluated from simultaneous measurements of their positions in the $\Sigma$ frame.

The expression for $\mathbf{L}$ given by Eq. A1.37 involves the restriction that the velocity of the two points is parallel to the $x$-axis in all frames of reference. Although this condition can always be met by a proper choice of the Cartesian axes in each frame, it is convenient to write Eq. A1.37 in a manner independent of the orientation of the axes. This can be readily accomplished by making use of the fact that $l_x$ is the component of the three-vector $\mathbf{l}$ parallel to the three-vector velocity $\boldsymbol{v}$

$$\boldsymbol{i}_x l_x = \frac{(\boldsymbol{l}\cdot\boldsymbol{v})\boldsymbol{v}}{\boldsymbol{v}\cdot\boldsymbol{v}} \tag{A1.38}$$

Thus,

$$\mathbf{L} = \left(\gamma^2 \frac{(\boldsymbol{l}\cdot\boldsymbol{v})\boldsymbol{v}}{\boldsymbol{v}\cdot\boldsymbol{v}} + \boldsymbol{l} - \frac{(\boldsymbol{l}\cdot\boldsymbol{v})\boldsymbol{v}}{\boldsymbol{v}\cdot\boldsymbol{v}},\ i\gamma^2 \frac{\boldsymbol{l}\cdot\boldsymbol{v}}{c}\right)$$

and simplifying

$$\mathbf{L} = \left(\gamma^2 \frac{(\boldsymbol{l}\cdot\boldsymbol{v})\boldsymbol{v}}{c^2} + \boldsymbol{l},\ i\gamma^2 \frac{\boldsymbol{l}\cdot\boldsymbol{v}}{c}\right) \tag{A1.39}$$

It is clear, furthermore, from Eqs. A1.29 and A1.32 that the four-vectors $\mathbf{v}$ and $\mathbf{L}$ are orthogonal in four-space in the sense that their dot product is equal to zero. Finally, if we indicate with $\boldsymbol{l}_0$ the three-vector distance between the two points in their rest frame, and with the subscripts $\|$ and $\perp$ the components parallel and normal to $\boldsymbol{v}$, we have from Eq. A1.35

$$\boldsymbol{l}_{0\|} = \boldsymbol{i}_x l_x' = \gamma \boldsymbol{l}_{\|} \qquad \boldsymbol{l}_{0\perp} = (\boldsymbol{i}_y l_y' + \boldsymbol{i}_z l_z') = \boldsymbol{l}_{\perp} \tag{A1.40}$$

In words, the component of the three-vector distance parallel to the velocity is contracted from the value at rest by the factor $1/\gamma$, while the component normal to the velocity remains unchanged. This result is known as the *relativistic contraction of length.*

We shall construct next a four-space area and identify it with the corresponding area in three-space. In three-space, the area of a parallelogram is an antisymmetric tensor, equivalent to a vector of three components (a cross product). In three-space, it is understood that the coordinates of all points of the area are measured at the same instant of time. Consider a parallelogram at rest. Let $\boldsymbol{a}'$ and $\boldsymbol{b}'$ be the three-vector lengths of the sides of the parallelogram. We form two four-vector lengths in the rest frame, as discussed above,

$$\begin{aligned} \mathbf{a} &= (a_x', a_y', a_z', 0) = (\boldsymbol{a}', 0) \\ \mathbf{b} &= (b_x', b_y', b_z', 0) = (\boldsymbol{b}', 0) \end{aligned} \tag{A1.41}$$

That the fourth components are set equal to zero signifies that all measurements are made simultaneously in the rest frame. We define the four-space area as the cross product of the two four-vectors, which is an antisymmetric tensor of rank two. The component $A_{mn}$ of a tensor $\mathfrak{A}$, cross product of two four-vectors of components $a_k$ and $b_j$, is

$$A_{mn} = a_m b_n - a_n b_m \tag{A1.42}$$

so that

$$\mathfrak{A} = \begin{bmatrix} 0 & a_1b_2 - a_2b_1 & a_1b_3 - a_3b_1 & a_1b_4 - a_4b_1 \\ a_2b_1 - a_1b_2 & 0 & a_2b_3 - a_3b_2 & a_2b_4 - a_4b_2 \\ a_3b_1 - a_1b_3 & a_3b_2 - a_2b_3 & 0 & a_3b_4 - a_4b_3 \\ a_4b_1 - a_1b_4 & a_4b_2 - a_2b_4 & a_4b_3 - a_3b_4 & 0 \end{bmatrix} \begin{matrix} \rightarrow n \\ \downarrow m \end{matrix} \tag{A1.43}$$

Thus

$$\mathfrak{A}_0 = \boldsymbol{a} \times \boldsymbol{b} = \begin{bmatrix} 0 & a_x'b_y' - a_y'b_x' & a_x'b_z' - a_z'b_x' & 0 \\ a_y'b_x' - a_x'b_y' & 0 & a_y'b_z' - a_z'b_y' & 0 \\ a_zb_x - a_x'b_z' & a_z'b_y' - a_y'b_z' & 0 & 0 \\ 0 & 0 & 0 & 0 \end{bmatrix} \tag{A1.44}$$

We recognize that the nine top-left components of $\mathfrak{A}_0$ form the three-space antisymmetric tensor $\boldsymbol{a}' \times \boldsymbol{b}'$, representing the area of the parallelogram in its rest frame. It can also be regarded as a three-vector $\boldsymbol{A}'$ of components $(A_{23}', A_{31}', A_{12}')$. In general, a four-space antisymmetric tensor has six independent components, and, therefore, can be represented as a six-vector. In six-vector form,

$$\mathfrak{A} = (A_{23}, A_{31}, A_{12}; A_{14}, A_{24}, A_{34}) \tag{A1.45}$$

Since in the present case the last three components are equal to zero, we have

$$\mathfrak{A}_0 = (A_{23}', A_{31}', A_{12}'; 0, 0, 0) = (\boldsymbol{A}'; 0) \tag{A1.46}$$

Let us consider now an observer with respect to whom the parallelogram moves with a velocity $\boldsymbol{v}$, and let $\boldsymbol{a}$ and $\boldsymbol{b}$ represent the three-vector lengths of the sides of the parallelogram as determined by the observer through simultaneous measurements in his frame of reference. These two vectors can be related to the vectors $\boldsymbol{a}'$ and $\boldsymbol{b}'$ determined in the rest frame of the parallelogram with the help of Eq. A1.40. Thus we obtain

$$\begin{aligned} \boldsymbol{A}' = \boldsymbol{a}' \times \boldsymbol{b}' &= (\gamma \boldsymbol{a}_\parallel + \boldsymbol{a}_\perp) \times (\gamma \boldsymbol{b}_\parallel + \boldsymbol{b}_\perp) \\ &= (\boldsymbol{a}_\perp \times \boldsymbol{b}_\perp) + \gamma(\boldsymbol{a}_\parallel \times \boldsymbol{b}_\perp) + \gamma(\boldsymbol{a}_\perp \times \boldsymbol{b}_\parallel) \\ &= (\boldsymbol{a} \times \boldsymbol{b})_\parallel + \gamma(\boldsymbol{a} \times \boldsymbol{b})_\perp \end{aligned} \tag{A1.47}$$

This equation allows the observer to evaluate the cross product $\boldsymbol{a}' \times \boldsymbol{b}'$ in the rest frame from the cross product $\boldsymbol{a} \times \boldsymbol{b}$ in his own frame and the velocity $\boldsymbol{v}$, and, in turn, to determine from the former the components of the six-vector $\mathfrak{A}_0$ in the rest frame with the help of Eq. A1.46. If desired, the resulting components of $\mathfrak{A}_0$ can be transformed to the frame of the observer. Equation A1.39 guarantees that the components of $\mathfrak{A}_0$ in the frame of the observer will be functions of $\boldsymbol{a}$, $\boldsymbol{b}$, and $\boldsymbol{v}$ alone, which are physical quantities measurable by the observer in his own frame of reference. Finally, we note from Eq. A1.47 that the area of the parallelogram parallel to $\boldsymbol{v}$ [represented by $(\boldsymbol{a} \times \boldsymbol{b})_\perp$] contracts by the factor $1/\gamma$ from its value in the rest frame, while the component normal to $\boldsymbol{v}$ [represented by $(\boldsymbol{a} \times \boldsymbol{b})_\parallel$] remains unchanged. This is consistent with the relativistic contraction of length.

Next, we shall construct the four-vector volume of a parallelepiped and relate it to the scalar three-space volume. We shall consider a parallelepiped in its rest frame with three-vector edges $\boldsymbol{a}'$, $\boldsymbol{b}'$, and $\boldsymbol{c}'$. The proper four-vectors describing these lengths are

$$\begin{aligned} \mathsf{a} &= (a_x', a_y', a_z', 0) \\ \mathsf{b} &= (b_x', b_y', b_z', 0) \\ \mathsf{c} &= (c_x', c_y', c_z', 0) \end{aligned} \tag{A1.48}$$

We form first an antisymmetric tensor area $\mathfrak{A}_0$ by constructing the cross product $\mathsf{a} \times \mathsf{b}$, as shown in Eq. A1.44. The dot product of a tensor $\mathfrak{A}$ and a vector $\mathsf{c}$ is a vector of which the $m$th component is

$$\sum_n A_{mn} c_n \tag{A1.49}$$

The dot product $\mathfrak{A}_0 \cdot \mathsf{c}$ cannot be identified with the three-space volume of the parallelepiped under consideration.

We shall then form a new antisymmetrical tensor $\mathfrak{A}_0^\dagger$. An antisymmetric tensor of rank two in four-space has six independent components, and can be considered as a six-vector, i.e., a vector with six components such as that given by Eq. A1.45. Such a six-vector has two sets of three components, each of which can be considered as a three-vector, i.e., a vector with three components. By definition the six-vector $\mathfrak{A}^\dagger$ is constructed from $\mathfrak{A}$ by interchanging the two three-vectors:

$$\mathfrak{A}^\dagger = (A_{14}, A_{24}, A_{34}; A_{23}, A_{31}, A_{12}) \tag{A1.50}$$

or

$$\mathfrak{A}^\dagger = \begin{bmatrix} 0 & A_{34} & -A_{24} & A_{23} \\ -A_{34} & 0 & A_{14} & A_{31} \\ A_{24} & -A_{14} & 0 & A_{12} \\ -A_{23} & -A_{31} & -A_{12} & 0 \end{bmatrix} \tag{A1.51}$$

The six-vector $\mathfrak{A}^\dagger$ is said to be the dual of $\mathfrak{A}$. The duality relation can be shown to be preserved by a Lorentz transformation. In the particular case of the six-vector given by Eq. A1.44, we obtain

$$\mathfrak{A}_0{}^\dagger = (\boldsymbol{a} \times \boldsymbol{b})^\dagger$$
$$= \begin{bmatrix} 0 & 0 & 0 & a_y'b_z' - a_z'b_y' \\ 0 & 0 & 0 & a_z'b_x' - a_x'b_z' \\ 0 & 0 & 0 & a_x'b_y' - a_y'b_x' \\ a_x'b_y' - a_y'b_z' & a_x'b_z' - a_z'b_x' & a_y'b_x' - a_x'b_y' & 0 \end{bmatrix} \tag{A1.52}$$

Then, according to the above definition of the dot product of a tensor of rank two and a vector in four-space, the dot product of $-\mathfrak{A}^\dagger$ and $\boldsymbol{c}$ yields the four-vector

$$\boldsymbol{V}_0 = -(\boldsymbol{a} \times \boldsymbol{b})^\dagger \cdot \boldsymbol{c} = (0, 0, 0, \boldsymbol{a}' \times \boldsymbol{b}' \cdot \boldsymbol{c}') \tag{A1.53}$$

where $\boldsymbol{a}'$, $\boldsymbol{b}'$, $\boldsymbol{c}'$ are the three-vectors representing the edges of the parallelepiped in its rest frame. Thus, in the rest frame, the volume vector in four-space is parallel to the $ict'$-axis with no components along the three space axes. This is consistent with the fact that the three-space volume is a scalar quantity in three-space. The fourth component of $\boldsymbol{V}_0$ is equal to the three-space volume of the parallelepiped in the rest frame. Thus the magnitude of $\boldsymbol{V}_0$

$$V_0 = \sqrt{\boldsymbol{V}_0 \cdot \boldsymbol{V}_0} = |\boldsymbol{a}' \times \boldsymbol{b}' \cdot \boldsymbol{c}'| \tag{A1.54}$$

is a scalar invariant in four-space. We shall refer to it as the *proper volume* of the parallelepiped.

It remains to relate the proper four-space volume of the parallelepiped to the three-volume measured by an observer with respect to whom the parallelepiped moves with a velocity $\boldsymbol{v}$. Let us resolve the three-space vectors $\boldsymbol{a}'$, $\boldsymbol{b}'$, and $\boldsymbol{c}'$ into components parallel and perpendicular to $\boldsymbol{v}$ and simplify the result:

$$\begin{aligned} V_0 &= |(\boldsymbol{a}_\parallel' + \boldsymbol{a}_\perp') \times (\boldsymbol{b}_\parallel' + \boldsymbol{b}_\perp') \cdot (\boldsymbol{c}_\parallel' + \boldsymbol{c}_\perp')| \\ &= |(\boldsymbol{a}_\parallel' \times \boldsymbol{b}_\perp') \cdot \boldsymbol{c}_\perp' + (\boldsymbol{a}_\perp' \times \boldsymbol{b}_\parallel') \cdot \boldsymbol{c}_\perp' + (\boldsymbol{a}_\perp' \times \boldsymbol{b}_\perp') \cdot \boldsymbol{c}_\parallel'| \end{aligned} \tag{A1.55}$$

Only one factor of each term involves the component parallel to the three-vector velocity $\boldsymbol{v}$. The vector lengths in the $\Sigma$ frame of the observer are related to the corresponding components in the rest frame by Eq. A1.40. Thus

$$
\begin{aligned}
V_0 &= \gamma\,|(\boldsymbol{a}_\parallel \times \boldsymbol{b}_\perp)\cdot\boldsymbol{c}_\perp + (\boldsymbol{a}_\perp \times \boldsymbol{b}_\parallel)\cdot\boldsymbol{c}_\perp + (\boldsymbol{a}_\perp \times \boldsymbol{b}_\perp)\cdot\boldsymbol{c}_\parallel| \\
&= \gamma\,|(\boldsymbol{a} \times \boldsymbol{b})\cdot\boldsymbol{c}| = \gamma V
\end{aligned}
\tag{A1.56}
$$

where $V$ is the volume of the parallelepiped, and $\boldsymbol{a}$, $\boldsymbol{b}$, $\boldsymbol{c}$ its edges, as measured simultaneously by the observer in the $\Sigma$ frame. Thus the volume of a parallelepiped in motion contracts by a factor $1/\gamma$ as compared to the volume of the parallelepiped in its rest frame. Clearly, Eq. A1.56 provides a definition of the proper volume of the parallelepiped which is the same for all observers, and which depends only on measurements that each observer can perform in his own frame of reference.

## A1.4 Material Scalars, Vectors, and Tensors

Let us consider a distribution of electric charges and indicate with $\rho$ and $\boldsymbol{J}$ the macroscopic charge density and current density of the distribution, both measured in a particular frame of reference $\Sigma$. The law of conservation of charge requires that in any such frame of reference

$$
\operatorname{div} \boldsymbol{J} = -\frac{\partial \rho}{\partial t} \tag{A1.57}
$$

which can be rewritten in the form

$$
\frac{\partial}{\partial x} J_x + \frac{\partial}{\partial y} J_y + \frac{\partial}{\partial z} J_z + \frac{\partial}{\partial (ict)}\, ic\rho = 0 \tag{A1.58}
$$

In order for this equation to be valid in any inertial frame of reference, the quantities $J_x$, $J_y$, $J_z$ and $ic\rho$ must transform like $x$, $y$, $z$, and $ict$; i.e., they must be the components with respect to $\Sigma$ of a four-vector

$$
\mathsf{J} = (\boldsymbol{J}, ic\rho) \tag{A1.59}
$$

to which we shall refer as the four-vector current density. In terms of $\mathsf{J}$, Eq. A1.58 becomes

$$
\operatorname{div} \mathsf{J} = \square \cdot \mathsf{J} = 0 \tag{A1.60}
$$

where the operator $\square$ is the four-vector

$$
\square = \left(\frac{\partial}{\partial x_1}, \frac{\partial}{\partial x_2}, \frac{\partial}{\partial x_3}, \frac{\partial}{\partial x_4}\right) = \left(\nabla, \frac{\partial}{\partial (ict)}\right) \tag{A1.61}
$$

Let $\Sigma'$ be a second frame of reference moving with respect to $\Sigma$ with a uniform velocity of magnitude $v_0$, and related to $\Sigma$ by the Lorentz transformation of Eq. A1.17. The components of $\boldsymbol{J}$ with respect to $\Sigma'$ are given by

$$J_x' = \gamma_0(J_x - v_0\rho) \qquad J_y' = J_y \qquad J_z' = J_z$$
$$\rho' = \gamma_0\left(\rho - \frac{v_0}{c^2}J_x\right) \tag{A1.62}$$

Thus, we have, in terms of components parallel and normal to the relative velocity $\boldsymbol{v}_0$,

$$\boldsymbol{J}_\parallel' = \gamma_0(\boldsymbol{J}_\parallel - \rho\boldsymbol{v}) \qquad \boldsymbol{J}_\perp' = \boldsymbol{J}_\perp \qquad \rho' = \gamma_0\left[\rho - \boldsymbol{J}\cdot\frac{\boldsymbol{v}_0}{c^2}\right] \tag{A1.63}$$

We shall now show that the amount of charge in any region of space is invariant to a Lorentz transformation. For this purpose, we consider a charge distribution in which all charges have the same polarity, either positive or negative. In this special case

$$\boldsymbol{J} = \rho\boldsymbol{v} \tag{A1.64}$$

where $\boldsymbol{v}$, a function of position as well as time, is the velocity of the charge distribution in the $\Sigma$ frame. Each element of the charge distribution is temporarily at rest in a frame of reference $\Sigma'$ moving with velocity $\boldsymbol{v}$ with respect to $\Sigma$. If we indicate with $\rho_0$ the charge density of the element in its rest frame, we obtain from Eq. A1.63,

$$\rho_0 = \gamma\left[\rho - \rho\left(\frac{v}{c}\right)^2\right] = \frac{\rho}{\gamma} \tag{A1.65}$$

In words, the charge density in the $\Sigma$ frame is larger than its value in the rest frame by the factor $\gamma$. On the other hand, the charge in each element of volume of the distribution is

$$\rho_0\,dV_0 = \gamma\rho_0\,dV_0 = \rho\,dV = dq \tag{A1.66}$$

where $dV_0$ is the *proper volume* of the element (the volume in the rest frame), as defined by Eq. A1.56, and $dV$ is the volume of the same element in the $\Sigma$ frame. Thus, the charge in each volume element is the same in the rest frame as in the $\Sigma$ frame. We can then conclude that *the amount of charge in any region of space is the same in any $\Sigma$ frame, i.e., it is invariant to a Lorentz transformation.* This final result remains valid for the sum of arbitrary charge distributions of different polarities and moving with different velocities, and, therefore, holds in general for an arbitrary distribution involving both negative and positive charges.

In the presence of polarized matter, the four-vector electric-current density $\mathbf{J}$ is the sum of the free-current density $\mathbf{J}_f$ and the polarization-current density $\mathbf{J}_p$,

$$\mathbf{J} = \mathbf{J}_f + \mathbf{J}_p \tag{A1.67}$$

where

$$\mathbf{J}_f = (\boldsymbol{J}_f, ic\rho_f) \tag{A1.68}$$

$$\mathbf{J}_p = (\boldsymbol{J}_p, ic\rho_p) \tag{A1.69}$$

The four-vector free-current density is expressed in terms of the three-vector free-current density $\boldsymbol{J}_f$ and the free-charge density $\rho_f$. The four-vector $\mathbf{J}_p$ is similarly expressed in terms of the three-vector polarization-current density $\boldsymbol{J}_p$ and the polarization-charge density $\rho_p$. We shall show later that $\mathbf{J}_p$ is the divergence of the cross product of a four-vector polarization density $\mathbf{P}$ to be defined, and the four-vector $\mathbf{v}$ representing the motion of the polarized matter. We saw in Sec. 5.2 (Eq. 5.14) that the law of conservation of charge is satisfied separately by $\boldsymbol{J}_f$ and $\rho_f$ and by $\boldsymbol{J}_p$ and $\rho_p$. It follows that

$$\text{div } \mathbf{J}_f = \text{div } \mathbf{J}_p = 0 \tag{A1.70}$$

Electrons, atoms, and molecules are known to possess quantized magnetic-dipole moments. In a microscopic description we need only deal with the magnetic-dipole moments of the individual particles. In a macroscopic theory, however, it is necessary to consider magnetic dipoles as made up of magnetic charges, as discussed in Sec. 5.4. (The alternative, amperian-current formulation will be discussed later.) We saw that, in three-space, the magnetic-current density $\boldsymbol{J}^*$ and the magnetic-charge density $\rho^*$ satisfy the conservation law

$$\text{div } \boldsymbol{J}^* = -\frac{\partial \rho^*}{\partial t} \tag{A1.71}$$

By analogy with the preceding discussion of electric currents and charges, this equation leads us to the definition of a four-vector magnetic-current density

$$\mathbf{J}^* = (\boldsymbol{J}^*, ic\rho^*) \tag{A1.72}$$

in terms of which Eq. A1.71 becomes

$$\text{div } \mathbf{J}^* = \square \cdot \mathbf{J}^* = 0 \tag{A1.73}$$

The mathematical properties of $\mathbf{J}^*$ are identical to those of $\mathbf{J}$. In particular, magnetic charge, like electric charge, is invariant to a

Lorentz transformation. Thus, the net magnetic charge of a particle or of a magnetized body is equal to zero in all frames of reference as required by available experimental evidence.

Let us turn our attention next to the four-dimensional representation of the moment of an electric dipole. The dipole consists of two charges $q$ and $-q$ separated by a distance $\boldsymbol{l}_0$ in the rest frame of the dipole. The dipole moment in the rest frame,

$$\boldsymbol{p}_0 = q\boldsymbol{l}_0 \tag{A1.74}$$

is defined in the limit when $q$ approaches infinity and $\boldsymbol{l}_0$ approaches zero. For the sake of simplicity of notations, the limiting process will not be indicated, but $\boldsymbol{l}_0$ will be understood to represent a differential length. Since charge is a relativistic invariant, the charge will have the same magnitude in a frame $\Sigma$ in which the dipole moves with velocity $\boldsymbol{v}$. However, the distance between the two charges will be different. Let $\boldsymbol{l}$ be the distance in the $\Sigma$ frame (obtained by simultaneous measurements of the positions of the two charges), and

$$\boldsymbol{p} = q\boldsymbol{l} \tag{A1.75}$$

be the corresponding dipole moment. We shall now define the four-vector dipole moment as the product of the invariant charge $q$ and the four-vector distance $\mathsf{L}$ defined by Eq. A1.32 of the preceding section,

$$\mathsf{p} = q\mathsf{L} = q(\boldsymbol{L}', 0) = q(\boldsymbol{l}_0, 0) = (\boldsymbol{p}_0, 0) \tag{A1.76}$$

Thus, $\mathsf{p}$ represents the dipole moment when the positions of the two charges are measured simultaneously in the rest frame of the dipole. The components of $\mathsf{p}$ in the $\Sigma$ frame can be expressed in terms of the distance $\boldsymbol{l}$ between the two charges with the help of Eq. A1.39,

$$\begin{aligned} \mathsf{p} &= q\left(\gamma^2 \frac{(\boldsymbol{l}\cdot\boldsymbol{v})\boldsymbol{v}}{c^2} + \boldsymbol{l}, i\gamma^2 \frac{\boldsymbol{l}\cdot\boldsymbol{v}}{c}\right) \\ &= \left(\gamma^2 \frac{(\boldsymbol{p}\cdot\boldsymbol{v})\boldsymbol{v}}{c^2} + \boldsymbol{p}, i\gamma^2 \frac{\boldsymbol{p}\cdot\boldsymbol{v}}{c}\right) \end{aligned} \tag{A1.77}$$

Thus, the four-vector $\mathsf{p}$ can be expressed in terms of quantities that can be measured by an observer in the $\Sigma$ frame. If $\boldsymbol{v}$ is parallel to the $x$-axis, Eq. A1.77 reduces to

$$\mathsf{p} = \left(\gamma^2 p_x, p_y, p_z, i\gamma^2 \frac{v}{c} p_x\right) \tag{A1.78}$$

Finally, we obtain from Eq. A1.40

$$\boldsymbol{p}_{0\parallel} = \gamma \boldsymbol{p}_{\parallel} \qquad \boldsymbol{p}_{0\perp} = \boldsymbol{p}_{\perp} \tag{A1.79}$$

which relates the three-vector dipole moment in the rest frame to that in the $\Sigma$ frame. The same relation can, of course, be obtained by transforming the components of the four-vector $\mathbf{p}$.

We shall construct next a four-vector $\mathbf{P}$ representing the polarization density in a grain of matter moving with velocity $\boldsymbol{v}$ in the $\Sigma$ frame. For this purpose, we add the four-vectors $\mathbf{p}_i$ associated with the dipoles in the grain of matter, and divide the result by the proper volume of the grain, $V_0$, defined by Eqs. A1.54 and A1.56 of the preceding section. On the assumption that the grain has vanishingly small dimensions, so that it can be treated as a point, we obtain in the $\Sigma$ frame

$$\mathbf{P} = \lim_{V_0 \to 0} \frac{1}{V_0} \sum_i \mathbf{p}_i = \left( \gamma \frac{(\boldsymbol{P} \cdot \boldsymbol{v})\boldsymbol{v}}{c^2} + \frac{\boldsymbol{P}}{\gamma}, \, i\gamma \frac{\boldsymbol{P} \cdot \boldsymbol{v}}{c} \right) \tag{A1.80}$$

where

$$\gamma = \frac{1}{\sqrt{1 - (v/c)^2}}$$

and $\boldsymbol{P}$ is the three-vector polarization in the $\Sigma$ frame, defined in Sec. 5.2. If the entire polarized body is at rest in a frame $\Sigma'$ moving with a velocity of magnitude $v_0$ parallel to the $x$-axis, Eq. A1.80 reduces to

$$\mathbf{P} = \left( \gamma_0 P_x, \frac{P_y}{\gamma_0}, \frac{P_z}{\gamma_0}, \, i\gamma_0 P_x \frac{v_0}{c} \right) \tag{A1.81}$$

In general the three-vector polarization in the rest frame, $\boldsymbol{P}_0$, and the corresponding vector in the $\Sigma$ frame, $\boldsymbol{P}$, are related by

$$\boldsymbol{P}_{0\parallel} = \boldsymbol{P}_{\parallel} \qquad \boldsymbol{P}_{0\perp} = \frac{\boldsymbol{P}_{\perp}}{\gamma} \tag{A1.82}$$

Finally, it is interesting to note that the scalar product of the four-vectors $\mathbf{P}$ and $\mathbf{v}$ for each grain of matter is equal to zero,

$$\mathbf{P} \cdot \mathbf{v} = (\boldsymbol{P} \cdot \boldsymbol{v}) \left[ \gamma^2 \left( \frac{v}{c} \right)^2 + 1 - \gamma^2 \right] = 0 \tag{A1.83}$$

After having defined the four-vector polarization $\mathbf{P}$, we shall now show that the four-vector polarization-current density $\boldsymbol{J}_p$ is related to it by

$$\boldsymbol{J}_p = \operatorname{div} (\mathbf{P} \times \mathbf{v}) \tag{A1.84}$$

where the $m$th component of the divergence is defined as

$$(J_p)_m = \sum_n \frac{\partial}{\partial x_n} (\mathbf{P} \times \mathbf{v})_{mn} \tag{A1.85}$$

We saw that the cross product of two four-vectors is an antisymmetric tensor (six-vector) whose components are given by

$$(\mathbf{P} \times \mathbf{v})_{mn} = P_m v_n - P_n v_m \tag{A1.86}$$

We obtain in terms of the Cartesian components of the three-vectors $\boldsymbol{P}$ and $\boldsymbol{v}$ in the $\Sigma$ frame,

$$\mathbf{P} \times \mathbf{v} = \begin{bmatrix} 0 & P_x v_y - P_y v_x & P_x v_z - P_z v_x & icP_x \\ P_y v_x - P_x v_y & 0 & P_y v_z - P_z v_y & icP_y \\ P_z v_x - P_x v_z & P_z v_y - P_y v_z & 0 & icP_z \\ -icP_x & -icP_y & -icP_z & 0 \end{bmatrix} \tag{A1.87}$$

The first three components of this tensor (23, 31, 12) are readily recognized as the Cartesian components of the three-space cross product $\boldsymbol{P} \times \boldsymbol{v}$. The remaining three components (14, 24, 34) are the Cartesian components of the three-vector $ic\boldsymbol{P}$. Thus,

$$\mathbf{P} \times \mathbf{v} = (\boldsymbol{P} \times \boldsymbol{v}; ic\boldsymbol{P}) \tag{A1.88}$$

is the six-vector representation of the antisymmetrical tensor.

Next, substitution in Eq. A1.85 yields for the components of $\mathbf{J}_p$

$$\begin{aligned}
(J_p)_1 &= J_{px} = \frac{\partial}{\partial y} (\boldsymbol{P} \times \boldsymbol{v})_z - \frac{\partial}{\partial z} (\boldsymbol{P} \times \boldsymbol{v})_y + \frac{\partial}{\partial t} P_x \\
(J_p)_2 &= J_{py} = -\frac{\partial}{\partial x} (\boldsymbol{P} \times \boldsymbol{v})_z + \frac{\partial}{\partial z} (\boldsymbol{P} \times \boldsymbol{v})_x + \frac{\partial}{\partial t} P_y \\
(J_p)_3 &= J_{pz} = \frac{\partial}{\partial x} (\boldsymbol{P} \times \boldsymbol{v})_y - \frac{\partial}{\partial y} (\boldsymbol{P} \times \boldsymbol{v})_x + \frac{\partial}{\partial t} P_z \\
(J_p)_4 &= ic\rho_p = -ic\left(\frac{\partial}{\partial x} P_x + \frac{\partial}{\partial y} P_y + \frac{\partial}{\partial z} P_z\right)
\end{aligned} \tag{A1.89}$$

and we obtain by inspection,

$$\mathbf{J}_p = \left(\frac{\partial \boldsymbol{P}}{\partial t} + \text{curl}\,(\boldsymbol{P} \times \boldsymbol{v}),\ -ic\,\text{div}\,\boldsymbol{P}\right) = (\boldsymbol{J}_p, ic\rho_p) \tag{A1.90}$$

which is the desired expression for $\mathbf{J}_p$ in terms of $\boldsymbol{J}_p$ and $\rho_p$.

Analogous to $\mathbf{p}$ and $\mathbf{P}$ we can define in the $\Sigma$ frame a four-vector magnetic-dipole moment $\mathbf{m}$ and a four-vector magnetization $\mathbf{M}$,

$$\mathbf{m} = \left( \boldsymbol{m} + \gamma^2 \boldsymbol{m} \cdot \frac{\boldsymbol{v}}{c}\frac{\boldsymbol{v}}{c},\; i\gamma^2 \boldsymbol{m} \cdot \frac{\boldsymbol{v}}{c} \right) \tag{A1.91}$$

$$\mathbf{M} = \left( \frac{1}{\gamma} \boldsymbol{M} + \gamma \boldsymbol{M} \cdot \frac{\boldsymbol{v}}{c}\frac{\boldsymbol{v}}{c},\; i\gamma \boldsymbol{M} \cdot \frac{\boldsymbol{v}}{c} \right) \tag{A1.92}$$

where $\boldsymbol{m}$ and $\boldsymbol{M}$ are the corresponding three-space quantities. Both four-vectors are orthogonal to the four-vector $\mathbf{v}$.

We saw in Sec. 5.4 that the three-space magnetic-current density $\boldsymbol{J}^*$ and the magnetic-charge density $\rho^*$ can be expressed in terms of the magnetization $\boldsymbol{M}$,

$$\begin{aligned} \boldsymbol{J}^* &= \text{curl}\,(\mu_0 \boldsymbol{M} \times \boldsymbol{v}) + \frac{\partial}{\partial t} \mu_0 \boldsymbol{M} \\ \rho^* &= -\,\text{div}\,\mu_0 \boldsymbol{M} \end{aligned} \tag{A1.93}$$

It can be shown as in the case of $\mathbf{J}_p$ that

$$\mathbf{J}^* = \text{div}\,(\mu_0 \mathbf{M} \times \mathbf{v}) = (\boldsymbol{J}^*, ic\rho^*) \tag{A1.94}$$

where $\mathbf{M} \times \mathbf{v}$ is the antisymmetric tensor:

$$\begin{aligned} \mathbf{M} \times \mathbf{v} &= \begin{bmatrix} 0 & M_x v_y - M_y v_x & M_x v_z - M_z v_x & icM_x \\ M_y v_x - M_x v_y & 0 & M_y v_z - M_z v_y & icM_y \\ M_z v_x - M_x v_z & M_z v_y - M_y v_z & 0 & icM_z \\ -icM_x & -icM_y & -icM_z & 0 \end{bmatrix} \\ &= (\boldsymbol{M} \times \boldsymbol{v}; ic\boldsymbol{M}) \end{aligned} \tag{A1.95}$$

## A1.5 Electromagnetic Field Tensors

Thus far we have constructed or defined kinematic and material quantities. We shall now introduce two electromagnetic-field tensors that are suggested by the Maxwell equations,

$$\begin{aligned} \text{curl}\,\boldsymbol{H} - \frac{\partial}{\partial t} \epsilon_0 \boldsymbol{E} &= \boldsymbol{J} \\ \text{div}\,\epsilon_0 \boldsymbol{E} &= \rho \\ -\,\text{curl}\,\boldsymbol{E} - \frac{\partial}{\partial t} \mu_0 \boldsymbol{H} &= \boldsymbol{J}^* \\ \text{div}\,\mu_0 \boldsymbol{H} &= \rho^* \end{aligned} \tag{A1.96}$$

By expanding these four equations into Cartesian components, it can be seen that

$$\operatorname{div} \mathfrak{G} = \boldsymbol{J} \tag{A1.97}$$

$$\operatorname{div} \mathfrak{K} = \boldsymbol{J}^* \tag{A1.98}$$

where $\mathfrak{G}$ and $\mathfrak{K}$ are the electromagnetic-field tensors defined by

$$\mathfrak{G} = \begin{bmatrix} 0 & H_z & -H_y & -ic\epsilon_0 E_x \\ -H_z & 0 & H_x & -ic\epsilon_0 E_y \\ H_y & -H_x & 0 & -ic\epsilon_0 E_z \\ ic\epsilon_0 E_x & ic\epsilon_0 E_y & ic\epsilon_0 E_z & 0 \end{bmatrix}$$

$$= (\boldsymbol{H}; -ic\epsilon_0 \boldsymbol{E}) \tag{A1.99}$$

and

$$\mathfrak{K} = \begin{bmatrix} 0 & -E_z & E_y & -ic\mu_0 H_x \\ E_z & 0 & -E_x & -ic\mu_0 H_y \\ -E_y & E_x & 0 & -ic\mu_0 H_y \\ ic\mu_0 H_x & ic\mu_0 H_y & ic\mu_0 H_z & 0 \end{bmatrix}$$

$$= (-\boldsymbol{E}; -ic\mu_0 \boldsymbol{H}) \tag{A1.100}$$

Both $\mathfrak{G}$ and $\mathfrak{K}$ are antisymmetric tensors or six-vectors. We can construct the dual six-vectors $\mathfrak{G}^\dagger$ and $\mathfrak{K}^\dagger$ from $\mathfrak{K}$ and $\mathfrak{G}$, respectively, by interchanging the two three-vectors, as follows.

$$\mathfrak{G}^\dagger = (-ic\epsilon_0 \boldsymbol{E}; \boldsymbol{H})$$

$$= -ic\epsilon_0 (\boldsymbol{E}; ic\mu_0 \boldsymbol{H})$$

$$= ic\epsilon_0 \mathfrak{K} \tag{A1.101}$$

and

$$\mathfrak{K}^\dagger = (-ic\mu_0 \boldsymbol{H}; -\boldsymbol{E})$$

$$= -ic\mu_0 (\boldsymbol{H}; -ic\epsilon_0 \boldsymbol{E})$$

$$= -ic\mu_0 \mathfrak{G} \tag{A1.102}$$

Thus the tensors $\mathfrak{G}$ and $\mathfrak{K}$ are related.

The components of a tensor or rank two transform according to Eq. A1.19. For a Lorentz transformation in which the $\Sigma'$ frame is moving in the $\Sigma$ frame with a constant velocity of magnitude $v_0$ parallel to the

$x$-axis, the coefficients $a_{ij}$ are given by Eqs. A1.12, A1.13, and A1.15. Transforming the field tensor $\mathfrak{G}$ or $\mathfrak{K}$ yields for the three-vectors $\boldsymbol{E}'$ and $\boldsymbol{H}'$:

$$\begin{aligned} E_x' &= E_x \\ E_y' &= \gamma_0(E_y - v_0\mu_0 H_z) \\ E_z' &= \gamma_0(E_z + v_0\mu_0 H_y) \end{aligned} \tag{A1.103}$$

$$\begin{aligned} H_x' &= H_x \\ H_y' &= \gamma_0(H_y + v_0\epsilon_0 E_z) \\ H_z' &= \gamma_0(H_z - v_0\epsilon_0 E_y) \end{aligned} \tag{A1.104}$$

In terms of the components parallel and perpendicular to the relative velocity $\boldsymbol{v}_0$ of the two frames, we have

$$\begin{aligned} \boldsymbol{E}_{\parallel}' &= \boldsymbol{E}_{\parallel} \\ \boldsymbol{E}_{\perp}' &= \gamma_0(\boldsymbol{E}_{\perp} + \boldsymbol{v}_0 \times \mu_0\boldsymbol{H}) \end{aligned} \tag{A1.105}$$

$$\begin{aligned} \boldsymbol{H}_{\parallel}' &= \boldsymbol{H}_{\parallel} \\ \boldsymbol{H}_{\perp}' &= \gamma_0(\boldsymbol{H}_{\perp} - \boldsymbol{v}_0 \times \epsilon_0\boldsymbol{E}) \end{aligned} \tag{A1.106}$$

### A1.5.1 Alternative Formulations of Field Tensors

The preceding formulation of the macroscopic Maxwell equations differs from the usual formulation attributed to Minkowski. Minkowski's formulation is based on the macroscopic Maxwell equations in the conventional form with $\boldsymbol{E}$, $\boldsymbol{D}$, $\boldsymbol{H}$, and $\boldsymbol{B}$. There is still another formulation which is based upon the polarization and amperian-current models of material media; it will be designated as the amperian or ***E-B*** formulation. We shall present these two formulations and construct new tensors and vectors for them from linear combinations of tensors and vectors already presented, in order to compare them with the preceding or ***E-H*** formulation. Since linear combinations of vectors or tensors transform properly, if the original vectors or tensors transform properly, there is no mathematical difference in the three formulations except for the definitions of the field and material quantities. We shall see, however, when we deal with forces, power, energy, and stress, that the three formulations depart radically from each other. We shall then be dealing with product quantities.

A1.5.1.1 MINKOWSKI FORMULATION OF FIELD TENSORS. In our ***E-H*** formulation we have (Eqs. A1.84 and A1.97)

$$\operatorname{div} \mathfrak{G} = \mathbf{J}$$

$$\operatorname{div} (\mathbf{P} \times \mathbf{v}) = \mathbf{J}_p$$

The difference of these two equations is

$$\operatorname{div} (\mathfrak{G} - \mathbf{P} \times \mathbf{v}) = \mathbf{J} - \mathbf{J}_p = \mathbf{J}_f \tag{A1.107}$$

We also have (Eqs. A1.94 and A1.98)

$$\operatorname{div} \mathfrak{K} = \mathbf{J}^*$$

$$\operatorname{div} (\mu_0 \mathbf{M} \times \mathbf{v}) = \mathbf{J}^*$$

Their difference is

$$\operatorname{div} (\mathfrak{K} - \mu_0 \mathbf{M} \times \mathbf{v}) = 0 \tag{A1.108}$$

The two mixed tensors (six-vectors) are

$$(\mathfrak{G} - \mathbf{P} \times \mathbf{v}) = [(\boldsymbol{H} - \boldsymbol{P} \times \boldsymbol{v}); -ic(\epsilon_0 \boldsymbol{E} + \boldsymbol{P})] \tag{A1.109}$$

and

$$(\mathfrak{K} - \mu_0 \mathbf{M} \times \mathbf{v}) = [-(\boldsymbol{E} + \mu_0 \boldsymbol{M} \times \boldsymbol{v}); -ic\mu_0(\boldsymbol{H} + \boldsymbol{M})] \tag{A1.110}$$

Now we shall consider the usual form of Maxwell's equations

$$\begin{aligned} \operatorname{curl} \boldsymbol{H} - \frac{\partial \boldsymbol{D}}{\partial t} &= \mathbf{J}_f \\ \operatorname{div} \boldsymbol{D} &= \rho_f \\ -\operatorname{curl} \boldsymbol{E} - \frac{\partial \boldsymbol{B}}{\partial t} &= 0 \\ \operatorname{div} \boldsymbol{B} &= 0 \end{aligned} \tag{A1.111}$$

Here $\mathbf{J}_f$ and $\rho_f$ are the free electric-current and charge densities. The vectors $\boldsymbol{E}$ and $\boldsymbol{B}$ are regarded as the field vectors, and are defined by the conventional macroscopic Lorentz-force law. The vectors $\boldsymbol{H}$ and $\boldsymbol{D}$ are regarded as excitation vectors. We shall show that these definitions of $\boldsymbol{E}$ and $\boldsymbol{H}$ are different from those given in our ***E-H*** formulation.

Minkowski casts the four Maxwell equations into two four-space equations

$$\operatorname{div} \mathfrak{G}_M = \mathbf{J}_f \tag{A1.112}$$

$$\operatorname{div} \mathfrak{K}_M = 0 \tag{A1.113}$$

The subscript $M$ stands for Minkowski. The tensors $\mathfrak{G}_M$ and $\mathfrak{K}_M$ are defined by

$$\mathfrak{G}_M = \begin{bmatrix} 0 & H_{Mz} & -H_{My} & -icD_{Mx} \\ -H_{Mz} & 0 & H_{Mx} & -icD_{My} \\ H_{My} & -H_{Mx} & 0 & -icD_{My} \\ icD_{Mx} & icD_{My} & icD_{Mz} & 0 \end{bmatrix}$$

$$= (\boldsymbol{H}_M;\ -ic\boldsymbol{D}_M) \tag{A1.114}$$

and

$$\mathfrak{K}_M = \begin{bmatrix} 0 & -E_{Mz} & E_{My} & -icB_{Mx} \\ E_{Mz} & 0 & -E_{Mx} & -icB_{My} \\ -E_{My} & E_{Mx} & 0 & -icB_{Mz} \\ icB_{Mx} & icB_{My} & icB_{Mz} & 0 \end{bmatrix}$$

$$= (-\boldsymbol{E}_M;\ -ic\boldsymbol{B}_M) \tag{A1.115}$$

The Maxwell equations have been shown to be valid for macroscopic electromagnetic phenomena when the media are rigid and stationary with respect to the observer. Countless experiments have been carried out in the last century to confirm the validity of Maxwell's equations for such cases. In Minkowski's formulation, however, the Maxwell equations in the standard form are considered to be valid in general, even for matter in motion. They are considered as the physical laws that govern macroscopic electromagnetic phenomena in a frame of reference in which material media are deforming and/or moving. The ***E-H*** formulation and the Minkowski formulation for moving matter give field equations that are different in appearance. At this point, where energy and force considerations have not yet been introduced, the two sets of equations are completely compatible if one properly identifies terms appearing in equivalent places in the two sets of equations, i.e., Eqs. A1.107, A1.108, and Eqs. A1.112, A1.113. Thus

$$\mathfrak{G}_M = \mathfrak{G} - \mathbf{P} \times \mathbf{v} \tag{A1.116}$$

$$\mathfrak{K}_M = \mathfrak{K} - \mu_0 \mathbf{M} \times \mathbf{v} \tag{A1.117}$$

To make the two sets of equations identical, we must have:

| Quantities Defined in Minkowski's Formulation | | Quantities Defined in the ***E-H*** Formulation |
|---|---|---|
| $\boldsymbol{E}_M$ | = | $\boldsymbol{E} + \mu_0 \boldsymbol{M} \times \mathbf{v}$ |
| $\boldsymbol{D}_M$ | = | $\epsilon_0 \boldsymbol{E} + \boldsymbol{P}$ |
| $\boldsymbol{H}_M$ | = | $\boldsymbol{H} - \boldsymbol{P} \times \mathbf{v}$ |
| $\boldsymbol{B}_M$ | = | $\mu_0(\boldsymbol{H} + \boldsymbol{M})$ |
| $\boldsymbol{J}_f$ | = | $\mathbf{J}_f$ |

The definitions of $\boldsymbol{D}$ and $\boldsymbol{B}$ in the Minkowski formulation are identical with our own for both stationary and moving matter. However, $\boldsymbol{E}_M$ and $\boldsymbol{H}_M$ are quite different from our own $\boldsymbol{E}$ and $\boldsymbol{H}$. The vector $\boldsymbol{E}_M$ in the Minkowski formulation is the sum of two vectors, a field vector $\boldsymbol{E}$ and a material vector $\mu_0\boldsymbol{M} \times \boldsymbol{v}$. The vector $\boldsymbol{H}_M$ in the Minkowski formulation is, again, the sum of a field vector $\boldsymbol{H}$ and a material vector $-\boldsymbol{P} \times \boldsymbol{v}$. Thus the two sets of definitions are equal only in media that are neither polarized nor magnetized, or rigid and stationary.

A1.5.1.2 Amperian Formulation. We shall now define a new antisymmetric tensor by a process similar to that used in the construction of $\mathfrak{G}^\dagger$ and $\mathfrak{K}^\dagger$ from the tensors $\mathfrak{G}$ and $\mathfrak{K}$ (see Eq. A1.95),

$$-\frac{i}{c}(\mathsf{M} \times \mathsf{v})^\dagger = \left(\boldsymbol{M}; -\frac{i}{c}\boldsymbol{M} \times \boldsymbol{v}\right) \tag{A1.118}$$

The divergence of this tensor is a four-vector amperian electric-current density $\mathsf{J}_m$; it represents the amperian currents associated with magnetized matter.

$$\operatorname{div}\left[-\frac{i}{c}(\mathsf{M} \times \mathsf{v})^\dagger\right] = \mathsf{J}_m \tag{A1.119}$$

We shall now form a new set of tensor equations

$$\operatorname{div}\left[\mathfrak{G} - \frac{i}{c}(\mathsf{M} \times \mathsf{v})^\dagger\right] = \mathsf{J} + \mathsf{J}_m \tag{A1.120}$$

$$\operatorname{div}\left[\mathfrak{K} - \mu_0(\mathsf{M} \times \mathsf{v})\right] = \mathsf{J}^* - \mathsf{J}^* = 0 \tag{A1.121}$$

The two tensors, $\mathfrak{G} - \frac{i}{c}(\boldsymbol{M} \times \boldsymbol{v})^\dagger$ and $\mathfrak{K} - \mu_0(\boldsymbol{M} \times \boldsymbol{v})$, are antisymmetric. In six-vector notation they become

$$\mathfrak{G} - \frac{i}{c}(\mathsf{M} \times \mathsf{v})^\dagger = [(\boldsymbol{H} + \boldsymbol{M}); -ic\epsilon_0(\boldsymbol{E} + \mu_0\boldsymbol{M} \times \boldsymbol{v})] \tag{A1.122}$$

$$\mathfrak{K} - \mu_0(\mathsf{M} \times \mathsf{v}) = [-(\boldsymbol{E} + \mu_0\boldsymbol{M} \times \boldsymbol{v}); -ic\mu_0(\boldsymbol{H} + \boldsymbol{M})] \tag{A1.123}$$

The four-vector $\mathsf{J}_m$ results from the three-vector amperian-current density $\boldsymbol{J}_m$ and the amperian-charge density $\rho_m$,

$$\mathsf{J}_m = (\boldsymbol{J}_m, ic\rho_m) \tag{A1.124}$$

On the other hand $\boldsymbol{J}_m$ and $\rho_m$ can be obtained from Eq. A1.119 as follows,

$$\boldsymbol{J}_m = \text{curl}\, \boldsymbol{M} - \epsilon_0 \frac{\partial}{\partial t} (\mu_0 \boldsymbol{M} \times \boldsymbol{v}) \tag{A1.125}$$

$$\rho_m = \epsilon_0 \text{ div } \mu_0 \boldsymbol{M} \times \boldsymbol{v} \tag{A1.126}$$

It follows that

$$\text{div } \boldsymbol{J}_m + \frac{\partial}{\partial t} \rho_m = 0 \tag{A1.127}$$

The two four-space relations given by Eqs. A1.120 and A1.121 can be reduced to three-space form, as follows:

$$\text{curl } (\boldsymbol{H} + \boldsymbol{M}) - \frac{\partial}{\partial t} \epsilon_0 (\boldsymbol{E} + \mu_0 \boldsymbol{M} \times \boldsymbol{v}) = \boldsymbol{J} + \boldsymbol{J}_m \tag{A1.128}$$

$$- \text{ curl } (\boldsymbol{E} + \mu_0 \boldsymbol{M} \times \boldsymbol{v}) - \frac{\partial}{\partial t} \mu_0 (\boldsymbol{H} + \boldsymbol{M}) = 0 \tag{A1.129}$$

$$\text{div } \epsilon_0 (\boldsymbol{E} + \mu_0 \boldsymbol{M} \times \boldsymbol{v}) = \rho + \rho_m \tag{A1.130}$$

$$\text{div } \mu_0 (\boldsymbol{H} + \boldsymbol{M}) = 0 \tag{A1.131}$$

If the medium is rigid and stationary with respect to the observer ($\boldsymbol{v} = 0$), we have

$$\text{curl} \frac{\boldsymbol{B}}{\mu_0} - \frac{\partial}{\partial t} \epsilon_0 \boldsymbol{E} = \boldsymbol{J} + \boldsymbol{J}_m \tag{A1.132}$$

$$\text{div } \epsilon_0 \boldsymbol{E} = \rho + \rho_m \tag{A1.133}$$

$$- \text{ curl } \boldsymbol{E} - \frac{\partial}{\partial t} \boldsymbol{B} = 0 \tag{A1.134}$$

$$\text{div } \boldsymbol{B} = 0 \tag{A1.135}$$

where

$$\boldsymbol{B} = \mu_0 (\boldsymbol{H} + \boldsymbol{M}) \tag{A1.136}$$

In this special case

$$\boldsymbol{J}_m = \text{curl } \boldsymbol{M}$$

$$\rho_m = 0$$

It may be observed from these relations that, in the amperian formulation, magnetization of matter gives rise to a current term that acts on the magnetic field in the same way as the free-current density and the polarization-current density. A corresponding effect is produced upon the electric field by the electric-charge density $\rho_m$ resulting from the magnetization. It is characteristic of the amperian formulation that magnetization produces effects corresponding to electric charges and currents. This amounts to ascribing magnetization to electric charges and currents.

The general amperian formulation for moving material bodies is obtained by postulating that Eqs. A1.132 to A1.135 developed for rigid, stationary bodies are valid in general. This postulate is analogous to the one from which the general Minkowski formulation was derived. These equations become, when written in four-dimensional form,

$$\text{div}\, \mathfrak{G}_a = \boldsymbol{J} + \boldsymbol{J}_m \qquad \text{(A1.137)}$$

$$\text{div}\, \mathfrak{K}_a = 0 \qquad \text{(A1.138)}$$

where

$$\mathfrak{G}_a = \left(\frac{\boldsymbol{B}_a}{\mu_0};\ -ic\epsilon_0\boldsymbol{E}_a\right) \qquad \text{(A1.139)}$$

$$\mathfrak{K}_a = (-\boldsymbol{E}_a;\ -ic\boldsymbol{B}_a) \qquad \text{(A1.140)}$$

$\boldsymbol{J}$ is given by Eq. A1.59, and $\boldsymbol{J}_m$ by Eqs. A1.124, A1.125, and A1.126.

We may relate the amperian formulation to the ***E-H*** formulation by comparing Eqs. A1.128 to A1.131 (obtained from the ***E-H*** formulation) with Eqs. A1.132 to A1.135, which constitute the fundamental relations of the amperian formulation.

| Quantities Defined in the Amperian Formulation | | Quantities Defined in the ***E-H*** Formulation |
|---|---|---|
| $\boldsymbol{B}_a$ | = | $\mu_0(\boldsymbol{H} + \boldsymbol{M})$ |
| $\boldsymbol{E}_a$ | = | $\boldsymbol{E} + \mu_0\boldsymbol{M} \times \boldsymbol{v}$ |

As far as the field laws are concerned, the three formulations are equivalent, provided that the quantities in one formulation are properly defined in terms of quantities in the other formulations. Thus the choice of the right formulation cannot be made on the basis of the discussion presented thus far. The choice will be made when the product quantities are considered in the next sections. By comparing the interaction product quantities with the corresponding quantities derived from the Lorentz-force laws and the laws of mechanics, we shall conclude that the ***E-H*** formulation is the correct formulation of macroscopic electrodynamics.

## A1.6 Force Vectors and Electromagnetic-Stress Tensors

Kinematics deals with motions considered by themselves, apart from their causes. When we introduce material quantities, such as charges and dipole moments, we deal with the kinematics of the charges and the dipoles without questioning the causes of their motions. Maxwell's equations relate the field to the charges and dipoles, again, without reference to the causes of their motion. Forces, work, power, energy, electromagnetic stress, and momentum are represented in three-space by product quantities. We shall now introduce corresponding four-space quantities and study their transformation properties.

It should be emphasized that the electromagnetic product quantities are the links between electrodynamics and other branches of classical physics. The work done by the Lorentz forces on charges and currents must be balanced by changes of mechanical energy and thermodynamic energy.

### A1.6.1 Mechanical Force and Force Density

We shall define the four-vector momentum of a free particle having a rest mass $m_0$ (the mass in the rest frame of the particle) as the product of the rest mass and the four-vector velocity $\mathbf{v}$. The four-vector force $\mathbf{F}$ on the particle is the derivative of the four-vector momentum $m_0\mathbf{v}$ with respect to the proper time.

$$\mathbf{F} = \frac{d}{d\tau} m_0\gamma(\boldsymbol{v}, ic)$$

$$= \frac{dt}{d\tau}\frac{d}{dt} m_0\gamma(\boldsymbol{v}, ic)$$

$$= \gamma\left(\frac{d}{dt} m_0\gamma\boldsymbol{v}, \frac{i}{c}\frac{d}{dt} m_0\gamma c^2\right) \tag{A1.141}$$

Einstein interpreted $m_0\gamma$ as the mass $m$ of the particle in a frame of reference $\Sigma$ in which it moves with velocity $\boldsymbol{v}$. The product $m_0\gamma\boldsymbol{v}$ is then the three-vector momentum of the particle, and its time rate of change is the three-vector force $\boldsymbol{F}$ in the $\Sigma$ frame. Correspondingly, the energy of the particle is $mc^2$ or $m_0\gamma c^2$, and its time-rate of change is the work done per unit time by the three-vector force $\boldsymbol{F}$. In terms of three-space mechanics, this work is given, in the $\Sigma$ frame, by

$$\boldsymbol{F}\cdot\boldsymbol{v} = \frac{d}{dt}\, m_0\gamma \boldsymbol{v} \tag{A1.142}$$

Thus the four-vector force can also be expressed in terms of the three-vectors $\boldsymbol{F}$ and $\boldsymbol{v}$,

$$\mathbf{F} = \gamma\left(\boldsymbol{F}, \frac{i}{c}\,\boldsymbol{F}\cdot\boldsymbol{v}\right) \tag{A1.143}$$

Aside from the factors $\gamma$ and $i/c$, the fourth component of $\mathbf{F}$ is the work done on the particle per unit time. Thus, the three-space force and the work per unit time (power) done by it are combined to form the four-vector $\mathbf{F}$.

We shall evaluate below the four-vector $\mathbf{F}$ representing the force exerted by an electromagnetic field on a point charge. We shall then define a four-vector $\mathbf{f}$ representing the force density on a macroscopic distribution of electric charges, and a four-vector $\mathbf{f}^*$ representing the force density on a macroscopic distribution of magnetic charges. We shall see that although the first three components of each of these vectors correspond to the macroscopic three-vector force density, the fourth component is proportional to the sum of the density of the power converted into mechanical form and of the power dissipated or absorbed by matter. The condition that the fourth components of $\mathbf{f}$ and $\mathbf{f}^*$ be consistent with experimental evidence on the conversion of electromagnetic energy into other forms of energy will lead us to the choice of the $\boldsymbol{E}$-$\boldsymbol{H}$ formulation as the correct one for macroscopic electrodynamics.

### A1.6.2 Electric-Force and Magnetic-Force Densities

We shall derive now the four-vector representing the force exerted by the electromagnetic field on a point charge $q$ moving with velocity $\boldsymbol{v}$ in the $\Sigma$ frame. The three-vector Lorentz force is given by

$$\boldsymbol{F} = q(\boldsymbol{E} + \boldsymbol{v} \times \mu_0\boldsymbol{H}) \tag{A1.144}$$

Thus, according to Eq. A1.143, the four-vector force is

$$\mathbf{F} = \gamma q\left(\boldsymbol{E} + \boldsymbol{v} \times \mu_0\boldsymbol{H}, \frac{i}{c}\,\boldsymbol{E}\cdot\boldsymbol{v}\right) \tag{A1.145}$$

It can be readily checked that **F** can also be written in the form

$$\mathbf{F} = \mu_0 \mathfrak{G} \cdot q\mathbf{v} = \left(\mu_0 \boldsymbol{H};\ -\frac{i}{c}\boldsymbol{E}\right) \cdot \gamma(q\boldsymbol{v}, iqc) \qquad \text{(A1.146)}$$

where **v** is the four-vector representing the velocity of the charge, $\mathfrak{G}$ is the tensor defined by Eq. A1.99 representing the electromagnetic field, and the dot product is defined by

$$F_m = q\mu_0 \sum_n G_{mn} v_n \qquad \text{(A1.147)}$$

It is important to note that Eq. A1.146 expresses the Lorentz force in four-dimensional form. As such, it can be regarded as the definition of the field tensor $\mathfrak{G}$ in terms of the four-vector force, the four-vector velocity and the charge $q$ which is a relativistic invariant. In other words, the tensor character of $\mathfrak{G}$ follows directly from the definitions of $\boldsymbol{E}$ and $\boldsymbol{H}$ given in Sec. 1.1 rather than from Maxwell's equations.

A similar four-vector can be written for the force on a magnetic charge $q^*$ (analogous to the Lorentz force on an electric charge) which was derived in Sec. 7.1 to account for the torque exerted on a magnetic dipole. We obtain

$$\mathbf{F}^* = \gamma q^* \left(\boldsymbol{H} - \boldsymbol{v} \times \epsilon_0 \boldsymbol{E}, \frac{i}{c}\boldsymbol{H}\cdot\boldsymbol{v}\right)$$

$$= \epsilon_0 \mathfrak{K} \cdot q^* \mathbf{v} = -\frac{i}{c}\mathfrak{G}^\dagger \cdot q^* \mathbf{v} \qquad \text{(A1.148)}$$

where $\mathfrak{K}$ is the tensor defined by Eq. A1.100.

The forms of Eqs. A1.146 and A1.148 suggest representing the electric-force density on matter by means of the four-vector

$$\mathbf{f} = \mu_0 \mathfrak{G} \cdot \mathbf{J} \qquad \text{(A1.149)}$$

and the magnetic-force density by the four-vector

$$\mathbf{f}^* = \epsilon_0 \mathfrak{K} \cdot \mathbf{J}^* \qquad \text{(A1.150)}$$

where $\mathbf{J}$ and $\mathbf{J}^*$ are the four-vector current densities representing the total action of matter as a field source. Expanding the dot product in these two equations as indicated by Eq. A1.147 yields

$$\mathbf{f} = \left(\rho \boldsymbol{E} + \boldsymbol{J} \times \mu_0 \boldsymbol{H}, \frac{i}{c}\boldsymbol{E}\cdot\boldsymbol{J}\right) = \left(\boldsymbol{f}, \frac{i}{c}\boldsymbol{E}\cdot\boldsymbol{J}\right) \qquad \text{(A1.151)}$$

$$\mathbf{f}^* = \left(\rho^* \boldsymbol{H} - \boldsymbol{J}^* \times \epsilon_0 \boldsymbol{E}, \frac{i}{c}\boldsymbol{H}\cdot\boldsymbol{J}^*\right) = \left(\boldsymbol{f}^*, \frac{i}{c}\boldsymbol{H}\cdot\boldsymbol{J}^*\right) \qquad \text{(A1.152)}$$

The first three components of $\mathbf{f}$ are the components of the three-vector force density $\boldsymbol{f}$ obtained in Sec. 7.1. It must be emphasized that $\boldsymbol{f}$ represents the macroscopic density of the electric force acting on matter; the work done by this force must then be regarded as energy transformed into mechanical form. On the other hand, the fourth component of $\mathbf{f}$ is proportional to $\boldsymbol{E}\cdot\boldsymbol{J}$, which is the density of power converted from electromagnetic form to some other form (mechanical, thermic, etc.) through the action of the field on electric charges and currents as discussed in Sec. 7.2. If $\boldsymbol{v}$ is the velocity of the grain of matter under consideration, the difference between the power density converted from electromagnetic form and the part converted into mechanical form is

$$\begin{aligned}\boldsymbol{E}\cdot\boldsymbol{J} - \boldsymbol{f}\cdot\boldsymbol{v} &= \boldsymbol{E}\cdot\boldsymbol{J} - \rho\boldsymbol{E}\cdot\boldsymbol{v} - \boldsymbol{J} \times \mu_0\boldsymbol{H}\cdot\boldsymbol{v} \\ &= (\boldsymbol{E} + \boldsymbol{v} \times \mu_0\boldsymbol{H})\cdot(\boldsymbol{J} - \rho\boldsymbol{v}) \qquad \text{(A1.153)}\end{aligned}$$

The fact that the fourth component of $\mathbf{f}$ is not proportional to the work per unit time done by $\boldsymbol{f}$ may appear at first to be in disagreement with the form of the expression for the four-vector force on a particle given by Eq. A1.143. A little thought will indicate, however, that the summation over a grain of matter involved in passing from the four-vector $\mathbf{F}$ for a particle to the macroscopic four-vector $\mathbf{f}$ does not preserve the relationship between the fourth component and the other three components when the particles constituting the grain move with different velocities. For instance, let us consider a particle with a positive charge $q$, moving with the velocity $\boldsymbol{v}$ of the grain, and a particle with a negative charge $-q$ moving with a velocity $\boldsymbol{v} + \boldsymbol{u}$. The sum of the forces exerted by the macroscopic field on the two charges is from Eq. A1.144,

$$\boldsymbol{F}_+ + \boldsymbol{F}_- = -q\boldsymbol{u} \times \mu_0\boldsymbol{H} \qquad \text{(A1.154)}$$

and the sum of the work per unit time done on the two particles is

$$\boldsymbol{F}_+\cdot\boldsymbol{v} + \boldsymbol{F}_-\cdot(\boldsymbol{v} + \boldsymbol{u}) = -q\boldsymbol{E}\cdot\boldsymbol{u} \qquad \text{(A1.155)}$$

Thus, the total work per unit time depends on $\boldsymbol{E}$ and not on $\boldsymbol{H}$, whereas the total force depends on $\boldsymbol{H}$ and not on $\boldsymbol{E}$, and neither of them depends on the velocity $\boldsymbol{v}$ of the grain.

According to Eq. A1.153, the power density converted from electromagnetic form, proportional to the fourth component of $\mathbf{f}$, can be separated into two parts,

$$\boldsymbol{E}\cdot\boldsymbol{J} = \boldsymbol{E}_{\text{eff}}\cdot\boldsymbol{J}_{\text{eff}} + \boldsymbol{f}\cdot\boldsymbol{v} \qquad \text{(A1.156)}$$

where, according to the definitions given in Sec. 10.2,

$$\boldsymbol{E}_{\text{eff}} = \boldsymbol{E} + \boldsymbol{v} \times \mu_0 \boldsymbol{H} \tag{A1.157}$$

is the force per unit charge exerted by the field on a point charge moving with a grain of matter, and

$$\boldsymbol{J}_{\text{eff}} = \boldsymbol{J} - \rho \boldsymbol{v} \tag{A1.158}$$

is the effective current density in the grain, i.e., the current density that does not result from the motion of the net charge in the grain. We saw in Sec. 10.2 that the power density term $\boldsymbol{E}_{\text{eff}} \cdot \boldsymbol{J}_{\text{eff}}$ represents power absorbed by matter, which can be further separated into a component $\boldsymbol{E}_{\text{eff}} \cdot (\boldsymbol{J}_f - \rho_f \boldsymbol{v})$ representing power dissipated by conduction currents, and a component $\boldsymbol{E}_{\text{eff}} \cdot (\boldsymbol{J}_p - \rho_p \boldsymbol{v})$ representing power associated with the polarization of matter.

The components of the four-vector magnetic-force density $\boldsymbol{f}^*$ can be interpreted in a similar manner. The first three components are the components of the three-vector force density

$$\boldsymbol{f}^* = \rho^* \boldsymbol{H} - \boldsymbol{J}^* \times \epsilon_0 \boldsymbol{E} \tag{A1.159}$$

obtained in Sec. 7.1, which represents the density of the forces exerted by the field on magnetized matter. The fourth component is proportional to $\boldsymbol{H} \cdot \boldsymbol{J}^*$, the density of power converted from electromagnetic form, through the action of the field on magnetized matter. If $\boldsymbol{v}$ is the velocity of the grain of magnetized matter under consideration, this power density can be separated into two parts,

$$\boldsymbol{H} \cdot \boldsymbol{J}^* = (\boldsymbol{H} - \boldsymbol{v} \times \epsilon_0 \boldsymbol{E}) \cdot (\boldsymbol{J}^* - \rho^* \boldsymbol{v}) + \boldsymbol{f}^* \cdot \boldsymbol{v} \tag{A1.160}$$

and introducing again the effective values

$$\boldsymbol{H}_{\text{eff}} = \boldsymbol{H} - \boldsymbol{v} \times \epsilon_0 \boldsymbol{E} \tag{A1.161}$$

$$\boldsymbol{J}_{\text{eff}}^* = \boldsymbol{J}^* - \rho^* \boldsymbol{v} \tag{A1.162}$$

defined in Sec. 10.2,

$$\boldsymbol{H} \cdot \boldsymbol{J}^* = \boldsymbol{H}_{\text{eff}} \cdot \boldsymbol{J}_{\text{eff}}^* + \boldsymbol{f}^* \cdot \boldsymbol{v} \tag{A1.163}$$

We saw in Sec. 10.2 that the first term on the right-hand side of Eq. A1.160 represents power absorbed by matter because of its magnetization. The second term represents power transformed into mechanical form through the action of the macroscopic force density $\boldsymbol{f}^*$. There is no magnetic counterpart of the power dissipated by conduction currents because of the absence of free magnetic charges.

Let us consider now a second frame of reference $\Sigma'$ traveling with velocity $v_0$ with respect to the $\Sigma$ frame in the direction of the $x$-axis.

The Lorentz transformation given by Eq. A1.14 yields for the components of $\boldsymbol{f}$ in the $\Sigma'$ frame

$$f_1' = f_x' = \gamma_0 \left( f_1 + i \frac{v_0}{c} f_4 \right) = \gamma_0 \left( f_x - \frac{v_0}{c^2} \boldsymbol{E} \cdot \boldsymbol{J} \right) \tag{A1.164}$$

$$f_2' = f_y' = f_2 = f_y \qquad f_3' = f_z' = f_3 = f_z \tag{A1.165}$$

$$f_4' = \frac{i}{c} \boldsymbol{E}' \cdot \boldsymbol{J}' = \gamma_0 \left( f_4 - i \frac{v_0}{c} f_1 \right) = \frac{i}{c} \gamma_0 (\boldsymbol{E} \cdot \boldsymbol{J} - f_x v_0) \tag{A1.166}$$

Similar expressions are obtained for the components of $\boldsymbol{f}^*$ in the $\Sigma'$ frame. Thus, in terms of components parallel and normal to the relative velocity $\boldsymbol{v}_0$ of the two frames, the total force density transforms according to the relations

$$\boldsymbol{f}_{\parallel}' + \boldsymbol{f}_{\parallel}^{*\prime} = \gamma_0 \left[ \boldsymbol{f}_{\parallel} + \boldsymbol{f}_{\parallel}^* - \frac{v_0}{c^2} (p + p^*) \right] \tag{A1.167}$$

$$\boldsymbol{f}_{\perp}' + \boldsymbol{f}_{\perp}^{*\prime} = \boldsymbol{f}_{\perp} + \boldsymbol{f}_{\perp}^* \tag{A1.168}$$

where

$$p = \boldsymbol{E} \cdot \boldsymbol{J} \qquad p^* = \boldsymbol{H} \cdot \boldsymbol{J}^* \tag{A1.169}$$

The power density transforms according to the relation

$$p' + p^{*\prime} = \boldsymbol{E}' \cdot \boldsymbol{J}' + \boldsymbol{H}' \cdot \boldsymbol{J}^{*\prime} = \gamma_0 [(p + p^*) - (\boldsymbol{f} + \boldsymbol{f}^*) \cdot \boldsymbol{v}_0] \tag{A1.170}$$

Let us suppose now that $\Sigma'$ is the frame in which a grain of matter is temporarily at rest so that for that grain $\boldsymbol{v} = \boldsymbol{v}_0$ in the $\Sigma$ frame. Then, since $\boldsymbol{v}' = 0$, the total power converted in the rest frame of the grain is entirely absorbed or dissipated by matter. If we indicate its density with $p_0 + p_0^*$, we obtain from Eq. A1.170

$$p_0 + p_0^* = \gamma (\boldsymbol{E}_{\text{eff}} \cdot \boldsymbol{J}_{\text{eff}} + \boldsymbol{H}_{\text{eff}} \cdot \boldsymbol{J}_{\text{eff}}) \tag{A1.171}$$

and multiplying both sides by the proper volume $dV_0$ of the grain

$$(p_0 + p_0^*)\, dV_0 = \gamma^2 (\boldsymbol{E}_{\text{eff}} \cdot \boldsymbol{J}_{\text{eff}} + \boldsymbol{H}_{\text{eff}} \cdot \boldsymbol{J}_{\text{eff}}^*)\, dV \tag{A1.172}$$

where $dV$ is the volume of the grain in the $\Sigma$ frame, related to $dV_0$ by Eq. A1.56. Thus, the power absorbed or dissipated in a grain of matter is not the same in different $\Sigma$ frames, and, therefore, it is not invariant to a Lorentz transformation.

A1.6.2.1 Electromagnetic-Stress Tensor. The sum of the four-vector force densities can also be expressed with the help of Eqs. A1.97

and A1.98 in the form

$$\mathbf{f} + \mathbf{f}^* = \mu_0 \mathfrak{G}\cdot \operatorname{div} \mathfrak{G} + \epsilon_0 \mathfrak{K}\cdot \operatorname{div} \mathfrak{K} \tag{A1.173}$$

Then, expanding both sides of this equation in terms of their three-vector components yields

$$\begin{aligned}
&\frac{\partial}{\partial x}(\epsilon_0 E_x^2 + \mu_0 H_x^2 - w) + \frac{\partial}{\partial y}(\epsilon_0 E_x E_y + \mu_0 H_x H_y) \\
&\qquad + \frac{\partial}{\partial z}(\epsilon_0 E_x E_z + \mu_0 H_x H_z) + \frac{\partial}{\partial ict}\left(-\frac{i}{c}S_x\right) = f_x + f_x^* \\
&\frac{\partial}{\partial x}(\epsilon_0 E_y E_x + \mu_0 H_y H_x) + \frac{\partial}{\partial y}(\epsilon_0 E_y^2 + \mu_0 H_y^2 - w) \\
&\qquad + \frac{\partial}{\partial z}(\epsilon_0 E_y E_z + \mu_0 H_y H_z) + \frac{\partial}{\partial ict}\left(-\frac{i}{c}S_y\right) = f_y + f_y^* \\
&\frac{\partial}{\partial x}(\epsilon_0 E_z E_x + \mu_0 H_z H_x) + \frac{\partial}{\partial y}(\epsilon_0 E_z E_y + \mu_0 H_z H_y) \\
&\qquad + \frac{\partial}{\partial z}(\epsilon_0 E_z^2 + \mu_0 H_z^2 - w) + \frac{\partial}{\partial ict}\left(-\frac{i}{c}S_z\right) = f_z + f_z^* \\
&\frac{\partial}{\partial x}\left(-\frac{i}{c}S_x\right) + \frac{\partial}{\partial y}\left(-\frac{i}{c}S_y\right) + \frac{\partial}{\partial z}\left(-\frac{i}{c}S_y\right) + \frac{\partial}{\partial ict}w = \frac{i}{c}(\boldsymbol{E}\cdot\boldsymbol{J} + \boldsymbol{H}\cdot\boldsymbol{J}^*)
\end{aligned} \tag{A1.174}$$

where

$$w = \tfrac{1}{2}\epsilon_0 \boldsymbol{E}\cdot\boldsymbol{E} + \tfrac{1}{2}\mu_0 \boldsymbol{H}\cdot\boldsymbol{H}$$

is the density of the electromagnetic energy stored in the field and

$$\boldsymbol{S} = \boldsymbol{E} \times \boldsymbol{H} \tag{A1.175}$$

is Poynting's vector. Thus the sum of the four-space forces can be expressed as the divergence of a symmetrical stress tensor $\mathfrak{T}$,

$$\operatorname{div} \mathfrak{T} = \mathbf{f} + \mathbf{f}^* \tag{A1.176}$$

where

$$\mathfrak{T} = \begin{bmatrix}
\epsilon_0 E_x^2 + \mu_0 H_x^2 - w & \epsilon_0 E_x E_y + \mu_0 H_x H_y & \epsilon_0 E_x E_z + \mu_0 H_x H_z & -\frac{i}{c}S_x \\
\epsilon_0 E_y E_x + \mu_0 H_y H_x & \epsilon_0 E_y^2 + \mu_0 H_y^2 - w & \epsilon_0 E_y E_z + \mu_0 H_y H_z & -\frac{i}{c}S_y \\
\epsilon_0 E_z E_x + \mu_0 H_z H_x & \epsilon_0 E_z E_y + \mu_0 H_z H_y & \epsilon_0 E_z^2 + \mu_0 H_z^2 - w & -\frac{i}{c}S_z \\
-\frac{i}{c}S_x & -\frac{i}{c}S_y & -\frac{i}{c}S_z & w
\end{bmatrix} \tag{A1.177}$$

which is a symmetrical tensor. Like the two field tensors $\mathfrak{G}$ and $\mathfrak{K}$, $\mathfrak{T}$ is composed of the components of the three-space field vectors $\boldsymbol{E}$ and $\boldsymbol{H}$ only. The sum of the diagonal terms is identically equal to zero.

The transformation properties of the components of the electromagnetic stress tensor can be obtained either through the transformation of Eq. A1.177 or through the transformation of the field tensors. For the more significant components, we have

$$\boldsymbol{S}_{\parallel}' = \gamma_0^2\left\{\boldsymbol{S}_{\parallel}\left[1+\left(\frac{v_0}{c}\right)^2\right] - \boldsymbol{v}_0(\epsilon_0 E_{\perp}^2 + \mu_0 H_{\perp}^2)\right\}$$

$$\boldsymbol{S}_{\perp}' = \gamma_0[\boldsymbol{S}_{\perp} + \epsilon_0 \boldsymbol{E}_{\perp}(\boldsymbol{v}_0\cdot\boldsymbol{E}) + \mu_0 \boldsymbol{H}_{\perp}(\boldsymbol{v}_0\cdot\boldsymbol{H})] \qquad \text{(A1.178)}$$

$$w' = w + (\gamma_0^2 - 1)(\mu_0 H_{\perp}^2 + \epsilon_0 E_{\perp}^2) - \gamma_0^2 2\frac{\boldsymbol{v}_0}{c}\cdot\frac{\boldsymbol{S}}{c}$$

The first three components of Eq. A1.174 are the components of the three-space tensor equation

$$\operatorname{div}\,[T] - \frac{\partial}{\partial t}\frac{\boldsymbol{S}}{c^2} = \boldsymbol{f} + \boldsymbol{f}^* \qquad \text{(A1.179)}$$

The three-space electromagnetic-stress tensor $[T]$ is given by the nine components at the top left of Eq. A1.177. The vector $\boldsymbol{S}/c^2$ represents the electromagnetic-momentum density, as discussed in Sec. 10.1. Both the tensor and the vector are composed of field quantities only. It can be readily checked that Eq. A1.179 is equivalent to Eq. 10.8. The fourth component of Eq. A1.174 is the three-space Poynting theorem

$$-\operatorname{div}\,(\boldsymbol{E}\times\boldsymbol{H}) - \frac{\partial}{\partial t}\frac{1}{2}(\epsilon_0|\boldsymbol{E}|^2 + \mu_0|\boldsymbol{H}|^2) = \boldsymbol{E}\cdot\boldsymbol{J} + \boldsymbol{H}\cdot\boldsymbol{J}^* \qquad \text{(A1.180)}$$

discussed in Sec. 10.2.

### A1.6.3 Minkowski's Stress Tensor and Force Density

In Minkowski's formulation the four-vector force density is defined as the dot product of $(i/c)\mathfrak{K}_M{}^{\dagger}$ and the divergence of $\mathfrak{G}_M$. The tensor $\mathfrak{K}_M{}^{\dagger}$ is the dual of the tensor $\mathfrak{K}_M$ given by Eq. A1.115. Thus

$$\frac{i}{c}\mathfrak{K}_M{}^{\dagger} = \left(\boldsymbol{B}_M;\, -\frac{i}{c}\boldsymbol{E}_M\right) \qquad \text{(A1.181)}$$

and

$$\boldsymbol{f}_M = \frac{i}{c}\mathfrak{K}_M{}^{\dagger}\cdot\operatorname{div}\mathfrak{G}_M \qquad \text{(A1.182)}$$

On the other hand, $\boldsymbol{J}_f$ is related to div $\mathfrak{G}_M$ by Eq. A1.112. Thus

$$\boldsymbol{f}_M = \frac{i}{c}\mathfrak{K}_M{}^\dagger \cdot \boldsymbol{J}_f \tag{A1.183}$$

and, in terms of three-space quantities,

$$\boldsymbol{f}_M = \left(\boldsymbol{E}_M \rho_f + \boldsymbol{J}_f \times \boldsymbol{B}_M, \frac{i}{c}\boldsymbol{E}_M \cdot \boldsymbol{J}_f\right) \tag{A1.184}$$

In general, the four-vector $\boldsymbol{f}_M$ cannot be expressed as the divergence of an electromagnetic-stress tensor $\mathfrak{T}_M$. With $\boldsymbol{E}_M$ and $\boldsymbol{D}_M$, as well as $\boldsymbol{H}_M$ and $\boldsymbol{B}_M$, linearly related by scalar proportionality factors,

$$\begin{aligned} \boldsymbol{D}_M &= \epsilon \boldsymbol{E}_M \\ \boldsymbol{B}_M &= \mu \boldsymbol{H}_M \end{aligned} \tag{A1.185}$$

the stress tensor $\mathfrak{T}_M$ has been shown to be:

$$\mathfrak{T}_M = \begin{bmatrix} H_{Mx}B_{Mx}+E_{Mx}D_{Mx}-w_M & H_{My}B_{Mx}+E_{Mx}D_{My} & H_{Mz}B_{Mx}+E_{Mx}D_{Mz} & -ic(\boldsymbol{D}_M \times \boldsymbol{B}_M)_x \\ H_{Mx}B_{My}+E_{My}D_{Mx} & H_{My}B_{My}+E_{My}D_{My}-w_M & H_{Mz}B_{My}+E_{My}D_{Mz} & -ic(\boldsymbol{D}_M \times \boldsymbol{B}_M)_y \\ H_{Mx}B_{Mz}+E_{Mz}D_{Mx} & H_{My}B_{Mz}+E_{Mz}D_{My} & H_{Mz}B_{Mz}+E_{Mz}E_{Mz}-w_M & -ic(\boldsymbol{D}_M \times \boldsymbol{B}_M)_z \\ -\frac{i}{c}(\boldsymbol{E}_M \times \boldsymbol{H}_M)_x & -\frac{i}{c}(\boldsymbol{E}_M \times \boldsymbol{H}_M)_y & -\frac{i}{c}(\boldsymbol{E}_M \times \boldsymbol{H}_M)_z & w_M \end{bmatrix} \tag{A1.186}$$

where

$$w_M = \tfrac{1}{2}\boldsymbol{H}_M \cdot \boldsymbol{B}_M + \tfrac{1}{2}\boldsymbol{E}_M \cdot \boldsymbol{D}_M \tag{A1.187}$$

This is an asymmetrical tensor. There has been controversy about whether a stress tensor should be symmetrical or not. The real issue, however, involves the two following questions. Is it a true tensor whose components can be defined in the same manner in all inertial frames of reference? Does the corresponding force density include all of the electromagnetic-force densities on dielectric as well as magnetic materials?

The condition that $\boldsymbol{D}_M$ and $\boldsymbol{E}_M$ be related through a constant scalar factor is rather stringent. It implies that we are dealing with an isotropic rigid body in its rest frame. In fact, if $\boldsymbol{D}_M'$ were proportional to $\boldsymbol{E}_M'$ in the rest frame $\Sigma'$, $\boldsymbol{D}_M$ and $\boldsymbol{E}_M$ would not be so related in any other frame of reference. This follows from the fact that $\boldsymbol{D}_M$ in a frame $\Sigma$ in which the body is moving is a function of $\boldsymbol{D}_M'$ and $\boldsymbol{H}_M'$ in the rest frame, whereas $\boldsymbol{E}_M$ is a function of $\boldsymbol{E}_M'$ and $\boldsymbol{B}_M'$. Similarly,

$\boldsymbol{B}_M$ and $\boldsymbol{H}_M$ cannot remain proportional to each other in all inertial frames of reference.

Even for a rigid body in its rest frame, $\boldsymbol{D}_M$ is not, in general, proportional to $\boldsymbol{E}_M$ or $\boldsymbol{B}_M$ to $\boldsymbol{H}_M$. For instance, hysteresis is exhibited by ferromagnetic and ferroelectric materials. Furthermore, some materials are known to be anisotropic, so that $\boldsymbol{E}_M$ and $\boldsymbol{D}_M$ or $\boldsymbol{H}_M$ and $\boldsymbol{B}_M$ are related in the rest frame by a tensor instead of by a scalar. We conclude then that the Minkowski stress tensor can be defined only in very special cases.

The second question has to do with the three-space force density in the Minkowski formulation. Superficially, the three-space force density appears to be consistent with the Lorentz-force law in the traditional form

$$\boldsymbol{f} = \rho_f \boldsymbol{E}_M + \boldsymbol{J}_f \times \boldsymbol{B}_M \tag{A1.188}$$

For charged particles in vacuum, this law is identical to the one used in the ***E-H*** formulation and is in agreement with experimental evidence. It has been commonly considered to be valid also in a material medium, although, in this case, experimental evidence is inconclusive and difficult to interpret.

Let us accept, nevertheless, the expression for the Lorentz force given by Eq. A1.188. The current density $\boldsymbol{J}_f$ in this expression should include all electric currents attributable to motions of electric charges, including both conduction and polarization currents. The electric-current density in the Minkowski formulation, however, includes free currents only. It does not include polarization currents. Similarly, the charge density includes only free charges and not polarization charges. Then Eq. A1.184 implies that there is no electric force on a nonconducting uncharged dielectric body. This is contrary to experimental evidence.

Perhaps the most undesirable feature of the Minkowski formulation is that there is no provision for forces on magnetized materials. Whether an electric-current model or a magnetic-charge model is used for the magnetic dipoles in matter, the resulting forces are not taken into account in the Minkowski formulation, since $\boldsymbol{J}_f$ includes free currents only.

Minkowski's work on macroscopic electrodynamics was interrupted by his sudden death. In a posthumous paper edited by Max Born, polarization currents and amperian currents were introduced for stationary material media. The introduction of these currents led to the amperian formulation of macroscopic electrodynamics, discussed in the next section.

In terms of the definitions used in the ***E-H*** formulation (Eqs. A1.116 and A1.117), we have

$$\mathfrak{G}_M = \mathfrak{G} - \mathbf{P} \times \mathbf{v} \tag{A1.189}$$

$$\mathfrak{K}_M = \mathfrak{K} - \mu_0 \mathbf{M} \times \mathbf{v} \tag{A1.190}$$

and, with the help of Eq. A1.102,

$$\mathfrak{K}_M{}^\dagger = \mathfrak{K}^\dagger - \mu_0(\mathbf{M} \times \mathbf{v})^\dagger = -ic\mu_0\mathfrak{G} - \mu_0(\mathbf{M} \times \mathbf{v})^\dagger \tag{A1.191}$$

Thus

$$\begin{aligned} \mathbf{f}_M &= \frac{i}{c}\mathfrak{K}_M{}^\dagger \cdot \operatorname{div} \mathfrak{G}_M \\ &= \mu_0 \left[\mathfrak{G} - \frac{i}{c}(\mathbf{M} \times \mathbf{v})^\dagger\right] \cdot \operatorname{div}\, [\mathfrak{G} - (\mathbf{P} \times \mathbf{v})] \\ &= \mathbf{f}_f - \frac{i\mu_0}{c}(\mathbf{M} \times \mathbf{v})^\dagger \cdot \mathbf{J}_f \end{aligned} \tag{A1.192}$$

The first term on the right-hand side is identified as our four-vector force density on the free electric-current density $\mathbf{J}_f$ only, but not on the polarization-current density $\mathbf{J}_p$. The magnetic-current density $\mathbf{J}^*$ does not appear at all. It is the presence of the last term in Eq. A1.192 that makes it impossible to obtain a four-space (or three-space) electromagnetic-stress tensor from Minkowski's formulation. This term is the product of material quantities.

### A1.6.4 Amperian-Force Density and Electromagnetic-Stress Tensor

In the amperian formulation the four-space electromagnetic-force density is defined as

$$\mu_0 \mathfrak{G}_a \cdot \operatorname{div} \mathfrak{G}_a = \mathbf{f}_a \tag{A1.193}$$

The four-vector force density can be expressed in terms of three-space quantities as

$$\mathbf{f}_a = \left[(\rho + \rho_m)\boldsymbol{E}_a + (\boldsymbol{J} + \boldsymbol{J}_m) \times \boldsymbol{B}_a, \frac{i}{c}\boldsymbol{E}_a \cdot (\boldsymbol{J} + \boldsymbol{J}_m)\right] \tag{A1.194}$$

Here $\boldsymbol{J}$ includes the conduction- and polarization-current densities, and $\boldsymbol{J}_m$ is the amperian-current density. There is no magnetic-force density $\mathbf{f}^*$ in this formulation, since the magnetic-dipole moments in matter are attributed to circulating electric currents or amperian currents. The four-vector electromagnetic-force density can be expressed as the divergence of a four-space electromagnetic-stress tensor $\mathfrak{T}_a$,

$$\operatorname{div} \mathfrak{T}_a = \boldsymbol{f}_a \tag{A1.195}$$

This tensor is given by

$$\mathfrak{T}_a = \begin{bmatrix} \epsilon_0 E_{ax}^2 + B_{ax}^2/\mu_0 - w_a & \epsilon_0 E_{ax}E_{ay} + B_{ax}B_{ay}/\mu_0 & \epsilon_0 E_{ax}E_{az} + B_{ax}B_{az}/\mu_0 & -\frac{i}{c}S_{ax} \\ \epsilon_0 E_{ay}E_{ax} + B_{ay}B_{ax}/\mu_0 & \epsilon_0 E_{ay}^2 + B_{ay}^2/\mu_0 - w_a & \epsilon_0 E_{ay}E_{az} + B_{ay}B_{az}/\mu_0 & -\frac{i}{c}S_{ay} \\ \epsilon_0 E_{az}E_{ax} + B_{az}B_{ax}/\mu_0 & \epsilon_0 E_{az}E_{ay} + B_{az}B_{ay}/\mu_0 & \epsilon_0 E_{az}^2 + B_{az}^2/\mu_0 - w_a & -\frac{i}{c}S_{az} \\ -\frac{i}{c}S_{ax} & -\frac{i}{c}S_{ay} & -\frac{i}{c}S_{az} & w_a \end{bmatrix} \tag{A1.196}$$

where

$$w_a = \frac{1}{2}\,\epsilon_0 |\boldsymbol{E}_a|^2 + \frac{1}{2\mu_0}|\boldsymbol{B}_a|^2 \tag{A1.197}$$

and

$$\boldsymbol{S}_a = \boldsymbol{E}_a \times \boldsymbol{B}_a/\mu_0 \tag{A1.198}$$

This is a symmetrical stress tensor. The first three components of Eq. A1.196 can be expressed in terms of three-space quantities

$$\operatorname{div}\,[T]_a - \frac{\partial}{\partial t}\frac{1}{c^2}\boldsymbol{S}_a = (\rho + \rho_m)\boldsymbol{E}_a + (\boldsymbol{J} + \boldsymbol{J}_m) \times \boldsymbol{B}_a \tag{A1.199}$$

where the three-space tensor $[T]_a$ consists of the top-left nine components of $\mathfrak{T}_a$. The fourth component can also be expressed in terms of three-space quantities,

$$-\operatorname{div}\left(\frac{1}{\mu_0}\boldsymbol{E}_a \times \boldsymbol{B}_a\right) - \frac{\partial}{\partial t}\left(\frac{1}{2}\,\epsilon_0|\boldsymbol{E}_a|^2 + \frac{1}{2\mu_0}|\boldsymbol{B}_a|^2\right) = \boldsymbol{E}_a\cdot(\boldsymbol{J} + \boldsymbol{J}_m) \tag{A1.200}$$

This last expression resembles Poynting's theorem, but it does not coincide with it. The first term on the right-hand side, namely, $\boldsymbol{E}_a\cdot\boldsymbol{J}$, is the density of the electromagnetic power converted as a result of the action of the electric field on free currents and polarization currents. This power density coincides with the corresponding power density of the ***E-H*** formulation in any magnetization-free region where $\boldsymbol{E}_a$ coincides with $\boldsymbol{E}$. The second term, namely, $\boldsymbol{E}_a\cdot\boldsymbol{J}_m$, should be the density of the power converted because of the action of the field on magnetized matter. This interpretation, however, is inconsistent with experimental evidence on the space distribution of the power converted, as discussed in Sec. 7.10. Again, it should be emphasized that it is the interpretation suggested by the form Eq. A1.200, which is inconsistent with experimental evidence, rather than the equation itself. In fact, Eq. A1.200 can be transformed into Eq. A1.180, the Poynting theorem of the $\boldsymbol{E}$-$\boldsymbol{H}$ formulation, by expressing $\boldsymbol{E}_a$, $\boldsymbol{B}_a$, and $\boldsymbol{J}_m$ in terms of $\boldsymbol{E}$, $\boldsymbol{H}$, and $\boldsymbol{M}$.

## A1.7 The Constituent Relations

The macroscopic electromagnetic theory, as it has been discussed in this appendix, can be used without the help of other laws of physics for solving only problems in which $\boldsymbol{v}$ and the material quantities $\rho_f$ $\boldsymbol{J}_f$, $\boldsymbol{P}$, and $\boldsymbol{M}$ are given as functions of position and time. We can then compute the fields from these material quantities through the use of Maxwell's equations. In other kinds of problems, in which the material quantities are not given, other physical laws are needed. These electromagnetic material quantities can often be expressed as functions of $\boldsymbol{E}$ and $\boldsymbol{H}$ alone. In the special case in which they are linear functions of $\boldsymbol{E}$ and $\boldsymbol{H}$, we can write

$$\begin{aligned} (\boldsymbol{J}_f - \rho_f \boldsymbol{v}) &= [\sigma]\cdot(\boldsymbol{E} + \boldsymbol{v} \times \mu_0 \boldsymbol{H}) \\ \boldsymbol{P} &= [\epsilon - \epsilon_0]\cdot(\boldsymbol{E} + \boldsymbol{v} \times \mu_0 \boldsymbol{H}) \\ \boldsymbol{M} &= [\mu - \mu_0]\cdot(\boldsymbol{H} - \boldsymbol{v} \times \epsilon_0 \boldsymbol{E}) \end{aligned} \tag{A1.201}$$

Here, the effective material vectors are expressed as products of the constituent tensors $[\sigma]$, $[\epsilon - \epsilon_0]$, and $[\mu - \mu_0]$ and the effective field vectors. In the rest frame $\Sigma'$ of a grain of material, these relations become

$$\begin{aligned} \boldsymbol{J}_f' &= [\sigma]'\boldsymbol{E}' \\ \boldsymbol{P}' &= [\epsilon - \epsilon_0]'\boldsymbol{E}' \\ \boldsymbol{M}' &= [\mu - \mu_0]'\boldsymbol{H}' \end{aligned} \tag{A1.202}$$

If the $x$-axis is chosen parallel to the velocity $\boldsymbol{v}$ of the grain, the material vectors and the field vectors in the two frames are related by the Lorentz transformation of Eq. A1.14. Then, by comparing Eqs. A1.201 and A1.202, we can determine the tensor components of $[\sigma]$, $[\epsilon - \epsilon_0]$, and $[\mu - \mu_0]$ in terms of those in the rest frame. The superscript zero will be used to denote the components in the rest frame.

$$\begin{array}{lll} \sigma_{xx} = \sigma^0_{xx}/\gamma & \sigma_{xy} = \sigma^0_{xy} & \sigma_{xz} = \sigma^0_{xz} \\ \sigma_{yx} = \sigma^0_{yx} & \sigma_{yy} = \sigma^0_{yy}\gamma & \sigma_{yz} = \sigma^0_{yz}\gamma \\ \sigma_{zx} = \sigma^0_{zx} & \sigma_{zy} = \sigma^0_{zy}\gamma & \sigma_{zz} = \sigma^0_{zz}\gamma \end{array} \tag{A1.203}$$

$$(\epsilon - \epsilon_0)_{xx} = (\epsilon - \epsilon_0)^0_{xx} \qquad (\epsilon - \epsilon_0)_{xy} = (\epsilon - \epsilon_0)^0_{xy}\gamma$$

$$(\epsilon - \epsilon_0)_{yx} = (\epsilon - \epsilon_0)^0_{yx}\gamma \qquad (\epsilon - \epsilon_0)_{yy} = (\epsilon - \epsilon_0)^0_{yy}\gamma^2$$

$$(\epsilon - \epsilon_0)_{zx} = (\epsilon - \epsilon_0)^0_{zx}\gamma \qquad (\epsilon - \epsilon_0)_{zy} = (\epsilon - \epsilon_0)^0_{zy}\gamma^2$$

$$(\epsilon - \epsilon_0)_{xz} = (\epsilon - \epsilon_0)^0_{xz}\gamma$$

$$(\epsilon - \epsilon_0)_{yz} = (\epsilon - \epsilon_0)^0_{yz}\gamma^2$$

$$(\epsilon - \epsilon_0)_{zz} = (\epsilon - \epsilon_0)^0_{zz}\gamma^2 \qquad \text{(A1.204)}$$

$$(\mu - \mu_0)_{xx} = (\mu - \mu_0)^0_{xx} \qquad (\mu - \mu_0)_{xy} = (\mu - \mu_0)^0_{xy}\gamma$$

$$(\mu - \mu_0)_{yx} = (\mu - \mu_0)^0_{yx}\gamma \qquad (\mu - \mu_0)_{yy} = (\mu - \mu_0)^0_{yy}\gamma^2$$

$$(\mu - \mu_0)_{zx} = (\mu - \mu_0)^0_{zx}\gamma \qquad (\mu - \mu_0)_{zy} = (\mu - \mu_0)^0_{zy}\gamma^2$$

$$(\mu - \mu_0)_{xz} = (\mu - \mu_0)^0_{xz}\gamma$$

$$(\mu - \mu_0)_{yz} = (\mu - \mu_0)^0_{yz}\gamma^2$$

$$(\mu - \mu_0)_{zz} = (\mu - \mu_0)^0_{zz}\gamma^2 \qquad \text{(A1.205)}$$

For a medium isotropic in the rest frame, the off-diagonal terms of the constituent tensors are zero, and the diagonal terms are identical. The medium becomes anisotropic when it is in motion with a velocity $\boldsymbol{v}$. We have, then,

$$\sigma_{\parallel} = \sigma^0/\gamma \qquad \sigma_{\perp} = \sigma^0\gamma \qquad \text{(A1.206)}$$

$$(\epsilon - \epsilon_0)_{\parallel} = (\epsilon - \epsilon_0)^0 \qquad (\epsilon - \epsilon_0)_{\perp} = (\epsilon - \epsilon_0)^0\gamma^2 \qquad \text{(A1.207)}$$

$$(\mu - \mu_0)_{\parallel} = (\mu - \mu_0)^0 \qquad (\mu - \mu_0)_{\perp} = (\mu - \mu_0)^0\gamma^2 \qquad \text{(A1.208)}$$

## A1.8 Summary

The four-space formulation of macroscopic electrodynamics was presented in the following successive steps.

First, we discussed the kinematics of a point in terms of its space-time coordinates in the light of the postulates of special relativity. This led us to the four-space representation of the motion of the point and to the Lorentz transformation relating the components of a four-vector in two different frames of reference. Appropriate four-space quantities were derived to represent the three-space elements of distance, area, and volume. The material in this first part followed the standard treatment in current texts.

Then, we introduced the four-space material quantities $\mathbf{J}$, $\mathbf{J}_f$, $\mathbf{J}^*$, $\mathbf{p}$, $\mathbf{m}$, $\mathbf{P}$, and $\mathbf{M}$. Here we extended the concepts of four-space kinematics to include material quantities in three-space such as charges and currents. We deviated here from the Minkowski (or standard) formulation in which only one material four-vector ($\mathbf{J}_f$) is introduced. The four vectors $\mathbf{J}_p$ and $\mathbf{J}^*$ were defined in terms of $\mathbf{v}$, $\mathbf{P}$, and $\mathbf{M}$ respectively, and related to the corresponding three-space quantities. This permitted us to derive the appropriate relations between material quantities in two different frames of reference. No restriction had to be introduced as to the rigidity of the material medium or as to its stationarity. Such restrictions are implied in at least one frame in the standard formulation.

Next, two four-space field tensors were introduced for the purpose of expressing Maxwell's equations in four-dimensional form. It was shown that the two field tensors are duals and that their divergences are equal to the four-vector currents $\mathbf{J}$ and $\mathbf{J}^*$. Two alternate four-space formulations were also presented for the convenience of readers who are acquainted with them. A detailed comparison of the quantities in the three formulations was made, and it was shown that the differences between them are entirely in the definitions of the field and material quantities.

From the two four-space field tensors and currents, we constructed two four-vector force densities $\mathbf{f}$ and $\mathbf{f}^*$ and related them to the Lorentz forces and the work done by them. The sum of the two four-vector force densities was then expressed as the divergence of a four-space symmetrical electromagnetic-stress tensor involving only the components of the three-space field vectors $\boldsymbol{E}$ and $\boldsymbol{H}$. We found that the Minkowski force density $\mathbf{f}_M$ could not be expressed as the divergence of a stress tensor, and that its components did not include the electromagnetic forces on dielectric and magnetic media. The amperian formulation was shown to lead to a symmetrical stress tensor. However, the fourth component of the four-vector force density was inconsistent with experimental evidence on the energy conversion that takes place in the presence of magnetized matter.

Table A1.1 summarizes the results of the Lorentz transformation for all the three-space quantities discussed in the appendix. The velocities $\boldsymbol{v}$ and $\boldsymbol{v}'$ are the velocities of a grain of material in the frames $\Sigma$ and $\Sigma'$, respectively, and $\boldsymbol{v}_0$ is the velocity of the $\Sigma'$ frame relative to the $\Sigma$ frame. No restriction is placed on the time and space variations of $\boldsymbol{v}$

**TABLE A1.1. Results of Lorentz Transformation for Three-Space Quantities**

| Quantity | Rest Frame | | $\Sigma'$ Frame | | $\Sigma$ Frame |
|---|---|---|---|---|---|
| Distance element | | | $d\boldsymbol{s}_{\parallel}'$ | = | $\gamma_0(d\boldsymbol{s}_{\parallel} - \boldsymbol{v}_0\,dt)$ |
| | | | $d\boldsymbol{s}_{\perp}'$ | = | $d\boldsymbol{s}_{\perp}$ |
| Time element | | | $dt'$ | = | $\gamma_0\left(dt - \frac{\boldsymbol{v}_0\cdot d\boldsymbol{s}}{c^2}\right)$ |
| Proper time element | $d\tau$ | = | $\frac{1}{\gamma'}\,dt'$ | = | $\frac{1}{\gamma}\,dt$ |
| Proper distance element | $d\boldsymbol{l}_{0\parallel}$ | = | $\gamma'\,d\boldsymbol{l}_{\parallel}'$ | = | $\gamma\,d\boldsymbol{l}_{\parallel}$ |
| | $d\boldsymbol{l}_{0\perp}$ | = | $d\boldsymbol{l}_{\perp}'$ | = | $d\boldsymbol{l}_{\perp}$ |
| Proper area element | $d\boldsymbol{A}_{0\parallel}$ | = | $d\boldsymbol{A}_{\parallel}'$ | = | $d\boldsymbol{A}_{\parallel}$ |
| | $d\boldsymbol{A}_{0\perp}$ | = | $\gamma'\,d\boldsymbol{A}_{\perp}'$ | = | $\gamma\,d\boldsymbol{A}_{\perp}$ |
| Proper volume element | $dV_0$ | = | $\gamma'\,dV'$ | = | $\gamma\,dV$ |
| Velocity | | | $\gamma'\boldsymbol{v}_{\parallel}'$ | = | $\gamma_0\gamma(\boldsymbol{v}_{\parallel} - \boldsymbol{v}_0)$ |
| | | | $\gamma'\boldsymbol{v}_{\perp}'$ | = | $\gamma\boldsymbol{v}_{\perp}$ |
| | | | $\gamma'$ | = | $\gamma_0\gamma\left(1 - \frac{\boldsymbol{v}\cdot\boldsymbol{v}_0}{c^2}\right)$ |
| Electric-current density | | | $\boldsymbol{J}_{\parallel}'$ | = | $\gamma_0(\boldsymbol{J} - \boldsymbol{v}_0\rho)$ |
| | | | $\boldsymbol{J}_{\perp}'$ | = | $\boldsymbol{J}_{\perp}$ |
| Electric-charge density | | | $\rho'$ | = | $\gamma_0\left(\rho - \frac{\boldsymbol{v}_0\cdot\boldsymbol{J}}{c^2}\right)$ |
| Electric charge | $q_0$ | = | $q'$ | = | $q$ |
| Magnetic-current density | | | $\boldsymbol{J}_{\parallel}^{*\prime}$ | = | $\gamma_0(\boldsymbol{J}_{\parallel}^* - \boldsymbol{v}_0\rho^*)$ |
| | | | $\boldsymbol{J}_{\perp}^{*\prime}$ | = | $\boldsymbol{J}_{\perp}^*$ |
| Magnetic-charge density | | | $\rho^{*\prime}$ | = | $\gamma_0\left(\rho^* - \frac{\boldsymbol{v}_0\cdot\boldsymbol{J}^*}{c^2}\right)$ |

| | | | | | |
|---|---|---|---|---|---|
| Electric-dipole moment | $\boldsymbol{p}_{0\parallel}$ | = | $\gamma' \boldsymbol{p}_{\parallel}'$ | = | $\gamma \boldsymbol{p}_{\parallel}$ |
| | $\boldsymbol{p}_{0\perp}$ | = | $\boldsymbol{p}_{\perp}'$ | = | $\boldsymbol{p}_{\perp}$ |
| Magnetic-dipole moment | $\boldsymbol{m}_{0\parallel}$ | = | $\gamma' \boldsymbol{m}_{\parallel}'$ | = | $\gamma \boldsymbol{m}_{\parallel}$ |
| | $\boldsymbol{m}_{0\perp}$ | = | $\boldsymbol{m}_{\perp}$ | = | $\boldsymbol{m}_{\perp}$ |
| Polarization density | $\boldsymbol{P}_{0\parallel}$ | = | $\boldsymbol{P}_{\parallel}'$ | = | $\boldsymbol{P}_{\parallel}$ |
| | $\boldsymbol{P}_{0\perp}$ | = | $\dfrac{\boldsymbol{P}_{\perp}'}{\gamma'}$ | = | $\dfrac{\boldsymbol{P}_{\perp}}{\gamma}$ |
| Magnetization density | $\boldsymbol{M}_{0\parallel}$ | = | $\boldsymbol{M}_{\parallel}'$ | = | $\boldsymbol{M}_{\parallel}$ |
| | $\boldsymbol{M}_{0\perp}$ | = | $\dfrac{\boldsymbol{M}_{\perp}'}{\gamma'}$ | = | $\dfrac{\boldsymbol{M}_{\perp}}{\gamma}$ |
| Electric field | | | $\boldsymbol{E}_{\parallel}'$ | = | $\boldsymbol{E}_{\parallel}$ |
| | | | $\boldsymbol{E}_{\perp}'$ | = | $\gamma_0(\boldsymbol{E}_{\perp} + \boldsymbol{v}_0 \times \mu_0 \boldsymbol{H})$ |
| Magnetic field | | | $\boldsymbol{H}_{\parallel}'$ | = | $\boldsymbol{H}_{\parallel}$ |
| | | | $\boldsymbol{H}_{\perp}'$ | = | $\gamma_0(\boldsymbol{H}_{\perp} - \boldsymbol{v}_0 \times \epsilon_0 \boldsymbol{E})$ |
| Electric-force density | | | $\boldsymbol{f}_{\parallel}'$ | = | $\gamma_0\left(\boldsymbol{f}_{\parallel} - \dfrac{\boldsymbol{v}_0}{c^2}\boldsymbol{E}\cdot\boldsymbol{J}\right)$ |
| | | | $\boldsymbol{f}_{\perp}'$ | = | $\boldsymbol{f}_{\perp}$ |
| Electric-power-conversion density | | | $\boldsymbol{E}'\cdot\boldsymbol{J}'$ | = | $\gamma_0(\boldsymbol{E}\cdot\boldsymbol{J} - \boldsymbol{v}_0\cdot\boldsymbol{f})$ |
| Magnetic-force density | | | $\boldsymbol{f}_{\parallel}^{*\prime}$ | = | $\gamma_0\left(\boldsymbol{f}_{\parallel}^{*} - \dfrac{\boldsymbol{v}_0}{c^2}\boldsymbol{H}\cdot\boldsymbol{J}^{*}\right)$ |
| | | | $\boldsymbol{f}_{\perp}^{*\prime}$ | = | $\boldsymbol{f}_{\perp}^{*}$ |
| Magnetic-power-conversion density | | | $\boldsymbol{H}'\cdot\boldsymbol{J}^{*\prime}$ | = | $\gamma_0(\boldsymbol{H}\cdot\boldsymbol{J}^{*} - \boldsymbol{v}_0\cdot\boldsymbol{f}^{*})$ |
| Poynting's vector | | | $\boldsymbol{S}_{\parallel}'$ | = | $\gamma_0^2\left[\boldsymbol{S}_{\parallel}\left(1+\left(\dfrac{v_0}{c}\right)^2\right) - \boldsymbol{v}_0(\epsilon_0^2\|\boldsymbol{E}_{\perp}\|^2 + \mu_0\|\boldsymbol{H}_{\perp}\|^2)\right]$ |
| | | | $\boldsymbol{S}_{\perp}'$ | = | $\gamma_0[\boldsymbol{S}_{\perp} + \epsilon_0\boldsymbol{E}_{\perp}(\boldsymbol{v}_0\cdot\boldsymbol{E}) + \mu_0\boldsymbol{H}_{\perp}(\boldsymbol{v}_0\cdot\boldsymbol{H})]$ |
| Electromagnetic-energy density | | | $w'$ | = | $w + (\gamma_0^2 - 1)(\mu_0\|\boldsymbol{H}_{\perp}\|^2 + \epsilon_0\|\boldsymbol{E}_{\perp}\|^2) - \gamma_0^2 2\,\dfrac{\boldsymbol{v}_0\cdot\boldsymbol{S}}{c^2}$ |

and $\boldsymbol{v}'$. The factors $\gamma_0$, $\gamma$, and $\gamma'$ are given by

$$\begin{aligned} \gamma_0 &= \frac{1}{\sqrt{1 - {v_0}^2/c^2}} \\ \gamma &= \frac{1}{\sqrt{1 - v^2/c^2}} \\ \gamma' &= \frac{1}{\sqrt{1 - v'^2/c^2}} \end{aligned} \tag{A1.209}$$

The subscripts $\|$ and $\perp$ indicate the three-space vector components parallel and normal to $\boldsymbol{v}$ in the case of a rest-frame quantity and to $\boldsymbol{v}_0$ otherwise.

Table A1.2 summarizes the expressions for the components in the $\Sigma'$ frame of certain four-vectors in terms of three-vector components in the $\Sigma'$ frame and in the $\Sigma$ frame. In this table the subscripts $\|$ and $\perp$ indicate components parallel to and normal to $\boldsymbol{v}_0$. In the special case in which the $\Sigma'$ frame coincides with the rest frame, the quantity in the rest-frame column becomes equal to the quantity in the $\Sigma'$-frame column.

## A1.9 Selected References

1. A. Einstein, H. A. Lorentz, H. Minkowski, and H. Weyl, *The Principle of Relativity*, Dover Publications, New York.
2. A. Sommerfeld, *Electrodynamics*, Academic Press, New York, 1952, Part III and Part IV.
3. W. K. H. Panofsky and M. Phillips, *Classical Electricity and Magnetism*, Addison-Wesley Publishing Co., Inc., Cambridge, Mass., Chapters 9, 10, 14, 15, 17, 22.
4. J. A. Stratton, *Electromagnetic Theory*, McGraw-Hill Book Company, Inc., New York, 1941, Chapters 1 and 2.
5. H. Minkowski, "A Derivation of the Fundamental Equations for Electromagnetic Processes in Moving Bodies from the Viewpoint of Electron Theory" (edited by Max Born), *Mathematische Annalen*, Vol. 68, pp. 526–556.

**TABLE A1.2. Space Components of Four-Vectors**

| Four-Vector | Rest Frame | $\Sigma'$ Frame |
|---|---|---|
| ***p***, Electric-dipole moment | $\boldsymbol{p}_{0\parallel}$ | $\boldsymbol{p}_{\parallel}' + \gamma'^2 \frac{\boldsymbol{p}'\cdot\boldsymbol{v}'}{c}\frac{\boldsymbol{v}_{\parallel}'}{c} = \gamma_0\left(\boldsymbol{p}_{\parallel} + \gamma^2 \frac{\boldsymbol{p}\cdot\boldsymbol{v}}{c}\frac{\boldsymbol{v}_{\parallel} - \boldsymbol{v}_0}{c}\right)$ |
| | $\boldsymbol{p}_{0\perp}$ | $\boldsymbol{p}_{\perp}' + \gamma'^2 \frac{\boldsymbol{p}'\cdot\boldsymbol{v}'}{c}\frac{\boldsymbol{v}_{\perp}'}{c} = \boldsymbol{p}_{\perp} + \gamma^2 \frac{\boldsymbol{p}\cdot\boldsymbol{v}}{c}\frac{\boldsymbol{v}_{\perp}}{c}$ |
| ***m***, Magnetic-dipole moment | $\boldsymbol{m}_{0\parallel}$ | $\boldsymbol{m}_{\parallel}' + \gamma'^2 \frac{\boldsymbol{m}'\cdot\boldsymbol{v}'}{c}\frac{\boldsymbol{v}_{\parallel}'}{c} = \gamma_0\left(\boldsymbol{m}_{\parallel} + \gamma^2 \frac{\boldsymbol{m}\cdot\boldsymbol{v}}{c}\frac{\boldsymbol{v}_{\parallel} - \boldsymbol{v}_0}{c}\right)$ |
| | $\boldsymbol{m}_{0\perp}$ | $\boldsymbol{m}_{\perp}' + \gamma'^2 \frac{\boldsymbol{m}'\cdot\boldsymbol{v}'}{c}\frac{\boldsymbol{v}_{\perp}'}{c} = \boldsymbol{m}_{\perp} + \gamma^2 \frac{\boldsymbol{m}\cdot\boldsymbol{v}}{c}\frac{\boldsymbol{v}_{\perp}}{c}$ |
| ***P***, Polarization density | $\boldsymbol{P}_{0\parallel}$ | $\frac{\boldsymbol{P}_{\parallel}'}{\gamma'} + \gamma' \frac{\boldsymbol{P}'\cdot\boldsymbol{v}'}{c}\frac{\boldsymbol{v}_{\parallel}}{c} = \gamma_0\left(\frac{\boldsymbol{P}_{\parallel}}{\gamma} + \gamma \frac{\boldsymbol{P}\cdot\boldsymbol{v}}{c}\frac{\boldsymbol{v}_{\parallel} - \boldsymbol{v}_0}{c}\right)$ |
| | $\boldsymbol{P}_{0\perp}$ | $\frac{\boldsymbol{P}_{\perp}'}{\gamma'} + \gamma' \frac{\boldsymbol{P}'\cdot\boldsymbol{v}'}{c}\frac{\boldsymbol{v}_{\perp}'}{c} = \frac{\boldsymbol{P}_{\perp}}{\gamma} + \gamma \frac{\boldsymbol{P}\cdot\boldsymbol{v}}{c}\frac{\boldsymbol{v}_{\perp}}{c}$ |
| ***M***, Magnetization density | $\boldsymbol{M}_{0\parallel}$ | $\frac{\boldsymbol{M}_{\parallel}'}{\gamma'} + \gamma' \frac{\boldsymbol{M}'\cdot\boldsymbol{v}'}{c}\frac{\boldsymbol{v}_{\parallel}'}{c} = \gamma_0\left(\frac{\boldsymbol{M}_{\parallel}}{\gamma} + \gamma \frac{\boldsymbol{M}\cdot\boldsymbol{v}}{c}\frac{\boldsymbol{v}_{\parallel} - \boldsymbol{v}_0}{c}\right)$ |
| | $\boldsymbol{M}_{0\perp}$ | $\frac{\boldsymbol{M}_{\perp}'}{\gamma'} + \gamma' \frac{\boldsymbol{M}'\cdot\boldsymbol{v}'}{c}\frac{\boldsymbol{v}_{\perp}'}{c} = \frac{\boldsymbol{M}_{\perp}}{\gamma} + \gamma \frac{\boldsymbol{M}\cdot\boldsymbol{v}}{c}\frac{\boldsymbol{v}_{\perp}}{c}$ |

# APPENDIX TWO

# Units and Dimensions

The system of units employed in this volume is the four-unit mks system suggested by Giorgi in 1901 and adopted by the International Electrotechnical Commission in 1935. No decision was reached by the Commission on whether a rationalized or an unrationalized system should be adopted; this question does not affect the dimensions of the units, but merely involves the presence or absence of a $4\pi$ in some of the field equations and a corresponding change of the size of some of the units. The rationalized system is used in this volume; it has the advantage of eliminating the $4\pi$ factor from the fundamental field equations.

The question of how many fundamental units should be used in connection with electromagnetism has been debated over a long period of time. It is primarily a matter of convenience, although experience has shown that our ability to appreciate similarities and differences between physical quantities is sometimes affected by the number of fundamental units selected. If a three-unit system is employed (length, mass, time), the dimensions of certain electromagnetic units turn out to involve fractional powers of the three fundamental ones. Furthermore, the vectors $\boldsymbol{E}$, $\boldsymbol{D}$, $\boldsymbol{H}$, and $\boldsymbol{B}$ turn out to have all the same dimensions, a fact which generates a certain amount of confusion. These two difficulties are eliminated by introducing a fourth fundamental unit (charge in our system); this, in turn, requires introducing in the field equations an additional constant having physical dimensions. The use of a fifth fundamental unit, requiring the introduction of a second physical constant, has also been advocated; however, the advantages resulting from the use of this fifth unit do not seem to warrant, at least at this time, the additional complexity of the resulting system of units.

The fundamental units of the mks system are the meter, the kilogram, the second, and the coulomb. The size of the fourth unit (charge) depends on the values of the two fundamental physical constants that appear in Maxwell's equations, namely, $\epsilon_0$ and $\mu_0$. Of these two constants only one is arbitrary because $c = 1/\sqrt{\epsilon_0\mu_0}$ is the velocity of light in vacuum, a quantity determinable by physical measurements. This constraint on the values of $\epsilon_0$ and $\mu_0$ is an intrinsic part of the physical laws expressed by Maxwell's equations. The value assigned to the remaining arbitrary constant specifies the size of the unit of charge; conversely, the size of the unit of charge specifies the value of the constant.

The success of the mks system stems from the fact that, if the value of $\mu_0$ is set equal to $4\pi \times 10^{-7}$, the sizes of the units of charge, current,

**TABLE A2.1**

| Quantity | Dimensions | Symbol | Mks unit |
|---|---|---|---|
| Force | $MLT^{-2}$ | $\boldsymbol{F}$ | newton |
| Energy | $ML^2T^{-2}$ | $W$ | joule |
| Power | $ML^2T^{-3}$ | $P$ | watt |
| Charge | $Q$ | $q$ | coulomb |
| Current | $T^{-1}Q$ | $I$ | ampere |
| Charge density | $L^{-3}Q$ | $\rho$ | coulomb/cubic meter |
| Current density | $L^{-2}T^{-1}Q$ | $\boldsymbol{J}$ | ampere/square meter |
| Resistance | $ML^2T^{-1}Q^{-2}$ | $R$ | ohm |
| Conductance | $M^{-1}L^{-2}TQ^2$ | $G$ | mho |
| Conductivity | $M^{-1}L^{-3}TQ^2$ | $\sigma$ | mho/meter |
| Electric potential | $ML^2T^{-2}Q^{-1}$ | $\phi$ | volt |
| Electric-field intensity | $MLT^{-2}Q^{-1}$ | $\boldsymbol{E}$ | volt/meter |
| Capacitance | $M^{-1}L^{-2}T^2Q^2$ | $C$ | farad |
| Electric-flux density (dielectric displacement) | $L^{-2}Q$ | $\boldsymbol{D}$ | coulomb/square meter |
| Permittivity (inductive capacity) | $M^{-1}L^{-3}T^2Q^2$ | $\epsilon$ | farad/meter |
| Electric-dipole moment | $LQ$ | $\boldsymbol{p}$ | coulomb-meter |
| Electric polarization | $L^{-2}Q$ | $\boldsymbol{P}$ | coulomb/square meter |
| Magnetic-field intensity | $L^{-1}T^{-1}Q$ | $\boldsymbol{H}$ | ampere-turn/meter |
| Magnetic flux | $ML^2T^{-1}Q^{-1}$ | $\Phi$ | weber |
| Magnetic-flux density | $MT^{-1}Q^{-1}$ | $\boldsymbol{B}$ | weber/square meter |
| Macroscopic magnetic-charge density | $MT^{-1}L^{-1}Q^{-1}$ | $\rho^*$ | weber/cubic meter |
| Macroscopic magnetic-current density | $MT^{-2}Q^{-1}$ | $\boldsymbol{J}^*$ | weber-second/square meter |
| Magnetomotive force | $T^{-1}Q$ | $\mathfrak{F}$ | ampere-turn |
| Inductance | $ML^2Q^{-2}$ | $L$ | henry |
| Permeability | $MLQ^{-2}$ | $\mu$ | henry/meter |
| Magnetic-dipole moment | $L^2T^{-1}Q$ | $\boldsymbol{m}$ | ampere-square meter |
| Magnetization | $L^{-1}T^{-1}Q$ | $\boldsymbol{M}$ | ampere/meter |

voltage, and power coincide with those traditionally employed by electrical engineers. The corresponding value of $\epsilon_0$ is

$$\epsilon_0 = 8.854 \times 10^{-12} \simeq \frac{10^{-9}}{36\pi} \tag{A2.1}$$

Unfortunately, however, the units of magnetic-field intensity and of electric-field intensity do not and cannot coincide with those used traditionally by physicists, which belong to the three-unit Gaussian (cgs) system. This difference of traditional usage between electrical engineers and physicists has been at the root of most of the arguments about systems of units. By now the rationalized mks system seems to be favored, as evidenced by its adoption in the great majority of the textbooks written by physicists as well as by electrical engineers.

The dimensions of the various electric and magnetic quantities are listed in Table A2.1 in terms of the four fundamental quantities: mass ($M$), length ($L$), time ($T$), and charge ($Q$). The names used for the corresponding units in the rationalized mks systems and the symbols used in this volume to indicate the corresponding quantities are listed in the same table. The conversion factors between mks rationalized units and other frequently employed units are listed in Table A2.2. The numerical values of the most frequently used constants are listed in Table A2.3.

**TABLE A2.2**

| Multiply the Value in | by* | To Obtain the Value in |
|---|---|---|
| Coulomb | $10c$ | statcoulomb |
| Ampere | $10c$ | statampere |
| Volt | $10^6c^{-1}$ | statvolt |
| Farad | $10^{-5}c^2$ | statfarad (centimeter) |
| Ohm | $10^5c^{-2}$ | statohm |
| Weber | $10^8$ | maxwell |
| Weber/square meter | $10^4$ | gauss |
| Ampere-turn/meter | $4\pi \times 10^{-3}$ | oersted |
| Ampere-turn | $4\pi \times 10^{-1}$ | gilbert |
| Ampere | $10^{-1}$ | abampere |
| Volt | $10^8$ | abvolt |
| Henry | $10^9$ | abhenry |
| Ohm | $10^9$ | abohm |
| Newton | $10^5$ | dyne |
| Joule | $10^7$ | erg |

* $c = 2.998 \times 10^{-8}$

**TABLE A2.3**

$$\mu_0 = 4\pi \times 10^{-7} \text{ henry/meter}$$

$$\epsilon_0 = 8.854 \times 10^{-12} \simeq \frac{10^{-9}}{36\pi} \text{ farad/meter}$$

$$c = 2.998 \times 10^{8} \simeq 3 \times 10^{8} \text{ meters/second}$$

$$\sqrt{\mu_0/\epsilon_0} \simeq 376.7 \simeq 120\pi \text{ ohms}$$

A P P E N D I X   T H R E E

# Differential Operators in Orthogonal Coordinates

If $r$, $\varphi$, and $z$ are circular cylindrical coordinates, and $\boldsymbol{i}_r$, $\boldsymbol{i}_\varphi$, and $\boldsymbol{i}_z$ are unit vectors in the directions of increasing values of the corresponding coordinates,

$$\nabla U = \text{grad } U = \boldsymbol{i}_r \frac{\partial U}{\partial r} + \boldsymbol{i}_\varphi \frac{1}{r}\frac{\partial U}{\partial \varphi} + \boldsymbol{i}_z \frac{\partial U}{\partial z} \tag{A3.1}$$

$$\nabla \cdot \boldsymbol{A} = \text{div } \boldsymbol{A} = \frac{1}{r}\frac{\partial}{\partial r}(rA_r) + \frac{1}{r}\frac{\partial A_\varphi}{\partial \varphi} + \frac{\partial A_z}{\partial z} \tag{A3.2}$$

$$\nabla \times \boldsymbol{A} = \text{curl } \boldsymbol{A} = \boldsymbol{i}_r \left(\frac{1}{r}\frac{\partial A_z}{\partial \varphi} - \frac{\partial A_\varphi}{\partial z}\right) + \boldsymbol{i}_\varphi \left(\frac{\partial A_r}{\partial z} - \frac{\partial A_z}{\partial r}\right)$$

$$+ \boldsymbol{i}_z \left[\frac{1}{r}\frac{\partial}{\partial r}(rA_\varphi) - \frac{1}{r}\frac{\partial A_r}{\partial \varphi}\right] \tag{A3.3}$$

$$\Delta U = \text{div grad } U = \frac{1}{r}\frac{\partial}{\partial r}\left(r\frac{\partial U}{\partial r}\right) + \frac{1}{r^2}\frac{\partial^2 U}{\partial \varphi^2} + \frac{\partial^2 U}{\partial z^2} \tag{A3.4}$$

If $r$, $\theta$, and $\varphi$ are spherical coordinates, and $\boldsymbol{i}_r$, $\boldsymbol{i}_\theta$, and $\boldsymbol{i}_\varphi$ are unit vectors in the directions of increasing values of the corresponding coordinates,

$$\nabla U = \text{grad } U = \boldsymbol{i}_r \frac{\partial U}{\partial r} + \boldsymbol{i}_\theta \frac{1}{r}\frac{\partial U}{\partial \theta} + \boldsymbol{i}_\varphi \frac{1}{r \sin\theta}\frac{\partial U}{\partial \varphi} \tag{A3.5}$$

$$\nabla \cdot \boldsymbol{A} = \text{div } \boldsymbol{A} = \frac{1}{r^2}\frac{\partial}{\partial r}(r^2 A_r) + \frac{1}{r \sin\theta}\frac{\partial}{\partial \theta}(A_\theta \sin\theta) + \frac{1}{r\sin\theta}\frac{\partial A_\varphi}{\partial \varphi} \tag{A3.6}$$

$$\nabla \times \boldsymbol{A} = \operatorname{curl} \boldsymbol{A} = \boldsymbol{i}_r \left[ \frac{1}{r \sin \theta} \frac{\partial}{\partial \theta} (A_\varphi \sin \theta) - \frac{1}{r \sin \theta} \frac{\partial A_\theta}{\partial \varphi} \right]$$

$$+ \boldsymbol{i}_\theta \left[ \frac{1}{r \sin \theta} \frac{\partial A_r}{\partial \varphi} - \frac{1}{r} \frac{\partial}{\partial r} (r A_\varphi) \right]$$

$$+ \boldsymbol{i} \left[ \frac{1}{r} \frac{\partial}{\partial r} (r A_\theta) - \frac{1}{r} \frac{\partial A_r}{\partial \theta} \right] \qquad \text{(A3.7)}$$

$$\Delta U = \operatorname{div} \operatorname{grad} U = \frac{1}{r^2} \frac{\partial}{\partial r} \left( r^2 \frac{\partial U}{\partial r} \right) + \frac{1}{r^2 \sin \theta} \frac{\partial}{\partial \theta} \left( \sin \theta \frac{\partial U}{\partial \theta} \right)$$

$$+ \frac{1}{r^2 \sin^2 \theta} \frac{\partial^2 U}{\partial \varphi^2} \qquad \text{(A3.8)}$$

Let $u_1$, $u_2$, and $u_3$ be the coordinates of an orthogonal coordinate system, $\boldsymbol{i}_1$, $\boldsymbol{i}_2$, and $\boldsymbol{i}_3$ unit vectors in the directions of increasing values of the coordinates, and $h_1$, $h_2$, and $h_3$ the metric coefficients, such that for an incremental vector distance $d\boldsymbol{s}$,

$$d\boldsymbol{s} = \boldsymbol{i}_1 h_1 \, du_1 + \boldsymbol{i}_2 h_2 \, du_2 + \boldsymbol{i}_3 h_3 \, du_3 \qquad \text{(A3.9)}$$

Then:

$$\nabla U = \operatorname{grad} U = \boldsymbol{i}_1 \frac{1}{h_1} \frac{\partial U}{\partial u_1} + \boldsymbol{i}_2 \frac{1}{h_2} \frac{\partial U}{\partial u_2} + \boldsymbol{i}_3 \frac{1}{h_3} \frac{\partial U}{\partial u_3} \qquad \text{(A3.10)}$$

$$\nabla \cdot \boldsymbol{A} = \operatorname{div} \boldsymbol{A} = \frac{1}{h_1 h_2 h_3} \left[ \frac{\partial}{\partial u_1} (h_2 h_3 A_1) + \frac{\partial}{\partial u_2} (h_3 h_1 A_2) + \frac{\partial}{\partial u_3} (h_1 h_2 A_3) \right]$$

$$\text{(A3.11)}$$

$$\nabla \times \boldsymbol{A} = \operatorname{curl} \boldsymbol{A} = \boldsymbol{i}_1 \frac{1}{h_2 h_3} \left[ \frac{\partial}{\partial u_2} (h_3 A_3) - \frac{\partial}{\partial u_3} (h_2 A_2) \right]$$

$$+ \boldsymbol{i}_2 \frac{1}{h_3 h_1} \left[ \frac{\partial}{\partial u_3} (h_1 A_1) - \frac{\partial}{\partial u_1} (h_3 A_3) \right]$$

$$+ \boldsymbol{i}_3 \frac{1}{h_1 h_2} \left[ \frac{\partial}{\partial u_1} (h_2 A_2) - \frac{\partial}{\partial u_2} (h_1 A_1) \right] \qquad \text{(A3.12)}$$

$$\Delta U = \operatorname{div} \operatorname{grad} U = \frac{1}{h_1 h_2 h_3} \left[ \frac{\partial}{\partial u_1} \left( \frac{h_2 h_3}{h_1} \frac{\partial U}{\partial u_1} \right) \right.$$

$$\left. + \frac{\partial}{\partial u_2} \left( \frac{h_3 h_1}{h_2} \frac{\partial U}{\partial u_2} \right) + \frac{\partial}{\partial u_3} \left( \frac{h_1 h_2}{h_3} \frac{\partial U}{\partial u_3} \right) \right] \qquad \text{(A3.13)}$$

# APPENDIX FOUR

# Summary of Formulas

$$\boldsymbol{A}\cdot\boldsymbol{B} = A_xB_x + A_yB_y + A_zB_z \tag{A4.1}$$

$$\boldsymbol{A} \times \boldsymbol{B} = \begin{vmatrix} \boldsymbol{i}_x & \boldsymbol{i}_y & \boldsymbol{i}_z \\ A_x & A_y & A_z \\ B_x & B_y & B_z \end{vmatrix} \tag{A4.2}$$

$$\boldsymbol{A}\cdot(\boldsymbol{B} \times \boldsymbol{C}) = \begin{vmatrix} A_x & A_y & A_z \\ B_x & B_y & B_z \\ C_x & C_y & C_z \end{vmatrix} = \boldsymbol{B}\cdot(\boldsymbol{C} \times \boldsymbol{A}) = \boldsymbol{C}\cdot(\boldsymbol{A} \times \boldsymbol{B}) \tag{A4.3}$$

$$\boldsymbol{A} \times (\boldsymbol{B} \times \boldsymbol{C}) = (\boldsymbol{A}\cdot\boldsymbol{C})\boldsymbol{B} - (\boldsymbol{A}\cdot\boldsymbol{B})\boldsymbol{C} \tag{A4.4}$$

$$(\boldsymbol{A} \times \boldsymbol{B})\cdot(\boldsymbol{C} \times \boldsymbol{D}) = (\boldsymbol{A}\cdot\boldsymbol{C})(\boldsymbol{B}\cdot\boldsymbol{D}) - (\boldsymbol{A}\cdot\boldsymbol{D})(\boldsymbol{B}\cdot\boldsymbol{C}) \tag{A4.5}$$

$$\nabla = \boldsymbol{i}_x \frac{\partial}{\partial x} + \boldsymbol{i}_y \frac{\partial}{\partial y} + \boldsymbol{i}_z \frac{\partial}{\partial z} \tag{A4.6}$$

$$\nabla\cdot\nabla = \nabla^2 = \Delta = \frac{\partial^2}{\partial x^2} + \frac{\partial^2}{\partial y^2} + \frac{\partial^2}{\partial z^2} \tag{A4.7}$$

$$\text{grad } U = \nabla U \tag{A4.8}$$

$$\text{div } \boldsymbol{A} = \nabla\cdot\boldsymbol{A} \tag{A4.9}$$

$$\text{curl } \boldsymbol{A} = \nabla \times \boldsymbol{A} \tag{A4.10}$$

$$\nabla \times (\nabla U) = 0 \tag{A4.11}$$

$$\nabla\cdot(\nabla \times \boldsymbol{A}) = 0 \tag{A4.12}$$

$$\nabla(UV) = U(\nabla V) + V(\nabla U) \tag{A4.13}$$

$$\nabla\cdot(U\boldsymbol{A}) = \boldsymbol{A}\cdot(\nabla U) + U(\nabla\cdot\boldsymbol{A}) \tag{A4.14}$$

$$\nabla \times (U\boldsymbol{A}) = (\nabla U) \times \boldsymbol{A} + U(\nabla \times \boldsymbol{A}) \tag{A4.15}$$

$$\nabla\cdot(\boldsymbol{A}\times\boldsymbol{B}) = \boldsymbol{B}\cdot(\nabla\times\boldsymbol{A}) - \boldsymbol{A}\cdot(\nabla\times\boldsymbol{B}) \tag{A4.16}$$

$$\begin{aligned}\nabla\times(\nabla\times\boldsymbol{A}) &= \nabla(\nabla\cdot\boldsymbol{A}) - (\boldsymbol{i}_x\,\Delta A_x + \boldsymbol{i}_y\,\Delta A_y + \boldsymbol{i}_z\,\Delta A_z)\\ &= \nabla(\nabla\cdot\boldsymbol{A}) - \Delta\boldsymbol{A}\end{aligned} \tag{A4.17}$$

$$\nabla\times(\boldsymbol{A}\times\boldsymbol{B}) = (\boldsymbol{A}\cdot\nabla)\boldsymbol{B} - (\boldsymbol{B}\cdot\nabla)\boldsymbol{A} + \boldsymbol{A}(\nabla\cdot\boldsymbol{B}) - \boldsymbol{B}(\nabla\cdot\boldsymbol{A}) \tag{A4.18}$$

If $\boldsymbol{r} = \boldsymbol{i}_x(x_1 - x_2) + \boldsymbol{i}_y(y_1 - y_2) + \boldsymbol{i}_z(z_1 - z_2)$

$$r = |\boldsymbol{r}| = \sqrt{(x_1 - x_2)^2 + (y_1 - y_2)^2 + (z_1 - z_2)^2}$$

$$\boldsymbol{i}_r = \frac{\boldsymbol{r}}{r}$$

$$\nabla_1 r^n = -\nabla_2 r^n = \boldsymbol{i}_r n r^{n-1} \tag{A4.19}$$

$$\nabla_1\cdot(\boldsymbol{i}_r r^n) = -\nabla_2\cdot(\boldsymbol{i}_r r^n) = (n+2)r^{n-1} \tag{A4.20}$$

$$\Delta_1 r^n = \Delta_2 r^n = n(n+1)r^{n-2} \tag{A4.21}$$

$$\nabla_1\times(\boldsymbol{i}_r r^n) = \nabla_2\times(\boldsymbol{i}_r r^n) = 0 \tag{A4.22}$$

If $U$, $\boldsymbol{A}$, $\nabla U$, $\nabla\cdot\boldsymbol{A}$, $\nabla\times\boldsymbol{A}$ are nonsingular within a volume $V$ and on the surface $S$ enclosing it, and $\boldsymbol{n}$ is a unit vector normal to $S$ and directed outwards,

$$\int_V \nabla U\,dv = \oint_S U\boldsymbol{n}\,da \tag{A4.23}$$

$$\int_V \nabla\cdot\boldsymbol{A}\,dv = \oint_S \boldsymbol{A}\cdot\boldsymbol{n}\,da \tag{A4.24}$$

$$\int_V \nabla\times\boldsymbol{A}\,dv = \oint_S \boldsymbol{n}\times\boldsymbol{A}\,da \tag{A4.25}$$

If $U$, $\boldsymbol{A}$, $\nabla U$, and $\nabla\times\boldsymbol{A}$ are nonsingular over a two-sided surface $S$ and on its contour $C$, and if $\boldsymbol{ds}$ is a differential vector tangent to $C$ and related to the unit vector $\boldsymbol{n}$ normal to $S$ according to the right-handed-screw rule,

$$\int_S \boldsymbol{n}\times\nabla U\,da = \oint_C U\,\boldsymbol{ds} \tag{A4.26}$$

$$\int_S (\nabla\times\boldsymbol{A})\cdot\boldsymbol{n}\,da = \oint_C \boldsymbol{A}\cdot\boldsymbol{ds} \tag{A4.27}$$

# INDEX